Vol. 55 1999

# Theilheimer's
# Synthetic Methods
## of Organic Chemistry

Editor **Alan F. Finch, Cambridge**

Assistant Editor Gillian Tozer-Hotchkiss, Derwent Information
Editorial Consultant William Theilheimer, Nutley, N.J.

Basel · Freiburg
Paris · London
New York · New Delhi
Bangkok · Singapore
Tokyo · Sydney

## Deutsche Ausgaben

| Vol. 1 | 1946 | 1. Auflage |
| --- | --- | --- |
| | 1948 | 2., unveränderte Auflage |
| | 1950 | 3., unveränderte Auflage |
| Vol. 2 | 1948 | |
| Vol. 3 | 1949 | with English Index key |
| | 1953 | 2., unveränderte Auflage |
| | 1966 | 3., unveränderte Auflage |
| | 1975 | 4., unveränderte Auflage |
| Vol. 4 | 1950 | with English Index key |
| | 1966 | 2., unveränderte Auflage |

## English Editions

| Vol. 1 | 1948 | Interscience Publishers |
| --- | --- | --- |
| | 1975 | (Karger) Second Edition |
| Vol. 2 | 1949 | Interscience Publishers |
| | 1975 | (Karger) Second Edition |
| Vol. 5 | 1951 | with Reaction Titles Vol. 1-5 and Cumulative Index |
| | 1966 | Second Edition |
| Vol. 6 | 1952 | |
| | 1975 | Second Edition |
| Vol. 7 | 1953 | |
| | 1975 | Second Edition |
| Vol. 8 | 1954 | |
| | 1975 | Second Edition |
| Vol. 9 | 1955 | |
| Vol. 10 | 1956 | with Reaction Titles Vol. 6-10 and Cumulative Index |
| | 1975 | Second Edition |
| Vol. 11 | 1957 | |
| | 1975 | Second Edition |
| Vol. 12 | 1958 | |
| | 1975 | Second Edition |
| Vol. 13 | 1959 | |
| | 1975 | Second Edition |
| Vol. 14 | 1960 | |
| | 1975 | Second Edition |
| Vol. 15 | 1961 | with Reaction Titles Vol. 11-15 and Cumulative Index |
| Vol. 16 | 1962 | |
| Vol. 17 | 1963 | |
| Vol. 18 | 1964 | |
| Vol. 19 | 1965 | |
| Vol. 20 | 1966 | with Reaction Titles Vol. 16-20 and Cumulative Index |
| Vol. 21 | 1967 | |
| Vol. 22 | 1968 | |
| Vol. 23 | 1969 | |
| Vol. 24 | 1970 | |
| Vol. 25 | 1971 | with Reaction Titles Vol. 21-25 and Cumulative Index |
| Vol. 26 | 1972 | |
| Vol. 27 | 1973 | |
| Vol. 28 | 1974 | |
| Vol. 29 | 1975 | |
| Vol. 30 | 1976 | with Reaction Titles Vol. 26-30 and Cumulative Index |
| Vol. 31 | 1977 | |
| Vol. 32 | 1978 | |
| Vol. 33 | 1979 | |
| Vol. 34 | 1980 | |
| Vol. 35 | 1981 | with Reaction Titles Vol. 31-35 and Cumulative Index |
| Vol. 36 | 1982 | |
| Vol. 37 | 1983 | |
| Vol. 38 | 1984 | |
| Vol. 39 | 1985 | |
| Vol. 40 | 1986 | with Reaction Titles Vol. 36-40 and Cumulative Index |
| Vol. 41 | 1987 | |
| Vol. 42 | 1988 | |
| Vol. 43 | 1989 | |
| Vol. 44 | 1990 | |
| Vol. 45 | 1991 | with Reaction Titles Vol. 41-45 and Cumulative Index |
| Vol. 46 | 1992 | |
| Vol. 47 | 1993 | |
| Vol. 48 | 1994 | |
| Vol. 49 | 1995 | |
| Vol. 50 | 1996 | with Reaction Titles Vol. 46-50 and Cumulative Index |
| Vol. 51 | 1997 | |
| Vol. 52 | 1997 | |
| Vol. 53 | 1998 | |
| Vol. 54 | 1998 | |

Library of Congress, Cataloging-in-Publication Data

Theilheimer's synthetic methods of organic chemistry = Synthetische Methoden der organischen Chemie. – Vol. 55 (1999) - Basel; New York: Karger, © 1982 -
v.
Continues: Synthetic methods of organic chemistry.
Editor: Alan F. Finch.
1. Chemistry, Organic – yearbooks    I. Finch, Alan F.    II. Theilheimer, William, 1914–
ISBN 3-8055-6889-4

All rights reserved.
No part of this publication may be translated into other languages, reproduced or utilized in any form or by any means, electronic or mechanical, including photocopying, recording, microcopying, or by any information storage and retrieval system, without permission in writing from the publisher.

© Copyright 1999 by S. Karger AG, Basel (Switzerland), and Derwent Information Ltd., London
Distributed by S. Karger AG, Allschwilerstrasse 10, P.O. Box, CH-4009 Basel (Switzerland)
Printed in Switzerland on acid-free paper by Schüler AG, Biel
ISBN 3-8055-6889-4

Theilheimer's
# Synthetic Methods
of Organic Chemistry

Vol. 55

## Contents

| | |
|---|---|
| Preface to Volume 55 | VI |
| Advice to the User | VII |
|     General Remarks | VII |
|     Methods of Classification | VIII |
|     High-Coverage Searches | X |
| Trends and Developments in Synthetic Organic Chemistry 1999 | XI |
| Systematic Survey | XXI |
| Abbreviations and Symbols | XXIII |
| Reactions | 1 |
| Reviews | 245 |
| Subject Index | 252 |
| Supplementary References | 296 |

# Preface

This is the first of the biannual volumes of *Theilheimer* for 1999 containing abstracts of new synthetic methods and supplementary data mainly from papers published in the scientific literature during March to September 1998.

For browsing purposes, abstracts are displayed according to the Systematic Classification (symbol notation) so that reactions of the same type and associated data appear together. For example, all deprotections appear in the early symbols (under HO⇅, HN⇅, HS⇅); reduction of oxo compds., imines and carbon-carbon multiple bonds under the HC⇓ sections; C-defunctionalization under the HC sections; oxy-functionalization under the OC sections; aminations, nitrations, peptide coupling etc. under the NC sections; halogenation under the HalC sections; sulfurations under the SC sections; selenation, stannylation, phosphorylation, etc. under the RemC sections; syntheses involving C-C bond formation in the latter half of the book under the CC sections; and data on resolutions (Res) at the end. A list of reaction symbols and references thereto is given in the Systematic Survey (p. XXI ).

The displayed data are supported by the customary in-depth Subject Index and access to supplementary data can be made in the usual manner via the Supplementary Reference Index, e.g. the reader interested in updates to palladium-catalyzed, asym. α-allylation (Synth. Meth. *48*, 772) will note from p. 302 that additional references can be found on p. 173 of this volume.

As usual, the volume contains a 'Reviews' section (p. 245), covering reviews published up to and including January 1999, and a 'Trends' section (p.XI) incorporating key developments in synthetic chemistry up to and including March 1999. Most of these latter references will appear as abstracts in the next volume.

I would like to express my gratitude to Dr. Theilheimer for his encouragement in the preparation of these yearbooks, and to my colleagues at Derwent Information Ltd., London, whose Journal of Synthetic Methods provides data for inclusion in these volumes. A special thankyou goes to my wife and to my colleagues at Derwent: to my assistant editor, Gillian Tozer-Hotchkiss, and to Rabeya Das, Kath Ince, and Jill Entwistle for handling the electronic processing by which these volumes are published.

April 1999 *A.F. Finch*, Editor

# Advice to the User

*General Remarks*

New methods for the synthesis of organic compounds and improvements of known methods are being recorded continuously in this series.

Reactions are classified on a simple though purely formal basis by symbols, which can be arranged systematically. Thus searches can be performed without knowledge of the current trivial or author names (e.g. 'Oxidation' and 'Friedel-Crafts reaction').

Users accustomed to the common notations will find these in the subject index. By consulting this index, use of the classification system may be avoided. It is thought that the volumes should be kept close at hand. The books should provide a quick survey, and obviate the immediate need for an elaborate library search. Syntheses are therefore recorded in the index by starting materials and end products, along with the systematic arrangement for the methods. This makes possible a sub-classification within the reaction symbols by reagents, a further methodical criterion. Complex compounds are indexed with cross reference under the related simpler compounds. General terms, such as synthesis, replacement, heterocyclics, may also be brought to the attention of the reader.

A brief review, *Trends and Developments in Synthetic Organic Chemistry*, stresses highlights of general interest and calls attention to key methods too recent to be included in the body of the text.

The abstracts are limited to the information needed for an appraisal of the applicability of a desired synthesis. In order to carry out a particular synthesis it is therefore advisable to have recourse to the original papers or, at least, to an abstract journal. In order to avoid repetition, selections are made on the basis of most detailed description and best yields whenever the same method is used in similar cases. Continuations of papers already included will not be abstracted, unless they contain essentially new information. They may, however, be quoted at the place corresponding to the abstracted papers. These supplementary references (see page 296) make it possible to keep abstracts of previous volumes up-to-date.

Syntheses that are divided into their various steps and recorded in different places can be followed with the help of the notations such as *startg. m. f.* (starting material for the preparation of ...).

## Method of Classification

*Reaction Symbols.* As summarized in the Systematic Survey (p. XXI), reactions are classified firstly according to the bond formed in the synthesis, secondly according to the reaction type, and thirdly according to the bond broken or the element eliminated. This classification is summarized in the reaction symbol, e.g.

$$\underset{\substack{\uparrow \\ \text{Bond formed}}}{\text{OC}} \underset{\substack{\uparrow \\ \text{Reaction} \\ \text{type}}}{\Uparrow} \underset{\substack{\uparrow \\ \text{Bond broken or} \\ \text{element eliminated}}}{\text{N}}$$

The first part of the symbol refers to the chemical bond formed during the reaction, expressed as a combination of the symbols for the two elements bonded together, e.g. HN, NC, CC. The order of the elements is as follows:

H, O, N, Hal (Halogen), S, Rem (Remaining elements), and C.

Thus, for the formation of a hydrogen-nitrogen bond, the notation is HN, not NH.

If two or more bonds are formed in a reaction, the 'principle of the latest position' applies. Thus, for the reduction

$$\text{RCH=O} + \text{H}_2 \longrightarrow \text{R-}\overset{\text{H}}{\underset{|}{\text{CH}}}\text{-OH}$$

in which both hydrogen-oxygen and hydrogen-carbon bonds are formed, the symbol is HC⇓OC and not HO⇓OC.

The second part of the symbol refers to the reaction type. Four types are distinguished: addition (⇓), rearrangement (∩), exchange (⇅), and elimination (⇑), e.g.

| | | |
|---|---|---|
| RCH=CH$_2$ + H$_2$O ⟶ R-CH(OH)-CH$_3$ | | OC⇓CC |
| (thiophene-allyl) ⟶ (cyclized product) | | CC∩SC |
| R-Cl + CN$^-$ ⟶ R-CN  [+ Cl$^-$] | | CC⇅Hal |
| R-CH(Br)-CH$_3$ ⟶ RCH=CH$_2$  [+ HBr] | | CC⇑Hal |

Monomolecular reactions are either rearrangements (∩), where the molecular weight of the starting material and product are the same, or eliminations (⇑), where an organic or inorganic fragment is lost; bimolecular and multicomponent reactions are either additions (⇓), such as intermolecular

Diels-Alder reactions, Michael addition and 1,4-addition of organometallics, or exchanges (↓↑), such as substitutions and condensations, where an organic or inorganic fragment is lost.

The last part of the symbol refers to the essential bond broken or, in the case of exchange reactions and eliminations, to a characteristic fragment which is lost. While the addition symbol is normally followed by the two elements denoting the bond broken, in the case of valency expansion, where no bonds are broken, the last part of the symbol indicates the atom at which the addition occurs, e.g.

| $R_2S$ ⟶ $R_2SO$ | OS⇅S |
| RONO ⟶ $RONO_2$ | ON⇅N |

For addition, exchanges, and eliminations, the 'principle of the latest position' again applies if more than one bond is broken. However, for rearrangements, the most descriptive bond-breakage is used instead. Thus, for the thio-Claisen rearrangement depicted above, the symbol is CC∩SC, and not CC∩CC.

Deoxygenations, quaternizations, stable radical formations, and certain rare reaction types are included as the last few methods in the yearbook. The reaction symbols for these incorporate the special symbols El (electron pair), Het (heteropolar bond), Rad (radical), Res (resolutions), and Oth (other reaction types), e.g.

| $R_2S=O$ ⟶ $R_2S$ | ElS↑O |
| $R_3N$ + R'Cl ⟶ $R_3N^+R'$ Cl⁻ | Het⇅N |

The following rules simplify the use of the reaction symbols:

1. The chemical bond is rigidly classified according to the structural formula without taking the reaction mechanism into consideration.

2. Double or triple bonds are treated as being equivalent to two or three single bonds, respectively.

3. Only stable organic compounds are usually considered: intermediates such as Grignard compounds and sodiomalonic esters, and inorganic reactants, such as nitric acid, are therefore not expressed in the reaction symbols.

*Reagents*. A further subdivision, not included in the reaction symbols, is based on the reagents used. The sequence of the reagents usually follows that of the periodic system. Reagents made up of several components are arranged according to the element significant for the reaction (e.g. $KMnO_4$ under Mn, NaClO under Cl). When a constituent of the reagent forms part of the product, the remainder of the reagent, which acts as a 'carrier' of this constituent, is the criterion for the classification; for example, phosphorus is the carrier in a chlorination with $PCl_5$ and sodium in a nitrosation with $NaNO_2$.

*High-Coverage Searches*

A search through *Synthetic Methods* provides a selection of key references from the journal literature. For greater coverage, as for bibliographies, a supplementary search through the following publications is suggested:

*Derwent Reaction Service*[1]. Designed for both current awareness and retrospective retrieval. Its monthly publication, the *Derwent Journal of Synthetic Methods*, covers the journal and patent literature, and provides 3,000 abstracts of recently published papers annually.

Access is available in-house via REACCS-JSM to over 100,000 reactions, including the data in all the abstracts in *Synthetic Methods*, while online access is provided on STN as DJSMONLINE.

*Science Citation Index*[2]. For which *Synthetic Methods* serves as a source of starting references. This is particularly useful for accessing papers quoting details of a particular method which has been included in these volumes from a preliminary communication.

*Chemical Abstracts Service*[3]. References may not be included in *Synthetic Methods* (1) to reactions which are routinely performed by well known procedures; (2) to subjects which can be easily located in handbooks and indexes of abstracts journals, such as the ring system of heterocyclics or the metal in case of organometallic compounds, and (3) to inadequately described procedures, especially if yields are not indicated.

References to less accessible publications such as those in the Chinese or Japanese language are usually only included if the method in question is not described elsewhere.

---

[1] Derwent Information Ltd., 14 Great Queen Street, London WC2B 5DF, England.
[2] Institute for Scientific Information, Philadelphia, Pa., USA.
[3] Chemical Abstracts Service, Columbus, Ohio, USA.

## Trends and Developments in Synthetic Organic Chemistry 1999

Though health authorities would not care to admit it, patients and medical staff in hospitals throughout the land are very much at risk to infection by MRSA (Methicillin-resistant *Staphylococcus aureus*). **Vancomycin** - a complex glycopeptide comprising a polycyclic aglycone linked to a disaccharide chain - is just about the last line of defence against this 'super-bug', and its emergence in this capacity has spurred the design of new, efficient synthetic routes to the molecule[1]. Recently, two procedures have been devised to append the disaccharide chain to the aglycone, each reliant on sequential attachment of the two monosaccharide units: one is based on sulfoxide coupling (cf. Synth. Meth. *45,* 106), and is notable in that conditions for the first attachment have been carefully designed to avoid undesirable orthoester formation[2]; the other is based on a suitably protected glycosyl trichloroacetimidate for the initial coupling, and a glycosyl fluoride for the second[3]. Then comes the Darwinian argument: what do we use when VRSA (Vancomycin-resistant *Staphylococcus aureus*) takes hold? One strategy might be to seek more potent analogs of vancomycin by modifying the disaccharide chain, for which Wong's ingenious 'one-pot', computer-linked procedure might well be adaptable. Here, a library of variously protected thioglycosides with *differential* reactivity is encoded, and an algorithm devised to select the best possible candidates for generating the given target (di- *or* oligo-saccharide!)[4]. Then there is the moral dilemma: do we simply continue to devise more and more potent drugs with the inevitable emergence of more and more potent drug-resistant organisms. Or should we call a moritoriam on developing and using such super-antibacterial agents?

Numerous experimental techniques have been introduced in recent years to avoid handling environmentally unfriendly and potentially harmful solvents, such as chlorinated hydrocarbons, HMPA[5] and DMF. The increasing use of aqueous media, and the associated development of water-soluble reagents[6] and routines, have been particularly welcome, and solid-state ('no-solvent') processes have been gaining ground[7]. Fluorous biphase technologies have introduced a further variable, principally as an aid to the recovery of product(s) and expensive reagents[8]. Now there is an alternative strategy: **syntheses in ionic liquids**! These are quaternary salts, such as 1,3-dialkylimidazolium fluoroborates or hexafluorophosphates, which are liquid at room temp. and support the same chemical reactivity and solubility profiles as traditional aprotic dipolar solvents[9]. Furthermore, they are readily recyclable, finely tunable, and provide simpler and more friendly work-up procedures than those offered by aq. organic routes. This is illustrated in ruthenium-catalyzed arene hydrogenation in imidazolium salts[10] and rhodium-catalyzed hydroformylation in phosphonium tosylates[10a], where the product can be simply decanted from the ionic liquid containing the catalyst. Diels-Alder cycloaddition can also be conducted in such media[11].

Particular advances have come to light in the field of heterogeneous catalysis with **mesoporous (alumino)silicates** as more active alternatives to the more familiar microporous zeolites[12]. The M41S family of molecular sieves - characterized by their uniform pore size and high surface area - have developed rapidly as acidic catalysts in their own right, notably with the advent of the aluminosilicate MCM-41. But more importance attaches to their tunability to enhance selectivity. *Doping* with transition metals has been a familiar ploy, as also *anchoring* transition metal complexes in order to enhance selectivity and facilitate bifunctional catalysis. More recently, palladium has been *grafted* onto the surface of silanized Nb-MCM-41 to produce a highly active catalyst for Heck arylation with either activated or unactivated aryl halides (the large pore size of the catalyst being able to accomodate the bulkiest of substituents)[13]. Surface modification by trimethyl-silylation has also been found to increase catalytic activity by rendering the surfaces hydrophobic, as illustrated by trimethylsilanized titanosilicate (Ti-MCM-41) for epoxidation with aq. $H_2O_2$[14]. Surface modification of the related mesoporous $SiO_2/TiO_2$ aerogels with amines is also reported. Here, a bifunctional catalyst with both Lewis acidic and Lewis basic sites is generated for the difficult epoxidation of alkyl-substituted cyclohexenols[15]. The development of bifunctional organo-silica mesophases, with either three-dimensional networks or linearly chanelled pores, has also been reported[16], while tuning of pore sizes themselves and doping with alkali metal cations to improve hydrothermal stability add another level of diversification[17].

A valuable review was published last year as a result of a ten-year survey of non-linear effects in **asym. synthesis**[18], and the reader will note the more specific reviews in this field by scanning the 'Reviews' section of this volume (p. 245). Of particular note is a review on syntheses with chiral 2-oxazolines[19], the utility of which is further exemplified by the recent catalytic asym. syntheses involving chiral transition metal 2-oxazoline complexes. These include asym. homogeneous hydrogenation of tri- and tetra-subst. olefins[20] and of ketones[21] with iridium(I) 2-(*o*-phosphinoaryl)-2-oxazoline and titanium bis(2-oxazoline) complexes, respectively; *endo*-specific asym. 1,3-dipolar cycloaddition with chiral (aqua)nickel(II) bis(2-oxazoline) complexes[22]; and asym. syntheses with allylstannanes in the presence of chiral rhodium(III) bis(2-oxazoline) complexes as air- and water-resistant Lewis acids[23]. Asym. aldol condensation has been elaborated via chiral zirconium[24] and platinum[25] enolates, and a novel procedure involving *in situ*-generated tin(IV) enolates is based on dual catalysis with a chiral silver(I) binap complex and an alkoxystannane regenerable in a catalytic cycle[26]; Mukaiyama-type aldol condensation is also possible in aq. media with the agency of a chiral copper(II) bis(2-oxazoline) complex[27], and the first asym. aldol polycondensation has been reported[28]. Chiral copper complexes are additionally represented in such diverse spheres as asym. Diels-Alder cycloaddition with chiral copper(II) phosphorodiamidite complexes[29], asym. imino-ene reaction with a chiral copper(I) binap complex[30], asym. 1,4-addition with a chiral copper(II) binol bisphosphite complex[31], and catalytic asym. cyclopropanation with diazo compds. in the presence of a chiral copper(I) bis(azaferrocene) complex[32]. Heterobimetallic catalysis is evident in the first catalytic asym. Mannich reaction with unmodified ketones through the cooperative effect of $La(OTf)_3$ and a chiral aluminum lithium binaphthoxide; in asym. Michael addition with a chiral aluminum lithium aminodiolate complex[34]; and in the asym. reduction of ketones with catecholborane using a chiral gallium lithium monothiobinaphthol complex[35]. Elaboration of asym. epoxidation with transition metal porphyrin complexes is never far from view[36], as also developments in palladium-catalyzed C-$\alpha$-allylation[37] and asym. addition of dialkylzincs to aldehydes[38] (these last mentioned reactions being effective barometers to assay new chiral ligands). Of special note with reference to the former is the asym. synthesis of cyclic $\alpha$-allylmalonates with the aid of a chiral cyclopentadienyl(tricarbonyl) manganese ligand substituted by both a P-chiral phosphine and a chiral 2-oxazoline ligand[39]; With reference to asym. addition of dialkylzincs to aldehydes, an interesting temperature dependence on enantioselectivity has been revealed[40], while resort to a recyclable 2-aminoalcohol *salt* as ligand has been made for the first time[41]. Desymmetrization and dynamic kinetic resolution [deracemization] are important subsets of asym. synthesis, perhaps the most notable addition to the latter being the recent syntheses of chiral 3-ene-1,2-diol monoethers[42] and chiral N-protected 3-ethylene-1,2-diamines[43], each involving the rapid interconversion of diastereoisomeric palladium $\pi$-allyl species as the 'handle' by which deracemization is effected.

**Combinatorial synthesis** is perhaps the fastest developing aspect of organic chemistry, being significant not only for the rapid generation and assay of potential drug candidates, but also for the synthesis and high throughput screening of catalyst libraries[44]. The latter is exemplified by catalytic 1,2-addition of dialkylzincs to aldehydes wherein a library of zinc complexes has been generated and screened from two points of diversity (the ligand and activator)[45]. Here, the most active candidate was found to effect the conversion in 100% yield and an enantiomeric excess of 99%! The integrated combinatorial synthesis and high through-put catalytic screening of ternary alloy mixtures has also been reported[46]. Notable reviews in combinatorial chemistry have been published recently[47], among which there is one devoted to monitoring solid-phase reactions on resin, and one on the application of sequestering agents for rapid purification protocols. Polymer-based syntheses in a non-combinatorial context are well and truly documented[48], particular emphasis being laid on new polymeric linkers[49] and polymer-supported reagents and sequestering agents[50]. In this respect, the 5-step route to 1,2,3,4-tetrasubst. pyrroles is remarkable in that each stage involves a different supported reagent or sequestering agent, work-up being so simple that chromatographic purification is not required[51].

Perhaps no single reaction type has captured more limelight in the last few years than **olefin and alkyne metathesis**[52], with particular emphasis on ruthenium- and tungsten-catalyzed ring closing and opening metathesis. Developments have been manifold. On the catalyst front, there have been three recent innovations: a new recyclable, readily prepared, air- and moisture-resistant ruthenium carbene complex possessing an internal metal-oxygen chelate structure[53]; more tunable alkylidene(dichloro)ruthenium bis(4-imidazolin-2-ylidene) complexes which exert higher catalytic activity through their enhanced Lewis basicity[54]; and an inexpensive combination of [(p-cymene)$RuCl_2$]$_2$ and $PCy_3$ which facilitates ring closing metathesis under neon light activation[55]. Higher-order ring closing metatheses have also emerged, such as a stereospecific double ring closure to produce bicyclic diallyl alcohols or ethers[56], and polyene cyclization by cascade ring closing metathesis[57]. The tandem coupling of diyne cycloisomerization with intermolecular olefin cross-metathesis is a further highlight[58], as also ring closing metathesis of siloxy-tethered dienes to secure silyl-protected oxy-functionalized ethylenic chains[59]. Desymmetrization and kinetic resolution can also be effected by ring closing metathesis through the agency of a chiral molybdenum carbene complex, as in a the synthesis of chiral 2,5-dihydrofurans[60].

In the field of **palladium-catalyzed synthesis,** Heck chemistry[61] will doubtless benefit from two new, highly active *o*-palladated complexes: an inexpensive *o*-palladated tris(2,4-di-*tert*-butylphenyl) phosphite[62], which effects Heck arylation with turnover numbers as high as 5 million(!), and a thermally stable, easily recoverable *o*-palladated imine for which turnover numbers exceeding 1 million are the norm[63]. Heck arylation of olefins can also be achieved in water at high temperature [without co-solvent or special ligand][64], and the same styrene synthesis can be performed with arylstannanes in place of the more familiar aryl halides[65]. Notable, also, is the emergence of *electron-rich* phosphine ligands, such as tri-*tert*-butylphosphine, for Heck arylation[66] [and, incidentally, for Suzuki coupling[67] and palladium-catalyzed α-arylation of ketones[68]] with either aryl bromides *or chlorides*. A 2-step estrane ring synthesis involving Heck vinylation and intramolecular Heck arylation has also been carried out by judicous choice of palladium complex for each step[69]. Developments in palladium-catalyzed N-arylation are numerous. These include the design of an *o*-phosphinoacetal[70] and the electron-rich 2-dimethylamino-2'-diphenylphosphino-1,1'-binaphthyl as ligand[71], both of which markedly accelerate N-arylation with aryl chlorides. Noteworthy, in other contexts, are tunable dendrimer-encapsulated palladium nanoparticles for use in the homogeneous hydrogenation of olefins in water[72], as well as clay-intercalated palladium(II) complexes for Suzuki biaryl synthesis[73]. **Platinum catalysis** is far less adaptable and generally more expensive. However, one might mention the novel synthesis of $C_2$-branched 2-deoxyglycosides via platinacyclobutanes[74], and a platinum-catalyzed O-alkylation with diazo compds[75]. **Rhodium catalysis** features in the unprecedented addition of chloroformic acid esters to terminal acetylene derivs.[76]; [5+2]-cycloadditon with vinylcyclopropanes to form cycloheptanoids[77]; a variant of the Pauson-Khand reaction[78]; asym. homogeneous hydrogenation in aq. micellar media[79]; the hydroacylation of olefins involving a remarkable C-cleavage of unstrained ketones under activation with an *o*-aminopyridine deriv.[80]; in the development of more refined ligands for regioselective hydroformylation[81] ; and in the novel 1,2-addition of arylboronic acids to ar. aldehydes in aq. media[82]. **Ruthenium catalysis,** on the other hand, is evident in the first anti-Markovnikov hydration of acetylene derivs. to aldehydes with fluorous ruthenium phosphine complexes[83]; the first transition metal-catalyzed addition of disulfides to olefins[84]; the first carbonylative [4+1]-cycloaddition of a 1,3-conjugated system (yielding unsatd. γ-lactams)[85]; and a three-component synthesis of (E)-vinyl chlorides[86].

New syntheses with **functionalized organozinc compds.** include nickel-catalyzed cross-coupling of functionalized alkylzinc halides with aryl chlorides[87], and cross-coupling of functionalized arylzinc bromides with primary iodides[88]; cyclopropanation with functionalized zinc carbenoids[89]; syntheses via α-silylalkylzinc bromides[90]; and catalytic asym. annelation via 1,4-addition-intramolecular aldol condensation[91]. Copper(I)-catalyzed regiospecific asym. synthesis of ethylene derivs. by coupling allyl chlorides with dialkylzincs is also possible through the agency of a chiral ferrocenyl-amine[92].

Particular highlights among new **radical-based methodologies** include a 'friendly' one-step radical benzylic allylation with allyl bromide involving initial abstraction of hydrogen with bromine atom[93]; Michael-type addition following radical generation at a remote unactivated site[94]; manganese(0)-mediated radical ring closure of ethyleneiodides[95]; asym. induction with chiral sulfinyl residues on radical ring closure[96]; a radical [non-metal catalyzed] cyclotrimerization of acetylene derivs. using a disilane as auxiliary[97]; further radical syntheses with xanthates as alternatives to less acceptable halides[98]; a new procedure for catalytic *in situ*-generation of organotin hydrides mediated by inexpensive polymethylhydrosiloxane[99]; and a high-yielding hydrocarbon functionalization by α-iminoester or nitrile formation[100].

In **protective group chemistry,** new procedures are available for the cleavage of propargyl-containing protective groups[101], and syntheses with borane-protected [and activated] amines and phosphines have diversified in the direction of enantiopure phosphine-boranes possessing chirality *at boron*[102].

Some further developments in brief:

**Chromium carbene chemistry** has been elaborated with a novel palladium-catalyzed synthesis of aryl allyl ketones via aroylpalladium π-allyl species[103], and by the coupling of chromium alkoxycarbene complexes with halides to provide β-keto-esters and bromomethyl ketones[104].

Further syntheses with **organozirconium compds.** include *m*-acylation of functionalized arenes with nitriles via zirconocene-benzyne complexes[105], and the synthesis of 2-cyclopentenones from *two* alkyne molecules via carbonylation of ate complexes generated from zirconacyclopentadienes and alkyllithiums[106]; there is also a review on zirconocene olefin and alkyne complexes[107].

An interesting asym. synthesis of carbocyclics has been developed by sparteine-mediated intramolecular eliminative **lithium**-ene reaction[108], and asym. synthesis of α,α-disubst. prim. amines can now be conducted via addition of organolithium compds. to N-sulfinyl*ket*imines[109]; asym. synthesis with chiral lithium amides has also been reviewed[110].

**Prins-type synthesis** of 4-hydroxytetrahydropyrans can be effected with either $Sc(OTf)_3$[111] or $Hg(OTf)_2$[112], while all-*cis*-2,4,6-trisubst. tetrahydropyrans are obtainable by a Prins-pinacol sequence with the aid of TfOH or $SnCl_4$[113]. A 3-component synthesis of 2,3-disubst. tetrahydro-furans and -pyrans is also available by sequential addition of ethyl glycolate and a nucleophile to the corresponding cyclic enolethers[114].

Further highlights include: a novel palladium-catalyzed C-α-allylation *with acetylene derivs.*[115]; Ponndorf-Meerwein-Verley-type alkylation of carbonyl compds.[116]; a mild and 'friendly' transfer-hydrogenation of ketones with alcohols as H-donor involving neither catalyst or base[117]; asym. reduction of ketones with cross-linked polymeric 1,3,2-oxazaborolidines under continuous flow in a membrane reactor[118]; a polymer-based aluminum aroxide as *solid* Lewis acid for the Diels-Alder reaction[119]; a new catalytic nucleophilic allylation of aldehydes with allylsilanes in the presence of a nucleophile-tolerant triarylcarbonium chloride[120] ...... and, in conclusion, the prospect of 'downsizing' laboratories with the advent of new micro-reactors and -analytical techniques[121].

[1] Vancomycin aglycone syntheses s. D.A. Evans et al., Angew. Chem. Int. Ed. Engl. *37*, 2700-4 (1998); K.C. Nicolaou et al., ibid. 2708-14.
[2] C. Thompson, D. Kahne et al., J. Am. Chem. Soc. *121*, 1237-44 (1999).
[3] K.C. Nicolaou et al., Angew. Chem. Int. Ed. Engl. *38*, 240-4 (1999).
[4] Z. Zhang, C.-H. Wong et al., J. Am. Chem. Soc. *121*, 734-53 (1999); reviews on oligosaccharide and glycopeptide synthesis s. *17*, 169s55 (p. 245); novel oligosaccharide synthesis via *n*-pentenyl glycosyl orthoesters s. J.G. Allen, B. Fraser-Reid, J. Am. Chem. Soc. *121*, 468-9 (1999).
[5] Use of quinuclidine N-oxide as an alternative to HMPA s. I.A. O'Neil et al., Chem. Commun. *1999*, 59-60.
[6] Review of the design and development of water-soluble functionalized phosphines s. Synth. Meth. *46*, 736s55 (p. 248).
[7] Review of solvent-free syntheses using focused microwaves s. Synth. Meth. *55*, 79s55 (p. 251).
[8] Reviews of fluorous biphase chemistry s. Synth. Meth. *53*, 57s55 (p. 250); Pd-catalyzed α-allylation in a fluorous biphase medium s. R. Kling, D. Sinou et al., Tetrahedron Lett. *39*, 9439-42 (1998).
[9] Overview s. M. Freemantle, Chem. Eng. News 77, No.1, 23-4 (1999).
[10] P.J. Dyson et al., Chem. Commun. *1999*, 25-6.
[10a] N. Korodia, J.-A. Andersen, Chem. Commun. *1998*, 2341-2.
[11] T. Fischer et al., Tetrahedron Lett. *40*, 793-6 (1999); s.a. M.J. Earle et al., Green Chem. 1, 23-5 (1999); French patent FR-2757850 (Inst Francais Du Petrole).
[12] Review s. Synth. Meth. *38*, 756s55 (p. 247).
[13] C.P.Mehnert et al., J. Am. Chem. Soc. *120*, 12289-96 (1998).
[14] M.B. D'Amore, S. Schwarz, Chem. Commun. *1999*, 121-2.
[15] M. Dusi, A. Baiker et al., Chem. Commun. *1999*, 197-8.
[16] S.R. Hall et al., Chem. Commun. *1999*, 201-2.
[17] Cation-doping s. D. Das et al., Chem. Commun. *1999*, 473-4.
[18] Synth. Meth. *47*, 646s55 (p. 248).
[19] Synth. Meth. *51*, 24s55 (p. 249).
[20] A. Lightfoot et al., Angew. Chem. Int. Ed. Engl. *37*, 2897-9 (1998).
[21] Asym. reduction of ketones via Ti-catalyzed hydrosilylation s. M. Bandini et al., Chem. Commun. *1999*, 39-40.
[22] S. Kanemasa et al., J. Am. Chem. Soc. *120*, 12355-6 (1998).

23 Y. Motoyama et al., Chem. Commun. *1999*, 131-2.
24 Asym. aldol condensation with carboxylic acid amides s. J.L. Vicario, E. Domínguez et al., Tetrahedron Lett. *39*, 9267-70 (1998).
25 Asym. aldol-type condensation with O-silyl O-alkyl keteneacetals s. O. Fujimura, J. Am. Chem. Soc. *120*, 10032-9 (1998).
26 A. Yanagisawa, H. Yamamoto et al., J. Am. Chem. Soc. *121*, 892-3 (1999).
27 S. Kobayashi et al., Chem. Lett. *1999*, 71-2.
28 K. Komura et al., Chem. Commun. *1999*, 35-6.
29 J.M. Brunel et al., Tetrahedron Lett. *39*, 9663-6 (1998).
30 W.J. Drury, III, T. Lectka et al., J. Am. Chem. Soc. *120*, 11006-7 (1998).
31 M. Yan et al., Chem. Commun. *1999*, 11-2.
32 M.M.-C. Lo, G.C. Fu, J. Am. Chem. Soc. *120*, 10270-1 (1998); review of chiral ferrocenes s. Synth. Meth. *52*, 497s55 (p. 250).
33 S. Yamasaki, M. Shibasaki et al., Tetrahedron Lett. *40*, 307-10 (1999).
34 G. Manickam, G. Sundararajan, Tetrahedron *55*, 2721-36 (1999).
35 A. Ford, S. Woodward, Angew. Chem. Int. Ed. Engl. *38*, 335-6 (1999).
36 For a recent epoxidation of unfunctionalized olefins with monopersulfate and a chiral Mn(III) salen complex s. P. Pietikäinen, Tetrahedron Lett. *40*, 1001-4 (1999).
37 Update s. Synth. Meth. *48*, 772s55 (p. 173).
38 Updates s. Synth. Meth. *42*, 616s55 (p. 120) and *44*, 565s55 (p. 121).
39 S. Kudis, G. Helmchen, Angew. Chem. Int. Ed. Engl. *37*, 3047-50 (1998); for a rapid microwave procedure s. U. Bremberg, A. Hallberg et al., J. Org. Chem. *64*, 1082-3 (1999).
40 H. Zhang, K.S. Chan, J. Chem. Soc. Perkin Trans. I *1999*, 381-2.
41 H.C. Hailes, J. Madden, Synlett *1999*, 105-7.
42 B.M. Trost et al., J. Am. Chem. Soc. *120*, 12702-3 (1998).
43 G.R. Cook et al., Angew. Chem. Int. Ed. Engl. *38*, 110-3 (1999).
44 Overview of a 'basic survival guide' for the combinatorial chemist s. G. Bhalay, Chem. Brit. *35*, No.3, 25-9 (1999); recent advances s. S. Borman, Chem. Eng. News 77, No.10, 33-48 (1999).
45 K. Ding et al., Angew. Chem. Int. Ed. Engl. *38*, 497-501 (1999).
46 P. Cong et al., Angew. Chem. Int. Ed. Engl. *38*, 484-8 (1999).
47 Reviews s. Synth. Meth. *50*, 555s55 (p. 249); multiple 'split-split' synthesiser approach to automated highly efficient, high-throughput solution-phase parallel synthesis s. P. Brooking et al., Tetrahedron Lett. *40*, 1405-8 (1999).
48 Annual reviews s. Synth. Meth. *50*, 555s55 (p. 249).
49 Recent novel polymer linkers include: a thioacetal-type, C.M. Huwe, H. Künzer, Tetrahedron Lett. *40*, 683-4 (1999); a decarboxylative-type, J.M. Cobb, C. Abell et al., ibid. 1045-8; and a (phosphine)chromium dicarbonyl-type, S.E. Gibson et al., ibid. 1417-8.
50 General method for sequestering by-products formed from activated acyl transfer in solution-phase synthesis s. J.J. Weidner et al., Tetrahedron Lett. *40*, 239-42 (1999).
51 M. Caldarelli, S.V. Ley et al., J. Chem. Soc. Perkin Trans. I *1999*, 107-8.
52 Overview of alkyne metathesis s. U.H.F. Bunz, L. Kloppenburg, Angew. Chem. Int. Ed. Engl. *38*, 478-81 (1999); review of ring opening metathesis s. Synth. Meth. *53*, 321s55, (p. 250).
53 J.S. Kingsbury, A.H. Hoveyda et al., J. Am. Chem. Soc. *121*, 791-9 (1999).
54 T. Weskamp, W.A. Herrmann et al., Angew. Chem. Int. Ed. Engl. *37*, 2490-3 (1998).

55 A. Fürstner, L. Ackermann, Chem. Commun. *1999*, 95-6.
56 M. Lautens, G. Hughes, Angew. Chem. Int. Ed. Engl. *38*, 129-31 (1999).
57 W.J. Zuercher, R.H. Grubbs et al., J. Org. Chem. *63*, 4291-8 (1998).
58 R. Stragies, S. Blechert et al., Chem. Commun. *1999*, 237-8.
59 Protected chiral 2-ene-1,4-diols s. P.A. Evans, V.S. Murthy, J. Org. Chem. *63*, 6768-9 (1998); chiral (E)-3-ethylenealcohols s. M. Ahmed et al., Tetrahedron *55*, 3219-32 (1999).
60 D.S. La, A.H. Hoveyda et al., J. Am. Chem. Soc. *120*, 9720-1 (1998).
61 Reviews s. Synth. Meth. *27*, 871s55 (p. 246) and *43*, 962s55 (p. 247).
62 D.A. Albisson et al., Tetrahedron Lett. *39*, 9793-6 (1998).
63 M. Ohff et al., Chem. Commun. *1999*, 357-8.
64 L.U. Gron, A.S. Tinsley, Tetrahedron Lett. *40*, 227-30 (1999).
65 K. Hirabayashi, A. Mori et al., Synlett *1999*, 99-101.
66 A.F. Littke, G.C. Fu, J. Org. Chem. *64*, 10-11 (1999).
67 A.F. Littke, G.C. Fu, Angew. Chem. Int. Ed. Engl. *37*, 3387-8 (1998); with an electron-rich 2-amino-2'-phosphinobiphenyl cf. D.W. Old, S.L. Buchwald, J. Am. Chem. Soc. *120*, 9722-3 (1998).
68 M. Kawatsura, J.F. Hartwig, J. Am. Chem. Soc. *121*, 1473-8 (1999).
69 L.F. Tietze et al., J. Am. Chem. Soc. *120*, 8971-7 (1998).
70 X. Bei, A.S. Guram et al., Tetrahedron Lett. *40*, 1237-40 (1999).
71 D.W. Old, S.L. Buchwald et al., J. Am. Chem. Soc. *120*, 9722-3 (1998).
72 M. Zhao, R.M. Crooks, Angew. Chem. Int. Ed. Engl. *38*, 364-6 (1999).
73 R.S. Varma, K.P. Naicker, Tetrahedron Lett. *40*, 439-42 (1999).
74 J. Beyer, R. Madsen, J. Am. Chem. Soc. *120*, 12137-8 (1998).
75 R. Schils, A. Demonceau et al., Tetrahedron Lett. *39*, 7849-52 (1998); under ruthenium catalysis cf. ibid. *40*, 63-6 (1999).
76 R. Hua et al, J. Am. Chem. Soc. *120*, 12365-6 (1998).
77 P.A. Wender et al., J. Am. Chem. Soc. *120*, 10976-7 (1998).
78 N. Jeong et al., Organometallics *17*, 3642-4 (1998).
79 T. Dwars et al., Angew. Chem. Int. Ed. Engl. *37*, 2851-3 (1998); with chiral amphiphilic rhodium di(phosphine) complexes in aq. media cf. European Patent EP-844250 (Degussa AG); with rhodium hybrid P-chiral di(phosphine) complexes cf. D. Carmichael et al., Chem. Commun. *1999*, 261-2.
80 C.-H. Jun, H. Lee, J. Am. Chem. Soc. *121*, 880-1 (1999).
81 Enhancement of regioselectivity (normal- *vs.* iso-ratio) with xanthene-based rhodium di(phosphine) complexes s. L.A. van der Veen et al. Angew. Chem. Intern. Ed. Engl. *38*, 336-8 (1999); with electronically dissymmetric DIPHOS ligands cf. C.P. Casey et al., J. Am. Chem. Soc. *121*, 63-70 (1999); with phosphite-capped cyclodextrins as ligand cf. R.M. Deshpande et al., Chem. Lett.. *1999*, 13-4.
82 M. Sakai et al., Angew. Chem. Int. Ed. Engl. *37*, 3279-81 (1998).
83 M. Tokunaga, Y. Wakatsuki, Angew. Chem. Int. Ed. Engl. *37*, 2867-9 (1998).
84 T. Kondo, T. Mitsudo et al., J. Am. Chem. Soc. *121*, 482-3 (1999).
85 T. Morimoto, S. Murai et al., J. Am. Chem. Soc. *121*, 1758-9 (1999).
86 B.M. Trost, A.B. Pinkerton, J. Am. Chem. Soc. *121*, 1988-9 (1999).
87 P. Knochel et al., Tetrahedron Lett. *40*, 197-200 (1999).
88 R. Giovannini, P. Knochel, J. Am. Chem. Soc. *120*, 11186-7 (1998).

[89] A.B. Charette et al., Tetrahedron Lett. *40*, 33-6 (1999).
[90] S. Matsubara et al., Synlett *1998*, 1315-6.
[91] R. Naasz, B.L. Feringa et al., J. Am. Chem. Soc. *121*, 1104-5 (1999).
[92] F. Dübner, P. Knochel, Angew. Chem. Int. Ed. Engl. *38*, 379-81 (1999).
[93] J.M. Tanko, M. Sudeghipour, Angew. Chem. Int. Ed. Engl. *38*, 159-61 (1999).
[94] G. Petrovic, Z. Cekovic, Tetrahedron *55*, 1377-90 (1999).
[95] J. Tang, K. Oshima et al., Tetrahedron *55*, 1893-904 (1999).
[96] C. Imboden, P. Renaud et al., Tetrahedron Lett. *40*, 495-8 (1999).
[97] J. Yang, J.G. Verkade, J. Am. Chem. Soc. *120*, 6834-5 (1998).
[98] Examples s. B. Sire, S.Z. Zard et al., Angew. Chem. Int. Ed. Engl. *37*, 2864-6 (1998); Tetrahedron Lett. *39*, 9435-8 (1998).
[99] I. Terstiege, R.E. Maleczka, Jr., J. Org. Chem. *64*, 342-3 (1999).
[100] Z. Zhang, C.L. Hill, Chem. Commun. *1998*, 2467-8.
[101] S. Rele et al., Tetrahedron Lett. *40*, 767-70 (1999); s.a. S. Sinha et al., ibid. 771-4; s.a. Y. Fukase et al., ibid. 1169-70.
[102] P. Vedrenne, T. Le Gall et al., J. Am. Chem. Soc. *121*, 1090-1 (1999); review of chemistry of phosphine- and amine-boranes s. Synth. Meth. *55*, 220s55 (p. 251); synthesis of BH$_3$-stabilized unsym. triarylphosphines by P-arylation s. B.H. Lipshutz et al., Tetrahedron Lett. *40*, 201-4 (1999).
[103] H. Sakurai et al., Chem. Lett. *1999*, 75-6.
[104] J.M. Concellon, P.L. Bernad, Jr., Tetrahedron Lett. *39*, 7967-70 (1998).
[105] T. Takahashi et al., J. Am. Chem. Soc. *121*, 1094-5 (1999).
[106] S. Akai, S.L. Buchwald et al., J. Am. Chem. Soc. *120*, 9119-25 (1998).
[107] Synth. Meth. *54*, 365s55 (p. 251).
[108] A. Dieters, D. Hoppe, Angew. Chem. Int. Ed. Engl. *38*, 546-8 (1999).
[109] D.A. Cogan, J.A. Ellman, J. Am. Chem. Soc. *121*, 268-9 (1999).
[110] Synth. Meth. *4*, 3s55 (p. 245).
[111] W.-C. Zhang et al., Chem. Commun. *1999*, 291-2.
[112] M. Nishizawa et al., Tetrahedron Lett. *40*, 1153-6 (1999).
[113] M.J. Cloninger, L.E. Overman, J. Am. Chem. Soc. *121*, 1092-3 (1999).
[114] A.K. Ghosh, R. Kawahama, Tetrahedron Lett. *40*, 1083-6 (1999).
[115] I. Kadota, Y. Yamamoto et al., J. Am. Chem. Soc. *120*, 10262-3 (1998).
[116] T. Ooi et al., J. Am. Chem. Soc. *120*, 10790-1 (1998).
[117] L. Bagnell, C.R. Strauss, Chem. Commun. *1999*, 287-8.
[118] World Intellectual Property Organization patent WO-9822415 (Forschungszentrum Jülich Gmbh); review of asym. reduction of ketones with chiral 1,3,2-oxazaborolidines s. Synth. Meth. *43*, 45s55 (p. 247).
[119] S. Saito et al., Synlett *1999*, 57-8.
[120] C.-T. Chen, S.-D. Chao, J. Org. Chem. *64*, 1090-1 (1999).
[121] M. Freemantle, Chem. Eng. News *77*, No.8, 27-36 (1999).

# Systematic Survey

| Reaction symbol | Page | | | | |
|---|---|---|---|---|---|
| HO↓↑N | 1 | ORem↓↑Hal | 32 | NC⇓CC | 65 |
| HO↓↑S | 1 | OC⇓HC | 33 | NC∩OC | 68 |
| HO↓↑Rem | 1 | OC⇓OC | 33 | NC∩SC | 68 |
| HO↓↑C | 2 | OC⇓NC | 34 | NC∩CC | 68 |
| HN↓↑O | 7 | OC⇓CC | 35 | NC↓↑H | 69 |
| HN↓↑N | 8 | OC∩HC | 41 | NC↓↑O | 70 |
| HN↓↑S | 8 | OC∩ON | 41 | NC↓↑N | 79 |
| HN↓↑C | 9 | OC∩NC | 42 | NC↓↑Hal | 80 |
| HS↓↑S | 11 | OC∩CC | 42 | NC↓↑S | 84 |
| HS↓↑C | 11 | OC↓↑H | 42 | NC↓↑Rem | 85 |
| HC⇓OC | 12 | OC↓↑O | 44 | NC↓↑C | 87 |
| HC⇓NC | 17 | OC↓↑N | 47 | NC⇑H | 88 |
| HC⇓CC | 18 | OC↓↑Hal | 50 | NC⇑O | 89 |
| HC↓↑O | 22 | OC↓↑S | 52 | NC⇑N | 90 |
| HC↓↑N | 24 | OC↓↑Rem | 53 | NC⇑Hal | 90 |
| HC↓↑Hal | 24 | OC↓↑C | 54 | NC⇑Rem | 90 |
| HC↓↑S | 25 | OC⇑H | 57 | HalS↓↑H | 90 |
| HC↓↑Rem | 26 | OC⇑O | 59 | HalRem↓↑Hal | 90 |
| HC↓↑C | 26 | OC⇑N | 59 | HalC⇓OC | 91 |
| HC⇑O | 27 | OC⇑S | 60 | HalC⇓NC | 92 |
| HC⇑S | 27 | OC⇑C | 60 | HalC⇓CC | 92 |
| HC⇑C | 27 | NN↓↑H | 62 | HalC↓↑H | 94 |
| ON⇓HN | 28 | NN⇑H | 62 | HalC↓↑O | 96 |
| ON⇓N | 28 | NN⇑O | 62 | HalC↓↑N | 97 |
| OS⇓S | 29 | NS↓↑O | 62 | HalC↓↑Hal | 98 |
| OS↓↑H | 30 | NS↓↑N | 63 | HalC↓↑S | 98 |
| OS↓↑Hal | 30 | NS↓↑Hal | 63 | HalC↓↑Rem | 98 |
| OS⇑H | 31 | NRem∩RemC | 63 | HalC↓↑C | 99 |
| ORem⇓Rem | 31 | NRem↓↑Hal | 64 | SS↓↑H | 99 |
| ORem↓↑H | 32 | NC⇓OC | 64 | SRem⇓Rem | 100 |
| | | NC⇓NN | 65 | SC⇓HC | 100 |
| | | NC⇓NC | 65 | SC⇓OC | 100 |

Systematic Survey                                                     XXII

| Reaction symbol | Page | | | | |
|---|---|---|---|---|---|
| SC⇓CC | 101 | RemC↓↑Hal | 112 | CC↓↑Rem | 202 |
| SC∩HC | 103 | RemC↓↑S | 115 | CC↓↑C | 222 |
| SC∩OS | 104 | RemC↓↑Rem | 116 | CC↑H | 227 |
| SC↓↑H | 104 | RemC↓↑C | 117 | CC↑O | 228 |
| SC↓↑O | 104 | CC⇓HC | 117 | CC↑N | 231 |
| SC↓↑N | 106 | CC⇓OC | 117 | CC↑Hal | 232 |
| SC↓↑Hal | 106 | CC⇓NC | 127 | CC↑S | 234 |
| SC↓↑S | 108 | CC⇓RemC | 129 | CC↑Rem | 235 |
| SC↓↑C | 108 | CC⇓CC | 130 | CC↑C | 237 |
| SC↑O | 109 | CC∩HC | 149 | ElN↑O | 240 |
| SC↑Rem | 109 | CC∩OC | 151 | ElN↑C | 240 |
| SC↑C | 109 | CC∩NC | 153 | ElS↑O | 241 |
| RemRem↓↑C | 109 | CC∩SC | 155 | ElRem↑O | 241 |
| RemC⇓OC | 110 | CC∩RemC | 155 | Het⇓N | 241 |
| RemC⇓CC | 110 | CC∩CC | 155 | Het⇓S | 242 |
| RemC∩CC | 112 | CC↓↑H | 157 | Het⇓Rem | 242 |
| RemC↓↑O | 112 | CC↓↑O | 159 | Res | 242 |
| RemC↓↑N | 112 | CC↓↑N | 173 | Oth | 244 |
| | | CC↓↑Hal | 177 | | |
| | | CC↓↑S | 199 | | |

# Abbreviations and Symbols

| | |
|---|---|
| abs. | absolute |
| alc. | alcoholic |
| aq. | aqueous |
| ar. | aromatic |
| atm. | atmosphere(s) |
| compd(s). | compound(s) |
| deriv(s). | derivative(s) |
| e.e. | enantiomeric excess |
| eq(s). | equivalent(s) |
| E. | Example |
| F.e.s. | Further example(s) see |
| M | molar |
| prepn. | preparation |
| prim. | primary |
| s55 | supplementary reference in Volume 55 |
| sec. | secondary |
| startg. m.f. | starting material for (the preparation of …) |
| subst. | substituted |
| sym. | symmetrical |
| tert. | tertiary |
| v.i. | via intermediates |
| w.a.r. | without additional reagents |
| Y * | Yield |
| ⚡ | Electrolysis |
| ⚟ | Irradiation |
| ○ | Ring closure |
| ◓ | Ring contraction |
| ○ | Ring expansion |
| ↻ | Ring opening |
| ⊕ | Ring hydrogenation |
| ← | 'see title on the left half of the page' |

\* Yields in parentheses refer to the immediately preceeding step of a multi-step reaction

**Derwent**
# Journal of Synthetic Methods

*Every month this service covers everything new and important in synthetic organic chemistry . . .*

**Reactions selected from worldwide journal and patent literature**

- Each reaction rigorously checked to ensure it only appears once
- Each reaction clearly illustrated with its own scheme
- Comprehensive indices, with an annual cumulation
- Retrospective retrieval through online access to over 100,000 reactions, including Theilheimer's 'Synthetic Methods'
- Structure-searchable either online on STN or in-house as REACCS-JSM.

**Available in a variety of formats to suit your needs.**

For further details contact Sales Support,
**Derwent Information Ltd,** 14 Great Queen Street, London WC2B 5DF UK
**Telephone +44 171 424 2347**   Fax +44 171 344 2972   Email salesup@derwent.co.uk

# Formation of H-O Bond

## Exchange ⇅

### Nitrogen ↑       HO ⇅ N

*Tri-n-butyltin hydride/azodiisobutyronitrile*     $Bu_3SnH/AIBN$
**Generation of alkoxyl radicals from N-alkoxyphthalimides under mild conditions** ←

1.

**Alcohols.** ca. 1 eq. $Bu_3SnH$ added to a 0.05 M soln. of N-benzyloxyphthalimide and a little AIBN in benzene, degassed for 20 min with $N_2$, and refluxed for 2 h → benzyl alcohol. Y 95%. Substrates with an alkenyl group underwent the expected radical ring closure to **cyclic ethers.** F.e., reactions, and prepn. of the substrates, also reduction with $(Me_3Si)_3SiH/AIBN$, s. S. Kim et al., Synlett *1998*, 471-2.

### Sulfur ↑      HO ⇅ S

*Magnesium/methanol*     *Mg/MeOH*
**O-Detosylation**     OTs → OH
with Na/naphthalene cf. *21*, 9; with Mg/MeOH, selectivity, s. M. Sridhar et al., Tetrahedron Lett. *39*, 2847-50 (1998).

### Remaining Elements ↑      HO ⇅ Rem

*Amberlite IRA 743*     ←
**Protection of diols as cyclic boronic acid esters**     C
cleavage of the protective group with 1,3-propanediol cf. *20*, 12; with Amberlite IRA 743, simplified polymer-based oligosaccharide synthesis, s. G.G. Cross, D.M. Whitfield, Synlett *1998*, 487-8; cleavage of polymer-based cyclic boronic acid esters in aq. acetone cf. Y. Liao, Z. Li, Synth. Commun. *28*, 3539-47 (1998).

*Trifluoroacetic acid*     $CF_3COOH$
*Tris(trimethylsilyl)silane*     $(Me_3Si)_3SiH$
**O-De-*tert*-butyldimethylsilylation**     $OSiMe_2Bu$-$t$ → OH
with $Bu_4NF$ s. *30*, 4; with retention of N-Boc groups, also with $(Me_3Si)_3SiH$ or $CF_3COOH$ (with simultaneous cleavage of N-Boc groups), s. G. Righi et al., Tetrahedron Lett. *39*, 2385-8 (1998).

*Pyridinium tosylate*     $C_5H_5NHOTs$
**Selective O-de-*tert*-butyldimethylsilylation**
s. *49*, 8s54; retention of N-Boc groups, also selective cleavage of ethoxyethyl ethers (cf. *20*, 22), s. J.H. Zaidi et al., Tetrahedron Lett. *39*, 4137-8 (1998).

*Iodine*     $I_2$
**O-De-*tert*-butyldimethylsilylation**
s. *51*, 3s52; preferential cleavage of alkyl *tert*-butyldimethylsilyl ethers with retention of aryl *tert*-butyldimethylsilyl ethers s. B.H. Lipshutz, J. Keith, Tetrahedron Lett. *39*, 2495-8 (1998).

*Hydrogen fluoride or chloride*      HF or HCl
**O-Desilylation**      OSi≦ → OH
with HCl s. *29*, 415; cleavage of polymer-based silyl ethers with 1 *M* HCl or 0.22 *M* HF s. B.R. Stranix et al., J. Org. Chem. *62*, 6183-6 (1997).

*Hydrogen chloride or Tetra-*n-*butylammonium fluoride*      HCl or Bu$_4$NF
**Protection of hydroxyl groups**      ←
**as 1,1,3,3-tetraisopropyl-3-[2-(triphenylmethoxy)ethoxy]disiloxan-1-yl ethers**
**Removal of the protective group**

2.

A soln. of startg. protected nucleoside in THF treated with 0.1 *M* Bu$_4$NF at room temp. for 1 min → product. Y ca. 100%. The new protective group can be introduced regiospecifically at the 5'-position of nucleosides (with 1-chloro-1,1,3,3-tetraisopropyl-3-[2-(triphenylmethoxy)ethoxy]-disiloxane in the presence of imidazole or pyridine), and is stable in NH$_3$/methanol at room temp.; it is also compatible with the standard conditions for solid-phase oligonucleotide coupling (using a terephthaloyl linker). F.e. and cleavage with 0.01 *M* HCl (at room temp.) s. I. Hirao et al., Tetrahedron Lett. *39*, 2989-92 (1998).

# Carbon ↑      HO ↓↑ C

*Irradiation (s.a. under N,N,N',N'-Tetramethylphenylenediamine)*      ⇝
**Protection of prim. alcohols as 9-phenyl-9-xanthyl [pixyl] ethers**      ←
**Photochemical removal of the protective group**

3.

**under neutral conditions.** A soln. of startg. *crystalline* pixyl ether in aq. acetonitrile (optimally 4:6 acetonitrile/water) irradiated in a quartz tube with low-pressure Hg-lamps at 254 nm for 13 min → product. Y 97%. The highly rigid and planar backbone of the pixyl group results in increased stability of the pixyl carbocation over similar groups such as dimethoxytrityl. No reactive by-products were formed, as in the photochemical cleavage of 2-nitrobenzyl ethers. The protective group is potentially valuable in the combinatorial synthesis of oligoribonucleotides. F.e. and protection procedure s. A. Misetic, M.K. Boyd, Tetrahedron Lett. *39*, 1653-6 (1998).

*Potassium* tert-*butoxide*      KOBu-t
**Protection of sulfate monoester groups**      ROSO$_2$OCH$_2$CF$_3$ → ROSO$_2$OH
as the Na-salts cf. *36*, 493; as alkyl 2,2,2-trifluoroethyl sulfates, **selective removal** of the protective group with KOBu-*t*, s. A.D. Proud et al., Tetrahedron Lett. *38*, 7243-6 (1997).

*Lithium azide*      LiN$_3$
**Phosphonic acid monoesters from diesters**      PO(OR)$_2$ → PO(OR)OH
with LiCl or LiBr cf. *17*, 11s*54*; more rapidly with LiN$_3$ or NaN$_3$ for cleavage of alkyl or aryl esters, acyclic nucleotides, s. A. Holý, Synthesis *1998*, 381-5.

*Sodium telluride*      Na$_2$Te
**Cleavage of carboxylic acid 2,2,2-trichloroethyl esters**      OCH$_2$CCl$_3$ → OH
with Cd-Pb cf. *24*, 9s*51*; with Na$_2$Te, selectivity, s. G. Blay, J.R. Pedro et al., Synth. Commun. *28*, 1405-14 (1998).

*N,N,N′,N′-Tetramethylphenylenediamine/irradiation*  ←
**Photochemical cleavage of phenacyl esters**   COOCH$_2$COAr → COOH
s. *29*, 2s*54*; sensitized cleavage, e.g. with N,N,N′,N′-tetramethylphenylenediamine, s. A. Banerjee, D.E. Falvey, J. Org. Chem. *62*, 6245-51 (1997); under UV- or visible-irradiation s. Tetrahedron Lett. *39*, 4635-8 (1998); under laser flash photolysis cf. J. Am. Chem. Soc. *120*, 2965-6 (1998).

*1,8-Diazabicyclo[5.4.0]undec-7-ene*   DBU
**Protection of carbonyl groups as 4-sulfonylmethyl-1,3-dioxolanes**   C̃
**Removal of the protective group under mild, non-aq. conditions**

4.

1.4 eqs. DBU added to a soln. of startg. 1,3-dioxolane in dichloromethane, and the mixture stirred at room temp. for 12 h → product. Y 80%. The non-nucleophilic base (DBU) is compatible with a variety of sensitive functional groups (e.g. THP-ethers, esters, sulfonamides, silyl ethers, and tosylates). The method is general (for protection of both aldehydes and ketones) and yields are high. F.e. and protection procedure s. S. Chandrasekhar, S. Sarkar, Tetrahedron Lett. *39*, 2401-4 (1998).

*Cupric chloride*   CuCl$_2$
**Cleavage of cyclic acetals**   C(OR)$_2$ → CO
with CuSO$_4$-SiO$_2$ cf. *20*, 20s*54*; cleavage of 1,3-dioxolanes with CuCl$_2$·2H$_2$O, also an asym. variant, s. P. Saravanan, V. Singh et al., Tetrahedron Lett. *39*, 3091-2 (1998).

*Zinc/ammonium chloride*   Zn/NH$_4$Cl
**Selective O-deallylation**   OCH$_2$CH=CH$_2$ → OH
**via regiospecific addition of perfluoroalkyl iodides**

5.

**under mild, neutral conditions.** Water added to a stirred soln. of startg. allyl ether and 2.5 eqs. perfluorohexyl iodide in acetonitrile at room temp., the mixture treated with 5 eqs. each of Na$_2$S$_2$O$_4$ and NaHCO$_3$, and stirred for 30 min → intermediate 2-(perfluoroalkyl)iodide (Y 99%), in abs. ethanol treated with 5 eqs. Zn-powder and 2 eqs. NH$_4$Cl, and the mixture refluxed for 15 min → product (Y 93%). This method is noteworthy for the fact that the O-deallylation proceeds **via a fluorous O-protective group**, which is potentially a synthon for further elaboration. Esters, thioethers, alcohols and cyclic acetals were unaffected. F.e. incl. cleavage of carboxylic acid allyl esters (aliphatic, carbohydrate and steroidal analogs) s. B. Yu et al., Tetrahedron Lett. *39*, 4871-4 (1998).

*Kaolinitic clay/anisole or Envirocat EPZG*   ←
**Cleavage of cinnamyl esters**   COOC-C=C → COOH
by mercuration-demercuration cf. *33*, 9; with kaolinitic clay/anisole or Envirocat EPZG, also cleavage of allyl esters, and selectivity, s. A.S. Gajare et al., Synth. Commun. *28*, 25-33 (1998).

*Graphite*   C$_8$
**Cleavage of tetrahydropyran-2-yl ethers**   OThp → OH
**under mild, heterogeneous conditions**
with zeolites (or bentonite) cf. *39*, 128s*53*; *45*, 10s*46*; using graphite, rapid procedure with retention of acid-sensitive functions, s. Z.-H. Zhang, T.-S. Li et al., J. Chem. Res., Synop *1998*, 152-3.

*Esterase*  ←
**Regiospecific O-deacylation of peracylated carbohydrates**  OAc → OH
s. *42*, 6s*48*, *49*; 6-O-deacylation of peracetylated hexopyranoses with the esterase from *Rhodosporidium toruloides*, and rearrangement to 4-O-deacylated derivs. s. T. Horrobin et al., J. Chem. Soc. Perkin Trans. I *1998*, 1069-80.

*Lipase*  ←
**Preferential enzymatic hydrolysis of carboxylic acid esters**  COOR → COOH
s. *44*, 10; separation of 4-subst. *cis/trans*-cyclohexanecarboxylates with recognition of diequatorial conformers s. K. Königsberger et al., Tetrahedron Lett. *37*, 9029-32 (1996).

**Aldehydes from acylals with kinetic resolution**  C(OAc)$_2$ → CO

6.

Racemic α-phenylpropionaldehyde diacetate added to the lipase from *Candida rugosa* in 0.01 *M* phosphate buffer (pH 7), and allowed to react for 70 min with periodic addition of 0.2 *M* NaOH to maintain neutrality → (R)-α-phenylpropionaldehyde (conversion 25%; e.e. 72%) and (S)-α-phenylpropionaldehyde diacetate (e.e. 62%). Other lipases were less effective. The degree of kinetic resolution decreased with increase in the size of the acyl chain. F.e.s. Y.S. Angelis, I. Smonou, Tetrahedron Lett. *38*, 8109-12 (1997); comparison with hydrolysis of sec. alcohol acetates s. ibid. *39*, 2823-6 (1998).

*Lipases or Immobilized lipases*  ←
**Preparation of chiral carboxylic acids and alcohols**  COOR → COOH + HOR
**by asym. hydrolysis of carboxylic acid esters**
s. *28*, 13s*54*; of ar. α-acoxyketones s. A.S. Demire et al., Tetrahedron:Asym. *9*, 1673-7 (1998); of α-acoxycarboxylic acid esters with lipases immobilized on Celite or pre-polymers *in water-satd. organic media* s. H. Akita et al., Chem. Pharm. Bull. *45*, 272-8 (1997); with the lipase from *Candida rugosa* in a 2-phase aq. organic medium s. A. Cipiciani et al., Tetrahedron *54*, 7883-90 (1998); carbasugars with the lipase from *Pseudomonas fragi* s. J. Chem. Soc. Perkin Trans. I *1998*, 1065-8; regiospecific asym. hydrolysis of acylated cyclobutane-type carbanucleosides s. N. Katagiri et al., Tetrahedron Lett. *39*, 2613-6 (1998); of azaadamantane derivs. s. D. Mölm, N. Risch, Liebigs Ann. *1995*, 1901-2; of bicyclo[n.1.0]alkan-1-ol esters and conversion to chiral α,α-disubst. cyclopentanones s. V. Morisson et al., Tetrahedron *54*, 7749-64 (1998); desymmetrization of 2-benzyl-1,3-propanediol derivs. s. T. Yokomatsu et al., ibid. 9341-56; of tetrahydrofuran-2,2-dimethanol derivs. s. K. Prasad et al., J. Org. Chem. *60*, 7693-6 (1995); of α-alkyl-α-aminomalonates s. S. Sano et al., Tetrahedron Lett. *39*, 5571-4 (1998).

*Papain*  ←
**Enzymatic cleavage of solubilizing choline esters**  COOCH$_2$CH$_2$N$^+$Me$_3$ → COOH
s. *51*, 5; nucleopeptides s. V. Jungmann, H. Waldmann, Tetrahedron Lett. *39*, 1139-42 (1998).

*Trifluoroacetic acid*  *CF$_3$COOH*
**Protection of phenols as alkyl carbonates**  ArOCOOBu-*t* → ArOH
**Removal of the protective group**
with HF cf. *24*, 5s*54*; protection of hindered phenols as *tert*-butyl carbonates with Boc$_2$O/DMAP (cf. *32*, 154), and cleavage of the protective group with CF$_3$COOH or 3 *M* HCl in dioxane, s. M.M. Hansen, J.R. Riggs, Tetrahedron Lett. *39*, 2705-6 (1998).

**Cleavage of polymer-based benzyl ethers** s. *37*, 152s*55*  OCH$_2$Ar → OH

*Thiophenol/potassium fluoride*                          *PhSH/KF*
**Carboxylic acids from carboxylic acid esters**         COOR → COOH
**Catalytic cleavage under neutral, non-hydrolytic conditions**

7.       o-ClC$_6$H$_4$COOMe   $\xrightarrow{[\text{PhS}^-]}$   o-ClC$_6$H$_4$COOH

A stirred mixture of startg. ester, 1 eq. thiophenol, and 10 mol% KF in dry N-methyl-2-pyrrolidone heated at 190° for 10 min under N$_2$ → product. Y 80%. The reaction is believed to occur via initial proton exchange between F- and thiophenol, followed by nucleophilic attack at the carbinol carbon of the ester by thiophenolate ion formed in a *catalytic* cycle. Functional groups such as ar. phenolethers, chloro, nitro and double-bonds remained unaffected. The method avoids the use of expensive and difficult-to-handle bases. F.e., also selective cleavage of methyl, benzyl and ethyl esters, s. M.K. Nayak, A.K. Chakraborti, Chem. Lett. *1998*, 297-8.

*Titanium tetrachloride*                                         *TiCl$_4$*
**Cleavage of carboxylic acid *tert*-butyl esters**         COOBu-*t* → COOH
with CF$_3$COOH cf. *16*, 201; cleavage of cephalosporin esters with inexpensive TiCl$_4$ or SnCl$_4$, also O-de-*p*-methoxybenzylation, s. M. Valencic et al., Tetrahedron Lett. *39*, 1625-8 (1998).

*n-Butylstannonic acid*                                  *BuSnO$_2$H*
**O-Deacylation** s. *55*, 109                           OAc → OH

*Ammonium nitrate-clay*                              *NH$_4$NO$_3$-clay*
**Selective cleavage of *p*-methoxybenzyl ethers**      OCH$_2$Ar → OH
under microwave irradiation on a solid support without solvent s. *55*, 17

*Tetra-n-butylammonium nitrite/acetic anhydride*        *Bu$_4$NNO$_2$/Ac$_2$O*
**Protection of hydroxyl groups as N-phenylcarbamates**    OCONHPh → OH
**Removal of the protective group under mild conditions**

8.

A soln. of 1,2:5,6-di-O-isopropylidene-3-O-(N-phenylcarbamoyl)-α-D-glucofuranose in pyridine treated with 4 eqs. Bu$_4$NNO$_2$ and 1.5 eqs. acetic anhydride at 0° for 10 min, warmed to 40° and kept at this temp. for 2 h, re-cooled to 0°, a further 1.2 eqs. acetic anhydride added, warmed again at 40° for 2 h, the process repeated with a further 1 eq. acetic anhydride, and quenched with satd. aq. NaHCO$_3$ → 1,2:5,6-di-O-isopropylidene-α-D-glucofuranose. Y 80%. O-Acetyl and O-benzoyl groups were unaffected, and there was no acyl or silyl migration from the 3-position. F.e. and with Bu$_4$NNO$_2$ or Bu$_4$NOAc/CsOAc/18-crown-6 (at 60-80°) s. S. Akai et al., Tetrahedron Lett. *39*, 5583-6 (1998).

*N-(Trimethylsilyl)fluorosulfonylimide*                *Me$_3$SiN(SO$_2$F)$_2$*
**Cleavage of acetals under mild, neutral conditions**     C(OR)$_2$ → CO

9.       p-MeOC$_6$H$_4$CH(OMe)$_2$   $\xrightarrow{\text{Me}_3\text{SiN(SO}_2\text{F)}_2}$   p-MeOC$_6$H$_4$CHO

5 Mol% N-(trimethylsilyl)fluorosulfonylimide added to a soln. of *p*-methoxybenzaldehyde dimethyl acetal in dichloromethane *at -78°* under N$_2$, the mixture allowed to react for 15 min, then quenched with satd. aq. NaHCO$_3$ → *p*-methoxybenzaldehyde. Y 95%. The method is general for regenerating aliphatic (including cyclic and steroidal) as well as aromatic aldehydes and ketones, although aromatic acetals were cleaved faster than their aliphatic counterparts. The

catalyst is highly efficient, particularly for acid-sensitive compds., and useful for the cleavage of 1,3-dioxolanes (with a stoichiometric amount of the catalyst) which are resistant to many other reagents (e.g. Me$_3$SiI). F.e.s. G. Kaur et al., J. Org. Chem. *63*, 2365-6 (1998).

*Pyridinium tosylate* $\qquad\qquad C_5H_5NHOTs$
**Selective cleavage of α-ethoxyethyl ethers** s. *20*, 22s*55* $\qquad$ OCH(OEt)Me → OH

*Sulfuric acid* $\qquad\qquad H_2SO_4$
**Cleavage of soluble polymer-supports by alcoholysis** s. *55*, 379 $\qquad$ OCOR → OH

*Ammonium chloride* $\qquad\qquad NH_4Cl$
**Cleavage of tetrahydropyran-2-yl ethers** s. *55*, 69 $\qquad$ OThp → OH

*Ferric chloride* $\qquad\qquad FeCl_3$
**Cleavage of benzyl ethers** $\qquad\qquad$ OCH$_2$Ar → OH
of *p*-phenylbenzyl ethers cf. *43*, 17; selective O-debenzylation of complex monosaccharides and oligosaccharides with anhydrous FeCl$_3$ s. R. Rodebaugh et al., Tetrahedron Lett. *37*, 5477-8 (1996).

*Dichloro[1,3-bis(diphenylphosphino)propane]nickel(II)/* $\qquad NiCl_2(dppp)/i\text{-}Bu_2AlH$
*diisobutylaluminum hydride*
**Nickel(0)-catalyzed deallylation** $\qquad\qquad$ OCH$_2$CH=CH$_2$ → OH

10.

**Cleavage of allyl ethers.** 1.5 eqs. 1.5 M DIBAL in toluene added dropwise under argon at 0° to a stirred soln. of allyl *p*-methoxyphenyl ether and 1 mol% NiCl$_2$(dppp) in ether, stirring continued for 5 min at 0°, then at room temp. for 2 h, the mixture diluted with ether, quenched with water, and stirred for 1 h → *p*-methoxyphenol. Y 90%. The procedure is simple, efficient, generally applicable to aliphatic (prim., sec., or tert.) and ar. allyl ethers, and highly specific for the allyl function [*tert*-butyldimethylsilyl, *p*-methoxyphenyl, benzyl, prenyl, MOM, and THP ethers, as well as O-acetyl, O-pivaloyl, and O-benzoyl groups (with NaBH$_4$ in place of DIBAL in 4:1 THF/ethanol), and O,O-isopropylidene groups being unaffected]. Reaction involves Ni-catalyzed hydroalumination, followed by β-elimination of propene in a catalytic cycle. F.e.s. T. Taniguchi, K. Ogasawara, Angew. Chem. Int. Ed. Engl. *37*, 1136-7 (1998); **N-deallylation** s. Tetrahedron Lett. *39*, 4679-82 (1998).

*Palladium-carbon/ammonium formate/acetic acid* $\qquad\qquad$ ←
**Reductive cleavage of carboxylic acid *p*-nitrobenzyl esters** $\qquad$ COOCH$_2$Ar → COOH
with Zn cf. *49*, 7; by homogeneous transfer-hydrogenation under mild conditions with Pd-C/HCOONH$_4$/AcOH (cf. *26*, 13s*54*), 3-cephem-4-carboxylic acids, s. D. Albanese, M. Zenoni et al., Tetrahedron Lett. *39*, 2405-8 (1998).

*Via intermediates* $\qquad\qquad$ *v.i.*
**Cleavage of *p*-nitrophenyl via *p*-acetamidophenyl glycosides** $\qquad$ OAr → OH

11.

**under mild conditions.** A soln. of *p*-nitrophenyl per-O-acetyl-β-D-xyloside in THF/Ac$_2$O (or Ac$_2$O) hydrogenated over Pd-black under 7 kg/cm$^2$ H$_2$ → intermediate *p*-acetamidophenyl glycoside (Y 100%), in 10:1 acetonitrile/water treated with 5 eqs. (NH$_4$)$_2$Ce(NO$_3$)$_6$ at 0° for 20 min → product (Y 99%). F.e.s. K. Fukase et al., Tetrahedron Lett. *37*, 3343-4 (1996).

# Formation of H-N Bond

## Exchange ⇅

## Oxygen ↑                  HN ⇅ O

*Zinc/calcium chloride*              $Zn/CaCl_2$
**Ar. amines from nitro compds.**              $NO_2 \rightarrow NH_2$
with $Zn/AlCl_3$ cf. *54*, 13; with $Zn/CaCl_2$, o-(2-arylthioethoxy)amines, s. X. Cai et al., J. Med. Chem. *41*, 1970-9 (1998).

*Borane-tetrahydrofuran*              $BH_3$-*THF*
**Prim. amines from siloximes**              C=NOSi≼ → $CHNH_2$

12.          $PhCH=NOSiMe_2Bu$-t   ⟶   $PhCH_2NH_2$

2 eqs. $BH_3$-THF added dropwise to a soln. of O-(*tert*-butyldimethylsilyl)benzaldoxime in THF under $N_2$, stirred at room temp. for 1 h, heated under reflux for 5 h, cooled to -40°, and quenched by careful addition of water and 3 *M* HCl → benzylamine. Y 83%. Cycloalkanone derivs. reacted similarly, but substrates with electron-releasing groups at the *p*-position of the benzene ring afforded a mixture of prim. amine and N-alkylaniline, the latter being formed by rearrangement. F.e.s. M. Ortiz-Marciales et al., J. Chem. Res., Miniprint *1998*, 0151-68.

*Borane-tetrahydrofuran/chiral 2-aminoalcohols/methylaluminum diphenoxide*              ←
**Prim. amines from alkoximes - Asym. reduction**              C=NOR → $CHNH_2$
s. *25*, 15s*42*; chiral 2-aminoalcohols from α-alkoximinoketones in the presence of $MeAl(OPh)_2$ s. Japanese patent JP-09241224 (Sumitomo Chem. Co. Ltd.).

*Sodium tetrahydridoborate/dialkyl sulfates*              $NaBH_4/R_2SO_4$
**Prim. amines from alkoximes**
with $NaBH_4/CF_3COOH$ cf. *25*, 15s*34*; with $NaBH_4$/sulfuric acid esters s. Japanese patent JP-09301932 (Sumika Fine Chem. Co. Ltd.).

*Titanium tetrachloride/aluminum*              $TiCl_4/Al$
**Acylamines from nitro compds.**              $NO_2 \rightarrow NHAc$
with Zn/NaOAc cf. *16*, 674; carboxylic acid anilides with $TiCl_4/Al$, also ar. amines with *t*-BuOH as proton source, s. J.-X. Wang et al., J. Chem. Res., Miniprint *1998*, 886-96.

*Ferric oxide-magnesium oxide/hydrazine*              $Fe_2O_3$-$MgO/N_2H_4$
**Ar. amines from nitro compds.**              $NO_2 \rightarrow NH_2$
with $FeCl_3/Me_2NNH_2$ cf. *27*, 15s*51*; with $Fe_2O_3$-$MgO/N_2H_4$ s. P.S. Kumbhar et al., Tetrahedron Lett. *39*, 2573-4 (1998).

*Tetrakis(triphenyl phosphite)nickel(0)/ammonium formate*              $Ni[P(OPh)_3]_4/HCOONH_4$
**Amines from nitro compds.** s. *47*, 35s*55*

*Palladium*              *Pd*
**Acylamines from nitro compds.** s. *55*, 11              $NO_2 \rightarrow NHAc$

*Palladium-carbon/ammonium formate*              $Pd$-$C/HCOONH_4$
**Prim. amines from oximes**              C=NOH → $CHNH_2$
s. *9*, 38s*52*; with retention of alkene groups s. G.K. Jnaneshwara et al., J. Chem. Res., Synop *1998*, 160-1.

*Palladium-on-polyolefin fibre*
**Prim. ar. amines from nitro compds. in a supercritical medium**  $NO_2 \rightarrow NH_2$

13.    MeOCO—⟨ ⟩—$NO_2$  ⟶  MeOCO—⟨ ⟩—$NH_2$

0.5 g Methyl 4-nitrobenzoate and 0.057 g Pd-on-polyolefin fibre in a batch reactor purged with $CO_2$, heated to 42°, the system charged with $CO_2$ and $H_2$ to a total pressure of 180 bar and a $H_2$ partial pressure of 15 bar, and the mixture stirred for 30 min → methyl 4-aminobenzoate (≥95% purity). This method is useful for aromatic amine production on an industrial scale. The solvent is easily separated from the product by depressurising the reaction mixture. When the solvent is in supercritical state, $H_2$ gas can be mixed easily to achieve the efficient mass transfers of a vapour-phase state but at significantly lower temp. Carbon dioxide, ethane, propane or mixtures of these can be used as solvent, and the catalyst may contain Pd, Pt, Cu, Cr or Ni. Methanol may be used as a modifier. F.e.s. World Intellectual Property Organization patent WO-9730967 (Valtion Teknillinen Tutkimuskeskus).

*Polymer-based (benzylamine-C,N)palladium(II) hydride complex*   ←
**Amines from nitro compds.** s. *55*, 40


# Nitrogen ↑    HN ↓↑ N

*Zinc bis(tetrahydridoborate)·triethylenediamine*   $Zn(BH_4)_2·dabco$
**Amines from azides**   $N_3 \rightarrow NH_2$
with $Zn(BH_4)_2$ cf. *23*, 27s*51*; with storable $Zn(BH_4)_2$·dabco for reduction of aliphatic and ar. azides, also carboxylic acid amides from their azides, s. H. Firouzabadi et al., Synth. Commun. *28*, 1257-73 (1998).

*Anion exchanger-supported tetrahydridoborate/cupric sulfate*   $[BH_4^-]/CuSO_4$
**Sec. amines from N-nitrosamines**   N-NO → NH
with $NaBH_4/TiCl_4$ s. *37*, 16; with readily removable anion exchanger-supported tetrahydridoborate/$CuSO_4$, selectivity, s. S.Y. Lee et al., Bull. Korean Chem. Soc. *18*, 1127-8 (1997).

*Tetrakis(triphenyl phosphite)nickel(0)/ammonium formate*   $Ni[P(OPh)_3]_4/HCOONH_4$
**Sulfonic acid amides from azides** s. *47*, 35s*55*   $SO_2N_3 \rightarrow SO_2NH_2$

*Palladium-carbon/ammonium formate*   $Pd-C/HCOONH_4$
**Amines from azo compds.**   N=NR → $NH_2$
with $Pd-C/N_2H_4$ cf. *22*, 24; with $Pd-C/HCOONH_4$, selectivity, s. G.K. Jnaneshwara et al., J. Chem. Res., Synop *1998*, 160-1.


# Sulfur ↑    HN ↓↑ S

*Electrolysis*   ↵
**Cathodic N-desulfonylation**   $NSO_2R \rightarrow NH$
s. *27*, 18; release of amines from polymer-based sulfonamides s. J.F. Pilard et al., Tetrahedron *54*, 9401-14 (1998).

*Samarium diiodide or Samarium diiodide/N,N'-dimethyl-N,N'-propyleneurea*   ←
**N-Desulfonylation**
s. *51*, 13; deprotection of N-(arylsulfonyl)glucosamines s. D.C. Hill et al., J. Org. Chem. *62*, 4864-6 (1997); cleavage of N-(dimethylaminosulfonyl) groups from indole nitrogen with $SmI_2$ s. A. Batch, R.H. Dodd, ibid. *63*, 872-7 (1998).

*Phenyldimethylsilyllithium*      *PhMe$_2$SiLi*
**N-Desulfonylation**      NSO$_2$R → NH

14.

**Preferential conversion.** 2 eqs. Phenyldimethylsilyllithium and startg. bis(sulfonamide) kept in dry THF for 6 h at 0° under argon, and quenched with satd. NH$_4$Cl → N-methyl-N'-(p-tolyl-sulfonyl)benzene-1,2-diamine. Y 78% (90% with toluene as solvent). The procedure is specific for the cleavage of *N,N-disubst.* sulfonamides. N-Sulfonylaziridines, however, underwent ring opening to **2-(sulfonylamino)silanes**. F.e. incl. cleavage of N-sulfonylindoles s. I. Fleming et al., J. Chem. Soc. Perkin Trans. 1 *1998*, 1229-35.

*Trifluoromethanesulfonic acid/anisole*      *CF$_3$SO$_3$H/PhOMe*
**Protection of amino groups as *tert*-butylsulfonamides**      NSO$_2$Bu-*t* → NH
**Removal of the protective group**

15.      Bn$_2$NSO$_2$Bu-t  ⟶  Bn$_2$NH

0.2 *N* Trifluoromethanesulfonic acid in methylene chloride added slowly at 0° to a soln. of N,N-dibenzyl-*tert*-butylsulfonamide and ca. 20 eqs. anisole in the same solvent (final concentration of TfOH = 0.1 *N*), and treated with 10% aq. NaOH after 1 h → dibenzylamine. Y 92% (90% with neat trifluoroacetic acid/anisole). The protective group ('Bus' derivs.) can be readily incorporated by reaction of the amine with *tert*-butylsulfinyl chloride followed by S-oxidation with *m*-chloroperoxybenzoic acid. Bus derivs. of prim. and sec. amines are stable towards strong bases (incl. RLi, RMgHal) and metalation conditions, but readily removable by mild acidic solvolysis. Furthermore, labile sec. derivs. may be cleaved under the above conditions (after 25 min) in the presence of prim. Bus derivs., while both prim. and sec. derivs. are removed on prolonging the reaction time to 2.5 h *at room temp.* F.e.s. P. Sun et al., J. Org. Chem. *62*, 8604-8 (1997).

## Carbon ↑      HN ↕ C

*Microwaves s. under AlCl$_3$ and SiO$_2$*      ←
*Triethylamine*      *Et$_3$N*
**N-Decarbamylation**      NCONH$_2$ → NH

16.

**of N-carbamylmaleimides.** N-Carbamylmaleimide in 120:1 ethyl acetate/triethylamine heated at 75° for 2 h, cooled to 15°, and stirred for 1 h → maleimide. Y 72.8%. F.e. and tert. amines s. Japanese patent JP-09268174 (Tosoh Corp.).

*Aluminum chloride-alumina/microwaves*      ←
**N-Decarbo-*tert*-butoxylation**      NCOOBu-*t* → NH
**under microwave irradiation on a solid support in the absence of solvent**

17.

**with retention of chirality.** N-*tert*-Butoxycarbonylproline methyl ester and 1 eq. AlCl$_3$-doped-on-neutral alumina mixed thoroughly on a vortex mixer, and irradiated *for 1 min* in an alumina-bath inside an unmodified domestic 2450 MHz microwave oven (*caution:* it is advisable that the microwave oven be operated carefully and for a short duration due to hazards associated with evolution of gases and possible higher localized temperatures) → proline methyl ester. Y 88%. The method is fast, simple, efficient, mild, and selective, leaving a variety of acid- and base-sensitive functional groups (e.g. esters, phenolethers, benzyl and silyl ethers, alcohols, and olefins) unaffected. Interestingly, benzyl carbamates were not deprotected. F.e.s. D.S. Bose, V. Lakshminarayana, Tetrahedron Lett. *39*, 5631-4 (1998); with silica gel as support cf. J.G. Siro et al., Synlett *1998*, 147-8; **cleavage of *p*-methoxybenzyl ethers** on clay-supported $NH_4NO_3$ s. J. Yadav et al., Tetrahedron Lett. *39*, 3043-6 (1998).

*Amberlyst 15/ammonia* ←
**N-Decarbo-*tert*-butoxylation** NCOOBu-*t* → NH
**Simultaneous deprotection and purification**

18.  n-$C_{18}H_{37}$NHCOOBu-t $\xrightarrow{\text{ⓟ-SO}_3\text{H}}$ [ n-$C_{18}H_{37}\overset{+}{N}H_3$ ⓟ-$SO_3^-$ ] $\xrightarrow{NH_3}$ n-$C_{18}H_{37}NH_2$

Clean Amberlyst 15 (2.5 g) added to a 1 g portion of N-(*tert*-butoxycarbonyl)octadecylamine in methylene chloride at room temp., the mixture gently shaken for 14 h, the resin filtered off and washed successively with hexane, THF and methanol, the resulting amine-bound resin transferred to 4 *M* methanolic ammonia, shaken for 50 min, and the liberated amine extracted with THF → octadecylamine. Y 96%. The method is applicable on both small and large scale, and tolerates hydroxyl, carboxy, and ar. amino and carbalkoxy groups; however, Boc-protected ar. amines reacted slowly. The procedure is applicable to solution-phase parallel syntheses. F.e. and selectivity s. Y.-S. Liu et al., J. Org. Chem. *63*, 3471-3 (1998); simultaneous esterification and purification with Amberlyst 15 on formation of α-aminocarboxylic acid esters s. R.C Anand, Vimal, Synth. Commun. *28*, 1963-5 (1998); simultaneous reduction and purification on formation of 2-amino-alcohols from α-aminocarboxylic acids with $NaBH_4$/LiCl in the presence of Amberlyst 15 s. Tetrahedron Lett. *39*, 917-8 (1998); scavenging excess of amine with Amberlyst 15 on displacement of chlorine and on urea formation from isocyanates in solution-phase parallel syntheses s. M.J. Suto et al., Tetrahedron *54*, 4141-50 (1998).

*Acetic acid* *AcOH*
**Sec. amines from N,N-disubst. arylcarboxamides** s. *55*, 154 $R_2NCOR → R_2NH$

*Trifluoroacetic acid* *$CF_3COOH$*
**N-Decarbo-*tert*-butoxylation** NCOOBu-*t* → NH
s. *27*, 110; *51*, 166; with simultaneous O-desilylation s. G. Righi et al., Tetrahedron Lett. *39*, 2385-8 (1998).

**Cleavage of N-benzyl-type polymer supports** ←
s. *22*, 30s*54*; release of a 2-chlorotrityl resin s. W.J. Hoekstra et al., Tetrahedron Lett. *38*, 2629-32 (1997).

*Acetyl chloride/alcohols* *AcCl/ROH*
**N-Decarbo-*tert*-butoxylation** s. *5*, 174s*55* NCOOBu-*t* → NH

*Silica gel/microwaves* ←
**N-Decarbo-*tert*-butoxylation**
under microwave irradiation on a solid support without solvent s. *55*, 17

*Hydrazine* *$N_2H_4$*
**Protection of amino groups as β-amino-α,β-ethyleneketones** N-C=C-CO → NH
cleavage of Dde derivs. cf. *27*, 402s*54*; with retention of N-Aloc groups s. B. Rohwedder et al., Tetrahedron Lett. *39*, 1175-8 (1998); cleavage of 1-(4-nitroindan-1,3-dion-2-ylidene)ethylamines (Nde) with *visual* monitoring s. B. Kellam et al., Tetrahedron *54*, 6817-32 (1998); appraisal of new Dde-type protective groups s. S.R. Chhabra et al., Tetrahedron Lett. *39*, 1603-6 (1998).

*Hydrogen fluoride* *HF*
**N-Decarbocyclohexyloxylation** s. *2*, 430s*55* NCOOR → NH

*Hydrogen chloride* *HCl*
**N-Subst. from N,N-disubst. sulfonic acid amides** NR → NH
Preferential N-dealkylation s. *55*, 372

*Dichloro[1,3-bis(diphenylphosphino)propane]nickel(II)/*
*diisobutylaluminum hydride*
**Catalytic N-deallylation** s. 55, 10

$NiCl_2(dppp)/i\text{-}Bu_2AlH$

$NCH_2CH{=}CH_2 \rightarrow NH$

*Palladium-carbon*
**3-Aminoalcohols from 5,6-dihydro-4H-1,3-oxazines**
with HCl cf. 29, 617; cyclic *trans*-3-aminoalcohols by hydrogenation over 10% Pd-C s. F. Fülöp et al., Synth. Commun. 28, 2303-9 (1998).

*Pd-C*
C

*Palladium(II) hydroxide-carbon/trifluoroacetic acid*
**α-*prim*-Amino-β-hydroxycarboxylic acids**
from 4,8-dioxa-1-azabicyclo[4.3.0]nonan-5-ones s. 55, 325

$Pd(OH)_2\text{-}C/CF_3COOH$

*Via intermediates*
**Sec. from tert. amines via thionocarbamic acid esters**

*v.i.*

$R_3N \rightarrow R_2NH$

$Et_3N \xrightarrow{ClC(S)OPh} Et_2NC(S)OPh \xrightarrow{Me_2SO_4} [\,Et_2N{=}C(SMe)OPh\,]^+ \longrightarrow Et_2NH_2^+ \, HSO_4^-$

1 eq. Phenyl chlorothionoformate added to a soln. of triethylamine in methylene chloride, and stirred under $N_2$ for 1 h → O-phenyl diethylthiocarbamate (Y 93%), refluxed with 2 eqs. dimethyl sulfate under $N_2$ for 2 h in methylene chloride, the solvent removed, the resulting imminium salt dissolved in water, and refluxed for 2 h → diethylamine (Y >95% as the hydrogen sulfate salt). Phenyl chlorothionoformate is similar in reactivity to 1-chloroethyl chloroformate (cf. 40, 13), and the resulting dialkyl thiocarbamates are readily hydrolyzed **under mild conditions**. N-Benzyl-, N-allyl-, and N-*tert*-butyl groups were cleaved in preference to N-methyl or N-ethyl groups. F.e.s. D.S. Millan, R.H. Prager, Tetrahedron Lett. 39, 4387-90 (1998).

# Formation of H-S Bond

## Exchange ↕

### Sulfur ↑    HS ↕ S

*Palladium-tin/carbon*
**Mercaptans from disulfides** s. 6, 47s55

*Pd-Sn/C*
$RSSR \rightarrow 2\,RSH$

### Carbon ↑    HS ↕ C

*Sodium methylmercaptide*
**S-Deacylation under mild conditions**

*NaSMe*
$SAc \rightarrow SH$

1 eq. 1 M Na-methylmercaptide in methanol added to a stirred soln. of startg. thioacetate in the same solvent at -10° under $N_2$, stirred for 30 min, and the mixture added to 0.1 N HCl → product. Y 82%. The method is useful for regenerating volatile or water-soluble mercaptans, and the deprotection protocol is superior to simple basic hydrolysis or ammonia treatment (NaSMe acting as a sacrificial reductant). The procedure is generally applicable to cleavage of prim., sec., tert. and ar. thioacetates. Functional groups such as enones, lactones, esters, acetals, alcohols, and amides remain unaffected. F.e.s. O.B. Wallace, D.M. Springer, Tetrahedron Lett. 39, 2693-4 (1998).

*Trifluoroacetic acid/triethylsilane* $\qquad$ *CF₃COOH/Et₃SiH*
**Removal of benzyl-type S-protective groups** $\qquad$ SR → SH
s. *16*, 172s*46, 48*; cleavage of 9*H*-xanthen-9-yl and 2-methoxy-9*H*-xanthen-9-yl S-protective groups, application to peptide synthesis with retention of the polymer anchor, also cyclic disulfides by S-deprotection-intramolecular oxidative coupling, s. Y. Han, G. Barany, J. Org. Chem. *62*, 3841-8 (1997).

*Palladium-tin/carbon* $\qquad$ *Pd-Sn/C*
**Mercaptans from thiocyanates** $\qquad$ SCN → SH
with LAH cf. *6*, 47; by catalytic hydrogenation over Pd-Sn on activated carbon, also from disulfides (cf. *19*, 38), s. World Intellectual Property Organization patent WO-9737971 (Du Pont de Nemours & Co.).

# Formation of H-C Bond

## Uptake $\qquad$ ⇓

## Addition to Oxygen and Carbon $\qquad$ HC ⇓ OC

*Electrolysis*
**Alcohols from oxo compds.** $\qquad$ CO → CHOH
**Electrochemical Meerwein-Ponndorf-Verley reduction**

21. $\qquad$ p-MeOC₆H₄CHO $\longrightarrow$ p-MeOC₆H₄CH₂OH

*p*-Methoxybenzaldehyde (*0.1* M *scale*) added to a satd. soln. of NaI in abs. ethanol contained in a cell equipped with two Al electrodes, stirred until thoroughly mixed, electrolyzed at a current density of 0.05 A/cm² for 6 h, and refluxed for 6-10 h under N₂ bubbling to remove acetaldehyde → *p*-methoxybenzyl alcohol. Y 92%. The concentration was very critical (yields being low at lower concentration, and more side-products being formed at higher concentration). Al(OEt)₃, the effective reductant, is produced *in situ*. The method is economical, convenient and inexpensive. F.e. and application on a large scale, s. W.-D. Yang et al., Synth. Commun. *28*, 2827-30 (1998).

*Electrolysis/alcohol dehydrogenase* $\qquad$ ←
**Asym. cathodic reduction of ketones**
s. *42*, 22s*52*; with alcohol dehydrogenase as electrocatalyst s. R. Yuan et al., J. Org. Chem. *62*, 2494-9 (1997).

*Zinc s. under FeCl₃* $\qquad$ Zn

*Borane-dimethyl sulfide/chiral 2-hydroxyphosphonic acid amides* $\qquad$ ←
**Asym. reduction of ketones** s. *43*, 45s*55*

*Sodium tetrahydridoborate/alumina* $\qquad$ *NaBH₄/Al₂O₃*
**Sec. alcohols from ketones**
with alumina impregnated with NaBH₄ cf. *35*, 20; with NaBH₄ and moist alumina (i.e. without preliminary preparation of the supported reagent) s. S. Yakabe et al., J. Chem. Res., Synop *1998*, 322-3.

*Sodium tetrahydridoborate/chiral 2-α-hydroxybenzimidazoles* $\qquad$ ←
**Asym. reduction of ketones**
with NaBH₄/chiral β-hydroxysulfoximines/Me₃SiCl cf. *49*, 35; with NaBH₄/chiral 2-α-hydroxybenzimidazoles s. D.K. Maiti, P.K. Bhattacharya, Synth. Commun. *28*, 99-108 (1998).

*Lithium tetrahydridoaluminate* $\qquad$ *LiAlH₄*
**Sec. alcohols from ketones**
s. *6*, 54; 5-hydroxy-1,3-dioxanes from 1,3-dioxan-5-ones, also with L-Selectride and stereoselectivity, s. D.C. Forbes et al., Synthesis *1998*, 879-82.

*Diisobutylaluminum hydride*                                                      i-$Bu_2AlH$
**Sec. alcohols from ketones**                                        CO → CHOH
stereospecific reduction s. *24*, 61s*29, 30*; of cyclic ketones to the thermodynamically more stable alcohol in ether (at 25° or reflux) s. J.S. Cha et al., Synlett *1997*, 1465-6.

*Lithium hydridotri-tert-butoxoaluminate*                                  $Li[AlH(OBu\text{-}t)_3]$
**Sec. alcohols from ketones**
regiospecific reduction s. *32*, 26s*33*; cyclic α,β-ethylene-γ-hydroxyketones from 2-ene-1,4-diones, regio- and stereo-selectivity, also with $NaBH_4$/MeOH, s. C. Liu, D.J. Burnell, J. Org. Chem. *62*, 3683-7 (1997).

*Chiral 1,3,2-oxazaborolidines/borane-dimethyl sulfide or borane-tetrahydrofuran*      ←
**Asym. reduction of ketones**
s. *43*, 45s*51, 53*; chiral 2-arylthio-2-ethylenealcohols from α-arylthio-α,β-ethyleneketones and ozonolysis to chiral α-hydroxythiolic acid esters s. R. Berenguer et al., Tetrahedron Lett. *39*, 2183-6 (1998); with chiral 2-hydroxyphosphinamides possessing both Lewis basic and acidic groups (cf. *43*, 45s*51*) cf. B. Burns et al., J. Chem. Soc. Perkin Trans. I *1998*, 1027-38; f. reductions s. Volume **52** (p.11); chiral 1,2-bromhydrins with configurationally constrained chiral 1,3,2-oxazaborolidines based on (1R,2S)-1-amino-2-tetralol s. R. Hett et al., Tetrahedron Lett. *39*, 1705-8 (1998); asym. reduction of ketones with oxazaborolidines based on (1S,3R,4R)-2-azanorbornyl-3-methanol cf. P. Pinho et al., Tetrahedron *54*, 7897-906 (1998); with borane-THF/(S)-2-amino-1,1-diphenyl-3-(2-naphthyl)-1-propanol cf. Y.-W. Zhang et al., Synth. Commun. *25*, 3407-11 (1995).

*Hydrotalcite/isopropanol*                                                                              ←
**Alcohols from oxo compds.**
**Heterogeneous Meerwein-Ponndorf-Verley reduction**

22.          t-Bu—⟨⟩=O    →    t-Bu—⟨⟩···OH

A mixture of 4-*tert*-butylcyclohexanone and a little hydrotalcite (Mg/Al *3:1;* calcined at *450°* under $N_2$) in isopropanol allowed to react at 82° for 4 h → 4-*tert*-butylcyclohexanol. Conversion 98%; selectivity >95% (*trans:cis* 85:15). This is a highly active, selective and regenerable catalyst. Its activity is substantially higher than that reported for alumina, silica-alumina or Y-zeolite, the high activity being attributed to the presence of both strongly basic and mildly acidic sites. Aldol condensation was not observed. F.e. for selective reduction of unsatd. aldehydes s. P.S. Kumbhar et al., Chem. Commun. *1998*, 535-6.

*Dichloroindium hydride*                                                                      $Cl_2InH$
**Reductions with dichloroindium hydride**                                           ←

23.      Ph⌒CHO    [$InCl_3$ + $Bu_3SnH$ / THF, $HInCl_2$(THF)]    →    Ph⌒⌒OH

**Prim. alcohols from aldehydes.** A mixture of 1 eq. $InCl_3$ and 1 eq. $Bu_3SnH$ in dry THF stirred for 10 min at -78° under $N_2$, cinnamaldehyde added, the mixture warmed to 0°, and after 1 h quenched with 1 *N* HCl then washed with aq. $NH_4F$ (to remove $Bu_3SnCl$) → cinnamyl alcohol. Y 99% (by GLC). The indium hydride is stable in THF soln. at ambient temp., but is not formed in toluene at this temp. suggesting that the coordination of THF effects both generation and stabilization of the reagent. Functional groups such as nitro, cyano, halides and esters remained unaffected. F.e. incl. reduction of aliphatic and ar. aldehydes, also debromination and 1,4-reduction of an enone, s. T. Miyai et al., Tetrahedron Lett. *39*, 1929-32 (1998).

*Alcohol dehydrogenases (s.a. under Electrolysis)* ←
**Asym. reduction of ketones** CO → CHOH
s. *41*, 38s*53*; kinetic resolution on reduction of *o*- and *m*-subst. (benzaldehyde)tricarbonylchromium(0) complexes with horse liver alcohol dehydrogenase s. C. Baldoli et al., Tetrahedron:Asym. 1497-504 (1998).

*Yeast* ←
**Asym. reduction of ketones**
s. *29*, 36s*53*; of 1-acetoxy-3-aryloxypropan-2-ones s. G. Egri et al., Tetrahedron:Asym. *9*, 271-83 (1998); of ethyl N-Boc-3-oxopyrrolidine-2-carboxylate s. R.M. Williams, J. Cao, Tetrahedron Lett. *37*, 5441-4 (1996); of 4-phenyl-2-ketobutyric acid esters s. D.H. Dao et al., Bull. Chem. Soc. Jpn. *71*, 425-32 (1998); of sulfur-containing trifluoromethyl ketones with the alcohol dehydrogenase from *Geotrichum* s. K. Nakamura et al., Tetrahedron *54*, 8393-402 (1998); *anti*-Prelog asym. reduction of aryl halogenomethyl or hydroxymethyl ketones s. Z.-L. Wei et al., ibid. 13059-72; prepn. of chiral 1,2-bromhydrins s. *55*, 34.

*Diphenylsilane/bis(norbornadiene)rhodium(I) perchlorate/chiral tripodal phosphite* ←
**Sec. alcohols from ketones via asym. hydrosilylation**
s. *49*, 42s*52*; with (S,S,S)-2,2′,2″-tris(2,4,8,10-tetra-*tert*-butyldibenzo[*d,f*][1,3,2]dioxaphosphepin-6-yl-6-oxy)tri-2-propylamine [(S,S,S)-TRISPHOS] and 2 mol% (NBD)$_2$Rh(I)ClO$_4$ s. S.D. Pastor, S.P. Shum, Tetrahedron:Asym. *9*, 543-6 (1998).

*Polymer-based organosilicon hydrides/chlorotris(triphenylphosphine)rhodium(I)* ←
**Alcohols from oxo compds. via polymer-based hydrosilylation**

24.

A mixture of 0.5 eq. polystyrene-diethylsilane, 4-biphenylylcarboxaldehyde, and 4 mol% RhCl(PPh$_3$)$_3$ in dry *N-methyl-2-pyrrolidone* (NMP) stirred at 60° for 2 h under argon, the mixture washed three times with NMP, dichloromethane and THF, the resin treated with 0.4 *M* HF/pyridine in THF, agitated for 2 h, methoxy(trimethyl)silane added (to scavenge excess HF), and agitated for a further 2 h → product. Y 88%. Use of coordinating NMP as solvent was essential for the success of the reaction, and prevented the deposition of metallic rhodium on the resin beads. Cleavage of the resin with HF/py is complementary to the non-invasive method with AcOH/THF/H$_2$O. F.e., **also polymer-based alkoxysilanes from alcohols,** s. Y. Hu, J.A. Porco, Jr., Tetrahedron Lett. *39*, 2711-4 (1998).

*Polymethylhydrosiloxane/tetra-n-butylammonium fluoride* ←
**Alcohols from oxo compds.**
with polymethylhydrosiloxane/ZnCl$_2$ cf. *36*, 670s*53*; more rapidly with Bu$_4$NF or [more cheaply] with Triton B as catalyst, chemo- and stereo-selectivity, also prim. alcohols from carboxylic acid esters (cf. *36*, 670s*37, 39*) or carboxylic acids with 0.02 mol% Bu$_4$NF, s. M.D. Drew et al., Synlett *1997,* 989-91.

*Sodium dithionite* $Na_2S_2O_4$
**Sec. alcohols from ketones**
s. *33*, 46s*39*; β-hydroxy- from β-keto-carboxylic acid esters, selectivity, s. J. Singh et al., Synth. Commun. *28*, 2253-7 (1998).

*Ferric chloride/zinc* $FeCl_3/Zn$
**Prim. alcohols from aldehydes** CHO → CH$_2$OH
with CoCl$_2$/Zn in aq. DMF cf. *44*, 42s*51*; with FeCl$_3$/Zn s. V.S. Sadavarte et al., Synth. Commun. *28*, 1139-42 (1998).

*Tetrakis(triphenyl phosphine)nickel(0)/ammonium formate* $Ni[P(OPh)_3]_4/HCOONH_4$
**Transfer-hydrogenation with nickel(0)** ←
sec. benzylalcohols with Ni/HCOONH$_4$ cf. *47*, 35; with Ni[P(OPh)$_3$]$_4$/HCOONH$_4$ for reduction of oxo compds. (incl. α,β-ethyleneoxo compds. and α-keto-acids), nitro compds., azomethines, and sulfonyl azides s. S. Iyer, A.K. Sattar, Synth. Commun. *28*, 1721-5 (1998).

*Nickel(II) chloride/lithium/naphthalene*                                                                         *Ni(0)*
**Reductions with active nickel(0) under mild conditions**                                     ←

25.                               $Et_2CO \longrightarrow Et_2CHOH$

**Alcohols from oxo compds.** Startg. ketone in THF added to a mixture of 1 eq. $NiCl_2 \cdot 2H_2O$, 8 eqs. Li powder, and 0.32 eq. naphthalene at room temp. under argon, and worked up after 12 h → product. Y 85%. Yields were lower from aldehydes due to competing pinacolization. Alcohols were also obtained **from α,β-ethyleneoxo compds.** with 2 eqs. reagent. The hydrated salt is essential since water serves as H-donor (thereby avoiding the use of $H_2$). F.e., **also sec. amines from azomethines** (preferably with DTBB as electron carrier), **and α-deuterio-alcohols and -amines** (with $NiCl_2 \cdot 2D_2O$), s. F. Alonso, M. Yus, Tetrahedron *54*, 1921-8 (1998).

*Dichloro(1,5-cyclooctadiene)ruthenium(II)/chiral 2,2′-di(phosphino)biphenyls/*        ←
    *triethylamine*
**Improved asym. Noyori hydrogenation of ketones**                                 CO → CHOH

26.

Chiral 2,2′-di(phosphino)biphenyls are more effective catalytically and enantioselectively than the original Noyori-type BINAP ligands (cf. *43*, 51) in the asym. hydrogenation of ketones. **E:** Catalytic amounts of $[Ru(cod)Cl_2]_n$ and (R)-2,2′-bis(diphenylphosphino)-5,5′-dichloro-4,4′,6,6′-tetramethylbiphenyl in toluene refluxed for 18 h in the presence of $Et_3N$, then, after removal of the solvent, stirred with hydroxyacetone in methanol at 65° for 16 h under 10 atm. $H_2$ → product. Conversion 100% (e.e. (R)-enantiomer 95.6%). F.e. and ligands s. European patent EP-826691 (Takasago Int Corp.); reduction of α-acylamino-β-ketoesters with dynamic kinetic resolution (using (R)-2,2′-dimethoxy-6,6′-bis(diphenylphosphino)biphenyl) s. E. Coulon et al., Tetrahedron Lett. *39*, 6467-70 (1998).

*($η^6$-Arene)dichlororuthenium(II) dimer/chiral 2-aminoalcohols/*                         ←
    *potassium isopropoxide/isopropanol*
*($η^6$-Arene)dichlororuthenium(II) dimer/chiral polymer-based N-sulfonyl-*               ←
    *1,2-diamines/potassium hydroxide/isopropanol*
*Chloro($η^6$-p-cymene)ruthenium(II)/L-prolinate/potassium hydroxide/*                      ←
    *isopropanol*
**Asym. transfer-hydrogenation of ketones**
with Ru(II) and chiral $o,o′$-bis($Δ^2$-oxazolin-2-yl)triarylphosphines as ligand cf. *51*, 26s*54*; with (1S,3R,4R)-2-azanorbornylmethanol as ligand s. D.A. Alonso et al., J. Org. Chem. *63*, 2749-51 (1998); with chiral polymer-based N-sulfonyl-1,2-diamino-1,2-diphenylethanes, also with the less stable $[Ir(COD)Cl]_2$ in place of $[Ru(arene)Cl_2]_2$ cf. R. ter Halle et al., Synlett *1997*, 1257-8; with (1R,2S)-*cis*-1-amino-2-indanol as ligand cf. M. Palmer et al., J. Org. Chem. *62*, 5226-8 (1997); with chloro($η^6$-*p*-cymene)ruthenium(II)/L-prolinate s. T. Ohta et al., Chem. Lett. *1998*, 491-2.

*Water-soluble ruthenium phosphine complex/β-cyclodextrins*                              ←
**Prim. alcohols from aldehydes**                                                    CHO → $CH_2OH$
with $RuCl_2(Ph_3P)_3$ under homogeneous conditions cf. *23*, 51s*33*; *in a 2-phase aq. media* for hydrogenation of water-insoluble aldehydes in the presence of a water-soluble Ru-complex ($RuCl_3/NaI/P(C_6H_4SO_3Na)_3$) and modified β-cyclodextrins as reverse phase transfer catalyst s. E. Monflier et al., Tetrahedron Lett. *39*, 2959-60 (1998).

*Dichlorotris(triphenylphosphine)ruthenium(II)/bis[4(R)-phenyl-Δ²-oxazolin-2-
  ylmethyl]amine/isopropanol/sodium isopropoxide*
**Asym. transfer-hydrogenation of aryl ketones**  CO → CHOH

27.

Both catalytic activity and enantioselectivity of ruthenium-catalyzed transfer-hydrogenation of ketones (method *51, 26s53*) are enhanced by using a *nitrogen-bridged* chiral bis(Δ²-oxazoline) as ligand. **E:** 1 Mol% RuCl$_2$(PPh$_3$)$_3$ and 1.1 mol% chiral ligand in isopropanol heated at 82° for 2 h, solvent removed *in vacuo*, the greenish residue washed with ether to remove free Ph$_3$P, the solid redissolved in isopropanol, acetophenone and 1 mol% NaOPr-*i* added, and heating continued at 82° for *10 min* → (S)-product. Conversion 91%; e.e. 97%. The catalyst can be sterically and electronically tuned, and has a higher thermal stability than previously reported bis(oxazolines). F.e.s. Y. Jiang et al., J. Am. Chem. Soc. *120*, 3817-8 (1998).

*Chiral* trans-*(diamine)dichloro[di(phosphine)]ruthenium(II) complexes/potassium*
  tert-*butoxide*
**Asym. homogeneous hydrogenation of ketones**

28.

Structurally defined and characterizable Ru(II)-complexes possessing both chiral di(phosphine) and chiral diamine ligands serve as shelf-stable pre-catalysts (in as little as *0.00004 mol%* ) for the rapid, efficient, and mild Noyori-type asym. hydrogenation of ketones. **E:** A soln. of acetophenone, 0.00004 mol% chiral Ru-complex, and 0.004 mol% KOBu-*t* in isopropanol degassed in a stainless steel autoclave, H$_2$ introduced to a pressure of 45 atm., and vigorously stirred at 30° for 48 h → (R)-product. Y 94% (e.e. 80%). The reaction rate and productivity are two orders of magnitude higher (the most active catalyst to date) than those obtained with the complex generated *in situ* (cf. *54*, 30). The catalysts are readily prepared, soluble in organic solvents, storable for a long period, and fairly air- and moisture-resistant. F.e. and complexes, also asym. hydrogenation of enones, s. H. Doucet et al., Angew. Chem. Int. Ed. Engl. *37*, 1703-7 (1998).

*Chiral cationic tris(μ-chlorine)halogenobis[2,2'-bis(diarylphosphino)-
  1,1'-binaphthyl]ruthenium(II) complexes*
**Asym. Noyori hydrogenation of ketones**
of β-ketoesters s. *43*, 51s*54*; with a stable *cationic* ruthenium(II) μ-chlorine complex cf. Japanese patent JP-09294932 (Takasago Perfumery Co. Ltd.).

*Polymer-based rhodium carbonyl clusters/formic acid*
**Heterogeneous transfer-hydrogenation of aldehydes**  CHO → CH$_2$OH
of ketoaldehydes s. *37*, 132s*53*; of α,β-ethylenealdehydes with HCOOH as H-donor s. J. Org. Chem. *63*, 2378-81 (1998).

*Chloro(1,5-cyclooctadiene)rhodium(I) dimer/chiral P,P′-1,2-phenylenebis-*  ←
*(endo-2,5-dialkyl-7-phosphabicyclo[2.2.1]heptane)/2,6-lutidine/potassium bromide*
**Asym. homogeneous hydrogenation of ketones** CO → CHOH

29.

Chiral, conformationally rigid, air-stable P,P′-1,2-phenylenebis(7-phosphabicyclo[2.2.1]heptanes) (PennPhos derivs.) are highly effective ligands for Rh-catalyzed asym. homogeneous hydrogenation of simple aryl alkyl ketones and *dialkyl* ketones in the presence of a *weak*, non-coordinating base as promotor. E: A soln. of 0.5 mol% [Rh(cod)Cl]$_2$ in methanol treated with 1 mol% PennPhos deriv., stirred at room temp. for 10 min, startg. ketone added, stirring continued for 2 min, a soln. of 0.8 eq. 2,6-lutidine and 1 eq. KBr in methanol added, and after 5 min hydrogenated in a Parr autoclave at room temp. under 30 atm H$_2$ for 75 h → (S)-product. Y 66% (e.e. 85%). This is the highest recorded enantioselectivity for the asym. hydrogenation of a simple alkyl methyl ketone. F.e., comparison of additives, structural effects, and prepn. of the reagents s. Q. Jiang et al., Angew. Chem. Int. Ed. Engl. *37*, 1100-3 (1998).

*Chiral rhodium(I) aminophosphine-phosphinite complexes*  ←
**Asym. homogeneous hydrogenation of ketones**
of α-aminoketones s. *23*, 51s*54*; s.a. French patent FR-2753193 (Sanofi SA).

*Chlorotris(triphenylphosphine)rhodium(I) s. under Organosilicon hydrides* RhCl(PPh$_3$)$_3$

*Palladium-carbon* Pd-C
**2-Aminoalcohols from oxazolidines** s. *55*, 152 ℃

**N-Protected α-aminocarboxylic acids from 5-oxazolidones**
with Et$_3$SiH/CF$_3$COOH or TiCl$_4$ cf. *38*, 32 and *50*, 250; N-Boc and N-Cbz derivs. by hydrogenation over Pd-carbon under *neutral* conditions s. G.V. Reddy et al., Tetrahedron Lett. *39*, 1985-6 (1998).

*Polymer-stabilized platinum cluster complex/cinchonidine/acetic acid*  ←
**α-Hydroxy- from α-keto-carboxylic acid esters** CO → CHOH
**Heterogeneous asym. hydrogenation**

30.

A mixture of methyl pyruvate, *n*-butanol (as internal standard), and catalytic amounts of cinchonidine and finely dispersed (*d* 1.4 nm) polyvinylpyrrolidone-stabilized platinum cluster complex in acetic acid stirred vigorously in a stainless steel autoclave under 4 MPa H$_2$ at 25° for 0.5 h → (R)-methyl lactate. Conversion 100% (e.e. 97.6%; >1.21 s$^{-1}$ turnover frequency). The catalyst is very stable, and enantioselectivity is effectively independent of the particle size (up to *d* 3.9 nm). Conversion and enantioselectivity were low in ethanol. F.e. and catalysts s. X. Zuo et al., Tetrahedron Lett. *39*, 1941-4 (1998).

## Addition to Nitrogen and Carbon        HC ⇓ NC

*Sodium tetrahydridoborate* NaBH$_4$
***o*-α-Hydroxycarboxylic acid amides from phthalimides** s. *55*, 154 ℃

*Lithium hydridotri-sec-butylborate* LiBH(s-Bu)$_3$
**Alkoxylamines from alkoximes with 1,3-asym. induction** C=NOR → CHNHOR
with Me$_4$NBH(OAc)$_3$ cf. *48*, 38; chiral β-alkoxylaminosulfoxides with L-Selectride s. K. Miyashita et al., Synlett *1995*, 1229-30.

*(S,S)-Ethylene-1,2-bis(η$^5$-4,5,6,7-tetrahydro-1-indenyl)titanium difluoride/*  ←
*phenylsilane/polymethylhydrosiloxane/piperidine/isobutylamine*
**Sec. amines from azomethines via asym. homogeneous hydrosilylation**  CH=NR → CHNHR

31.

The use of prim. amines as additives in Ti-catalyzed asym. hydrosilylation of imines (cf. *52*, 24) greatly expands the scope of the reaction, notably to the reduction of N-*benzyl*imines which normally fail to react. **E:** 3.5 Mol% each of phenylsilane, piperidine and methanol added via syringe to ca. 1 mol% (S,S)-ethylene-1,2-bis(η$^5$-4,5,6,7-tetrahydro-1-indenyl)titanium difluoride in dry THF at 60° under argon, stirred for 15-20 min, further THF and 9.3 eqs. polymethylhydrosiloxane added via syringe, the sealed flask cooled to room temp., placed in an argon-filled glove box, N-benzyl-1-indanimine added, heated to 65°, ca. 2 eqs. isobutylamine added *slowly* over 2.5 h via syringe pump, cooled to room temp., diluted with ether, and stirred with 1 *M* HCl for 0.5 h (*caution:*vigorous bubbling) → product. Y 95%; e.e. 92%. Acyclic imines are reduced with higher levels of enantioselectivity compared to hydrogenation with Brintzinger-type catalysts, irrespective of the E/Z geometry of the substrates. Furthermore, the procedure allows the use of cheap polymethylhydrosiloxane. F.e.s. X. Verdaguer et al., Angew. Chem. Int. Ed. Engl. *37*, 1103-7 (1998).

*Tetrakis(triphenyl phosphite)nickel(0)/ammonium formate*  Ni[P(OPh)$_3$]$_4$/HCOONH$_4$
**Sec. amines from azomethines** s. *47*, 35s55

*Nickel(II) chloride/lithium/naphthalene*  ←
**Sec. amines from azomethines** s. *55*, 25

*Polymer-based (benzylamine-C,N)palladium(II) hydride complex*  ←
**Hydrogenation of carbon-nitrogen multiple bonds** s. *55*, 40  ←

## Addition to Carbon-Carbon Bonds         HC ⇓ CC

*Irradiation s. under Zeolites*  ⋕

*Triphenylphosphine copper(I) hydride hexamer/phenylsilane*  [(Ph$_3$P)CuH]$_6$/PhSiH$_3$
**Carbonyl compds. from α,β-ethylenecarbonyl compds.**  C=C-CO → CHCHCO
with copper(I) hydride complexes cf. *54*, 34; *catalytic* procedure with 0.5 mol% [(Ph$_3$P)CuH]$_6$ and 1.5 eqs. PhSiH$_3$ or Bu$_3$SnH s. B.H. Lipshutz et al., Tetrahedron Lett. *39*, 4627-30 (1998).

*Zinc bis(tetrahydridoborate)/N,N-dimethylaniline*  Zn(BH$_4$)$_2$/PhNMe$_2$
**1,2,3,4-Tetrahydroquinolines from quinolines**  Ⓗ
with NaBH$_3$CN/BF$_3$ cf. *49*, 53s*52*; with Zn(BH$_4$)$_2$/PhNMe$_2$ (cf. *31*, 39s*43*), and reduction of other benzo-condensed N-hetarenes s. B.C. Ranu et al., Synth. Commun. *28*, 485-92 (1998).

*Lithium tetrahydridoaluminate*  LiAlH$_4$
**Pyrazolidines from pyrazolium salts**
**Stereospecific reduction**

32.

2 eqs. LAH added portionwise at room temp. to a stirred soln. of startg. pyrazolium salt in ether, and quenched after 1 h by dropwise addition of satd. NH$_4$Cl → *trans*-2-ethyl-3-methyl-4-nitro-1-phenylpyrazolidine. Y 77% (single stereoisomer). The functional group at the 4-position (NO$_2$, Br, CO$_2$Et) markedly increases the reactivity of the nucleus towards hydride attack. F.e. and with NaBH$_4$, also with simultaneous reduction of 4-acyl groups, s. L.A. Bañuelos et al., Tetrahedron *52*, 9193-206 (1996).

*Triethylaluminum/titanocene dichloride* — $Et_3Al/Cp_2TiCl_2$
**(Z)-Ethylene derivs. from acetylene derivs.**     $C\equiv C \rightarrow CH=CH$

with $Cp_2TiCl_2$/*i*-BuMgBr cf. *36*, 43; with $Cp_2TiCl_2$/$Et_3Al$ **via catalytic hydroalumination** (cf. *47*, 44), also 1,4-dienes by cross-coupling of the intermediate enalanes with allyl chloride, s. A.G. Ibragimov et al., Mendeleev Commun. *1996*, 231-2.

*Zeolites/hexane/irradiation*     ←
**Zeolite-supported regio- and stereo-specific photochemical reduction**     $C=C \rightarrow CHCH$

33.

**of $\Delta^4$-3-ketosteroids.** A soln. of testosterone acetate in hexane stirred with activated, anhydrous NaY zeolite (Si/Al 2.5) for 12 h, the solid washed with hexane, slurried with the same solvent, and irradiated with a 450 W medium-pressure Hg-lamp through a Pyrex filter for 2-4 h → product. Y 80-90% (combined yield from five runs); selectivity 85%. Interestingly, cations within the zeolite direct reduction of the adsorbed steroid from the *more* hindered β-face, the solvent providing the hydrogen source. There was no reduction with cation-free supports, nor in hexane without the zeolite, while homogeneous reduction in isopropanol predominantly took place, predictably, from the less hindered face. F.e.s. V.J. Rao et al., J. Am. Chem. Soc. *120*, 2480-1 (1998).

*Yeast*     ←
**1,2-Bromhydrins from α-bromo-α,β-ethyleneketones**     ←
**Asym. reduction**

34.

A mixture of baker's yeast, D-glucose, and tap water stirred for 10 min at 38-40°, a soln. of 2-bromoinden-1-one in the minimum of ethanol added dropwise, and stirring continued for 24 h at the same temp. → (1S,2R)-product. Y 75% (e.e. 99%). F.e.s. J. Aleu et al., Tetrahedron:Asym. *9*, 1589-96 (1998).

*Titanocene dichloride s. under $Et_3Al$*     $Cp_2TiCl_2$

*Tri-n-butyltin hydride*     $Bu_3SnH$
**Ethylene derivs. from acetylenedicobalt hexacarbonyl complexes**     $C\equiv C \rightarrow CH=CH$
**via reductive decomplexation**

35.

**Cyclic ethylene derivs.** A degassed mixture of startg. acetylenedicobalt complex and 12 eqs. $Bu_3SnH$ in benzene stirred at 65° for 1 h → product. Y 81%. The method not only complements oxidative decomplexation procedures but also provides a simple, high-yielding, stereo-defined (generally *cis*-specific) preparation of ethylene derivs.; furthermore, reduction is applicable to both *exo-* and *endo*-cyclic complexes. A variety of sensitive functional groups (e.g. alcohols, cyclic ethers, esters, and silyl or THP ethers) are compatible with these conditions, and double bond migration is not a problem below 70°. F.e., also enesilanes via regiospecific hydrosilylation, s. S. Hosokawa, M. Isobe, Tetrahedron Lett. *39*, 2609-12 (1998); reductive decomplexation of (π-allyl)tricarbonyliron-lactone complexes with $NaBH(OAc)_3$ s. S.V. Ley et al., Chem. Commun. *1998*, 229-30.

*Diimide*  *HN=NH*
**Diimide reduction**  C≡C → CHCH
s. *28*, 39; chlorins from porphyrins, regioselectivity, s. M.O. Senge et al., Tetrahedron *54*, 3781-98 (1998).


*Nickel(0)/triphenylphosphine*  *Ni(0)/Ph₃P*
**Hydrogenation with active nickel(0)**  ←
s. *16*, 72s*53*; ketones from α,β-ethyleneketones, and nitriles from α,β-ethylenenitriles s. P. Boudjouk et al., Tetrahedron Lett. *39*, 3951-2 (1998).


*Nickel(II) chloride/lithium/naphthalene*  ←
**Alcohols from α,β-ethyleneoxo compds.** s. *55*, 25  C≡C-CO → CHCHCHOH


*Chiral ruthenium(II) 2,2′-bis(diphenylphosphino)-1,1′-binaphthyl complexes*  ←
*(s.a. under [Rh(COD)(S)-BINAP]⁺ClO₄⁻)*
**Noyori-type asym. hydrogenation**  C≡C → CHCH
s. *42*, 45s*54*; asym. hydrogenation of 3-acyl-4-methylene-2-oxazolidones with ((R)-BINAP)-Ru(O₂CCF₃)₂ or other chiral (BINAP or BIPHEMP)ruthenium complexes s. P. Le Gendre et al., J. Org. Chem. *63*, 1806-9 (1998); of eneurethans with [(R)-BINAP]Ru(TFA)₂ s. A. Couture et al., J. Chem. Soc. Perkin Trans. I *1998*, 1403-7.


*Chiral rhodium phosphine or phosphinite complexes*  ←
**Asym. homogeneous hydrogenation**
update s. *27*, 57s*54*; with cylindrically chiral, air-stable ferrocenyldiphosphines as ligand s. J. Kang et al., Tetrahedron Lett. *39*, 5523-6 (1998); with carbohydrate phosphinites s. T.V. RajanBabu et al., J. Org. Chem. *62*, 6012-3 (1997); asym. hydrogenation of dehydroaminoacids with chiral bisphosphinites s. G. Zhu, X. Zhang, ibid. *63*, 3133-6 (1998); chiral *erthyro*-α-acylamino-β-siloxycarboxylic and *threo*-β-acoxy-α-acylaminocarboxylic acid esters with chiral rhodium(I) ferrocenyldi(phosphine) complexes s. R. Kuwano et al., ibid. 3499-503.


*Chiral 1,2-bis[alkyl(methyl)phosphino]ethane(norbornadiene)rhodium(I) fluoroborate*  ←
**Asym. homogeneous hydrogenation**

36.

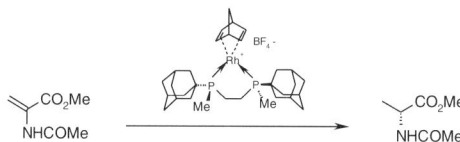

A new class of thermally stable, *symmetrically* substituted, *P-chiral* 1,2-bis[alkyl(methyl)-phosphino]ethanes is now available as highly efficient ligands for Rh-catalyzed asym. homogeneous hydrogenation. **E:** A soln. of startg. ester in methanol hydrogenated with 0.2 mol% chiral Rh-catalyst under 2 atm. H₂ until reaction complete (0.2 to 2 h) → product. Conversion 100%; e.e. >99.9%. The ligands form 5-membered C₂-symmetric chelates thereby imposing an asymmetric environment which leads to high enantioselectivity. β-Subst. substrates required an increase in pressure (6 atm), but enantioselectivity was disappointedly low with β,β-disubst. substrates. F.e. and catalysts s. T. Imamoto et al., J.Am. Chem. Soc. *120*, 1635-6 (1998).

*Cyclooctadiene[(S)-2,2'-bis(diphenylphosphino)-1,1'-binaphthyl]rhodium(I)*
*perchlorate/dibromo[(S)-2,2'-bis(diphenylphosphino)-1,1'-binaphthyl]ruthenium(II)/*
*triethylamine*
**N-Protected γ-amino-β-hydroxycarboxylic acid esters**   C=C → CHCH
**from γ-amino-γ,δ-ethylene-β-ketocarboxylic acid esters**
**One-pot sequential asym. hydrogenation under dual catalysis**

37.

**Statine analogs.** Startg. ethylene(keto)ester and 1 eq. Et₃N in ethanol hydrogenated in the presence of 1 mol% [Rh(COD)(S)-BINAP]⁺ClO₄⁻ and 1 mol% RuBr₂[(S)-BINAP] at 40° under *10 atm.* H₂ for 24 h, the H₂ pressure increased to *90 atm.*, and hydrogenation continued for 24 h → (3R,4R)-product. Y 99% (e.e. >95%). The (3R,4S)-isomer was obtained predominantly with [Rh(COD)(S,S)-DIP]⁺ClO₄⁻. F.e.s. T. Doi et al., J. Org. Chem. *63*, 428-9 (1998).

*Chiral rhodium bis(phospholane) complexes*
**α-Acoxycarboxylic from α-acoxy-α,β-ethylenecarboxylic acid esters**
**Asym. homogeneous hydrogenation**

38.

Burk's asym. homogeneous hydrogenation (*47*, 48) has been successfully applied to α-acoxy-α,β-ethylenecarboxylic acid esters. **E:** A 0.5 *M* soln. of startg. ester (E/Z 3) in deoxygenated methanol containing 0.2 mol% [(COD)Rh(S,S)-Et-DuPHOS]⁺TfO⁻ pressurized to 60 psig H₂ in a Fisher-Porter tube, and stirred at room temp. for 48 h → (S)-2-(benzoyloxy)pentanoic acid methyl ester. Conversion 100% (e.e. 98%). The products are readily converted to the corresponding **chiral glycols and α-hydroxycarboxylic acid esters** with no loss of chirality. F.e.s. M.J. Burk et al., J. Am. Chem. Soc. *120*, 4345-53 (1998); asym. hydrogenation of acyclic enol acetates, incl. 2-acetoxy-1,3-dienes and 2-acetoxy-1,3-enynes, s. N.W. Boaz, Tetrahedron Lett. *39*, 5505-8 (1998).

*Palladium-carbon*   Pd-C
**1,5-Diols from 2-ene-1,5-diols** s. *55*, 35

**α,β-Dideuterio-α-*prim*-aminocarboxylic acids**   C=C → CDCD
**from 3-alkylidene-2,5-piperazinediones via asym. deuteriation**

39.

A soln. of (Z,S)-3-benzylidene-6-(1-methylethyl)piperazine-2,5-dione in 1:1 methanol-OD/DMF deuteriated using D₂ gas (0.5 MPa) in the presence of 10 mol% Pd-C for 2 h, the catalyst filtered off, the soln. evaporated, the resin hydrolyzed with 6 *M* DCl at 120° for 20 h, and worked up first on a Dowex 50W-X8 column (Na⁺ form) to separate valine from deuteriated phenylalanine, then after acidification with concd. HCl (pH 1) on a Dowex 50W-X8 column (H⁺ form) → L-*threo*-[2,3-²H₂]phenylalanine. Y 85% (*threo:erythro* 97:3; e.e. 91%). N,N'-Di-Boc-protected substrates afforded the corresponding chiral *erythro* isomers. F.e.s. M. Oba et al., J. Chem. Soc. Perkin Trans. 1 *1998*, 1275-81.

*Palladium-carbon/ammonium formate*  Pd-C/HCOONH$_4$
**Carbonyl from α,β-ethylenecarbonyl compds.**  C≕C → CHCH
s. *34*, 46s*48-50*; α-alkoxylactones from α-alkoxy-α,β-ethylenelactones, also 3-deoxyaldono-lactones with simultaneous O-debenzylation, s. C. Choquet-Farnier et al., Carbohydr. Res. *303*, 185-91 (1997).

*Polymer-based (benzylamine-C,N)palladium(II) hydride complex*  ←
**Heterogeneous hydrogenation**  ←

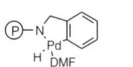

**of ethylene derivs.** A stirred soln. of hex-1-ene in DMF hydrogenated under 1 atm. H$_2$ in a glass reactor in the presence of a little polymer-based (benzylamine-C,N)palladium hydride complex (prepared from aminopolystyrene, Pd(OAc)$_2$, and benzaldehyde in acetic acid, followed by activation on stirring under 1 atm. H$_2$ at 80° for 1 h in DMF) for 1.2 h → hexane. Y 86%. The procedure is rapid, simple, reproducible, and generally applicable to hydrogenation of ethylene and acetylene derivs., ar. and aliphatic nitro compds. (the latter at ca. 70° under a higher pressure), nitriles and Schiff bases (to prim. amines), and phthalic anhydride (to phthalide). The catalyst is safe, readily accessible, storable and reusable (even after 7-8 cycles). F.e. incl. reduction of ar. nitro compds. with retention of *o*- and *p*-chlorine s. M. Islam et al., J. Chem. Res., Synop *1998*, 44-5.

## Exchange  ⇅

## Oxygen ↑  HC ⇅ O

*Electrolysis*  ⚡
**Phthalides from phthalic acid derivs.** s. *11*, 123s*55*  ←

*Borane-tetrahydrofuran*  BH$_3$-THF
**Amines from carboxylic acid amides**  CON< → CH$_2$N<
s. *20*, 71; di-*sec*-amines s. L.R. Orelli et al., Synth. Commun. *28*, 1625-39 (1998).

**Cyclic tert. amines from dicarboxylic acid imides**  ←
with NaBH$_4$/BF$_3$ cf. *35*, 34; hindered compds. with BH$_3$-THF s. M.R. Akula, G.W. Kabalka, Synth. Commun. *28*, 2063-70 (1998).

*Lithium tetrahydridoborate/dicyclohexylcarbodiimide*  LiBH$_4$/RN≕C≕NR
**Prim. alcohols from carboxylic acids via *in situ*-generated active esters**  COOH → CH$_2$OH
N-protected 2-amino-*prim*-alcohols with NaBH$_4$/*i*-BuOCOCl/N-methylmorpholine cf. *47*, 54; with LiBH$_4$/dicyclohexylcarbodiimide via O-acylisoureas, selectivity, s. J.M. Herbert et al., Synth. Commun. *28*, 823-32 (1998).

*Sodium tetrahydridoborate*  NaBH$_4$
**Reductions with sodium tetrahydridoborate**  ←
s. *12*, 110; *23*, 79; *26*, 57; in diglyme at 125-162° cf. C. Yang, C.U. Pittman, Jr., Synth. Commun. *28*, 2027-41 (1998).

*Sodium tetrahydridoborate/lithium chloride*  NaBH$_4$/LiCl
**Prim. alcohols from carboxylic acid esters**  COOR → CH$_2$OH
s. *15*, 71; with retention of azido groups s. H.-O. Kim, Synth. Commun. *28*, 1713-20 (1998); **also from carboxylic acids** in diglyme, and f. reductions, s. C. Yang, C.U. Pittman, Jr., ibid. 2027-41.

*Sodium tetrahydridoborate/lithium chloride/Amberlyst 15*  ←
**2-Aminoalcohols from α-aminocarboxylic acids** s. *55*, 18  COOH → CH$_2$OH

*Sodium tetrahydridoborate/methyl iodide* $\qquad$ $NaBH_4/MeI$
**Amines from carboxylic acid amides** $\qquad$ CON< → $CH_2$N<
with $NaBH_4$ in py or $Et_3N$ cf. *23, 79*; in toluene with added alkyl halide or HCl s. Japanese patent JP-10077251 (Sumika Fine Chem Co. Ltd.).

*Sodium tetrahydridoborate/benzotriazol-1-yloxytris(dimethylamino)phosphonium* ←
  *hexafluorophosphate/ethyldiisopropylamine*
**Prim. alcohols from carboxylic acids via 1-acoxybenzotriazoles** $\qquad$ COOH → $CH_2$OH
**One-pot procedure under mild conditions**

41.

1.2 eqs. Ethyldiisopropylamine added to a stirred suspension of 5-azidopentanoic acid and 1.1 eqs. BOP reagent in THF at room temp., stirred for 5 min, 1 eq. $NaBH_4$ added (*caution*: evolution of gas), and stirred again for 20 min → product. Y 93%. The procedure is generally applicable, convenient, and rapid, and leaves such functions as nitro groups, halides (Br or I), nitriles, azides, and ester groups unaffected. Rigorous drying of the solvent is not essential. F.e. incl. reduction of hindered tert. carboxylic acids, electron-poor arylcarboxylic acids, α,β-unsatd. carboxylic acids, and chiral N-protected amino acids, s. R.P. McGeary, Tetrahedron Lett. *39*, 3319-22 (1998).

*Lithium tetrahydridoaluminate* $\qquad$ $LiAlH_4$
**Acetoxy compds. from carboxylic acid esters** $\qquad$ COOR → $CH_2$OAc
reductive O-acylation with *i*-$Bu_2AlH/Ac_2O$ cf. *27, 68*; with LAH/EtOAc, also from ketones and a carboxylic acid, s. Z. Guo, R.D. Sindelar, Synth. Commun. *28*, 1031-9 (1998).

*Sodium dihydridobis(2-methoxyethoxo)aluminate/morpholine* $\qquad$ ←
**Aldehydes from carboxylic acid esters** $\qquad$ COOR → CHO
s. *18*, 99s*33*; anthracenecarboxaldehydes with added morpholine s. G. Zagotto et al., Bioorg. Med. Chem. Lett. *8*, 121-6 (1998).

*Samarium diiodide/lithium chloride* $\qquad$ $SmI_2/LiCl$
**Carbonyl from α-heterosubst. carbonyl compds.** $\qquad$ O- → H
ketones cf. *41, 63*; carboxylic acid amides, incl. enantioenriched atropisomeric carboxylic acid anilides, with $SmI_2$ or $SmI_2$/LiCl s. A.D. Hughes, N.S. Simpkins, Synlett *1998*, 967-8; effect of co-solvent on reducing power of $SmI_2$ in THF s. M. Shabangi et al., Tetrahedron Lett. *39*, 4429-32 (1998).

*Dicyclohexylcarbodiimide s. under* $LiBH_4$ $\qquad$ RN=C=NR

*Diphenylsilane/carbonylhydridotris(triphenylphosphine)rhodium(I)* $Ph_2SiH_2/RhH(CO)(PPh_3)_3$
**Tert. amines from N,N-disubst. carboxylic acid amides** $\qquad$ CON< → $CH_2$N<

42. $\quad$ p-$(MeO_2C)C_6H_4CONEt_2$ $\quad$ → $\quad$ p-$(MeO_2C)C_6H_4CH_2NEt_2$

2.1 eqs. Diphenylsilane added at room temp. to a mixture of startg. tert. amide and 0.1 mol% $RhH(CO)(PPh_3)_3$ in THF, and allowed to react for 4.5 h → product. Y 70%. Unlike other hydride reductants, the reagent left carboxylic acid esters, epoxides and aromatic bromides unaffected. The rate of the reaction (but not the yield) was affected by the steric environment of the N-atom as well as the carbonyl group. Overall, the method is mild, simple and high-yielding. However, reduction of α,β-unsatd. amides or those with α-hydrogens led to complicated mixtures. F.e.s. R. Kuwano et al., Tetrahedron Lett. *39*, 1017-20 (1998).

*Polymethylhydrosiloxane/tetra-n-butylammonium fluoride* $\qquad$ ←
**Prim. alcohols from carboxylic acids or acid esters** s. *36*, 670s*55* $\qquad$ COO(H,R) → $CH_2$OH

*Titanium tetraisopropoxide/isopropylmagnesium chloride*            $Ti(OPr\text{-}i)_4/i\text{-}PrMgCl$
**Acetylene derivs. from 2-acetylenealcohol O-derivs.**         C≡C-C-O- → C≡C-CH
Asym. hydrolysis and deuterolysis s. 55, 347

*Copper chromite/sodium methoxide*                                                ←
**Amines from carboxylic acid amides**                         CON< → $CH_2$N<
**Catalytic hydrogenation**
prim. amines over barium copper chromite cf. 12, 116; tert. amines over copper chromite/ NaOMe s. World Intellectual Property Organization patent WO-9803262 (Stepan Co.).

*Nickel/molybdenum*                                                                                Ni/Mo
**Phthalides from phthalic anhydrides**                                            ←
with Raney nickel cf. 11, 123; more rapidly with Raney nickel doped with Mo, Cu or Re s. German patent DE-19627697 (BASF AG); by electrolysis, also from phthalic acids, esters or amides cf. DE-19618854.

*Ruthenium(III) acetoacetonate/1,1,1-tris(diphenylphosphinomethyl)ethane/triethylamine*    ←
**Prim. alcohols from carboxylic acid esters**                           COOR → $CH_2OH$

43.                           PhCOOBn    ⟶    $PhCH_2OH$

A soln. of benzyl benzoate, 0.05 mol% Ru(acac)$_3$, 0.06-0.08 mol% 1,1,1-tris(diphenylphosphinomethyl)ethane, and 9 mol% Et$_3$N in 1,1,1,3,3,3-hexafluoropropan-2-ol hydrogenated in a stainless steel autoclave at 120° under 85 atm H$_2$ for 16 h → benzyl alcohol. Y 95% (conversion 97%; TON 2071). Reaction is applicable to both aliphatic and aromatic esters. F.e. and additives s. H.T. Teunissen, C.J. Elsevier, Chem. Commun. 1998, 1367-8.

*Carbonylhydridotris(triphenylphosphine)rhodium(I) s. under Ph$_2$SiH$_2$*         $RhH(CO)(PPh_3)_3$

## Nitrogen ↑                                                                       HC ↓↑ N

*Lithium tetrahydridoaluminate*                                                     $LiAlH_4$
**Aldehydes from hydroxamic acid esters**                           CON(OMe)R → CHO
peptide aldehydes s. 45, 510s51; details s. J. Org. Chem. 62, 6792-6 (1997); Fmoc-protected α-aminoaldehydes s. J.J. Wen, C.M. Crews, Tetrahedron:Asym. 9, 1855-8 (1998).

*Tri-n-butyltin hydride*                                                         $Bu_3SnH$
**Replacement of aliphatic nitro groups by hydrogen**                $NO_2$ → H
s. 37, 58; chiral N-protected α-aminocarboxylic acid esters s. M.J. Crossley et al., J. Chem. Soc. Perkin Trans. I 1998, 1123-30.

## Halogen ↑                                                                      HC ↓↑ Hal

*Irradiation s. under Bu$_3$SnH*                                                        ⫫
*Sodium tetrahydridoborate s.a. under Organotin halides*                   $NaBH_4$

*Sodium tetrahydridoborate/lithium chloride*                           $NaBH_4/LiCl$
**Replacement of ar. halogen by hydrogen**                                Hal → H
in diglyme cf. 25, 62; dechlorination of pentachlorophenol and 1,2,4-trichlorobenzene with NaBH$_4$ in tetraglyme, or with NaBH$_4$/LiCl, s. C. Yang, C.U. Pittman, Jr., Synth. Commun. 28, 517-25 (1998).

*Sodium tetrahydridoborate/dichloro[1,1'-bis(diphenylphosphino)-*       $NaBH_4/PdCl_2(dppf)$
*ferrocene]palladium(II)*
**Replacement of ar. halogen by hydrogen**
with NaBH$_4$/PdCl$_2$ s. 37, 49; selective cleavage of highly chlorinated benzenes with NaBH$_4$/ PdCl$_2$(dppf) and TMEDA as base support s. L. Lassová et al., J. Org. Chem. 63, 3538-43 (1998).

*Dichloroindium hydride*                                                         $Cl_2InH$
**Replacement of bromine by hydrogen** s. 55, 23                        Br → H

*1,1,2,2-Tetraphenyldisilane/triethylborane or azodiisobutyronitrile*     *(Ph$_2$SiH)$_2$/Et$_3$B or AIBN*
**Replacement of bromine by hydrogen** s. 55, 278     Br → H

*Tri-n-butyltin hydride/azodiisobutyronitrile/irradiation*     ←
**Tin hydride-mediated syntheses with halides**     ←
**Improved work-up under mild conditions**

44.     Ph⟶OAc/Br  —Bu$_3$SnH/Me$_3$Al→  Ph⟶OAc    [ + Bu$_3$SnMe ]

Tri-*n*-butyltin halides, formed as by-products on Bu$_3$SnH-mediated syntheses with halides (e.g. debromination, Giese-type 1,4-addition), can be removed more easily by work-up with Me$_3$Al, which converts the tin(IV) halide into the highly polar, hexane-soluble Bu$_3$SnMe. **E**: A soln. of startg. halide, 1.2 eqs. Bu$_3$SnH, and 2.5 mol% AIBN in benzene irradiated at 10° under N$_2$ for 2 h, 1.2 eqs. 1 *M* Me$_3$Al in hexane added, stirred at room temp. for 2 h, hydrolyzed with 1 *M* aq. NaOH, the organic layer separated, washed with brine, dried over MgSO$_4$, the crude product filtered through silica gel with hexane to remove Bu$_3$SnMe, then with hexane/EtOAc to elute the reduced product → 2-acetoxy-1-phenylpropane. Y 85%. Work-up with 1 N aq. NaOH is preferred for non-polar or completely apolar products (the resulting emulsion containing Bu$_3$SnOH and (Bu$_3$Sn)$_2$O being removed by absorption on silica gel). F.e.s. P. Renaud et al., Tetrahedron Lett. *39*, 2123-6 (1998).

*Hexabutyldistannane/thiophenol/malonic acid/azodiisobutyronitrile*     ←
**Thiyl-mediated replacement of halogen by hydrogen**     Hal → H
with organosilicon hydrides cf. *45*, 35; with Bu$_3$SnSnBu$_3$/malonic acid as an alternative to the standard tin hydride route s. K.-M. Kim, B.P. Roberts, J. Chem. Res., Synop *1998*, 132-3.

*Polymer-based organotin halides/sodium tetrahydridoborate/azodiisobutyronitrile*     ←
**Catalytic reduction with *in situ*-generated polymer-based organotin hydrides**     ←

45.     Br-Ad  —(P)-(CH$_2$)$_4$Sn(I)Bu$_2$ / NaBH$_4$→  Ad

1-Bromoadamantane (and dodecane as internal standard) in ethanol added under N$_2$ to a dry Schlenk tube containing 0.2 eq. polymer-supported organotin iodide (based on a macroporous polystyrene cross-linked with divinylbenzene), NaBH$_4$, and AIBN in the same solvent, and slowly stirred for 12 h at 65° → adamantane. Y 93% (Y 75% with 0.05 eq. polymer-based tin halide). Significantly, there was no pollution of the product with tin residues (as evident in reduction with Bu$_3$SnCl/NaBH$_4$), and the reagent can be readily recovered and reused without loss of activity. Details and comparison with other reagents s. G. Dumartin et al., Tetrahedron Lett. *39*, 4663-6 (1998).

*Dichloro[1,1'-bis(diphenylphosphino)ferrocene]palladium(II) s. under NaBH$_4$*     *PdCl$_2$(dppf)*

# Sulfur ↑                                                                 HC ↓↑ S

*Sodium*     *Na*
**Replacement of organothio groups by hydrogen**     SR → H
cleavage of 1,1-fluorothioethers cf. *44*, 70; of 2-hydroxythioethers, and further desulfurizations, s. Z. Yu, J.G. Verkade, Tetrahedron Lett. *39*, 2671-4 (1998).

*tert-Butyllithium/tert-butylmagnesium chloride*     *t-BuLi/t-BuMgCl*
**Replacement of sulfinyl groups by deuterium**     S(O)R → D
with *t*-BuLi cf. *41*, 77s*45*; 2-deuterioaziridines with *t*-BuLi/*t*-BuMgCl with retention of configuration, also trapping of the intermediate 2-lithiated aziridines with other electrophiles, s. T. Satoh et al., Tetrahedron Lett. *39*, 2345-8 (1998).

*Samarium diiodide*                                         $SmI_2$
**Replacement of sulfonyl groups by hydrogen**            $SO_2R \rightarrow H$
s. *41*, 63s*46, 51*; chiral β-aminocarboxylic acid esters s. H. Matsuyama et al., Chem. Lett. *1997*, 375-6.

*Raney nickel (W-2)/sodium hypophosphite*                $Ni/NaH_2PO_2$
**Hydrocarbon groups from thioethers**                      $SR \rightarrow H$
with Raney nickel cf. *2*, 112/3; sec. alcohols with Raney nickel (W-2)/sodium hypophosphite (cf. *28*, 524) with retention of chirality, also from β-hydroxysulfoxides (cf. *4*, 117; *22*, 836), and desulfurization of benzyl and ar. thioethers (with retention of benzyl ethers), s. M. Node et al., Tetrahedron *53*, 12883-94 (1997).

## Remaining Elements ↑                                    HC ↓↑ Rem

*Potassium hydride/18-crown-6 polyether*                     *KH/crown*
**Syntheses via silicon-potassium exchange**                    ←
with $KNH_2$/liq. $NH_3$ cf. *19*, 104; syntheses via ($\eta^6$-potassioarene)tricarbonylchromium complexes by desilylation with KH/18-crown-6 s. S.K. Mandal, A. Sarkar, J. Org. Chem. *63*, 1901-5 (1998).

*Cuprous chloride or Hydrogen chloride*                     *CuCl or HCl*
**Replacement of vinylic stannyl groups by hydrogen**     $C=C(Sn\leqslant) \rightarrow C=CH$
cleavage of 2-silylenestannanes with $HI/Bu_4NI$ cf. *47*, 77; (E)- or (Z)-α,β-ethylene-β-stannylcarboxylic from (E)- or (Z)-α,β-ethylene-α,β-di(stannyl)carboxylic acid esters with HCl or CuCl s. E. Piers et al., J. Org. Chem. *62*, 6034-40 (1997).

*Magnesium chloride*                                             $MgCl_2$
**Replacement of phosphonyl groups by hydrogen**         $PO(OR)_2 \rightarrow H$
ketones cf. *52*, 40s*53*; α-fluoromalonic acid esters from α-fluoro-α-phosphonylmalonic acid esters s. D.Y. Kim, J.Y. Kim, Synth. Commun. *28*, 2483-9 (1998).

*Trifluoroacetic acid*                                          $CF_3COOH$
**Cleavage of arylsilyl-linked polymer supports**               $Si\leqslant \rightarrow H$
with $Bu_4NF$ cf. *31*, 65s*54*; with $CF_3COOH$ s. K.A. Newlander et al., J. Org. Chem. *62*, 6726-32 (1997).

## Carbon ↑                                                                 HC ↓↑ C

*Trifluoroacetic acid/triethylsilane*                          $CF_3COOH/Et_3SiH$
**Removal of polymer supports by decarbalkoxylation** s. *55*, 164, 349    $COOR \rightarrow H$

*Lithium perchlorate/triethylamine*                          $LiClO_4/Et_3N$
**α-Bromocarboxylic from α-bromo-β-ketocarboxylic acid esters**     $Ac \rightarrow H$

46.

2 eqs. Each of $LiClO_4$ and $Et_3N$ (freshly distilled from $CaH_2$) added to a soln. of methyl α-bromo-α-[3-(2-furyl)propyl]acetoacetate in freshly distilled ether, the mixture stirred at room temp. for 4 h, then quenched with water → product. Y 83%. The method is simple, efficient and high-yielding. It is compatible with cyclic acetals and leaves the furan ring intact. F.e.s. Y. Hu, D. Bai, Tetrahedron Lett. *39*, 2375-6 (1998).

## Elimination ⇑

## Oxygen ↑           HC ⇑ O

*Diisobutylaluminum hydride/trimethylsilyl chloride/triethylamine*      ←
**Aldehydes from carboxylic acids via silyl esters**      COOH → CHO

47.  $CH_2=CH(CH_2)_8COOH \xrightarrow{Me_3SiCl} [CH_2=CH(CH_2)_8COOSiMe_3] \longrightarrow CH_2=CH(CH_2)_8CHO$

**One-pot conversion.** 10-Undecenoic acid in dichloromethane treated with 1 eq. each of $Et_3N$ and $Me_3SiCl$ at 0°, the mixture cooled to -78°, 1 eq. $i$-$Bu_2AlH$ added over 30 min, and allowed to react until completion → 10-undecanal. Y 85%. The method is mild, simple and general, leaving olefins, bromides, aromatic chlorides, phenolethers and aromatic nitro compds. unaffected. F.e. incl. ar. aldehydes s. S. Chandrasekhar et al., Tetrahedron Lett. *39*, 909-10 (1998).

*Triethylsilane/Amberlyst 15*      ←
**Cyclic ethers from lactols**      OH → H
with $Et_3SiH/BF_3$ cf. *37*, 76; with $Et_3SiH$/Amberlyst 15 s. M.C. Hansen et al., J. Org. Chem. *63*, 2360-1 (1998).

*Palladium-carbon/acetic acid*      Pd-C/AcOH
*Palladium-carbon/acetic anhydride/p-toluenesulfonic acid*      $Pd$-$C/Ac_2O/TsOH$
**Replacement of hydroxyl groups by hydrogen**
s. *13*, 733; arylacetic acids from mandelic acids s. Japanese patent JP-10053555 (Sumika Fine Chem Co. Ltd.); carboxylic acid esters from α-hydroxycarboxylic acid esters s. World Intellectual Property Organization patent WO-9738963 (Du Pont de Nemours & Co.).

## Sulfur ↑           HC ⇑ S

*Nickel boride*      $Ni_2B$
**Desulfuration with nickel boride**      ←
s. *45*, 43; 2$H$-pyrrolenines from $\Delta^3$-pyrroline-2-thiones s. C.J. Hawker et al., J. Chem. Soc. Perkin Trans. I *1998*, 1493-508.

## Carbon ↑           HC ⇑ C

*Trialkylamines/sodium hydroxide*      $R_3N/NaOH$
**Ar. decarboxylation** s. *55*, 101      COOH → H

*Tri-n-butylphosphine*      $Bu_3P$
**Aldimines from α-iminocarboxylic acids**
**Decarboxylation under mild conditions**

48.

2 Mol% tri-$n$-butylphosphine added to a stirred soln. of startg. iminocarboxylic acid and dry THF (or pyridine) at room temp. under argon, and allowed to react for 2 h → product. Y 99%. The method is simple, general and efficient for preparing ar. aldimines. Strong acids and bases are not required (in fact, they have an adverse effect on yields and reaction times). Sterically hindered imines also gave low yields with longer reaction times. F.e. and **one-pot procedure** from α-ketocarboxylic acids and prim. amines, s. D.H.R. Barton, F. Taran, Tetrahedron Lett. *39*, 4777-80 (1998).

# Formation of O-N Bond

## Uptake ⇓

### Addition to Hydrogen and Nitrogen     ON ⇓ HN

*Titanium silicate/hydrogen peroxide*     ←
**N,N-Disubst. hydroxylamines from sec. amines**     $\geq$N → $\geq$NOH

49.     Et$_2$NH ⟶ Et$_2$NOH

A mixture of diethylamine, *tert*-butanol, and a little titanosilicalite (prepared essentially from ethyl silicate and TiF$_4$, and containing 0.9% Ti, 0.07% F, 0.8% K, and 0.045% Na) heated to reflux (79-80°), 35% H$_2$O$_2$ added over 1 h, and heating discontinued after a further 15 min → diethylhydroxylamine. Conversion 87% (87% selectivity). F.e.s. European patent EP-835688 (Elf Atochem SA).

### Addition to Nitrogen     ON ⇓ N

*Perfluoro-cis-dialkyloxaziridines*     ←
**Amine oxides from tert. amines**     $\geqslant$N → $\geqslant$N→O
with N-sulfonyloxaziridines cf. *44*, 82; with perfluoro-*cis*-dialkyloxaziridines, selectivity, also pyridine N-oxides with retention of carbon-carbon double bonds, s. A. Arnone et al., Tetrahedron *54*, 7831-42 (1998).

*Molybdenum trioxide/hydrogen peroxide/sulfuric acid*     *MoO$_3$/H$_2$O$_2$/H$_2$SO$_4$*
*Methylrhenium oxide/hydrogen peroxide*     *MeReO$_3$/H$_2$O$_2$*
**Cyclic N-oxides from N-heterocyclics**
with MeReO$_3$/H$_2$O$_2$ s. *51*, 45; pyridine N-oxides from simple 3- and 4-subst. pyridines incl. electron-deficient derivs., also with retention of ethylene groups, s. K.B. Sharpless et al., J. Org. Chem. *63*, 1740-1 (1998); with MoO$_3$/H$_2$O$_2$/H$_2$SO$_4$, and further catalysts (incl. WO$_3$) and oxyacids (cf. *27*, 184), s. Japanese patent JP-09087251 (Tama Kagaku Kogyo KK).

*Perrhenic acid/bis(trimethylsilyl) peroxide*     *HReO$_4$/Me$_3$SiOOSiMe$_3$*
**Pyridine N-oxides from pyridines**

50.     MeO$_2$C—⟨N⟩ ⟶ MeO$_2$C—⟨N⟩→O

A mixture of methyl isonicotinate and 0.5 mol% HReO$_4$ (65-70% aq. soln.) in dichloromethane treated with 1.5 eqs. bis(trimethylsilyl) peroxide, and stirred at 24° (water-bath) for 6 h → methyl isonicotinate N-oxide. Y 98%. A trace of water was essential. Reaction with only 0.1 mol% HReO$_4$ required 40 h for completion. The method is mild and general, work-up is easy, and reagents are inexpensive, readily available and non-toxic. Bromine, chlorine, and alkenyl, cyano and nitro groups on the pyridine ring remained unaffected. F.e., also with ReO$_3$ for the oxidation of 2-picoline, s. C. Copéret et al., Tetrahedron Lett. *39*, 761-4 (1998).

# Formation of O-S Bond

## Uptake ⇓

## Addition to Sulfur                                            OS ⇓ S

*Microwaves s. under PhI(OAc)$_2$*                              ←

*Cupric nitrate*                                                $Cu(NO_3)_2$
**Sulfoxides from thioethers**                                  $>S \rightarrow >SO$
with Cu(NO$_3$)$_2$·N$_2$O$_4$ or Fe(NO$_3$)$_3$·N$_2$O$_4$ cf. *29*, 84s*54*; with Cu(NO$_3$)$_2$·3H$_2$O in ethyl acetate, or with Fe(NO$_3$)$_3$ without solvent (cf. *29*, 84s*53*), s. H. Firouzabadi et al., Synth. Commun. *28*, 1179-87 (1998).

*Enzymes*                                                       ←
**Sulfoxides from thioethers - Asym. oxidation**
s. *24*, 100s*47-9*; of ar. bicyclic sulfides with the vanadium-containing bromoperoxidase from *Corallina officinales* (with continous *slow* addition of H$_2$O$_2$) s. M. Andersson et al., J. Org. Chem. *62*, 8455-8 (1997).

*Cyclohexanone monooxygenase*                                   ←
**Cyclic diol sulfates from sulfites with kinetic resolution**  (RO)$_2$SO → (RO)$_2$SO$_2$

51.

Racemic *cis*-4-benzyloxymethyl-1,3,2-dioxathiolane 2-oxide stirred at 25° in Tris-HCl buffer (pH 8.6) containing NADP, glucose-6-phosphate, cyclohexanone monooxygenase (from *Acinetobacter* NCIB 9871) and glucose-6-phosphate dehydrogenase with O$_2$-bubbling for 30 min (34% conversion) → (R,R$^S$)-4-benzyloxymethyl-1,3,2-dioxathiolane 2-oxide (e.e. 44%) and the corresponding (S)-cyclic sulfate (e.e. 85%). After 90 min the e.e. was >99% for the sulfite and 47% for the sulfate (74% conversion). F.e.s. S. Colonna et al., Chem. Commun. *1998*, 415-6.

*Iodosobenzene/hexadecyltrimethylammonium bromide*              PhIO/Me$_3$C$_{16}$H$_{33}$NBr
**Sulfoxides from thioethers under mild, neutral conditions**   $>S \rightarrow >SO$

52.                     p-MeC$_6$H$_4$SMe  ⟶  p-MeC$_6$H$_4$S(O)Me

**in reverse micellar medium.** Addition of a catalytic amount of hexadecyltrimethylammonium bromide (to activate PhIO and increase its solubility) and water expands the scope of thioether oxidation using hypervalent iodine(III) in solvents ranging from water to *n*-hexane. **E:** 1.2 eqs. Iodosobenzene added to a stirred suspension of 10 mol% hexadecyltrimethylammonium bromide in 500:1 toluene/water at room temp., stirring continued for 30 min, a soln. of methyl *p*-tolyl sulfide in toluene added, and the mixture stirred for a further 6 h → product. Y quantitative. The reaction does not proceed in the absence of either the catalyst or water. F.e. incl. cyclic sulfoxides, also with Et$_4$NBr **in micellar medium** (i.e. with water as solvent) s. H. Tohma et al., Tetrahedron Lett. *39*, 4547-50 (1998).

*Phenyl iodosoacetate/alumina/microwaves*                       ←
**Sulfoxides from thioethers**
in the absence of solvent with PhIO/montmorillonite cf. *54*, 54; under microwave irradiation with PhI(OAc)$_2$ on neutral alumina, notably for oxidation of long-chain thioethers, s. R.S. Varma et al., J. Chem. Res., Synop *1998*, 120-1.

*Titanium tetraisopropoxide/diethyl tartrate/hydroperoxides* ←
*Titanium tetraisopropoxide/chiral hydroperoxides* $Ti(OPr\text{-}i)_4/ROOH$
**Sulfoxides from thioethers - Asym. oxidation** $>S \rightarrow >SO$
with *t*-BuOOH cf. *39*, 83s*54*; enhanced enantioselectivity with steroid-derived 2-α-hydroperoxyfurans, also with kinetic resolution (cf. *49*, 994s*52*), s. L. Palombi et al., Tetrahedron:Asym. *9*, 1817-22 (1998); asym. oxidation of alkyl aryl thioethers with $Ti(OPr\text{-}i)_4$ and chiral hydroperoxides (via kinetic resolution) cf. W. Adam et al., J. Org. Chem. *63*, 3423-8 (1998).

*Bismuth(III) nitrate* $Bi(NO_3)_3$
**Sulfoxides from thioethers**
by aerobic oxidation with catalytic amounts of $Bi(NO_3)_3 \cdot 5H_2O$ and $BiBr_3$ cf. *54*, 55; with a stoichiometric amount of $Bi(NO_3)_3 \cdot 5H_2O$ s. S.H. Mashraqui et al., Synth. Commun. *28*, 939-43 (1998).

*Hydrogen peroxide* $H_2O_2$
**Sulfoxides from thioethers under mild conditions in a fluorous solvent**

53.    $PhSCH_2CH=CH_2 \longrightarrow PhS(O)CH_2CH=CH_2$

2 eqs. 30% aq. $H_2O_2$ added to a stirred soln. of allyl phenyl sulfide in *1,1,1,3,3,3-hexafluoro-2-propanol* (HFIP) at 25°, stirring continued for a further 5 min, and the mixture quenched with 10% $Na_2SO_3$ in brine → allyl phenyl sulfoxide. Y 99%. The method is fast, simple, general, and efficient, and work-up (by toluene extraction) is easy. It is thought that hydrogen-bonding between the solvent and the oxygen atom of the sulfoxide prevents over-oxidation to the sulfone. Significantly, olefinic unsaturations were unaffected. F.e.s. K.S. Ravikumar et al., Tetrahedron Lett. *39*, 3141-4 (1998).

# Exchange ⇕

# Hydrogen ↑ OS ⇕ H

*Via intermediates* *v.i.*
**Sulfenic acid esters from mercaptans and alcohols via sulfenyl chlorides** $SH \rightarrow SOR$

54.  $p\text{-}ClC_6H_4SH \xrightarrow{Cl_2/CCl_4} [\,p\text{-}ClC_6H_4SCl\,] \xrightarrow{HOCH_2CH_2OMe} p\text{-}ClC_6H_4SOCH_2CH_2OMe$

$Cl_2$ gas (freshly dried by passing through a column of concd. $H_2SO_4$) bubbled slowly into carbon tetrachloride (freshly distilled over $P_2O_5$) at -5 to 0° for ca. 5 min, a soln. of *p*-chlorobenzenethiol in dry carbon tetrachloride added dropwise over 1 h with continued $Cl_2$-bubbling, volatiles removed *in vacuo*, the crude intermediate sulfenyl chloride in dry ether added dropwise to a vigorously stirred soln. of 1.2 eqs. glycol monomethyl ether and 1.2 eqs. $Et_3N$ in the same solvent at 0° under $N_2$, and the mixture stirred at 0° for 30 min → product. Y 85%. The method is simple, efficient and versatile, being compatible with ar. fluorides, phenolethers, ar. nitro compds. and trifluoromethyl groups. F.e.s. S.R. Harring, T. Livinghouse, Synth. Commun. *28*, 893-902 (1998).

# Halogen ↑ OS ⇕ Hal

*Triethylamine* $Et_3N$
**Sulfenic acid esters from sulfenyl chlorides** s. *55*, 54  $SCl \rightarrow SOR$

## Elimination ⇑

### Hydrogen ↑      OS ⇑ H

p-*Toluenesulfonyl chloride/triethylamine*     $TsCl/Et_3N$
**4-Hydroxy-1,2-oxathianes from 2,4-dihydroxymercaptans**

55.

A soln. of startg. 2,4-dihydroxymercaptan in dichloromethane treated with $Et_3N$, followed by *slow* addition of TsCl → product. Y 93% (single diastereoisomer). The reaction occurs via the thiolate which promotes S-tosylation in preference to O-tosylation; this is followed by cyclization to form the S-O bond by nucleophilic displacement at sulfur with retention of configuration at two stereogenic centres. The method is applicable to tert. mercaptans, the S-tosyl deriv. existing in a favoured conformation for ring closure. F.e.s. J. Eames et al., Tetrahedron Lett. *39*, 1251-4 (1998).

# Formation of O-Rem Bond

## Uptake ⇓

### Addition to Remaining Elements     ORem ⇓ Rem

*Iodine*     $I_2$
**Oligonucleotide synthesis**     ←
by the phosphoramidite method, update, s. *17*, 169s*54*; coupling of hindered *tert*-alkyl phosphoramidites s. C. Scheuer-Larsen et al., Tetrahedron Lett. *39*, 8361-4 (1998); preparation of biotin-containing phosphoromonoamidites for multiple non-radioactive labelling of oligonucleotides s. V.A. Korshun et al., Synth. Commun. *26*, 2531-47 (1996); phosphitylation with phosphoromonoamidites using trialkylsilyl halide and other Ge or Sn catalysts s. World Intellectual Property Organization patent WO-9734853 (Polish Academy of Sciences); solid-phase stereoselective synthesis of oligonucleoside phosphorothioates (review s. *17*, 169s*49*) by the phosphoromonoamidite method using a bicyclic 1,3,2-oxazaphospholidine s. R.P. Iyer et al., Tetrahedron Lett. *39*, 2491-4 (1998); attachment of N-unprotected deoxyribonucleosides to solid supports and use in oligonucleotide synthesis by the H-phosphonate method s. T. Wada et al., ibid., 5593-6; sulfamide-linked dinucleosides s. J. Micklefield, K.J. Fettes, ibid. *38*, 5387-90 (1997); acetylene-linked dinucleosides s. S. Wendeborn et al., ibid. *37*, 5511-4 (1996); oligonucleoside methyl phosphonates, prevention of transamination, s. M.P. Reddy et al., ibid. 8691-4; $R_P$-diastereoselective synthesis of dinucleotide methylphosphonates by the phosphonamidite method s. S.P. Schell, J.W. Engels, ibid. *39*, 8629-32 (1998); dinucleoside phosphoramidimidates s. K. Bjergårde et al., ibid. *35*, 2941-4 (1994); 2'-deoxyribonucleoside 5'-(α-P-borano)triphosphates s. B.K. Krzyzanowska et al., Tetrahedron *54*, 5119-28 (1998); formal-linked dinucleosides s. E. Rozners, R. Strömberg, J. Org. Chem. *62*, 1846-50 (1997).

## Exchange ↕↑

### Hydrogen ↑           ORem ↕↑ H

*Bis(2-oxazolidon-3-yl)phosphoryl chloride/pyridine/iodine*
**Mixed phosphoric acid diesters**     P-H → P-OR
**from phosphorous acid monoesters and alcohols**
via H-phosphonates with $CCl_4/Et_3N$ cf. *22*, 106; glycosyl hydrogen phosphates via glycosyl H-phosphonates with bis(2-oxazolidon-3-yl)phosphoryl chloride/pyridine/iodine, regio- and stereo-specific conversion, s. L. Knerr et al., Tetrahedron Lett. *39*, 273-4 (1998).

*Chlorotris(triphenylphosphine)rhodium(I)*     $RhCl(PPh_3)_3$
**Polymer-based alkoxysilanes from alcohols** s. *54*, 24     OH → OSi≤

### Halogen ↑          ORem ↕↑ Hal

*Sodium iodide/triethylamine*     $NaI/Et_3N$
**Enoxysilanes from ketones**     CHCO → C=C(OSi≤)
s. *43*, 89; isolation of the thermodynamic enoxysilanes from a mixture of regioisomers (derived from α,α'-dienolizable ketones) by work-up with $Et_3N·HCl$ s. A. Deyine et al., Synth. Commun. *28*, 1817-21 (1998).

*Triethylamine*     $Et_3N$
**N,N-Disiloxyenamines from aliphatic nitro compds.**     $CHCHNO_2$ → C=C-N(OSi≤)$_2$
**via nitronic acid silyl esters**

56.     NO$_2$ $\xrightarrow{Me_3SiBr}$ [ N$^+$(O$^-$)=CH-OSiMe$_3$ ] $\xrightarrow{Me_3SiBr}$ N(OSiMe$_3$)$_2$-CH=CH

**One-pot conversion**. A soln. of 2.2 eqs. trimethylsilyl bromide in 1,2-dichloroethane added dropwise to a soln. of nitroethane and 2.3 eqs. $Et_3N$ in the same solvent at 0°, kept at the same temp. for 3 h then at 20° for 7 h with occasional stirring, and the mixture added to petroleum ether and dil. aq. $NaHSO_4$ (pH 2-3) → product. Y 97% (87% after distillation). The second silylation occurs regioselectively, resulting exclusively in the formation of the terminal double bond. The optimum conditions (temp. and time) were dependent on the stability and the structure of the substrate. Reaction failed with certain sec. and hindered nitro compds., although products were obtainable from the intermediate nitronates (prepared with DBU as base instead of $Et_3N$). F.e. and (E)-selectivity s. A.D. Dilman et al., Synthesis *1998*, 181-5.

*Zinc*     Zn
**O-Silyl O-alkyl keteneacetals from α-halogenocarboxylic acid esters**     C=C(OSi≤)OR
with Na cf. *44*, 89; with inexpensive Zn powder s. Japanese patent JP-10017576 (Mitsubishi Rayon Co. Ltd.).

# Formation of O-C Bond

## Uptake ⇓

### Addition to Hydrogen and Carbon     OC ⇓ HC

*Pyridine N-oxides*     ←
**Carboxylic acids from aldehydes**     CHO → COOH
with NaH/pyrazole under base-catalyzed autoxidation cf. *38*, 92; with a little pyridine N-oxide under air s. World Intellectual Property Organisation patent WO-9714668 (Union Carbide Chem & Plastics Technology).

*Ruthenium/cerium dioxide*     $Ru/CeO_2$
**Carboxylic acids from aldehydes** s. *55*, 113

### Addition to Oxygen and Carbon     OC ⇓ OC

*Microwaves* s. under Montmorillonite     ←

*Chiral ferrocenyl-fused 4-dimethylaminopyridines/benzoic acid*     ←
**α-Acylaminocarboxylic acid esters from $\Delta^2$-5-oxazolones**     C
**with dynamic kinetic resolution**

57.

A soln. of 10 mol% benzoic acid and 1.5 eqs. methanol in toluene added to a soln. of 5 mol% chiral ferrocenyl-fused 4-dimethylaminopyridine and startg. azlactone (0.1 *M*) in the same solvent, and stirred at room temp. for 48 h → product. Y 98% (e.e. 54%). Ring opening of the L-azlactone enantiomer is much faster than that of the D-enantiomer, while the latter rapidly inverts so that deracemization can be achieved dynamically. With isopropanol, enantioselectivity was higher (e.e. 78%), although reaction was much slower (half-life ca. 1 week). F.e.s. J. Liang et al., J. Org. Chem. *63*, 3154-5 (1998).

*Montmorillonite/microwaves*     ←
**Acylals from aldehydes on a solid support in the absence of solvent**     CHO → $CH(OAc)_2$
on montmorillonite cf. *51*, 55s*53*; general, rapid procedure under microwave irradiation s. D. Karmakar et al., J. Chem. Res., Synop *1998*, 382-3.

*Lanthanum tris[bis(trimethylsilyl)amide]*     $La[N(SiMe_3)_2]_3$
**Tishchenko reaction**     2 CHO → $COOCH_2$

58.     2 PhCHO $\xrightarrow{La[N(SiMe_3)_2]_3}$ $PhCOOCH_2Ph$

Homoleptic lanthanide tris[bis(trimethylsilyl)amides] are highly efficient Lewis acids for the Tishchenko reaction, being more active than the conventional Al-triisopropoxide (cf. *4*, 154). E: Benzaldehyde (5 g scale) added with stirring to 1 mol% $La[N(SiMe_3)_2]_3$ under an inert atmosphere at 21° (exothermic), and the product isolated by distillation after 1 day → benzyl benzoate. Y 98% (turnover frequency 87). The catalysts, namely the above and the Sm and Y analogs, are easy to prepare, have a high turnover frequency (especially the La amide), retain their activity after several days, and are more efficient than Al(OPr-$i$)$_3$ (Y 51% with a turnover frequency of 8). Work-up is very simple. F.e. incl. dimerization of furfural s. H. Berberich, P.W. Roesky, Angew. Chem. Int. Ed. Engl. *37*, 1569-71 (1998).

*2-Aminopropylsilyl-modified mesoporous silica*
**α-Acoxyglycols from 2,3-epoxyalcohols** $\quad\overset{\longleftarrow}{\triangledown_\text{O}}\!\nearrow \to$ C(OH)C(OAc)
with Ti(OPr-$i$)$_4$ cf. *44*, 104; with 2-aminopropylsilyl-modified mesoporous silica under heterogeneous catalysis s. A. Cauvel et al., J. Org. Chem. *62*, 749-51 (1997).

*Trimethylsilyl chloride/sodium iodide* $\qquad\qquad\qquad\qquad\qquad\qquad\qquad Me_3SiCl/NaI$
**Acylals from aldehydes** $\qquad\qquad\qquad\qquad\qquad\qquad\qquad\qquad\qquad$ CHO $\to$ CH(OAc)$_2$
with I$_2$ cf. *38*, 100s*53*; rapid and inexpensive procedure with Me$_3$SiCl/NaI s. N. Deka et al., J. Chem. Res., Synop *1998*, 94-5.

*Methylrhenium oxide* $\qquad\qquad\qquad\qquad\qquad\qquad\qquad\qquad\qquad\qquad MeReO_3$
**1,3,5-Trioxanes from aldehydes by catalytic cyclotrimerization**

59.

Acetaldehyde and 1% MeReO$_3$ allowed to stand for 1 day at room temp. (with monitoring by GC-MS) $\to$ 2,4,6-trimethyl-1,3,5-trioxane. Y >99%. No other products (e.g. dimers, tetramers, or aldol condensation products) were observed. Water inhibited the reaction, it being completely blocked with 20 mol% or more. The yields decreased as the size of the substituent increased, and aldehydes containing very bulky or electron-withdrawing substituents in the α-position did not react at all. This method was also found to be applicable to diethyl ketomalonate but not to other non-aldehyde carbonyl compounds. **Mixed trioxanes** were formed by reacting one aldehyde taken in a limiting amount and a second aldehyde as solvent (5 eqs.) with 1% MeReO$_3$. F.e., and with chloroform or benzene as solvent s. Z. Zhu, J.H. Espenson, Synthesis *1998*, 417-22.

## Addition to Nitrogen and Carbon $\qquad\qquad\qquad$ OC ⇓ NC

*Samarium diiodide/hexamethylphosphoramide* $\qquad\qquad\qquad\qquad SmI_2/HMPA$
**Tert. urethans from tert. alcohols and isocyanates** $\qquad\qquad\qquad$ NCO $\to$ NHCOOR

60. $\qquad\qquad$ n-BuN=C=O $\;+\;$ HOBu-t $\;\longrightarrow\;$ n-BuNHCOOBu-t

0.1 eq. 0.1 M SmI$_2$ in THF added to *n*-butyl isocyanate, 1 eq. *tert*-butyl alcohol, and 0.6 (or 6) eq. *HMPA* in THF at -78°, and the mixture stirred at this temp. for a few (<3) min before quenching with 1 N HCl $\to$ product. Y 97% (96% at 0°, and 97% at 25°). This method is mild, rapid, high-yielding, and applicable to reaction of tertiary alcohols with primary or secondary alkyl isocyanates; furthermore, functional groups such as double or triple bonds, esters or bromide groups on the alcohol were unaffected. There was no reaction in the absence of HMPA. F.e.s. Y.H. Kim, H.S. Park, Synlett *1998*, 261-2.

*Trimethylsilyl chloride* $\qquad\qquad\qquad\qquad\qquad\qquad\qquad\qquad\qquad Me_3SiCl$
**Carboxylic acid amides from nitriles under mild, solvent-less conditions** $\quad$ CN $\to$ CONH$_2$

61. $\qquad\qquad\qquad$ EtO$_2$CCH$_2$CN $\;\longrightarrow\;$ EtO$_2$CCH$_2$CONH$_2$

2 eqs. Trimethylsilyl chloride added to startg. nitrile at 0-5°, the mixture treated dropwise with 2 eqs. water, and allowed to warm to 25° over 2-4 h $\to$ product (as the hydrochloride). Y 83%. The method is mild (esters and tert. amines being unaffected) and general for aliphatic and aromatic nitriles. Yields were poor in THF, nitromethane or methylene chloride. F.e.s. M.K. Basu, F.-T. Luo, Tetrahedron Lett. *39*, 3005-6 (1998).

## Addition to Carbon-Carbon Bonds       OC ⇓ CC

*Potassium carbonate/irradiation*       $K_2CO_3/⭝⭝⭝$
**6-Azabicyclo[3.1.0]hex-3-en-2-ols from pyridinium salts**       ←

62.

**Stereospecific conversion.** A deoxygenated ($N_2$) aq. soln. of 1-(2-methoxyethyl)pyridinium chloride and $K_2CO_3$ irradiated at 253.7 nm with cooling for 14 h in a double-walled quartz vessel using a Srinivasan-Griffin (Rayonet-RPR-100) apparatus fitted with RPR lamps → (1RS,2RS,5RS)-6-(2-methoxyethyl)-6-azabicyclo[3.1.0]hex-3-en-2-ol. Y 57%. F.e. and conversion to **4-amino-3,5-dihydroxycyclopentenes** s. E.A. Acar et al., Helv. Chim. Acta *81*, 1095-104 (1998).

*Methyl(triphenylphosphine)gold(I)/sulfuric acid*       $[Me(Ph_3P)Au]/H_2SO_4$
*Tris(p-fluorophenyl)phosphinegold(I) nitrate/boron fluoride*       $[(Ar_3P)Au]NO_3/BF_3$
**Gold(I)-catalyzed addition of alcohols to acetylene derivs. under neutral conditions**       ←

63.

**2,5-Dialkoxy-1,4-dioxanes.** Propargyl alcohol (freshly distilled), ca. 4 eqs. methanol, and ca. 1 eq. concd. $H_2SO_4$ mixed while heating to 55°, a little methyl(triphenylphosphine)gold(I) in dioxane added during 10 h, and stirred for a further 10 h → *trans*-2,5-dimethyl-2,5-dimethoxy-1,4-dioxane. Y 93%. **Ketals** were obtained similarly **from terminal acetylene derivs.** by regiospecific attack of the alcohol at the substituted carbon atom. The catalyst is more active (with turnover numbers of up to $10^5$ moles of product per mole of catalyst with turnover frequencies of up to 5400 $h^{-1}$) than conventional Hg(II) or Au(III) complexes which are quickly reduced to the catalytically inactive metal. F.e.s. J.H. Teles et al., Angew. Chem. Int. Ed. Engl. *37*, 1415-7 (1998); ketals with tris(*p*-fluorophenyl)phosphinegold(I) nitrate/boron fluoride, also methyl ketones with water, and addition of carboxylic acids, s. German patent DE-19546610 (BASF AG).

*Mercuric acetate/sodium tetrahydridoborate*       $Hg(OAc)_2/NaBH_4$
**2-Deoxyaldoses from glycals**       ←
via acetochlorosugars and methyl glycosides cf. *19*, 201; by oxymercuration-demercuration with $Hg(OAc)_2/NaBH_4$, mono-, di-, and tri-saccharides, s. E. Bettelli et al., Tetrahedron *54*, 6011-8 (1998).

*Mercuric trifluoroacetate/lithium tetrahydridoaluminate*       $Hg(OCOCF_3)_2/LiAlH_4$
**Alcohols from cyclopropanes by oxymercuration-demercuration**       ↶
1,3-diols cf. *41*, 125; regio- and stereo-specific ring opening of bi- and ter-cyclopropane arrays s. A.G.M. Barrett, W. Tam, J. Org. Chem. *62*, 4653-64 (1997).

*Sodium perborate s. under $KMnO_4$*       $NaBO_3$

*Dinitratocerium(IV) chromate*       $Ce(NO_3)_2CrO_4$
**Protection of alcohols as tetrahydropyran-2-yl ethers**       OH → OThp
with $(NH_4)_2Ce(NO_3)_6$ cf. *48*, 120s49; mild, rapid procedure with $Ce(NO_3)_2CrO_4$ or trinitratocerium(IV) paraperiodate s. H.A. Oskooie et al., Synth. Commun. *28*, 2281-5 (1998).

*Novozym s. under $H_2O_2$*       ←

tert-*Butyl hydroperoxide/titanium tetraisopropoxide/chiral polymer-based tartrate*
**Heterogeneous Sharpless epoxidation**  C=C → \o/   ←

64.

25 Mol% Ti(OPr-*i*)₄ added via syringe to a mixture of 4 Å molecular sieves, 50 mol% polymer-based (L)-tartrate, and methylene chloride under N₂ at -20°, stirred for ca. 1 h, 2 eqs. *t*-BuOOH added via syringe, stirred for at least 1 h at -20°, a soln. of 1 eq. *trans*-hex-2-en-1-ol in methylene chloride added dropwise via syringe at -15° to -20°, stirred for 6 h at the same temp., and stored in a freezer for 12 h → product. Y 53% (e.e. 87%). The polymer-based catalyst is simply removed and recovered by filtration at the end of the reaction. The optimum polymer-branching ratio was 3-11% with a ligand:titanium ratio of 2:1. F.e. and preparation of the ligands s. J.K. Karjalainen et al., Tetrahedron:Asym. *9*, 1563-75 (1998); with a linear soluble poly(tartrate) cf. L. Canali et al., Chem. Commun. *1997*, 123-4.

*Dimethyldioxirane*   ←
**Epoxidation**
s. *44*, 117s*54*; stereospecific epoxidation of highly unactivated double bonds, e.g. of phosphonyl-subst. α,β-ethylenecarboxylic acid quaternary ammonium salts, s. P. de Macedo Puyan, J.J. Perie, Synth. Commun. *28*, 2679-83 (1998); preparation of dimethyldioxirane solns. with a 4- to 5-fold increase in concentration s. M. Ferrer et al., Tetrahedron Lett. *37*, 3585-6 (1996).

m-*Chloroperoxybenzoic acid*   m-*ClC₆H₄COO₂H*
**Epoxidation**
s. *20*, 112s*51, 54*; of alkylidenecyclobutanes s. T. Fujiwara et al., Chem. Lett. *1998*, 741-2; 5-functionalized N-protected *threo*-2,3-epoxyamines, and *erythro*-isomers with CF₃COO₂H s. A.J. Jensen, K. Luthman, Tetrahedron Lett. *39*, 3213-4 (1998); 5-siloxy-2,3-epoxyalcohols from 2-ethylene-5-siloxyalcohols, effect of siloxy group on enantioselectivity (cf. *33*, 131), s. K. Maruyama et al., ibid. 4517-20.

m-*Chloroperoxybenzoic acid/lithium carbonate*   m-*ClC₆H₄COO₂H/Li₂CO₃*
**Baeyer-Villiger oxidation**   ←
s. *31*, 105; spirocyclic bislactones, substituent effect on regioselectivity, s. J. Cossy et al., Tetrahedron Lett. *39*, 4459-62 (1998); γ-spiro-γ-lactones with added Li₂CO₃ (cf. *34*, 116) s. A.B. Bueno, L.S. Hegedus, J. Org. Chem. *63*, 684-90 (1998).

m-*Chloroperoxybenzoic acid/trifluoroacetic acid*   m-*ClC₆H₄COO₂H/CF₃COOH*
**Acid-catalyzed Baeyer-Villiger oxidation**   ←
s. *45*, 70; 3,4-dihydro-1,5-benzodioxepin-2-ones from 4-chromanones s. T. Yasunaga et al., J. Med. Chem. *40*, 1252-7 (1997); of γ-oxocarboxylic acid esters s. H.-U. Reissig et al., Liebig Ann. *1997*, 2119-24.

m-*Chloroperoxybenzoic acid/stannic chloride*   m-*ClC₆H₄COO₂H/SnCl₄*
**Asym. Baeyer-Villiger oxidation of spirocyclic ketals**   ○

65.

**Chiral γ-lactones.** A soln. of startg. ketal (obtained from 3-phenylcyclobutanone and (2R,4R)-2,4-pentanediol by standard acid-catalyzed condensation) and 2 eqs. *m*-chloroperoxybenzoic acid (82% purity) in methylene chloride cooled to -78°, 5 eqs. SnCl$_4$ added, stirred for 1.5 h at the same temp., warmed to room temp., and poured into 2 N HCl → product. Y 100% (e.e. 89%). This is the first example of a Lewis acid-promoted Baeyer-Villiger reaction involving an acetal. Other Lewis acids and solvents gave poor or negative results. F.e.s. T. Sugimura et al., Tetrahedron Lett. *38*, 6019-22 (1997).

*Titanium silicate/hydrogen peroxide*                                                          ←
**3-Hydroxy-O-heterocyclics from ethylenealcohols**                                             ○

66.

A mixture of but-3-en-1-ol, 1 eq. 30 wt% aq. H$_2$O$_2$ and 20 wt% titanium silicate TS-1 (Si/Ti = 27) in butan-2-ol allowed to react at room temp. for 18 h → product. Y 82%. Reaction in water was faster, 93.6% conversion being achieved after 6 h, but selectivity decreased to 75.5%. The method is highly regioselective. F.e. and stereoselectivity, also 2-α-hydroxytetrahydro-furans and -pyrans, and with acetone as solvent, s. A. Bhaumik, T. Tatsumi, Chem. Commun. *1998*, 463-4.

*Titanium tetraisopropoxide s. under t-BuOOH*                                                   Ti(OPr-i)$_4$
*Trimethylsilyl iodide*                                                                         Me$_3$SiI
**Protection of alcohols as tetrahydropyran-2-yl ethers**                                       OH → OThp
s. *41*, 135; general procedure with added Ph$_3$P to scavenge HI s. K.H. Cha et al., Synth. Commun. *28*, 2131-6 (1998).

*Vanadyl triisopropoxide/tert-butyl hydroperoxide*                                              VO(OPr-i)$_3$/t-BuOOH
**Epoxidation in dense liquid-phase carbon dioxide**                                            C=C → ⟨O⟩

67.

**of 2-ethylenealcohols.** A soln. of startg. allyl alcohol in liq. CO$_2$ (10.3 atm.) stirred with 3.5 mol% VO(OPr-*i*)$_3$ and an excess of *tert*-butyl hydroperoxide in stainless steel high-pressure cells for 24 h at room temp. → product. Conversion >99%; selectivity >99%. Reactivity parallels that reported in conventional solvents. There was no advantage in operating above the critical point for CO$_2$ (i.e. under supercritical conditions). F.e. and epoxidation **of 3-ethylenealcohols**, also asym. epoxidation with diisopropyl L-tartrate as ligand, s. D.R. Pesiri et al., Chem. Commun. *1998*, 1015-6.

*Hydrogen peroxide s.a. under Titanium silicate*                                                H$_2$O$_2$
*Hydrogen peroxide or urea-hydrogen peroxide/dicyclohexylcarbodiimide/*                         ←
  *potassium hydrogen carbonate*
**Epoxidation**
with urea-H$_2$O$_2$/maleic anhydride cf. *46*, 123s*50*; with urea-H$_2$O$_2$/dicyclohexylcarbodiimide/ KHCO$_3$ s. R.W. Murray, K. Iyanar, J. Org. Chem. *63*, 1730-1 (1998); with H$_2$O$_2$ and a little KHCO$_3$ cf. G. Majetich et al., ibid. 2564-73.

*Hydrogen peroxide/Novozym*                                                                     ←
**Acoxyepoxides from ethylenealcohols and carboxylic acid esters**
**Enzymatic epoxidation-transesterification**

68.

ca. 700 U Novozym 435 (the immobilized form of *Candida antarctica* on acrylic resin) added to startg. unsatd. alcohol (5 mmol scale) in ethyl butyrate, stirred for 15 min, 5 eqs. 60% H$_2$O$_2$ added automatically by Methrom Dosimat in 15 µl portions every 15 min, and stirring continued for 16 h at room temp. → product. Y 89% (unoptimized). Allyl alcohol failed to provide high yields. F.e. incl. epoxystearylacylates s. M. Rüsch gen. Klaas, S. Warwel, Synth. Commun. *28*, 251-60 (1998).

*Urea-hydrogen peroxide or triethylenediamine-hydrogen peroxide/
immobilized poly-L-leucine*  ←
**Asym. epoxidation of α,β-ethyleneketones**  C=C → \o/
s. *37*, 127s*54*; with immobilized poly-L-leucine, also with triethylenediamine-hydrogen peroxide as oxidant, s. M.W. Cappi et al., Chem. Commun. *1998*, 1159-60.

*p-Toluenesulfonic acid/silica gel*  $TsOH/SiO_2$
**Thiolic acid esters from 1-acetylene-1-thioethers**  C≡C(SR) → $CH_2C(O)SR$
via hydroboration cf. *11*, 87s*46*; with TsOH (or $CF_3COOH$) and silica gel, selectivity, s. A.L. Braga et al., Tetrahedron Lett. *39*, 3395-6 (1998).

*Potassium peroxymonosulfate/ketones*  $KHSO_5/R_2CO$
**Epoxidation**  C=C → \o/
catalytic conversion s. *37*, 128s*54*; with 0.1 eq. 6-oxo-1,1,4,4-tetramethylhexahydro-1,4-diazepinium bis(triflate) in aq. MeCN s. S.E. Denmark, Z. Wu, J. Org. Chem. *63*, 2810-1 (1998).

*Potassium peroxymonosulfate/chiral ketones or cyclic azomethinium salts*  ←
**Asym. epoxidation**
s. *51*, 65s*53*; of ethylenealcohols, effect of pH on enantioselectivity s. J. Org. Chem. *63*, 3099-104 (1998); regiospecific asym. monoepoxidation of 1,3-dienes with a fructose-derived chiral ketone as catalyst s. M. Frohn et al., ibid. 2948-53; chiral 3-acetyleneepoxides from 1,3-enynes s. G.-A. Cao et al., Tetrahedron Lett. *39*, 4425-8 (1998); asym. epoxidation with chiral 3,4-dihydroisoquinolinium salts s. P.C. Bulman Page et al., J. Org. Chem. *63*, 2774-7 (1998).

*Molybdenum peroxide-amine oxide complexes/bis(trimethylsilyl) peroxide*  ←
**Epoxidation**
with chlorodioxomolybdenum complexes/*t*-BuOOH cf. *42*, 233s*46*; with Mo, W or Re peroxide complexes with amine, arsine, phosphine or stibine oxides as ligand, e.g. $[MoO_5(ON)(C_{12}H_{25})_3]$ with bis(trimethylsilyl) peroxide as reoxidant, s. World Intellectual Property Organization patent WO-9732867 (BASF AG).

*Tetraalkylammonium zinc-containing polyoxometalates/hydrogen peroxide*  ←
**Epoxidation**
with heteropolyacids/$H_2O_2$/hexadecylpyridinium chloride cf. *42*, 233s*46, 47*; with tetraalkylammonium zinc-containing polyoxometalates, e.g. $[(n-C_4H_9)_4N]_5PZnMo_2W_9O_{39}$, also aryl ketones from alkylarenes, s. S. Tangestaninejad, B. Yadollahi, Chem. Lett. *1998*, 511-21.

*Sodium hypochlorite/chiral quaternary ammonium salts*  $NaOCl/R_4N^+$
**Asym. epoxidation of α,β-ethyleneketones**
with chiral crown ethers cf. *18*, 193s*44*; of *trans*-enones with N-anthracenylmethylcinchonidinium salts as phase transfer catalyst s. B. Lygo, P.G. Wainwright, Tetrahedron Lett. *39*, 1599-602 (1998).

*Ammonium chloride*  $NH_4Cl$
**Protection of alcohols as tetrahydropyran-2-yl ethers**  OH → OThp

69.  +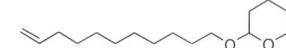

1 eq. Commercial $NH_4Cl$ added to an equimolar mixture of startg. alcohol and dihydropyran in THF (pH 5.93), and heated at reflux for 3 h → product. Y 90%. The method is mild, inexpensive, and does not require high temp. or a strongly acidic reagent. Cleavage can be effected with 1.2 eqs. $NH_4Cl$ in *methanol* (pH 5.25) at reflux for 4 h. Functional groups such as TBDPS and TBDMS, MPM and benzyl ethers, double bonds, acetonides, and esters remained unaffected both on protection and deprotection. F.e.s. J.S. Yadav et al., Synth. Commun. *28*, 1399-404 (1998).

*Manganese(II) sulfate/1,4,7-trimethyl-1,4,7-triazacyclononane/hydrogen peroxide*  ←
**Epoxidation**  C=C → \o/
of *cis*-alkenes cf. *39*, 124s*51*; of terminal or electron-deficient olefins in the presence of an oxalate buffer s. Tetrahedron Lett. *39*, 3221-4 (1998).

*Water-soluble manganese(III) porphyrin complexes/imidazole/sodium hypochlorite/Brij 25*
**Catalytic epoxidation in aq. micellar media**   $C=C \to \underset{O}{\triangle}$

Manganese(III) porphyrin complexes bearing a water-soluble [neutral or cationic] side-chain are effective catalysts for epoxidation of simple olefins in aq. micellar media. E: 10 eqs. 1 $M$ Aq. NaOCl (buffered to pH 10.5) added in ten portions over 2 h to a 1-3 x $10^{-2}$ $M$ soln. of surfactant Brij 35 containing 10 mol% Mn(III)-porphyrin complex, 2 eqs. imidazole, and cyclooctene, and worked up when GC-MS indicated completion of reaction → product. Y 85%. For epoxidation of the less hydrophilic cyclohexene, a porphyrin complex possessing a quaternary ammonium side chain was more effective (in the presence of cetyltrimethylammonium bromide). F.e.s. D. Monti et al., Angew. Chem. Int. Ed. Engl. *37*, 1131-3 (1998).

*Amberlite IRA 900-supported 5,10,15,20-tetrakis(sulfoaryl)porphyrinatomanganese(III)/*
  *imidazole/sodium periodate*
**Epoxidation**
with a polymer-based tetraarylporphyrinatomanganese(III) complex cf. *39*, 124s*48*; with Amberlite IRA 900-supported 5,10,15,20-tetrakis(sulfoaryl)porphyrinatomanganese(III) in the presence of imidazole as co-catalyst and NaIO$_4$ (as reoxidant) s. S. Tangestaninejad, M. Moghadam, Synth. Commun. *28*, 427-32 (1998).

*Chiral manganese(III) salen complex/4-phenylpyridine N-oxide or ammonium acetate/*
  *hydrogen peroxide or iodosobenzene or dimethyldioxirane or sodium hypochlorite*
**Asym. epoxidation**
with N-heterocyclic bases as co-catalyst cf. *46*, 106s*46-50*; with carboxylate salts, such as NH$_4$OAc, for asym. epoxidation of unfunctionalized di- and tri-subst. alkenes with either aq. H$_2$O$_2$ or anhydrous urea-H$_2$O$_2$ s. P. Pietikäinen, Tetrahedron *54*, 4319-26 (1998); with a Mn(III) salen complex possessing a carboxylate-substituted ethylenediamine moiety, chiral chromene epoxides (cf. *53*, 68), s. Y.N. Ito, T. Katsuki, Tetrahedron Lett. *39*, 4325-8 (1998); chiral isoflavone epoxides with dimethyldioxirane or NaOCl as reoxidant and 4-phenylpyridine N-oxide as oxygen donor s. A. Lévai et al., Tetrahedron *54*, 13105-14 (1998).

*Chiral manganese(III) salen complex/4-phenylpyridine N-oxide/iodosobenzene*
**Asym. epoxidation of allenes with kinetic resolution** s. *55*, 500

*Chiral fluorous manganese(III) salen complex/N-hexylimidazole/pivalaldehyde*
**Asym. aerobic epoxidation**
s. *48*, 134s*50*; under fluorous biphase catalysis in perfluorooctane/CH$_2$Cl$_2$ with a chiral fluorous (C$_2$-symmetric) manganese(III) salen complex s. G. Pozzi et al., Chem. Commun. *1998*, 877-8.

*Potassium permanganate/sodium perborate*   $KMnO_4/NaBO_3$
**Stereospecific epoxidation**
β-epoxidation of unsatd. steroids with KMnO$_4$/CuSO$_4$ cf. *45*, 72s*51*; of Δ$^5$-steroids with KMnO$_4$/Na-perborate s. J.R. Hanson et al., J. Chem. Res., Synop *1998*, 50-1.

*Dodecacarbonyltriruthenium*   $Ru_3(CO)_{12}$
**Enol phosphinates from terminal acetylene derivs.**   $C\equiv CH \to C(OPOR_2)=CH_2$

**Regiospecific addition.** A mixture of oct-1-yne, 1.2 eqs. diphenylphosphinic acid, and 2.5 mol% Ru$_3$(CO)$_{12}$ in toluene heated at 140° for 5 h → 1-octen-2-yl diphenylphosphinate. Y 88%. The method is simple and general leaving cyclic olefins and nitriles unaffected, and Markovnikov adducts were obtained with high selectivity. Internal alkynes, however, failed to react. F.e. incl. bis(enol phosphinates), and with $RuCl_2(p$-cymene$)(PPh_3)$ as catalyst, s. R. Hua, M. Tanaka, Chem. Lett. *1998*, 431-2.

*Palladous acetate/2-(p-tolylsulfinyl)-5-tert-butyl-1,4-benzoquinone/sulfuric acid* ←
**4-Acoxy-2-ethyleneethers from 1,3-dienes**     C=C-C=C → (AcO)C-C=C-C(OR)
**Regio- and stereo-specific conversion**

72.  AcOH + [2-phenyl-1,3-cyclohexadiene] + HOMe ⟶ AcO⋯[cyclohexene with Ph]⋯OMe

2-Phenyl-1,3-cyclohexadiene added via a syringe pump over 4 h to a stirred soln. of 10 eqs. acetic acid, 20 eqs. methanol, 10 mol% $Pd(OAc)_2$, 10 mol% 2-(p-tolylsulfinyl)-5-*tert*-butyl-1,4-benzoquinone, 5 mol% $H_2SO_4$ and a little iron phthalocyanine in methylene chloride at 40°, and stirring continued at the same temp. for 24 h under an atm. of $O_2$ → *trans*-1-acetoxy-4-methoxy-2-phenyl-2-cyclohexene. Y 63% (chemoselectivity >98%; stereoselectivity >95%). The pH must be controlled within a narrow range in order to prevent formation of the 2-ene-1,4-diol ethers or esters (cf. *44*, 131*s47*). Reaction is generally applicable to prim., sec. and [with slight modification] tert. alcohols. F.e. with high regio- and stereo-selectivity s. E. Hupe et al., Tetrahedron *54*, 5375-84 (1998); 4-trifluoroacetoxy derivs. and 2-ene-1,4-diol acetate trifluoroacetates s. J. Org. Chem. *63*, 2523-9 (1998).

*Tris(dibenzylideneacetone)dipalladium/1,1′-bis(diphenylphosphino)ferrocene   $Pd_2(dba)_3$/dppf*
**Acoxy-2-ethylenes from allenes**     C=C=C → C=CHC(OAc)
**via palladium π-allyl complexes**
**Regio- and stereo-specific conversion under mild conditions**

73.  Ph-CH=C=CH₂ + [HPdOAc] (from AcOH, Pd(0)) ⟶ [Ph-CH=CH-CH₂-PdOAc] ⟶ Ph-CH=CH-CH₂-OAc

Phenylallene and 1.1 eqs. acetic acid added to 1 mol% $Pd_2(dba)_3·CHCl_3$ and 2 mol% dppf in dry THF, and heated at 80° for 4 h → cinnamyl acetate. Y 83%. Reaction is presumed to involve formation of a palladium π-allyl complex, and is generally applicable to a variety of arylallenes and carboxylic acids (incl. cinnamic acid and N-protected α-amino acids). Aliphatic allenes and α-aryl-γ-methylallenes, however, underwent isomerization to the corresponding **1,3-dienes**, β-hydride elimination predominating over reductive coupling. F.e. incl. a 3-acoxythioenolether from an allenyl thioether s. M. Al-Masum, Y. Yamamoto, J. Am. Chem. Soc. *120*, 3809-10 (1998).

*Osmium tetroxide/N-methylmorpholine N-oxide*     $OsO_4/R_3NO$
**Stereospecific dihydroxylation**     C=C → C(OH)C(OH)
s. *21*, 858s*51*; of chiral N-(α,β-ethyleneacyl)sultams with asym. induction s. J. Raczko et al., Helv. Chim. Acta *81*, 1264-76 (1998).

**Steric protection of functional groups within ansa macrolides**
***syn*-Addition to 1,2-disubst. (E)-ethylene derivs.**

74.  [starting diol with OBn, OH, OAc] ⇢ [ansa macrolide intermediate] → [dihydroxylated ansa macrolide] ⇢ [final open-chain tetraol p-toluate]

High *syn*-addition on dihydroxylation or epoxidation of simple 1,2-disubst. (E)-ethylene derivs. (i.e. those lacking an allylic function) can be achieved via an ansa macrolide, the benzene ring of which effectively shields one side of the olefin. **E:** *cis*-**Glycols.** A soln. of startg. ansa macrolide (readily prepared from the acyclic ethylene deriv.) in aq. acetone treated with $OsO_4$ and N-methylmorpholine N-oxide at 0° to room temp. for 12 h under standard conditions for dihydroxylation → product. Y 76-92% (diastereoselectivity >20:1). Such high diastereoselectivity in the direct dihydroxylation of unfunctionalized acyclic double bonds is not possible because of high conformational mobility. The product is readily cleaved to give a protected polyol. F.e. and stereospecific epoxidation s. J. Mulzer et al., Angew. Chem. Int. Ed. Engl. *37*, 1566-8 (1998).

*Potassium osmate/potassium hexacyanoferrate/silica-supported bis(9-O-dihydroquinidine)pyrazinopyrazines/potassium carbonate*
**Asym. dihydroxylation**  $C=C \rightarrow C(OH)C(OH)$
with $OsO_4/K_3[Fe(CN)_6]/K_2CO_3$ and polymer-based alkaloids cf. *43*, 121s*46*; of unfunctionalized alkenes with silica-supported bis(9-O-dihydroquinidine)pyrazinopyrazines in the presence of $K_2OsO_2(OH)_4$ and $K_3[Fe(CN)_6]/K_2CO_3$ in 1:1 *t*-BuOH/water s. C. Bolm et al., Chem. Commun. *1997*, 2353-4.

*Via intermediates*
**Epoxides from ethylene derivs. via 1,2-halogenhydrins**
via 1,2-bromohydrins cf. *12*, 206; via 1,2-iodohydrins (method s. *50*, 276) for acid-sensitive compds. s. A.M. Sanseverino, M.C.S de Mattos, Synth. Commun. *28*, 559-72 (1998).

# Rearrangement

## Hydrogen/Carbon Type

*Chloro(η⁵-indenyl)bis(triphenylphosphine)ruthenium(II)/potassium hydroxide*
**Racemization of sec. alcohols**
with Ru-hydride complex cf. *53*, 500; with chloro(η⁵-indenyl)bis(triphenylphosphine)ruthenium(II)/KOH and comparison of catalysts s. J.H. Koh et al., Tetrahedron Lett. *39*, 5545-8 (1998).

## Oxygen/Nitrogen Type

*Triethylamine*  $Et_3N$
**Beckmann rearrangement of O-tosyloximes**  $C(=NOTs)R \rightarrow CONHR$
without reagent cf. *20*, 116; chiral α,α-disubst. α-acylaminocarboxylic acid esters with retention of configuration (with $Et_3N$) s. R.P Frutos, D.M. Spero, Tetrahedron Lett. *39*, 2475-8 (1998).

*Aluminum chloride*  $AlCl_3$
**Beckmann rearrangement**
with $BF_3$ cf. *11*, 217; in the *solid phase* with ground, anhydrous $AlCl_3$ s. M. Ghiaci, G.H. Imanzadeh, Synth. Commun. *28*, 2275-80 (1998).

*Methyl trifluoromethanesulfonate*  $CF_3SO_3Me$
**Epoxyaldehydes from 3-(alkenyl)oxaziridines**
**Stereospecific intramolecular epoxidation**

2 eqs. Methyl triflate added dropwise to a stirred soln. of startg. oxaziridine in freshly distilled methylene chloride under $N_2$, further 2 equivalent portions of the triflate added every 90 min until TLC indicated completion of reaction, treated with satd. aq. $NaHCO_3$, and stirred vigorously for 20 min → product. Y 60%. F.e. and regioselectivity s. A. Armstrong, A.G. Draffan, Synlett *1998*, 646-8.

## Nitrogen/Carbon Type                             OC ∩ NC

*Without additional reagents*                                    w.a.r.
**Δ²-Oxazolines from 1-acylaziridines**                            ○
with Bu₃N cf. *20*, 239; in chloroform with retention of configuration, chiral N-(Δ²-oxazolin-4-ylcarbonyl)-2-imidazolidones and conversion to chiral α-amino-β-hydroxycarboxylic acids s. G. Cardillo et al., Tetrahedron Lett. *38*, 6953-6 (1997).

## Carbon/Carbon Type                                OC ∩ CC

*Aluminum chloride*                                              AlCl₃
**2,3-Dihydrobenzofurans from *o*-allylphenols**                   ○
with HBr/AcOH cf. *23*, 182; 7-nitro-derivs. with AlCl₃ s. S.K. Kang et al., Bull. Korean Chem. Soc. *18*, 1128-30 (1997); with I₂ (cf. *50*, 70) s. World Intellectual Property Organization patent WO-9747615 (Korean Research Institute of Chemical Technology).

*Titanium tetrachloride*                                         TiCl₄
**Cyclic ethers from ethylenealcohols**
**Regio- and stereo-specific ring closure with 1,2-silyl group migration**

76.

*trans*-**2-Subst. 3-silyltetrahydropyrans.** A soln. of startg. enesilane and 5 mol% TiCl₄ in chloroform allowed to react at room temp. for 2.3 h → product. Y 93% (*trans/cis* 97/3). Trisubstitution of the double bond appears essential, and ether and ester groups remained unaffected. Reaction is presumed to involve acid-catalyzed reversible isomerization of an intermediate tetrahydrofuran leading to the thermodynamically favoured product. The corresponding ring closure of silylated 3-ethylenealcohols to *trans*-**3-silyltetrahydrofurans** was much slower. F.e. and with HCl gas or acetyl chloride as catalyst s. K. Miura et al., J. Org. Chem. *62*, 8292-3 (1997).

*Iodine*                                                          I₂
**2,3-Dihydrobenzofurans from *o*-allylphenols** s. *23*, 182s55

## Exchange                                             ⇅

## Hydrogen ↑                                         OC ⇅ H

*Cupric oxide*                                                   CuO
**Regiospecific α-sulfonyloxylation of ketones**                 H → OSO₂R
*in situ*-prepn. with Tl(OAc)₃/DMSO cf. *54*, 62; isolation of α-nosyloxy-, α-mesyloxy- and α-tosyloxy-ketones from methyl ketones with CuO s. Tetrahedron Lett. *39*, 3171-2 (1998).

*Cuprous salts/chiral bis(Δ²-oxazolines)*                          ←
**Asym. Kharasch acoxylation**                                   H → OAc
chiral acoxy-2-ethylenes s. *51*, 72; with C₂-symmetric chiral 2,6-bis(Δ²-oxazolin-2-yl)pyridines as ligand in acetone s. G. Sekar et al., J. Org. Chem. *63*, 2961-7 (1998); with chiral dinuclear copper complexes prepared from Cu(I)(MeCN)₄PF₆ cf. C.J. Fahrni, Tetrahedron *54*, 5465-70 (1998); chiral acoxy-2-acetylenes from acetylene derivs. s. J.S. Clark et al., Tetrahedron Lett. *39*, 4913-6 (1998).

*N-Hydroxyphthalimide/cobalt(II) acetate*                          ←
**N-Hydroxyphthalimide-catalyzed aerobic oxidation**               ←
aryloxo compds. cf. *51*, 76; arylcarboxylic acids from methylarenes, incl. partial oxidation of *o*- and *p*-xylenes, s. J. Org. Chem. *62*, 6810-3 (1997).

*Nucleoside oxidase*  ←
**Nucleoside-5′-carboxylic acids from nucleosides**  CH$_2$OH → COOH

77.

Aristeromycin added to the clarified crude nucleoside oxidase from *Stenotrophomonas maltophilia* (FERM BP-2252), and incubated with stirring at 25° overnight → product. Y 76%. The enzyme has a surprisingly wide substrate specificity, being suitable for the oxidation of both natural and unnatural nucleosides, as well as carbocyclic analogs, and being tolerant of functions at the 2- and 6-positions (e.g. chloro, hydroxy, 2-phenylethylamino). The N$^5$ nitrogen may also be methylated or be in the form of the N-oxide. F.e. and with the immobilized enzyme s. M. Mahmoudian et al., Tetrahedron *54*, 8171-82 (1998).

*Poly[styrene(iodosoacetate)]*  ←
**α-Arylcarboxylic acid esters from acylophenones** s. *41*, 132s55  ←

*Chromium trioxide/sulfuric acid*  CrO$_3$/H$_2$SO$_4$
**Carboxylic acids from prim. alcohols**  CH$_2$OH → COOH
s. *16*, 225; 1-thiouronic acids from thioglycosides under ultrasonication, selectivity, s. N.M. Allanson et al., Tetrahedron Lett. *39*, 1889-92 (1998).

*Manganese(III) salen complexes/iodosobenzene or sodium hypochlorite*  ←
**Benzylic oxidation under mild condition**  ←

78.

**Benzolactones**. 3 eqs. Buffered NaOCl (pH 11.3) added to a mixture of isobenzochroman and 8 mol% Mn(III)-salen catalyst in dichloromethane, and stirred at 0° for 4 h under N$_2$ → product. Y 87% (98% conversion). The method is mild and regioselective, indicating the electrophilic nature of the manganese-oxo intermediate. There was no reaction with Mn(OAc)$_2$ or Mn(OAc)$_3$, and no hydroxylation. F.e. incl. benzolactams and **aryloxo compds. from alkylarenes,** also with PhIO as re-oxidant and with the racemic complex, s. N.H. Lee et al., Tetrahedron Lett. *39*, 1385-8 (1998).

*Cobalt(II) acetate s. under N-Hydroxyphthalimide*  Co(OAc)$_2$

*Cobalt(II) and manganese(II) p-aminobenzoate/silica gel*  ←
**Quinones from phenols**  ←
with an azomethine-type cobalt(II) complex under O$_2$ cf. *16*, 222s32; *p*-quinones under co-catalysis with cobalt(II) and manganese(II) *p*-aminobenzoate/silica gel s. M.M. Hashemi, Y.A. Beni, J. Chem. Res., Synop *1998*, 138-9.

*Ruthenium/cerium dioxide*  Ru/CeO$_2$
**Carboxylic acids from prim. alcohols** s. *55*, 113  CH$_2$OH → COOH

*Dichlorotris(triphenylphosphine)ruthenium(II)*  RuCl$_2$(PPh$_3$)$_3$
**Urethans from alcohols and formamides** s. *55*, 133  OH → OCON<

*Via intermediates*  v.i.
**Carboxylic acid esters from aldehydes via acetals** s. *55*, 107  CHO → COOR

## Oxygen↑                       OC ↓↑ O

*Without additional reagents*                                                *w.a.r.*
**Carboxylic acid esters from acids and isoureas**             COOH → COOR
s. *29*, 547; diphenylmethyl esters with N,N′-diisopropyl-O-diphenylmethylisourea s. K.H. Cha et al., Synth. Commun. *28*, 2207-11 (1998).

*Microwaves (s.a. under I₂)*                                                   ←
**Acetylation under microwave irradiation in the absence of solvent**    OH → OAc

79.

**of phenols.** A mixture of salicylic acid and 5 eqs. acetic anhydride in a large, loosely capped vial irradiated in a 2450 MHz commercial microwave oven (Sam Sung, Model # RE-555 TCW) for 5 min, and the cooled mixture quenched with satd. $Na_2CO_3$ soln. → 2-acetoxybenzoic acid. Y 92%. The method is simple and very rapid, and electron-withdrawing groups such as Cl or $CO_2H$ did not retard the reaction. F.e. and N-acetylation of prim. ar. amines, also ar. nitration, s. P.-S. Kwon et al., Bull. Korean Chem. Soc. *18*, 1118-9 (1997).

*Lithium or Sodium hydroxide*                                    *LiOH or NaOH*
**O-Alkylation with dialkyl sulfates** s. under OC↓↑S                  OH → OR

*Copper(II) nitrate*                                                        $Cu(NO_3)_2$
**O-Acetylation under mild conditions**                               OH → OAc

80.

(-)-Menthol and 1 eq. $Cu(NO_3)_2·3H_2O$ in acetic acid stirred vigorously under reflux for 3.5 h → (-)-menthol acetate. Y 98%. This method allows efficient **O-acetylation and O-formylation** (in ethyl formate) of primary and secondary alcohols (including benzylalcohols with electron-withdrawing groups) with retention of chirality. The reagent is cheap and readily available, and the procedure and work-up are simple. Primary alcohols can be selectively acetylated in the presence of secondary alcohols in ethyl acetate, e.g. a mixture of 3-phenylpropan-1-ol and 1-phenylpropanol gave 100% conversion of the former and only 10% conversion of the latter in refluxing ethyl acetate after 6 h. However, sugars and other polyfunctionalized molecules formed complexes with the Cu(II) ion preventing acetylation. F.e. and Cu(II)-catalysts s. N. Iranpoor et al., Synth. Commun. *28*, 1923-34 (1998).

*Montmorillonite*                                                                  ←
**O-Acetylation**                                                                     OH → OAc
s. *54*, 79; per-O-acetylation of carbohydrates s. Tetrahedron Lett. *39*, 2215-8 (1998).

**Sym. ethers from alcohols**                                  2 ROH → ROR
with $Al_2O_3$ cf. *19*, 226; 5(6)/5′(6′)-unsatd. 3β,3′β-disteryl ethers with montmorillonite s. T. Li et al., Synth. Commun. *26*, 2497-502 (1996).

*Zeolite*                                                                             ←
**1,3-Dioxolanes from oxo compds.**                               CO → $C(OR)_2$
with montmorillonite cf. *28*, 141s52; with reusable zeolite HSZ-360, selectivity, s. R. Ballini et al., Tetrahedron Lett. *39*, 1615-8 (1998).

*Boron fluoride* $BF_3$
**O-Benzylation** $OH \rightarrow OCH_2Ar$
with benzyl trichloroacetimidate cf. *37*, 152; protection of hydroxyl groups as polymer-based benzyl ethers in the presence of $BF_3$-etherate, and cleavage with trifluoroacetic acid, s. S. Hanessian, F. Xie, Tetrahedron Lett. *39*, 733-6 (1998); N-protected α-aminocarboxylic acid *tert*-butyl and 2-phenylisopropyl esters with the appropriate alkyl trichloroacetimidate s. J. Thierry et al., ibid. 1557-60; protection of hydroxyl groups as *p*-methoxybenzyl and 3,4-dimethoxybenzyl ethers with the appropriate trifluoroacetimidates using pyridinium tosylate, TfOH or camphorsulfonic acid as catalyst, s. N. Nakajima et al., ibid. 5565-8.

*Cerium(III) chloride* $CeCl_3$
**Preferential Lewis acid-catalyzed O-acylation** $OH \rightarrow OAc$

81.

A 0.05 *M* soln. of 10-deacetylbaccatin III in THF treated with butyric anhydride at 25° for 3 h in the presence of 0.1 eq. $CeCl_3$ → 10-butyryl deriv. Y 100%. $ZnCl_2$ was almost as effective. F.e., **also preferential O-carbamylation** (with isocyanates in the presence of 1 eq. $CuCl_2$), **and preferential O-silylation** (with N,O-bis(triethylsilyl)trifluoroacetamide in the presence of a little Li-bis(trimethylsilyl)amide), s. R.A. Holton et al., Tetrahedron Lett. *39*, 2883-6 (1998).

*Dicyclohexylcarbodiimide/polymer-based 1-hydroxybenzotriazole* ←
**N-Hydroxysuccinimide esters from carboxylic acids** ←
with polymer-based carbodiimide cf. *16*, 236s52; improved procedure with dicyclohexylcarbodiimide/polymer-based 1-hydroxybenzotriazole s. K.G. Dendrinos, A.G. Kalivretenos, Tetrahedron Lett. *39*, 1321-4 (1998); general procedure with diphenyl or diethyl phosphorochloridate and $NaHCO_3$ (cf. *36*, 85) s. P. Pöchlauer, W. Hendel, Tetrahedron *54*, 3489-94 (1998).

*Immobilized lipase* ←
**Kinetic resolution by asym. enzymatic esterification** ←
with 'Lipase My' cf. *41*, 175; asym. esterification of 2-arylpropionic acids with immobilized *Rhizomucor miehei* lipase, systematic study, s. M.T. López-Belmonte et al., J. Org. Chem. *62*, 1831-40 (1997).

*Amberlyst 15* ←
**α-Aminocarboxylic acid esters from acids** s. *55*, 18 $COOH \rightarrow COOR$

*Acetyl chloride/alcohols* $AcCl/ROH$
**Carboxylic acid esters from acids**
N-protected α-amino esters with HCl in methanol cf. *5*, 174; with an *exact* concentration of HCl generated *in situ* from acetyl chloride in methanol, also with simultaneous N-decarbo-*tert*-butoxylation, and further acid-catalyzed conversions, s. A. Nudelman et al., Synth. Commun. *28*, 471-4 (1998).

*Chloroacetyl chloride* $ClCH_2COCl$
**Carboxylic acid phenyl esters from carboxylic acids** $COOH \rightarrow COOPh$

82. $n\text{-}C_8H_{17}COOH$ + $HOPh$ ⟶ $n\text{-}C_8H_{17}COOPh$

**under mild conditions.** A mixture of 5 g nonanoic acid, 3.93 g chloroacetyl chloride, and 2.97 g phenol *in acetonitrile* refluxed at 80° for 19 h under $N_2$ → phenyl nonanoate. Y 83% (>97% purity). F.e. and functionalized acetyl chlorides s. United States patent US-5710296 (Clorox Co.).

83.

*Di-n-butyltin oxide/methyl orthoformate* $Bu_2SnO/HC(OMe)_3$
**Sym. 1,4-dioxane-2,5-diones from α-hydroxycarboxylic acid esters**

A mixture of 416.4 g DL-methyl lactate and 2.1 g Bu$_2$SnO heated (from 160°/600 mmHg) to 200° over 4 h under N$_2$ with removal of methanol, heating continued at 200° and 200 mmHg over 1 h then at 10 mmHg over 1 h, 2.46 g methyl orthoformate added at atm. pressure under N$_2$, and heated at 200° for 2 h → 210.1 g lactide (99.4% purity). The orthoester facilitates removal of water and undesirable carboxylic acids. The procedure is simple and inexpensive. F.e.s. European patent EP-834511 (Mitsubishi Gas Chem Co. Inc.).

*Stannous chloride* $SnCl_2$
**Acetals from oxo compds.** $CO \rightarrow C(OR)_2$
with TiCl$_4$ cf. *18*, 234; unstable acetals with SnCl$_2$, CeCl$_3$·6H$_2$O, BiCl$_3$ or Ti-salts s European patent EP-771779 (Kuraray Co. Ltd.).

*Phosphorous acid diesters/carbon tetrachloride/potassium carbonate/* ←
  *benzyltriethylammonium chloride*
**Carboxylic acid esters from acids** s. *34*, 358s55 $COOH \rightarrow COOR$

*Diphenyl phosphorochloridate/sodium hydrogen carbonate* $(PhO)_2P(O)Cl/NaHCO_3$
**N-Hydroxysuccinimide esters from carboxylic acids** s. *16*, 236s55 $COOH \rightarrow COON{<}$

*Tantalum pentachloride/silica* $TaCl_5/SiO_2$
**O-Acetylation of alcohols** $OH \rightarrow OAc$

84.

Startg. alcohol and 1.5 eqs. acetic anhydride added to a stirred soln. of 5 mol% TaCl$_5$-on-silica gel in dry dichloromethane, and the mixture stirred at room temp. under N$_2$ until reaction complete by TLC → product. Y 76%. The method is general for simple aliphatic, allylic or benzylic alcohols as well as phenols. Tert. alcohols, however, gave low yields due to concomitant dehydration. Olefins, cyclic ethers, chlorides and cyclic acetals survived these mildly acidic conditions. F.e. and [less efficiently] in the absence of silica, **also kinetic resolution of sec. alcohols** with TaCl$_5$ and (-)-2,3-O-isopropylidene-1,1,4,4-tetraphenyl-L-threitol (e.e. up to 40%), s. S. Chandrasekhar et al., Tetrahedron Lett. *39*, 3263-6 (1998).

*Pyridinium tosylate* $C_5H_5NHOTs$
**Protection of hydroxyl groups** $OH \rightarrow OCH_2Ar$
as p-methoxybenzyl or 3,4-dimethoxybenzyl ethers s. *37*, 152s55

*Iodine/microwaves* ←
**Acetals from oxo compds. under microwave irradiation** $CO \rightarrow C(OR)_2$
s. *41*, 172s*51, 54*; *51*, 84s*53*; with I$_2$ as catalyst in THF cf. D.J. Kalita et al., Tetrahedron Lett. *39*, 4573-4 (1998).

*Ferric sulfate* $Fe_2(SO_4)_3$
**Carboxylic acid esters from acids** $COOH \rightarrow COOR$
α,β-ethylenecarboxylic acid esters s. *42*, 163; esterification of simple aliphatic carboxylic acids and dicarboxylic acids s. G.-S. Zhang, Synth. Commun. *28*, 1159-62 (1998).

*Polymer-based ferric chloride* ←
**Carboxylic acid esters from acids**
with FeCl$_3$ cf. *28*, 148s*34*; with moisture-resistant, readily removable polymer-based ferric chloride, **also acetalation**, s. Y. Huirong, L.B.C. Yingde, Synth. Commun. *28*, 1233-8 (1998).

*Dichlorotris(triphenylphosphine)ruthenium(II)*      $RuCl_2(PPh_3)_3$
**Diol monoallyl ethers from diols and 3-ethylenealcohols via migration of the double bond and allyl rearrangement** ←

85.

**Preferential O-allylation.** A mixture of 1-phenyl-3-buten-1-ol and 4 mol% $RuCl_2(PPh_3)_3$ in 1,3-butanediol stirred at 90-100° for 2 h under air → product. Y 58%. Prim. hydroxyl groups reacted preferentially over sec. ones, and no formation of bisether was observed. F.e.s. D. Wang, C.-J. Li, Synth. Commun. *28*, 507-15 (1998).

# Nitrogen ↑                                      OC ↓↑ N

*Without additional reagents*                                                        *w.a.r.*
**O-Acylation with 1-acylimidazoles**                                OH → OAc
with NBS in methylene chloride cf. *32,* 161; in the *solid* phase, selective O-acetylation of prim. alcohols and phenols, s. H. Hagiwara et al., Synth. Commun. *28*, 2001-6 (1998).

**O-Acylation with N-acylcyclimmonium salts**
with 1-acyl-3-benzylimidazolium salts cf. *38,* 158; O-acylation of chiral sec. alcohols with N-acylpyridinium triflates or fluoroborates s. R. Wagner et al., Synthesis *1998*, 883-8.

*Sodium/oxalic acid*                                                        $Na/(COOH)_2$
**Aldehydes from $\Delta^2$-imidazolines**
with $Na_3$/liq. $NH_3$/EtOH cf. *10,* 177; with Na in ethanol, followed by distillation of the crude imidazolidine from oxalic acid soln., s. Z. Shi, H. Gu, Synth. Commun. *27*, 2701-7 (1997).

*Sodium hydride*                                                                             NaH
**O-*p*-Methoxybenzylation**                                                 OH → $OCH_2Ar$

86.

**of alcohols.** A soln. of 1 eq. N-(*p*-methoxybenzyl)-*o*-benzenedisulfonimide in dry THF added dropwise to a soln. of 1-phenylethanol and 1.5 eqs. NaH in the same solvent, and the mixture stirred overnight at room temp. → *p*-methoxybenzyl 1-phenethyl ether. Y 78%. The acidic by-product, *o*-benzenedisulfonimide, is readily soluble in water and easy to remove. F.e. incl. O-*p*-methoxybenzylation of phenols, and preparation of the disulfonimide, s. P.H.J. Carlsen, Tetrahedron Lett. *39*, 1799-802 (1998).

*Hexamethylenetetramine-bromine complex*                                ←
**Oxo compds. from oximes under mild, neutral conditions**      C=NOH → CO

87.

A mixture of 4-bromobenzophenone oxime and 1.03 eqs. hexamethylenetetramine-bromine complex in 10:1 carbon tetrachloride/water stirred at 25° for 2 h → 4-bromobenzophenone. Y 90%. Reaction is generally applicable to cleavage of both aldoximes and ketoximes, and there was no over-oxidation. The oxidant is readily prepared, and work-up is simple. F.e. incl. chemoselective cleavage of ketoximes in preference to aldoximes, **also cleavage of tosylhydrazones,** s. B.P. Bandgar et al., J. Chem. Res., Synop *1998*, 154-5.

*Pyridine*                                                                                         $C_5H_5N$
**Polymer-based benzotriazol-1-yl carbonates from chloroformic acid esters** s. *55*, 134     ←

*Cupric acetoacetonate* $\hspace{5cm} Cu(acac)_2$
**α-Acoxyketones from α-diazoketones** $\hspace{2cm} COCN_2 \rightarrow COCH(OAc)$
with CuCl$_2$ cf. *9*, 287; with Cu(acac)$_2$, selectivity, s. T. Shinada et al., Tetrahedron Lett. *39*, 3757-60 (1998).

*Silver benzoate* $\hspace{8cm} AgOCOPh$
**Carboxylic acids from α-diazoketones** $\hspace{2cm} COCHN_2 \rightarrow CH_2COOH$
with Ag$_2$O/Na$_2$S$_2$O$_3$ cf. *22*, 813; chiral N-Fmoc-protected β-aminocarboxylic acids with AgOCOPh in aq. dioxane under sonication s. A. Müller et al., Synthesis *1998*, 837-41.

*Lanthanum(III) iodide* $\hspace{8cm} LaI_3$
**Carboxylic acid esters from 3-acyl-2-oxazolidones and alcohols** $\hspace{1cm}$ CON< → COOR
**under mild, neutral conditions**

88.

3 eqs. Benzyl alcohol added to 1 eq. 0.1 *M* LaI$_3$ in THF at room temp., the mixture stirred for 10 min, startg. 2-oxazolidone added, and stirring continued for a further 15 h → product. Y 99%. The method is free from by-products (due to oxazolidine ring opening), racemization is minimal, and the reagent is inexpensive and readily available. The by-product, (S)-3-isopropyl-2-oxazolidone, can be readily separated by column chromatography (Y 87%) and re-used. F.e. incl. chiral derivs. with retention of configuration, also with SmI$_3$ or YbI$_3$ (the latter being less efficient with benzyl alcohol), and catalytic procedure s. S. Fukuzawa, Y. Hongo, Tetrahedron Lett. *39*, 3521-4 (1998).

*Formic acid* $\hspace{9cm} HCOOH$
**Cleavage of hydrazones** $\hspace{6cm} C{=}N\text{-}N< \rightarrow CO$
with pyruvic acid cf. *6*, 290, 891; aliphatic and ar. ketones from phenylhydrazones with formic acid in 50% ethanol or in aq. media s. M. Chakrabarty, S. Khasnobis, Synth. Commun. *28*, 1361-8 (1998).

*Oxalic acid* $\hspace{9cm} (COOH)_2$
**Cleavage of hydrazones**
s. *39*, 581; of chiral N-[2-(methoxymethyl)pyrrolidino]ketimines (SAMP-hydrazones) with retention of chirality, selectivity, s. D. Enders et al., Synlett *1998*, 721-2.

*1,1,1-Triacetoxy-1,2-benziodoxol-3-one* $\hspace{6cm} \leftarrow$
**Ketones from ketoximes** $\hspace{6cm} C{=}NOH \rightarrow CO$
with PhI(OAc)$_2$ cf. *42*, 173; aryl ketones with 1,1,1-triacetoxy-1,2-benziodoxol-3-one, selectivity, s. S.S. Chaudhari, K.G. Akamanchi, Tetrahedron Lett. *39*, 3209-12 (1998).

*Clay-supported ammonium nitrate* $\hspace{5cm} NH_4NO_3\text{-}clay$
**Oxo compds. from oximes under mild conditions**

89.

Clayan (containing 7 eqs. NH$_4$NO$_3$-on-montmorillonite K 10) added to a soln. of 5-methoxy-tetralone oxime in *dichloromethane*, and the mixture stirred at room temp. under N$_2$ for 12 h → product. Y 86%. The method is simple, metal-ion free, and general (for aliphatic or aromatic aldehydes and ketones), and the reagent is inexpensive and eco-friendly. Alumina, silica or other clays were found to be unsuitable supports. F.e. and preparation of Clayan s. H.M. Meshram et al., Synth. Commun. *28*, 2593-600 (1998).

*Ozone* $O_3$
**Cleavage of hydrazones** C=N-N< → CO
s. *16*, 257s*48*; aldehydo sugars s. R.P. Spencer et al., J. Org. Chem. *62*, 4507-9 (1997).

*Trifluoromethanesulfonic anhydride/pyridine* $(CF_3SO_2)_2O/C_5H_5N$
**Carboxylic acid esters from amides under nearly neutral conditions** CON< → COOR

90.  PhCH$_2$CH$_2$CONEt$_2$  $\xrightarrow{Tf_2O}$  [ PhCH$_2$CH$_2$C(OTf)=NEt$_2$ TfO$^-$ ]  $\xrightarrow{HOEt}$  PhCH$_2$CH$_2$COOEt

1.3 eqs. Trifluoromethanesulfonic anhydride added slowly to a soln. of N,N-diethylhydrocinnamide and 3 eqs. pyridine in methylene chloride under argon at -40°, allowed to warm slowly to 0° (ca. 2 h) with stirring, >30 eqs. ethanol added after a further 10 h, allowed to warm to room temp., stirring continued for 12 h, diluted with ether, and washed with 1 *N* HCl → ethyl hydrocinnamate. Y 94%. The method is applicable to both N-subst. and N,N-disubst. amides, and a number of acid- or base-sensitive functional groups (e.g. OTBDPS, OAc, OPMB, O,O-isopropylidene) remained unaffected. Furthermore, there was little racemization of substrates possessing a chiral centre at the α-position. F.e.s. A.B. Charette, P. Chua, Synlett *1998*, 163-5.

*Ammonium chlorochromate-alumina* $[NH_4][CrO_3Cl]-Al_2O_3$
**Oxo compds. from oximes** C=NOH → CO
with [MeNH$_3$][CrO$_3$Cl]-alumina cf. *54*, 86; aryloxo compds. with ammonium chlorochromate-alumina, selectivity, s. Synth. Commun. *28*, 2221-5 (1998).

*Bromine-amine complexes s. under Hexamethylenetetramine* ←

*1-Benzyl-4-aza-1-azoniabicyclo[2.2.2]octane periodate* $R_4NIO_4$
**Oxo compds. from oximes**
ketones with HIO$_4$ cf. *29*, 201s*31*; also aldehydes under neutral conditions, and cleavage of chiral β-oximinosulfoxides with retention of chirality, with 1-benzyl-4-aza-1-azoniabicyclo[2.2.2]octane periodate s. A.R. Hajipour, N. Mahboubhah, J. Chem. Res., Synop *1998*, 122-3.

*Hydrogen chloride* *HCl*
**γ-Lactols from 2-aminotetrahydrofurans** s. *55*, 432 N< → OH

**α-*tert*-Aminoketones from (Z)-ene-1,2-di-*tert*-amines** s. *55*, 346 C=C(N<) → CHCO

*Bis(tetraethylammonium) tribromotricarbonylrhenate/silver trifluoromethanesulfonate/* ←
*potassium salt*
**3-Component synthesis of tricarbonyl(η$^5$-acoxycyclopentadienyl)rhenium complexes** ←

91.  AcOK + [cyclopentadiene with N$_2$]  $\xrightarrow{[(MeCN)_3Re(CO)_3]^+ TfO^-}$  AcO-[cyclopentadienyl]-Re(CO)$_3$

A soln. of (Et$_4$N)$_2$[ReBr$_3$(CO)$_3$] in anhydrous acetonitrile treated with 3 eqs. AgOTf, the precipitate of AgBr filtered off, the supernatant added to a soln. of 1.2 eqs. diazocyclopentadiene and 2 eqs. KOAc in the same solvent, and heated at 80° for 45 min → product. Y 62%. Both aliphatic and ar. carboxylates participate in the coupling, which tolerates free alcohol, phenol and amide NH-groups. There was no coupling, however, with mercaptans or acetylides as nucleophile. The procedure is of potential for securing radio-labelled pharmaceuticals. F.e.s. F. Minutolo, J.A. Katzenellenbogen, J. Am. Chem. Soc. *120*, 4514-5 (1998).

*Nickel/acetic acid* *Ni/AcOH*
**γ-Lactols from γ-hydroxynitriles** ○

92.  Ph-CH(OH)-CH$_2$-CH$_2$-CN  →  Ph-[tetrahydrofuran]-OH

**Chiral γ-lactols.** Raney nickel (0.4 g) added to a soln. of 4 g (R)-3-benzyl-4-hydroxybutyronitrile in deaerated 50% aq. acetic acid, and heated at 50° for 7 h in an autoclave under a pressure of 10 kg/cm$^2$ → 2.5 g product. The procedure is industrially viable. F.e. and acids s. Japanese patent JP-09077758 (Kuraray Co. Ltd.).

*Tetra*-n-*propylammonium perruthenate/N-methylmorpholine N-oxide/silver acetate/*   ←
*potassium carbonate*
**Ketones from sec. nitro compds.**   CHNO$_2$ → CO
**Catalytic conversion under mild conditions**

93.
    NO$_2$
    |
 MeCHCH(Ph)CH$_2$COOMe  ⟶  MeCOCH(Ph)CH$_2$COOMe

10 Mol% tetra-*n*-propylammonium perruthenate added to a suspension of startg. nitro compd., 1.5 eqs. N-methylmorpholine N-oxide, 2 eqs. AgOAc, 5 eqs. K$_2$CO$_3$, and 4 Å molecular sieves in dry acetonitrile, and stirred at 40° for 10 h → methyl 4-oxo-3-phenylpentanoate. Y 89%. Prim. nitro compds. gave an intractable mixture. F.e. and silver(I) salts s. Y. Tokunaga et al., J. Chem. Soc. Perkin Trans. I *1997*, 207-9.

*Via intermediates*   *v.i.*
**Aldehydes from nitriles via oxazolidines** s. *55*, 152   CN → CHO

# Halogen ↑      OC ↓↑ Hal

*Microwaves* s. *under KOBu-*t   ←

*Sodium hydride*   *NaH*
**Carboxylic acid esters from difluoromethylene compds.**   C=CF$_2$ → CHCOOR
s. *36*, 203; α-aryl-α-(trifluoromethyl)carboxylic acid esters with NaH s. I.H. Jeong et al., Synth. Commun. *28*, 1981-7 (1998).

*Potassium* tert-*butoxide/microwaves*   ←
**Nucleophilic substitution of ar. halogen under microwave irradiation**   ←
of ar. nitrochlorides cf. *45*, 96s*48*; *tert*-butyl phenolethers (with KOBu-*t*) and ar. amines s. G.V. Salmoria et al., Tetrahedron Lett. *39*, 2471-4 (1998).

*Sodium peroxide*   *Na$_2$O$_2$*
**Carboxylic acid esters from aldehydes and halides**   CHO → COOR

94.     PhCHO   +   MeBr  ⟶  PhCOOMe

**One-pot procedure.** Benzaldehyde treated with 1 eq. Na-peroxide in DMF or dimethylacetamide at 15-20°, CO$_2$ introduced, 1.1 eqs. methyl bromide or iodide added, and worked up after 24 h → methyl benzoate. Y 80-95%. F.e.s. Russian patent RU-2074853 (Univ. Kuban Agric.).

*Sodium carbonate/2,2,6,6-tetramethylpiperidine N-oxyl/sodium hypochlorite*   ←
**Ar. aldehydes from benzyl chlorides via benzylalcohols** s. *55*, 99   CH$_2$Cl → CHO

*Cesium fluoride/Celite*   *CsF/Celite*
**Carboxylic acid esters from acids**   COOH → COOR

95.   [cyclohexyl-CH(OH)-COOH]   +   EtI  ⟶  [cyclohexyl-CH(OH)-COOEt]

Startg. carboxylic acid and 1.5 eqs. CsF-Celite as *solid* base in *acetonitrile* treated with 2 eqs. ethyl iodide, and the mixture stirred at reflux for 2.5 h → product. Y 93%. The reagent was prepared by stirring CsF and Celite 521 in water for 20 min, removing the water *in vacuo*, shaking the solid in acetonitrile, and drying it in a desiccator. This is a clean and practical method which is applicable to aromatic, aliphatic, and heteroaromatic (including base-sensitive) carboxylic acids. Esterification of chiral α-substituted carboxylic acids proceeded in excellent yields **with retention of chirality.** Replacing acetonitrile by THF reduced the yields and increased reaction times, as did

*Triethylamine/(S)-1-methyl-2-(N-benzyl-N-methyl)aminomethylpyrrolidine* ←
**Desymmetrization of glycols by asym. mono-O-acylation**  OH → OCOR
with a chiral diamine cf. *54*, 88; with Et₃N/(S)-1-methyl-2-(N-benzyl-N-methyl)aminomethyl-pyrrolidine s. Tetrahedron Lett. *39*, 3529-32 (1998).

*Zinc*  *Zn*
**Carboxylic acid esters from carboxylic acid chlorides and alcohols**  COCl → COOR
**under mild conditions**

96.

1 eq. Activated Zn-dust added to a soln. of startg. acid chloride in benzene, the suspension stirred for 10 min, a soln. of 1 eq. *tert*-butanol in benzene added, and stirring continued for a further 12 min → product. Y 93%. The method is fast, yields are high, and conditions are almost neutral. It is general for a variety of acid chlorides, and for prim., sec. and tert. alcohols, including allyl and benzyl derivs. Conjugated or isolated olefins and acetylenes, aromatic chlorides and phenolethers were unaffected. It is believed that the presence of Zn helps to increase the electrophilic character of the acyl group by complexation of polar groups to the surface of the metal. F.e. and with toluene as solvent in comparable yield s. J.S. Yadav et al., Synth. Commun. *28*, 2337-42 (1998).

*Triphenylcarbonium tetrakis(pentafluorophenyl)borate*  *[Ph₃C][Ar₄B]*
**β-Glycosides from β-glycosyl fluorides**  F → OR

97.

Methyl 2,4,6-tri-*O*-benzyl-α-D-glucopyranoside and 1.3 eqs. 2,3,4,6-tetra-O-benzyl-β-D-glucopyranosyl fluoride added successively at -10° in 5:1 benzotrifluoride/pivalonitrile to a stirred suspension of 0.2 eq. trityl tetrakis(pentafluorophenyl)borate and Drierite in the same solvent, stirred for 14 h at this temp., and quenched with satd. aq. NaHCO₃ → methyl 2,4,6-tri-O-benzyl-3-O-(2,3,4,6-tetra-O-benzyl-D-glucopyranosyl)-α-D-glucopyranoside. Y 93% (α/β 9:91). This is the first example of activation of an anomeric C-F bond using a trityl cation. F.e.s. K. Takeuchi, T. Mukaiyama, Chem. Lett. *1998*, 555-6.

*2,2,6,6-Tetramethylpiperidine N-oxyl s. under Na₂CO₃*  ←

*Silica gel*  *SiO₂*
**Partial O-acetylation of sym. diols**  OH → OAc

98.

A soln. of butane-1,4-diol in ether treated with silica gel, solvent removed under reduced pressure, the obtained solid and 9 eqs. acetyl chloride added to cyclohexane, and refluxed for 2 h → butane-1,4-diol monoacetate. Y 99.5% (100% selectivity). Even with 20 eqs. acetyl chloride only monoacetylation was observed. The diol is presumably adsorbed as a mono-molecular layer on the surface of the silica gel, which thus acts as a protecting agent for one hydroxyl group. While aliphatic prim. diols reacted quantitatively, lower yields were obtained with cyclohexane-1,4-diol or benzene-1,4-dimethanol. F.e.s. H. Ogawa et al., Chem. Commun. *1998*, 495-6.

*Dimethyltin dichloride/potassium carbonate*  *Me₂SnCl₂/K₂CO₃*
**Mono-O-acylation of diols via O,O'-stannylene derivs.**
with (Bu₃Sn)₂O cf. *33*, 205; *32*, 85; mono-O-benzoylation of chiral diols with Me₂SnCl₂/K₂CO₃, also selective and regiospecific mono-O-benzoylation of glycols, s. T. Maki et al., Tetrahedron Lett. *39*, 5601-4 (1998).

*Stannic chloride*     $SnCl_4$
**Glycosides from glycosyl bromides**     Br → OR
acylglycosides with Ag(I)-γ-hydroxyvalerate cf. *26*, 203; with $SnCl_4$, with retention of configuration, also from peracylated arabinofuranose, galactofuranose, and rhamnopyranose derivs. (cf. *34*, 209), s. A.K. Pathak et al., Tetrahedron Lett. *39*, 1497-1500 (1998).

*Sulfated zirconia*     ←
**Glycosides from glycosyl fluorides**     F → OR
α-glycosides from β-glycosyl fluorides with $SnCl_2$/$AgClO_4$ cf. *37*, 182s39; with 5 wt% sulfated zirconia, also β-glycosides with 100 wt% sulfated zirconia/5 Å molecular sieves, s. K. Toshima et al., Synlett *1998*, 643-5.

*Chlorotris(triphenylphosphine)cobalt(I)*     $Co(PPh_3)_3Cl$
**Ar. aldehydes from benzyl bromides under mild conditions**     $CH_2Br$ → CHO

99.

$O_2N-C_6H_4-CH_2Br \xrightarrow{O_2} [O_2N-C_6H_4-CH_2OO^\bullet] \longrightarrow O_2N-C_6H_4-CHO$

Air bubbled through a mixture of *p*-nitrobenzyl bromide and 1 eq. anhydrous Co(I)(PPh$_3$)$_3$Cl in dry benzene/ethyl acetate at 0 to -10° for 15 to 30 min → *p*-nitrobenzaldehyde. Y 80%. The method is mild and neutral, and is believed to occur via a benzylperoxyl radical, formation of which is favoured over C-C coupling. Functional groups such as methoxy, carbethoxy, phthalimido and nitro remained unaffected under these conditions. F.e.s. S. Goswami, A.K. Mahapatra, Tetrahedron Lett. *39*, 1981-4 (1998); **from benzyl chlorides** via benzylalcohols in one pot with $Na_2CO_3$/2,2,6,6-tetramethylpiperidine N-oxyl/NaOCl s. Japanese patent JP-09087226 (Ihara Nikkei Kagaku Kogyo KK).

## Sulfur ↑     OC ↓↑ S

*Lithium hydroxide*     LiOH
**O-Alkylation of phenols with dialkyl sulfates**     ArOH → ArOR

100.

[Structure: N-acetyl tyrosine ethyl ester + Me$_2$SO$_4$ → N-acetyl O-methyl tyrosine ethyl ester]

**under mild, non-aq. conditions.** Startg. phenol treated with 1 eq. LiOH·H$_2$O in dry THF at room temp. for 10 min, 1 eq. dimethyl sulfate added, and the mixture stirred at room temp. for 1 h → product. Y 100%. In the non-aq. medium, hydrolytic decomposition of the sulfates is avoided, and a quantitative transfer of alkyl groups is possible. N-Alkylation did not compete, and a variety of functional groups (e.g. amides, esters, nitriles, phenolethers, and aromatic chlorides and nitro compds.) were unaffected. F.e. and O-ethylation s. A. Basak et al., Tetrahedron Lett. *39*, 4883-6 (1998).

*Sodium hydroxide (s.a. under $R_3N$)*     NaOH
**Nucleophilic substitution of sulfonyl groups**     ←
s. *21*, 256; 5-functionalized tetrazoles s. M.A. Glotsberg, G.I. Koldobskii, Khim. Geterotsikl. Soedin. *1996*, 1515-9 (Russ.).

*Trialkylamines/sodium hydroxide* $\quad R_3N/NaOH$
**Arylcarboxylic acid esters** $\quad COOH \rightarrow COOR$
**from arylcarboxylic acids and dialkyl sulfates in a 2-phase aq. organic medium**

101.

$$\text{F}_4\text{C}_6(\text{COOH})_2 \longrightarrow [\text{F}_3\text{C}_6\text{H-COOH}] \xrightarrow{Et_2SO_4} \text{F}_3\text{C}_6\text{H-COOEt}$$

**with ar. decarboxylation.** A mixture of 311 g tetrafluorophthalic acid, 150 g of a $C_8$-$C_{10}$ mixture of trialkylamines, and water/diphenylmethane/xylene adjusted to pH 6-7 with $H_2SO_4$, stirred at 110° for 9 h, water and ca. half the volume of xylene removed over 2 h at 110°, the resulting mixture containing 2,3,4,5-tetrafluorobenzoic acid (234.9 g) recombined with the distillate, treated dropwise with 856.9 g diethyl sulfate over 4 h at 40° and pH 7-8 (periodically adding aq. NaOH), stirred for 75 min, treated with $NH_4Cl$, stirring continued for 2 h, and filtered at pH 8.2 → ethyl 2,3,4,5-tetrafluorobenzoate. Y 84% overall. F.e. and with added phase transfer catalyst s. European patent EP-811601 (Clariant GMBH).

*Hydroximinochlorides/triethylamine* $\quad RC(=NOH)Cl/Et_3N$
**Ureas from thioureas** s. *55*, 208 $\quad CS(N<)_2 \rightarrow CO(N<)_2$

*N-Iodosuccinimide/trifluoromethanesulfonic acid or trimethylsilyl triflate* $\quad \leftarrow$
*Methyl trifluoromethanesulfonate/2,6-di-*tert*-butylpyridine* $\quad \leftarrow$
**Glycosides from thioglycosides** $\quad SR \rightarrow OR$
with $NIS/CF_3SO_3SiMe_3$ s. *39*, 189s*54*; f. N-acetylneuraminic acid glycosides s. A.V. Demchenko, G.-J. Boons, Tetrahedron Lett. *39*, 3065-8 (1998); *two-directional* glycosidation for the convergent assembly of oligosaccharides s. T. Zhu, G.-J. Boons, ibid. 2187-90; coupling of 2-sulfonylamino-2-deoxythioglycosides with polymer-based glycals using MeOTf/2,6-di-*tert*-butylpyridine (cf. *39*, 189s*46*) s. C. Zheng, S. Danishefsky et al., Angew. Chem. Int. Ed. Engl. *37*, 786-9 (1998).

# Remaining Elements ↑     OC ↕ Rem

*Cupric acetate/triethylamine* $\quad Cu(OAc)_2/Et_3N$
**Diaryl ethers from phenols and arylboronic acids** s. *55*, 166 $\quad ArOH \rightarrow ArOAr'$

*Phenyl iodosoacetate/sodium iodide* $\quad PhI(OAc)_2/NaI$
**Enolesters** $\quad C=C\text{-}B(OH)_2 \rightarrow C=C(OAc)$
**from α,β-ethyleneboronic acids or acid esters with inversion of configuration**

102.

$$\text{CH}_3(\text{CH}_2)_5\text{CH=CH-B(OH)}_2 \xrightarrow{PhI(OAc)_2} \text{CH}_3(\text{CH}_2)_5\text{CH=CH-OAc}$$

**(Z)-Enolesters.** A soln of (E)-oct-1-en-1-ylboronic acid, 1.1 eqs. phenyl iodosoacetate, and 1.1 eqs. NaI in DMF stirred at room temp. for 16 h → (Z)-oct-1-en-1-yl acetate. Y 85% (>99% purity). There was no reaction in the absence of NaI. Reaction is thought to involve *anti*-addition of *in situ*-generated acetyl hypoiodite, followed by acetate-induced *anti*-deiodoboration. F.e. and from the corresponding boronic acid esters s. M. Murata et al., J. Chem. Soc. Perkin Trans. 1 *1998*, 1465-6.

*Phenyl iodosoacetate/trifluoromethanesulfonic acid* $\quad PhI(OAc)_2/CF_3SO_3H$
**Oxidative solvolysis of 1-siloxybicyclo[n.1.0]alkanes** $\quad \circlearrowleft$
ethylenecarboxylic acids in glacial AcOH cf. *51*, 97; in aq. media with a little $CF_3SO_3H$, also esters in alcoholic media, s. Synth. Commun. *28*, 1947-56 (1998).

*Zirconocene dichloride/silver trifluoromethanesulfonate* $\quad Cp_2ZrCl_2/AgOSO_2CF_3$
**Glycosides from glycosyl fluorides and alkoxysilanes** $\quad F \rightarrow OR$
with $ZrCl_4$ cf. *40*, 122s*53*; with $Cp_2ZrCl_2/AgOSO_2CF_3$, α-selectivity, s. T. Zhu, G.-J. Boons, Tetrahedron Lett. *39*, 2187-90 (1998).

*Triphenylphosphine/carbon tetrabromide* $Ph_3P/CBr_4$
**Acoxy compds. from *tert*-butyldimethylsilyl ethers** s. *55*, 110   $OSiMe_2Bu\text{-}t \rightarrow OAc$

## Carbon ↑                                                                    OC ↓↑ C

*Irradiation* s. under RSH                                                          ⇊

*Potassium carbonate*                                                      $K_2CO_3$
**Transesterification of carbazic acid esters**       >NNHCOOR → >NNHCOOR'

103.            $H_2$NNHCOOMe  +  HOBn  ⟶  $H_2$NNHCOOBn

A mixture of 45 g methyl carbazate, 54 g benzyl alcohol, and 2 g $K_2CO_3$ heated for 3 h at 130° with distillation of methanol → 46.5 g product (97% benzyl carbazate). F.e and catalysts (alkali and alkaline earth metal hydroxides, carbonates, bicarbonates, or alcoholates, amino compds., or titanium or tin compds.) s. European patent EP-770598 (Bayer AG).

*Kaolinitic clay or Zeolites/microwaves*                                              ←
**Transesterification of β-ketocarboxylic acid esters**           COOR → COOR'
with sulfated stannic oxide cf. *51*, 104; with kaolinitic clay s. D.E. Ponde et al., J. Org. Chem. *63*, 1058-63 (1998); with zeolite Hβ, also acceleration under microwave irradiation, s. B.S. Balaji, B.M. Chanda, Tetrahedron *54*, 13237-52 (1998).

*Boron fluoride*                                                                $BF_3$
**β-Acyl glycosides from polymer-based glycosides**                      OR → OAc

104. [reaction scheme: polymer-bound silyl-tethered glycoside + $(EtCO)_2O$ → tetra-O-Bz glycoside with anomeric OCOEt]

Glycosides bound anomerically to a polymer support through a *silyl tether* are stable under basic conditions, but can be cleaved stereoselectively *with simultaneous functionalization at the anomeric centre*. E: A mixture of startg. polymer-based carbohydrate in toluene treated with 4 eqs. each of propionic anhydride and $BF_3$-etherate at room temp. for 24 h → product. Y ≥56% (β/α 14:1). F.e.s. D. Weigelt, G. Magnusson, Tetrahedron Lett. *39*, 2839-42 (1998).

*Graphite*                                                                       $C_8$
**Protection of alcohols as methoxymethyl ethers**                OH → $OCH_2OMe$
with montmorillonite cf. *39*, 214s*54*; with expansive graphite s. T.-S. Jin et al., Synth. Commun. *28*, 837-41 (1998).

**Acoxy compds. from ethers under neutral conditions**                  OR → OAc

105.           PhCOBr  +  t-BuO$C_8H_{17}$-n  ⟶  PhCOO$C_8H_{17}$-n

A mixture of startg. ether, 2 eqs. benzoyl bromide and graphite in 1,2-dichloroethane refluxed at 50° for 2 h → product. Y 94%. Benzyl, allyl and tert. alkyl groups were cleaved selectively regardless of the nature of the other alkyl residues, while prim. and sec. alkyl ethers were inert. Cleavage of benzyl ethers was chemoselective, double and triple bonds and other ether linkages remaining intact. The reaction occurs via O-acylation followed by cleavage to give the more stable carbonium ion. F.e. incl. **ω-acoxyhalides from cyclic ethers** s. Y. Suzuki et al., Chem. Lett. *1998*, 319-20.

*2,3-Dichloro-5,6-dicyanoquinone/molecular sieves*                                    ←
**O-Tritylation under mild, neutral conditions**                          OH → OTr

106. Ph-CH(OH)-$CH_2$OH  +  BnOTr  ⟶  Ph-CH(OH)-$CH_2$OTr

1.5 eqs. DDQ added to a suspension of 1.1 eqs. benzyl trityl ether (BTE), 1-phenylethane-1,2-diol, and activated 4 Å molecular sieves in dry dichloromethane under $N_2$, and the mixture allowed to react at 30° for 18 h before quenching with satd. aq. NaHCO$_3$ → product. Y 73%. Simple alcohols gave moderate to excellent yields. In general sec. alcohols reacted slower than prim. alcohols, thereby allowing **preferential O-tritylation**. Addition of molecular sieves was crucial to remove moisture and suppress the formation of triphenylmethanol as side-product. A benzaldehyde-complexed triphenylcarbonium ion, formed by oxidation of BTE, is considered to be the effective tritylating species. F.e. incl. carbohydrate derivs. s. M. Oikawa et al., Synlett *1998*, 757-60.

*Lipase* ←
*Lipase/microwaves* ←
**Asym. O-acylation with enolesters**  OH → OAc
s. *44*, 214s*54*; resolution of 1-(2-pyridyl)- and 1-[6-(2,2′-bipyridyl)]-ethanols s. J. Uenishi et al., J. Org. Chem. *63*, 2481-7 (1998); of tert. alcohols s. S.-T. Chen, J.-M. Fang, ibid. *62*, 4349-57 (1997); of *endo*-bicyclo[3.3.0]octen-2-ols s. T. Iimori et al., Chem. Pharm. Bull. *45*, 207-8 (1997); enhancement under microwave irradiation s. G. Lin, W.-Y. Lin, Tetrahedron Lett. *39*, 4333-6 (1998); desymmetrization of 2-subst. *meso*-1,3-propanediols s. B. Morgan et al., J. Org. Chem. *62*, 7736-43 (1997); of *meso*-spirodiols s. T. Fujita et al., ibid. 3824-30; of *meso*-2-aryl-2-fluoro-1,3-propanediols s. G. Guanti et al., Tetrahedron:Asym. *9*, 1859-62 (1998).

*Immobilized subtilisin* ←
**Carboxylic acid esters from enolesters and alcohols**  COOCH=CH$_2$ → COOR
with lipase cf. *42*, 220; N-acetyl-L-phenylalaninates with immobilized subtilisin s. R.C. Lloyd et al., Tetrahedron:Asym. *9*, 551-61 (1998).

*Amberlyst 15/boron fluoride/m-chloroperoxybenzoic acid/* ←
*1,8-diazabicyclo[5.4.0]undec-7-ene*
**Carboxylic acid esters from aldehydes via acetals**  CHO → COOR
**One-pot procedure**

107.  PhCHO + HC(OMe)$_3$ ⟶ [ PhCH(OMe)$_2$ ] ⟶ PhCOOMe

**Carboxylic acid methyl esters**. Wet Amberlyst 15 and 4 eqs. methyl orthoformate added to a soln. of benzaldehyde in dry chloroform at ambient temp. under argon, stirred under reflux for 3 h, cooled to room temp., 10 mol% BF$_3$-etherate and 1 eq. *m*-chloroperoxybenzoic acid (72%) added, followed by 1 eq. DBU, stirred for 1 h at ambient temp., and quenched with 0.5 N NaOH → methyl benzoate. Y 95%. The method is simple and high-yielding. F.e.s. H. Rhee, J.Y. Kim, Tetrahedron Lett. *39*, 1365-8 (1998).

m-*Chloroperoxybenzoic acid* s. under Amberlyst 15  m-ClC$_6$H$_4$CO$_3$H

tert-*Dodecanethiol/triphenylphosphine/irradiation* ←
**Prim. alcohols from carboxylic acids via 3-acoxy-Δ$^4$-thiazoline-2-thiones**  COON< → OH
**Radical degradation with loss of 1 C-atom**

108.

A vigorously stirred soln. of 3-(3α,7α-diacetoxy-5β-cholanoxy)-4-methylthiazole-2(3*H*)-thione (readily prepared from the corresponding cholanic acid) in toluene containing 4 eqs. *tert*-dodecanethiol irradiated under O$_2$ using a 100 W Xenophot lamp, stirring continued at room temp. for 30-120 min, 1.5 eqs. triphenylphosphine added, and stirred for a few more min → 3α,7α-diacetoxy-23-hydroxy-24-nor-5β-cholane. Y 60%. 3-Acoxy-Δ$^4$-thiazoline-2-thiones are much less sensitive to light and significantly more robust towards hydrolysis than the more familiar N-acoxy-2-pyridinethiones so that radicals can be generated slowly without undue ionic side reactions. F.e.s. D.H.R. Barton et al., Tetrahedron *54*, 6751-6 (1998).

*Titanium(IV) alkoxides*                                                         *Ti(OR)$_4$*
**Transesterification**                                                    COOR → COOR'
s. *37*, 214; with sterically hindered alcohols in the absence of solvent, selectivity, s. P. Krasik, Tetrahedron Lett. *39*, 4223-6 (1998).

n-*Butylstannonic acid*                                            *BuSnO$_2$H*
**Transesterification of carboxylic acid esters under mild, neutral conditions**

109.

A soln. of (-)-dimethyl 2,3-O,O-benzylidene-L-tartrate, 5 eqs. benzyl alcohol and 0.2 eq. *n*-BuSnO$_2$H in toluene refluxed for 19 h → (-)-dibenzyl 2,3-O,O-benzylidene-L-tartrate. Y 90%. The mild and non-basic/non-acidic conditions ensure the survival of sensitive functional groups, such as cyclic acetals, lactams, conjugated double and triple bonds, chlorides and bromides. The method is applicable to prim. and sec. alcohols, but adamantanol failed to react. F.e. incl. transesterification of peptide esters, and in the absence of solvent, also application to the protection/deprotection of alcohols [by O-acetylation with ethyl acetate, and O-deacetylation with methanol], s. R.L.E. Furlán et al., Tetrahedron Lett. *39*, 2257 60 (1998).

*Triphenylphosphine/carbon tetrabromide*                           *Ph$_3$P/CBr$_4$*
**O-Acylation of prim. alcohols by transesterification under mild conditions**    OH → OAc

110.

**Preferential O-acetylation.** A soln. of startg. diol and 0.5 eq. each of triphenylphosphine and carbon tetrabromide in ethyl acetate stirred at room temp. under N$_2$ until TLC indicated completion of reaction → 5-hydroxynonyl acetate. Y 82%. It is thought that transesterification is facilitated by HBr liberated from the two reagents. Sec. alcohols reacted considerably more slowly, although with the more reactive ethyl and methyl formate **O-formylation** of both types of alcohol takes place. The procedure is simple and avoids the complications which arise by standard O-acylation procedures, e.g. with Ac$_2$O/py/DMAP. Furthermore, **acoxy compds.** (acetates or formates) may also be obtained in one pot **from *tert*-butyldimethylsilyl or tetrahydropyran-2-yl ethers** in the presence of 2-3 drops of water. F.e.s. H. Hagiwara et al., Tetrahedron *54*, 5845-52 (1998).

*Hydrogen peroxide/formic acid*                                         *H$_2$O$_2$/HCOOH*
**Hydroxylactones from ethylenecarboxylic acid esters**
δ-hydroxy-γ-lactones with Br$_2$-Ag$_2$SO$_4$/H$_2$SO$_4$ cf. *23*, 261; with H$_2$O$_2$/HCOOH s. German patent DE-19600034 (Huels AG).

*Trimethylsilyl triflate*                                                       *Me$_3$SiOSO$_2$CF$_3$*
**Glycosides from glycosyl trichloroacetimidates**                      OC(=NH)CCl$_3$ → OR
s. *44*, 211s*51, 52, 54*; α- and β-linked disaccharides with 2-deoxysugar residues s. J.C. Castro-Palomino, R.R. Schmidt, Synlett *1998*, 501-3; solvent effect on solid-phase glycosidation (acetonitrile favouring β-product) s. S. Manabe et al., ibid. 628-30; solid-phase synthesis of a branched pentasaccharide s. J. Rademann et al., Angew. Chem. Int. Ed. Engl. *37*, 1241-5 (1998); β-D-mannopyranosides (with BF$_3$) s. A. Fürstner, I. Konetzki, Tetrahedron Lett. *39*, 5721-4 (1998).

p-*Toluenesulfonic acid*      TsOH
**1,2-Acoxytosylates from 2-furyl ketones and glycols**     ←
**Furan as leaving group under non-oxidative conditions**

111.

A stirred mixture of 2-acetylfuran, 3 eqs. ethylene glycol, 3 eqs. p-TsOH·H$_2$O and benzene refluxed under N$_2$ for 14 h → product. Y 52%. Chiral glycols reacted **with inversion of configuration** via backside attack of the tosylate on the intermediate 1,3-dioxolanium ion. F.e.s. J.A. Bender et al., Tetrahedron Lett. *39*, 2051-4 (1998).

## Elimination ⇑

## Hydrogen ↑      OC ⇑ H

*Irradiation s. under PhI(OAc)$_2$*     ///
*Microwaves s. under CuSO$_4$, PhI(OAc)$_2$ and Benzimidazolium dichromate*     ←

*Cupric sulfate/ammonia*      CuSO$_4$/NH$_3$
**Aldonohydrazonolactones from aldose hydrazones**     ○

112.

1 eq. CuSO$_4$ added to a soln. of D-fucose phenylhydrazone in 95% ethanol adjusted to pH 10-11 with aq. NH$_3$, and air bubbled through the mixture for ca. 20 min → product. Y 75%. The procedure is simple, inexpensive, safe, high-yielding, widely applicable, and considerably faster than a previously reported method involving air oxidation in 95% ethanol at pH 12-14 (with KOH). F.e. and method s. J. Wang et al., Synth. Commun. *28*, 2317-24 (1998).

*Cupric sulfate/alumina/microwaves*     ←
**Aryloxo compds. from benzylalcohols**      CHOH → CO
**Microwave irradiation on an inorganic support without solvent**
with Fe(NO$_3$)$_3$ on montmorillonite cf. *53*, 108; benzils from benzoins with CuSO$_4$-Al$_2$O$_3$ s. R.S. Varma et al., J. Chem. Res., Synop *1998*, 324-5.

*Hydrotalcites s.a. under Ruthenium*     ←

*2,2,6,6-Tetramethylpiperidine N-oxyl/trichloroisocyanuric acid*
*or 1,3-dichloro-5,5-dimethylhydantoin*
**Oxo compds. from alcohols**
with PhI(OAc)$_2$ as reoxidant cf. *45*, 120s*54*; with trichloroisocyanuric acid or 1,3-dichloro-5,5-dimethylhydantoin s. European patent EP-775684 (Hoffmann la Roche & Co. AG).

*Phenyl iodosoacetate/alumina/microwaves*     ←
**Oxo compds. from alcohols**
aryloxo compds. s. *37*, 234s*54*; general application without over-oxidation s. J. Chem. Res., Synop *1998*, 120-1.

*Phenyl iodosoacetate/iodine/irradiation*     ←
**Ring closures of alcohols via alkoxyl radicals**     ○
s. *39*, 228s*53*; 3-oxabicyclo[3.3.0]hexane from cyclopentylcarbinol ring s. L.A Paquette et al., J. Am. Chem. Soc. *119*, 8438-50 (1997).

*2,3-Dichloro-5,6-dicyanoquinone/molecular sieves* ←
**O,O-(*p*-Methoxybenzylidene) derivs. by oxidative ring closure** ○
s. *37*, 226; poly-acetates and -propionates by diastereoselective acetalation of pseudo-$C_2$-symmetric 1,3,5-triols s. J.N. Shepherd et al., J. Org. Chem. *62*, 4558-9 (1997).

*Pyridinium dichromate* $(C_5H_5NH)_2Cr_2O_7$
**Oxazolidines from 2-aminoalcohols**
with $MnO_2$ cf. *35*, 157; 3-aryl derivs. with pyridinium dichromate s. J.T. Yli-Kauhaluoma et al., Tetrahedron Lett. *39*, 2269-72 (1998).

*Isoquinolinium dichromate* ←
**Oxo compds. from alcohols under mild conditions** CHOH → CO
with quinolinium dichromate cf. *42*, 234; with storable isoquinolinium dichromate, for oxidation of prim. and sec. alcohols, incl. α-di- from α-hydroxy-ketones, and α-hydroxyketones from glycols, s. R. Srinivasan et al., Synth. Commun. *28*, 2245-51 (1998).

*Benzimidazolium dichromate/microwaves* ←
**Oxo compds. from alcohols**
allylic and benzylic oxidation with imidazolium dichromate cf. *42*, 235; with benzimidazolium dichromate under microwave irradiation in acetone, selectivity, s. Q.-H. Meng et al., Synth. Commun. *28*, 1097-102 (1998).

*Chromium trioxide-alumina* $CrO_3$-$Al_2O_3$
**Oxo compds. from alcohols**
with $CrO_3$-$Al_2O_3$ in protic media cf. *12*, 33s*49*; aryloxo compds. more rapidly with $CrO_3$ on wet alumina (without solvent) s. R.S. Varma, R.K. Saini, Tetrahedron Lett. *39*, 1481-2 (1998).

*Quinolinium bromochromate* ←
**Oxo compds. from alcohols**
aryloxo compds. with pyridinium bromochromate cf. *42*, 235; also oxidation of aliphatic prim. and sec. alcohols with quinolinium bromochromate s. B. Özgün, N. Degirmenbasi, Synth. Commun. *26*, 3601-6 (1996).

*Sodium bromite/alumina* $NaBrO_2/Al_2O_3$
**Lactones from diols** ○
s. *39*, 233s*49*; in methylene chloride with acidic alumina s. Synth. Commun. *28*, 123-30 (1998).

*Sodium bromate/ammonium chloride* $NaBrO_3/NH_4Cl$
**Ketones from sec. alcohols** CHOH → CO
with $NaBrO_3$/HBr cf. *29*, 233s*41*; also ar. aldehydes from benzylalcohols, s. A. Shaabani, M. Ameri, J. Chem. Res., Synop *1998*, 100-1.

*Bis(µ-oxo)dimanganese(IV) oxamato complex/pivalaldehyde/oxygen*
**Ketones from sec. alcohols**
**Catalyzed aerobic oxidation**
with a Co(II) Schiff base complex and isobutanal cf. *50*, 126s*50*; oxidation of benzylic and aliphatic sec. alcohols with bis(µ-oxo)dimanganese(IV) oxamato complex and pivalaldehyde s. R. Ruiz et al., Chem. Commun. *1998*, 989-90.

*Ruthenium-aluminum-magnesium hydrotalcite/oxygen* ←
*Ruthenium/cerium dioxide/oxygen* $Ru/CeO_2/O_2$
**Heterogenous catalytic oxidation with dioxygen under mild conditions** ←

113.      MeCH(OH)C$_6$H$_{13}$-n   ⟶   MeCOC$_6$H$_{13}$-n

**Ketones from sec. alcohols.** A mixture of 2-octanol and Ru/$CeO_2$ (containing 1 eq. $CeO_2$ and 3.3 mol% Ru) stirred in a Schlenk tube, and $O_2$ bubbled at the surface of the mixture via a metal cannula for 6 h at 140° → 2-octanone. Y 96%. The reagent is easy to prepare (by heating 30:1 $CeO_2$/$RuCl_3$ with 37% formaldehyde in water), inexpensive, storable, and permits selective dioxygen oxidation of various prim. and sec. alcohols and aldehydes. The products are isolated by simple filtration, and the system is easily regenerated. F.e.s. F. Vocanson et al., Synth. Commun.

28, 2577-82 (1998); oxidation of allyl and benzyl alcohols with a Ru/Al/Mg hydrotalcite $(Mg_6Al_2Ru_{0.5}(OH)_{16}CO_3)$ cf. K. Kaneda et al., J. Org. Chem. 63, 1750-1 (1998).

*Dichlorotris(triphenylphosphine)ruthenium(II)/hydroquinone/potassium carbonate/oxygen* ←
**Oxo compds. from alcohols** $CHOH \rightarrow CO$
**Catalyzed aerobic oxidation**
ketones with added acetone cf. 24, 261s47, 52; aldehydes from unactivated prim. alcohols with added hydroquinone (with retention of sec. alcohols) s. A. Hanyu et al., Tetrahedron Lett. 39, 5557-60 (1998).

*Palladous acetate/sodium hydrogen carbonate/oxygen* $Pd(OAc)_2/NaHCO_3/O_2$
**Oxo compds. from alcohols**
**Catalyzed aerobic oxidation**
with $PdCl_2/NaOAc/O_2$ s. 33, 252 (ketones) and 41, 243s49 (enones); aryloxo compds. and α,β-ethyleneoxo compds. with $Pd(OAc)_2/NaHCO_3/O_2$ s. K.P. Peterson, R.C. Larock, J. Org. Chem. 63, 3185-9 (1998).

*Bis(dibenzylideneacetone)palladium(0)/air/potassium hydrogen carbonate* ←
**3-Chromenes from *o*-allylphenols** ○

114.

**Improved procedure**. A soln. of startg. phenol, 1.1 eqs. $KHCO_3$, and 5 mol% $Pd(dba)_2$ in 9:1 DMSO/water heated for 3 days at 60° in the presence of air → product. Y 80%. The choice of base, catalyst, and solvent is critical in order to prevent formation of the regioisomeric dihydrobenzofurans. Interestingly, for small-scale conversion, air is more suitable than pure oxygen. However, substrates with electron-withdrawing groups *para* to the hydroxyl group gave a low yield. F.e.s. R.C. Larock et al., Synlett *1998*, 522-4.

## Oxygen ↑                                         OC ⇑ O

*Montmorillonite/microwaves* ←
**4-Chromones from *o*-hydroxy-β-diketones** ○
with HCl cf. 8, 342; under microwave irradiation on montmorillonite in the absence of solvent, flavones, s. R.S. Varma et al., J. Chem. Res., Synop *1998*, 348-9.

*Potassium dichromate/sulfuric acid* $K_2Cr_2O_7/H_2SO_4$
**Furans from 2-ene-1,4-diols**
with $Pd(OAc)_2/CuOAc/O_2$ cf. 38, 232; in a 2-phase aq. organic medium with $K_2Cr_2O_7/H_2SO_4$ s. G.A. Kraus, X. Wang, Synth. Commun. 28, 1093-6 (1998).

*Tris(dibenzylideneacetone)dipalladium/1,4-bis(diphenylphosphino)butane* $Pd_2(dba)_3/dppb$
**2-Vinyl-O-heterocyclics from (Z)-2-ene-1,n-diol 1-monocarbonates**
**Regio- and stereo-specific ring closure**

115.

A soln. of startg. carbonate in THF treated with a little Pd-catalyst (prepared in a Schlenk tube from 2.5 mol% $Pd_2(dba)_3$ and 1 mol% dppb in THF), and heated at 50° for 24 h → (E)-2-styryltetrahydrofuran. Y 30% (E/Z 100/0). Reaction proceeds by 5-*exo-trig*-cyclization. F.e., also pyran analogs by 6-*exo-trig* cyclization, and in the presence of chiral di(phosphines) with low enantioselectivity s. C. Fournier-Nguefack et al., J. Chem. Res., Miniprint *1998*, 614-34.

## Nitrogen ↑                                        OC ⇑ N

*Tri-n-butyltin hydride/azodiisobutyronitrile* $Bu_3SnH/AIBN$
**Cyclic ethers from N-alkenyloxyphthalimides** s. 55, 1 ○

## Sulfur ↑      OC ↥ S

Mercuric chloride/mercuric oxide      $HgCl_2/HgO$
N-Iodosuccinimide/trifluoroacetic acid      $NIS/CF_3COOH$
**Lactolides from hydroxymonothioacetals**      ○
with $AgBF_4$/collidine cf. 45, 319; septanosides with $NIS/CF_3COOH$ s. J.C. McAuliffe, O. Hindsgaul, Synlett 1998, 307-9; β-furanosides with $HgCl_2/HgO$, inversion of configuration, s. J. Org. Chem. 62, 1234-9 (1997).

## Carbon ↑      OC ↥ C

Mercuric acetate/sodium tetrahydridoborate      $Hg(OAc)_2/NaBH_4$
**Aldehydes from enolethers**      $C{=}CH(OR) \rightarrow CHCHO$
with $HClO_4$ cf. 14, 876; by oxymercuration-demercuration s. E. Bettelli et al., Tetrahedron 54, 6011-8 (1998).

Magnesium chloride      $MgCl_2$
**Carbonic from oxalic acid aryl esters** s. 55, 117      $(COOR)_2 \rightarrow CO(OR)_2$

Amberlyst 15      ←
**Macrocyclics by stereospecific intramolecular transacetalation**      ○

116.

A 0.004 M soln. of startg. aldehydoacetal in methylene chloride treated with Amberlyst-15 acidic resin and 4 Å molecular sieves at room temp. until reaction complete → product. Y ≥88%. A single stereoisomer with an equatorial configuration at $C_{15}$ was formed under thermodynamic control. This is the key step in the generation of the 20-membered cryostatin skeleton. F.e.s. P.A. Wender et al., J. Am. Chem. Soc. 120, 4534-5 (1998).

Tetraphenylphosphonium chloride      $Ph_4PCl$
**Decarbonylation of α-ketocarboxylic acid esters**      $COCOOR \rightarrow COOR$

117.      PhOCOCOOPh ⟶ PhOCOOPh [+ CO]

**Carbonic from oxalic acid esters.** 6 g Diphenyl oxalate and 0.093 g tetraphenylphosphonium chloride heated to 255° under atm. pressure for 3 h → diphenyl carbonate. Y 95.2%. This method is also adaptable to the preparation of carboxylic acid esters, as well as halogenoformic acid esters from oxalic acid halide esters. F.e.s. European patent EP-826658 (Ube Ind. Ltd.); with $MgCl_2$ cf. Japanese patent JP-09077722.

Pyridinium chlorochromate      $[C_5H_5NH][CrO_3Cl]$
**α,β-Ethyleneoxo compds. from alkoxy-2-ethylenes**      $CHOR \rightarrow CO$

118.

**under mild conditions.** A soln. of startg. allyl ether in methylene chloride refluxed with 4 eqs. pyridinium chlorochromate for 4 h → product. Y 80% (100% conversion). Satd. aliphatic ethers were inert, suggesting that reaction proceeds via an allyl- or benzyl-stabilized carbonium ion. F.e., **also ar. aldehydes** from benzyl ethers, s. J. Cossy et al., Tetrahedron Lett. *39*, 2561-4 (1998).

*2,2'-Bipyridinium chlorochromate*
**Oxo compds. from tetrahydropyran-2-yl ethers**     ←     CH(OThp) → CO
with nicotinium chlorochromate cf. *34*, 249s*53*; with 2,2'-bipyridinium chlorochromate in acetonitrile s. I. Mohammadpoor-Baltork, B. Kharamesh, J. Chem. Res., Synop *1998*, 146-7.

*Sodium periodate*                                                         $NaIO_4$
**Carboxylic acids from α-hydroxyketones**         COC(OH)< → COOH
with C-cleavage s. *55*, 233

*Sodium periodate/silica*                                              $NaIO_4/SiO_2$
**Aldehydes from glycols**                              CH(OH)CH(OH) → CHO
s. *44*, 249; improved procedure with a free-flowing powdered reagent s. Y.-L. Zhong, T.K.M. Shing, J. Org. Chem. *62*, 2622-4 (1997).

*Tetramethylammonium [o-phenylenebis(N'-methyloxamidate)]cobalt(III)ate/*     ←
*pivalaldehyde*
**Ketones from α-hydroxycarboxylic acids**             C(OH)COOH → CO
**Catalytic aerobic decarboxylation under mild conditions**

119.

**Acylophenones.** A soln. of startg. mandelic acid in acetonitrile added to a stirred mixture of ca. 6 mol% tetramethylammonium [*o*-phenylenebis(N'-methyloxamidate)]cobalt(III)ate and 3 eqs. pivalaldehyde in the same solvent under $O_2$ at 0°, and stirring continued for 6 h → product. Y 90%. Reaction is generally useful for the preparation of *prim-*, *sec-* and *tert-*alkyl, allyl or benzyl ketones. Isolated double bonds (at 0°), phenolethers, and terminal carboxyl groups remained unaffected. Furthermore, the method is inexpensive, convenient, and requires only a catalytic amount of metal complex. F.e.s. G. Blay et al., Tetrahedron Lett. *39*, 3327-30 (1998).

*Dichlorotris(triphenylphosphine)ruthenium(II)/allyl acetate/carbon monoxide*     ←
**Ketones from 3-ethylene-*tert*-alcohols**       $C(OH)CH_2CH=CH_2$ → CO
**C-Cleavage by catalyzed β-allyl elimination**

120.

A soln. of startg. alcohol in THF treated with excess of allyl acetate and 5 mol% $RuCl_2(PPh_3)_3$ under 10 atm. CO at 180° for 15 h → product. Y 91%. This is the first example of such a catalytic C-deallylation via an (alkoxy)metal intermediate, the driving force for which is the formation of a stable allylruthenium species. The presence of both allyl acetate and CO (the latter as an effective π-acid for promoting reductive elimination of propene from the presumed allyl(hydrido)-ruthenium intermediate) was crucial. F.e. incl. ring opening of 2-vinylcycloalkanols s. T. Kondo et al., J. Am. Chem. Soc. *120*, 5587-8 (1998).

## Formation of N-N Bond

### Exchange ↕

#### Hydrogen ↑      NN ↕ H

*Mercuric oxide/iodine*      $HgO/I_2$
**Sym. ar. azo compds. from prim. ar. amines**      2 $ArNH_2 \rightarrow ArN{=}NAr$
with $Ag_2CO_3$/Celite cf. *7*, 365s*31*; with $HgO/I_2$ for conversion of acid- or base-sensitive compds., also oxidation of benzylamines, s. K. Orito et al., Tetrahedron *54*, 8403-10 (1998).

### Elimination ↑

#### Hydrogen ↑      NN ↑ H

*Ferric chloride*      $FeCl_3$
**N,N′-Carbonyldi(azo compds.) from carbohydrazides**      N=NCON=N
with NBS/py cf. *16*, 58s*54*; with $FeCl_3$ s. Y. Wang et al., Synth. Commun. *28*, 2287-90 (1998).

#### Oxygen ↑      NN ↑ O

*Electrolysis*
**2H-Indazoles from o-nitrobenzylamines**

121.

**Continuous flow electrolysis.** A deoxygenated soln. of startg. *o*-nitrobenzylamine in 4:1 methanol/aq. acetate-acetic buffer under $N_2$ pumped through a flow cell fitted with graphite felt electrodes at room temp. under a current of 3 A until polarographic monitoring failed to detect the intermediate nitroso compd., and the mixture neutralized with $NaHCO_3$ (pH 7-8) → product. Y 70%. Reaction is also applicable to 2-alkyl- and 2-aryl-indazoles (the rate of cyclization being fastest with substrates possessing electron-donating groups). F.e.s. B.A. Frontana-Uribe, C. Moinet, Tetrahedron *54*, 3197-206 (1998).

## Formation of N-S Bond

### Exchange ↕

#### Oxygen ↑      NS ↕ O

*Triphenylphosphine/bromine/triethylamine/sodium salt*
**Sulfonic acid amides from sulfonic acids and amines**      $SO_3H \rightarrow SO_2N{<}$

122. $PhSO_3Na \xrightarrow{Ph_3P.Br_2} [PhSO_2Br] \xrightarrow{H_2NBn} PhSO_2NHBn$

**via sulfonic acid halides.** 1 eq. $Br_2$ added dropwise to a suspension of 1 eq. $Ph_3P$ in acetonitrile at 0° until the colour of $Br_2$ did not disappear, a trace of $Ph_3P$ added (to consume excess of $Br_2$), followed by sodium benzenesulfonate in portions at room temp., the mixture allowed to react for 1 h, 1 eq. benzylamine and 1 eq. Et$_3$N added dropwise in this order at 0°, and allowed to react for a further 30 min → N-(benzyl)benzenesulfonamide. Y 83%. This method is mild, generally applicable to arene- and alkane-sulfonamides, and proceeds under neutral conditions with the formation of Ph$_3$PO as by-product rather than the more toxic and corrosive POCl$_3$ or SO$_2$ as in previous methods. F.e. and via sulfonyl chlorides, **also sulfonic acid esters** by treatment of the intermediate sulfonyl halide with alcohol/pyridine, s. T. Kataoka et al., Synthesis *1998*, 423-6.

## Nitrogen ↑     NS ⇅ N

*Ferrous chloride*     $FeCl_2$
**Iron(II)-catalyzed transfer of carbo-*tert*-butoxynitrene**     ←

123.
$$\underset{Bn}{\overset{Me}{S}} + N_3COOBu\text{-}t \longrightarrow \underset{Bn}{\overset{Me}{S}}=NCOOBu\text{-}t$$

**N-Carbo-*tert*-butoxysulfilimines from thioethers.** A mixture of *tert*-butoxycarbonyl azide, 2.5 eqs. benzyl methyl sulfide, and 10 mol% FeCl$_2$ in dry methylene chloride cooled to 0°, dry DMF (10 vol%) added slowly (N$_2$ evolution), and stirred for a further 1 h at 0° then overnight at room temp. → product. Y 68%. F.e. and **N-carbo-*tert*-butoxysulfoximines from sulfoxides** s. T. Bach, C. Körber, Tetrahedron Lett. *39*, 5015-6 (1998).

## Halogen ↑     NS ⇅ Hal

*Cuprous trifluoromethanesulfonate*     $CuOSO_2CF_3$
*Cuprous trifluoromethanesulfonate/chiral bis(Δ²-oxazoline)*     ←
**N-Tosylsulfilimines from thioethers**     >S → >S=NTs
**Catalytic asym. sulfimidation**

124.

Phenyl(tosylimino)iodinane and 1 eq. startg. thioether added to a soln. of 5 mol% CuOTf and 6 mol% chiral bis(oxazoline) in toluene, and the mixture stirred under N$_2$ at 25° for 48 h → product. Y 75% (e.e. 71%). Acetonitrile was used as solvent in the absence of chiral ligand. F.e.s. H. Takada, S. Uemura et al., Chem. Commun. *1996*, 931-2; details, **also N-allyl-N-tosyl-sulfenamides** from 2-ethylenethioethers via asym. [2.3]-sigmatropic rearrangement, s. J. Org. Chem. *62*, 6512-8 (1997); **N-tosylsulfoximines from sulfoxides** with retention of chirality (using CuOTf) s. J.F.K. Müller, P. Vogt, Tetrahedron Lett. *39*, 4805-6 (1998).

# Formation of N-Rem Bond

## Rearrangement     ∩

## Remaining Elements/Carbon Type     NRem ∩ RemC

n-*Butyllithium*     *BuLi*
**C→N-Phosphonyl group migration** s. *55*, 369     ←

## Exchange ⇅

### Halogen ↑          NRem ⇅ Hal

*Triethylamine/sodium hydride*  
**N-Phosphinylaziridines from 2-aminoalcohols**      $Et_3N/NaH$  
One-pot procedure via N,O-diphosphinylation

125.

**Chiral N-phosphinylaziridines.** 2 eqs. Diphenylphosphinyl chloride and 3 eqs. Et$_3$N added to a soln. of (2S)-2-amino-3-phenylpropanol in THF under N$_2$ at 0°, the resulting suspension stirred at 0° to room temp. for 20 h, re-cooled to 0°, ca. 13 eqs. NaH added, the suspension stirred at 0° to room temp. for a further 20 h, and ca. 13 eqs. water added → (S)-N-diphenylphosphinyl-2-benzylaziridine. Y 86%. F.e. and dephosphinylation, also nucleophilic ring opening, s. A.A. Cantrill et al., Tetrahedron *54*, 2181-208 (1998).

*Ethyldiisopropylamine/1H-tetrazole*      ←  
**Phosphonic acid amide esters from dichlorides**      $RPOCl_2 \rightarrow RPO(OR')N\mathord{<}$  
via phosphonochloridates

126.

**One-pot catalytic conversion.** 0.8 eq. Methanol in benzene added dropwise at 0° to a soln. of phenylphosphonic dichloride, 5 eqs. *i*-Pr$_2$NEt, and *a little tetrazole* in the same solvent, stirred for 1.5 h at room temp., 2 eqs. *n*-butylamine added, and stirring continued for 12 h → product. Y 98% (43% without 1H-tetrazole). Yields were lower on reversing the order of addition of the nucleophiles. F.e. incl. reaction with hindered alcohols and amines, s. G. Yang et al., Tetrahedron Lett. *39*, 2449-50 (1998).

# Formation of N-C Bond

## Uptake ⇓

### Addition to Oxygen and Carbon          NC ⇓ OC

*Without additional reagents*      *w.a.r.*  
**Dicarboxylic acid monoamides from anhydrides**  
s. *4*, 308; regiospecific cleavage of aspartic and glutamic anhydrides with aniline s. X. Huang et al., J. Org. Chem. *62*, 8821-5 (1997).

*Lithium azidohydridodiisobutylaluminate*      $i\text{-}Bu_2AlH/LiN_3$  
**2-Azidoalcohols from epoxides**      ▽O → C(OH)C(N$_3$)  
with Et$_3$Al/Me$_3$SiN$_3$ cf. *40*, 176s*41*; with LiAlH(*i*-Bu)$_2$N$_3$ (prepared *in situ* from *i*-Bu$_2$AlH and LiN$_3$), regioselectivity, also carboxylic acid azides from their chlorides, s. Y.S. Youn et al., Tetrahedron Lett. *39*, 4337-8 (1998).

*Ytterbium(III) triflate/(R)-1,1'-binaphthol*      ←  
**2-Aminoalcohols from epoxides by asym. aminolysis**      ▽O → C(OH)C(N<)  
with chiral lanthanide complexes s. *48*, 269s*53*; with Yb(OTf)$_3$/(R)-BINOL, desymmetrization with anilines, s. X.-L. Hou et al., Tetrahedron:Asym. *9*, 1747-52 (1998).

*Di-n-butyltin diiodide/hexamethylphosphoramide* $\qquad$ $Bu_2SnI_2/HMPA$
**2-Oxazolidones from epoxides and isocyanates** ○
with $Bu_2SnI_2/Ph_3PO$ cf. 42, 108; 3-sulfonyl-2-oxazolidones with $Bu_2SnI_2/HMPA$ or $ZnCl_2$ s. World Intellectual Property Organization patent WO-9801432 (Nissan Chem. Ind. Ltd.).

*Chiral chromium(III) salen complex* ←
**2-Siloxyazides from epoxides - Asym. ring opening** $\diagdown_O\diagup \to C(OSi\in)C(N_3)$
s. 51, 121; asym. ring opening of fused epoxides s. S.E. Schaus et al., J. Org. Chem. 62, 4197-9 (1997); of 1,4-cyclohexadiene monoepoxide s. M.H. Wu, E.N. Jacobsen, Tetrahedron Lett. 38, 1693-6 (1997).

*Lithium perchlorate* $\qquad$ $LiClO_4$
**2-Aminoalcohols from epoxides** $\diagdown_O\diagup \to C(OH)C(N{<})$
s. 46, 267s47, 49; solution-phase combinatorial synthesis of 3β-aminomethyl-3α-hydroxy-5α-androstan-17-ones s. R. Maltais, D. Poirier, Tetrahedron Lett. 39, 4151-4 (1998).

## Addition to Nitrogen-Nitrogen Bonds $\qquad$ NC ⇓ NN

*Without additional reagents* $\qquad$ w.a.r.
**Regiospecific ene reaction with azodicarbonyl compds.** ←
with 1,2,4-triazoline-3,5-diones s. 36, 285s39; diastereoselective ene reaction with allyl alcohols (and O-derivs.) s. W. Adam et al., Tetrahedron Lett. 39, 2625-8 (1998); regiospecific ene reaction of 3-ethylenesilanes with diethyl azodicarboxylate s. T.K. Sarkar et al., ibid. 37, 6607-10 (1996).

*Stannic chloride* $\qquad$ $SnCl_4$
**Lewis acid-catalyzed ene reaction with azodicarboxylic acid esters** ←
s. 49, 256; with asym. induction from chiral azodicarboxylates s. M.A. Brimble, C.K.Y. Lee, Tetrahedron:Asym. 9, 873-84 (1998).

## Addition to Nitrogen and Carbon $\qquad$ NC ⇓ NC

*Without additional reagents* $\qquad$ w.a.r.
**Biguanides from guanidines** $\qquad$ $RN{=}C(NHR)N{=}C(N{<})_2$
and cyanamides cf. 6, 357; and carbodiimides, also under acid catalysis with bulky guanidines, and prepn. of a polymer-based biguanide, s. G. Gelbard, F. Vielfaure-Joly, Tetrahedron Lett. 39, 2743-6 (1998).

*Sodium azide/ammonium chloride/dodecyltrimethylammonium bromide* ←
*Sodium azide/amine hydrochlorides* ←
**Tetrazoles from nitriles** ○
with $NaN_3/NH_4Cl$ cf. 13, 371; 17, 503s51; in aq. micellar media with dodecyltrimethylammonium bromide, 5-aryltetrazoles, s. B.S. Jursic, B.W. LeBlanc, J. Heterocycl. Chem. 35, 405-8 (1998); with added $Me_2NH·HCl$ cf. V.Y. Zubarev et al., Khim. Geterotsikl. Soedin. 1997, 1494-501 (Russ.); with $Et_3N·HCl$ s. K. Koguro et al., Synthesis 1998, 910-4.

*Cesium phosphotungstate* ←
**N-Subst. carboxylic acid amides from nitriles** $\qquad$ $CN \to CONHR$
with concd. $H_2SO_4$ cf. 3, 275; with 'friendly', reusable phospho-tungstates or -molybdates s. United States patent US-5712413 (Lubrizol Corp.).

## Addition to Carbon-Carbon Bonds $\qquad$ NC ⇓ CC

*Without additional reagents* $\qquad$ w.a.r.
**Michael addition of amines to α,β-ethylenecarboxylic acid esters** $\qquad$ $C{=}C \to CHC(N{<})$
cf. 6, 364; double addition to bis(enoates) with asym. induction s. E.P. Schreiner, A. Pruckner, J. Org. Chem. 62, 5380-4 (1997); α-amino-β-(arylseleno)succinic acid esters, stereoselectivity, s. M. Bella et al., Tetrahedron Lett. 38, 7917-8 (1997); rapid procedure under microwave irradiation in the absence of solvent s. N.N. Romanova, Y.G. Bundel et al., Mendeleev Commun. 1997, 235-6.

**Michael addition of amines to α,β-ethylenenitriles**
s. *19*, 382; and reduction to hindered 1,3-diamines s. T. Suzuki et al., Synth. Commun. *28*, 701-12 (1998).

**Polymer-based Michael addition of amines** s. *55*, 349

**Azides from ethylene derivs.**  C=C → CHC($N_3$)
and $HN_3$ s. *30*, 222; Michael addition to enoates and α,β-ethylenelactones s. P. Lakshmipathi, A.V. Rama Rao, Tetrahedron Lett. *38*, 2551-2 (1997).

**Δ³-1,2,4-Oxadiazoline-5-carboxylic acid esters from 5-alkoxyoxazoles**  ←

127.

A soln. of 5-methoxy-2-methyl-4-(*p*-nitrophenyl)oxazole and nitrosobenzene in dry acetonitrile stirred at room temp. for 16.5 h under $N_2$ → product. Y 98%. F.e.s. H. Suga, T. Ibata, Chem. Lett. *1991*, 1221-4; details s. Bull. Chem. Soc. Japan *71*, 1231-6 (1998).

*Microwaves*  ←
**Michael addition of amines under microwave irradiation**  C=C → CHC(N≤)
in the absence of solvent s. *6*, 364s55

*Lithium amides*  LiN≤
**Amines from ethylene derivs.**
with BuLi s. *6*, 367s*44*; 2-arylalkylamines from styrenes, incl. reaction with lithium benzylamide as $LiNH_2$ equivalent, s. J.A. Seijas, M.P. Vázquez-Tato et al., Tetrahedron Lett. *39*, 5073-6 (1998).

**Asym. Michael addition**
to arylmenthol-derived enoates cf. *42*, 290s*51*; to chiral γ-trityloxy- or γ-*tert*-butyldiphenylsiloxy-subst. enoates s. N. Asao et al., J. Org. Chem. *62*, 6274-82 (1997); asym. addition of chiral Li-amides to α,β-ethylenecarboxamides s. S.G. Davies et al., Rec. Trav. Chim. Pays-Bas *114*, 175-83 (1995).

*Sodium azide/manganese(III) acetate/trifluoroacetic acid*  ←
**1,2-Diazides from ethylene derivs.**  C=C → C($N_3$)C($N_3$)
with $NaN_3/Fe_2(SO_4)_3/FeSO_4/H_2O_2$ cf. *19*, 393; with $NaN_3/Mn(OAc)_3/CF_3COOH$, from alkenes and glycals, s. B.B. Snider, H. Lin, Synth. Commun. *28*, 1913-22 (1998).

*Triethylamine*  $Et_3N$
**Polymer-based synthesis of 2-imidazolidones**  ○
from 2-ethyleneamines and isocyanates s. *55*, 158

*N-Methylmorpholine N-oxide/triethylamine*  ←
**2-Ethylenehydroxamic acids**  CON(OH)C-C=C
from hydroximinochlorides and ethylene derivs.
via ene reaction with *in situ*-generated acylnitroso compds.

128.

A soln. of startg. hydroximinochloride in dichloromethane added to a stirred soln. of 1.1 eqs. N-methylmorpholine N-oxide, 1 eq. $Et_3N$ and an excess (20 eqs.) of tetramethylethylene in the same solvent, and the mixture stirred at room temp. for 12 h → product. Y 99%. The method is simple, general and mild. However, competing 1,3-dipolar cycloaddition was also observed with

1,1- or 1,2-disubst. ethylenes and with cyclopentene. F.e. incl. aliphatic hydroxamic acid analogs, and regiospecific reaction with unsym. subst. ethylene derivs., s. P. Quadrelli et al., Tetrahedron Lett. *39*, 3233-6 (1998).

*Magnesium bromide/chiral bis($\Delta^2$-oxazolines)* ←
**β-(Benzyloxylamino)- from α,β-ethylene-carboxylic acid amides**   $C=C \rightarrow CHC(NHOR)$
**Lewis acid-catalyzed asym. Michael addition**

129.

**Effect of catalyst on face selectivity.** The first example of a highly enantioselective Michael addition of an N-nucleophile in the presence of a *catalytic* amount of a chiral Lewis acid is reported, the face selectivity being determined by the nature of the catalyst. **E:** 1.1 eqs. O-Benzylhydroxylamine added to a soln. of startg. crotonamide in methylene chloride containing 30 mol% MgBr$_2$-etherate and chiral bis($\Delta^2$-oxazoline) at -60°, and worked up after 22 h → (R)-product. Y 80% (e.e. 92%). With 1 eq. Y(OTf)$_3$ under the same conditions, the (S)-product was obtained predominantly (Y 67%; e.e. 59%). With the Lewis acid in stoichiometric amount, catalytic amidolysis of the product takes place to some extent with, in one instance, kinetic resolution so that the optical activity of the slower-reacting enantiomer is enhanced. The origin of the reversal of face selectivity is unclear. F.e.s. M.P. Sibi et al., J. Am. Chem. Soc. *120*, 6615-6 (1998); large-scale synthesis of O-benzylhydroxylamine s. F. Bonaccorsi, R. Giorgi, Synth. Commun. *27*, 1143-7 (1997).

*Manganese(III) acetate s. under NaN$_3$*   $Mn(OAc)_3$

*Potassium osmate/1,4-bis(9-O-dihydroquin(id)ine)phthalazine/Chloramine-T*   ←
**Regiospecific asym. oxyamination of ethylene derivs.**   $C=C \rightarrow C(NHTs)C(OH)$
s. *51*, 132; chiral α-hydroxy-β-tosylamino- from α,β-ethylene-phosphonic acid esters s. G. Cravotto et al., Tetrahedron:Asym. *9*, 745-8 (1998); taxol side-chain s. Acta Chem. Scand. *50*, 649-51 (1996); f. ligands and reagents s. World Intellectual Property Organization patent WO-051887 (Scripps Research Institute).

*Potassium osmate/1,4-bis(9-O-dihydroquin(id)ine)-anthraquinone or -phthalazine/*   ←
   tert-*butyl hypochlorite/sodium hydroxide*
**Asym. oxyamination - Reversal of regioselectivity**   $C=C \rightarrow C(NHCOOR)C(OH)$

130.

The regioselectivity of Sharpless asym. oxyamination (cf. *51*, 132) is reversed dramatically by replacing 1,4-bis(9-O-dihydroquinidine)phthalazine by 1,4-bis(9-O-dihydroquinidine)-anthraquinone as ligand. **E: Chiral N-protected α-amino-β-hydroxycarboxylic acid esters.** A vigorously stirred aq. soln. of 3.05 eqs. NaOH was diluted with the same volume of *n*-propanol, 3.1 eqs. benzyl carbamate added, followed by dropwise addition of 3.05 eqs. freshly prepared *t*-BuOCl, after 5 min 4 mol% 1,4-bis(9-O-dihydroquinidine)anthraquinone in *n*-propanol and 4 mol% K$_2$[OsO$_2$(OH)$_4$] in aq. alkali added, and quenched with NaHSO$_3$ after 1.5 h → (2S,3R)-product. Y 62% (e.e. 92%). Electron-poor cinnamates were less suitable substrates, but aliphatic enoates reacted with only slightly decreased regioselectivity. F.e. and reversal of face selectivity with the quinine analog as ligand s. B. Tao et al., Tetrahedron Lett. *39*, 2507-10 (1998); **chiral N-protected α-arylglycines** via asym. oxyamination of styrenes s. J. Am. Chem. Soc. *120*, 1207-17 (1998); chiral N-protected β-amino-α-hydroxycarboxylic acid esters with (DHQ)$_2$PHAL as ligand cf. Tetrahedron Lett. *39*, 3667-70 (1998).

## Rearrangement ⋂
## Oxygen/Carbon Type                                              NC ⋂ OC

*Ammonium hydrogen carbonate*                                          $NH_4HCO_3$
**1,4-O→N-Acyl group migration**                                             ←
with $NaHCO_3$ cf. *14*, 400; α-subst. serine-containing peptides with aq. $NH_4HCO_3$ s. M. Horikawa et al., Synlett *1998*, 609-10.

*1,8-Diazabicyclo[5.4.0]undec-7-ene/potassium carbonate*              $DBU/K_2CO_3$
*N-Bromosuccinimide*                                                        NBS
**2-Ethylene(trichloroacetyl)amines from 2-ethylenealcohols**                ←
**via [3.3]-sigmatropic rearrangement**
with trichloroacetonitrile/$KF-Al_2O_3$ cf. *29*, 325s*52*; improved procedure with DBU and powdered $K_2CO_3$ s. T. Nishikawa, M. Isobe et al., J. Org. Chem. *63*, 188-92 (1998); 3-phosphonyl- and 3-cyano-(E)-2-ethylene(trichloroacetyl)amines with NBS cf. H. Shabany, C.D. Spilling, Tetrahedron Lett. *39*, 1465-8 (1998); (E)-olefin dipeptide isosteres by thermal rearrangement (cf. *29*, 325) s. H. Imogaï et al., Synlett *1997*, 615-7.

*Hydrogen chloride*                                                          HCl
**4-Hydroxyindoles from 4-aminobenzofurans**                                 ←
s. *28*, 297; also with glacial AcOH, $CF_3COOH$, or $HClO_4$ in AcOH, and one-pot conversion from 4-nitrobenzofurans with $SnCl_2$/HCl, s. A. Chilin et al., Synthesis *1998*, 309-12.

*Dichloro[(S)-2-(2-(diphenylphosphino)phenyl)-4-benzyl-$\Delta^2$-oxazoline]-*   ←
*palladium(II)/silver fluoroborate*
**2-Ethyleneacylamines from 2-ethyleneiminoesters**                          ←
**Asym. [3.3]-sigmatropic rearrangement**
with a chiral cyclopalladated complex cf. *54*, 138; improved enantioselectivity with dichloro[(S)-(+)-2-(2-(diphenylphosphino)phenyl)-4-benzyl-$\Delta^2$-oxazoline]palladium(II)/$AgBF_4$ s. Y. Uozumi et al., Tetrahedron:Asym. *9*, 1065-72 (1998).

## Sulfur/Carbon Type                                              NC ⋂ SC

*Cuprous trifluoromethanesulfonate/chiral bis($\Delta^2$-oxazolines)*        ←
**N-Allyl-N-tosylsulfenamides from 2-ethylenethioethers**                    ←
via asym. [2.3]-sigmatropic rearrangement s. *55*, 124

## Carbon/Carbon Type                                              NC ⋂ CC

*Lithium bis(trimethylsilyl)amide/silver trifluoromethanesulfonate*   $LiN(SiMe_3)_2/AgOSO_2CF_3$
**5-Alkylidene-2-pyrrolidones from γ,δ-acetylenecarboxylic acid amides**     ○
with $Bu_4NF$ cf. *52*, 145; (Z)-isomers with $LiN(SiMe_3)_2/AgOSO_2CF_3$ s. Y. Koseki et al., Tetrahedron Lett. *39*, 3517-20 (1998).

*Tetrakis(acetonitrile)palladium(II) fluoroborate*                    $Pd(MeCN)_4(BF_4)_2$
*Tetrakis(triphenylphosphine)palladium(0)*                             $Pd(PPh_3)_4$
**Cyclic enamines from acetyleneamines**
s. *43*, 271s*47*; f. catalysts, incl. $Pd(MeCN)_4(BF_4)_2$ and $Rh(COD)(DIPAMP)BF_4$, s. T.E. Müller, Tetrahedron Lett. *39*, 5961-2 (1998); cyclic N-tosylamines with $Pd(PPh_3)_4$ (cf. *54*, 333) s. L.B. Wolf et al., ibid. 5081-4.

## Exchange ↕

### Hydrogen ↑              NC ↕ H

*Without additional reagents*       w.a.r.
**N-Cyanation**       NH → NCN
with BrCN s. *4*, 435; of azoles s. P.P. Purygin, S.V. Pankov, Zh. Org. Khim. *31*, 934-6 (1995) (Russ.).

*Potassium bis(trimethylsilyl)amide/trisyl azide*       $KN(SiMe_3)_2/ArSO_2N_3$
**Replacement of α-hydrogen by azido groups**       H → $N_3$
with asym. induction s. *30*, 232s*50*; chiral α-azido-ω-bromocarboxylic acids s. J.T. Lundquist IV, T.A. Dix, Tetrahedron Lett. *39*, 775-8 (1998); chiral 3,3-diaryl-2-azidopropionic acids s. J. Lin et al., ibid. 3117-20; isocyclic α-azidophosphonic acid esters s. C. Guéguen et al., Synth. Commun. *26*, 4131-3 (1996).

*Cupric nitrate-clay*       $Cu(NO_3)_2$-clay
**Ar. mononitration**       H → $NO_2$
s. *30*, 239s*44*; of electron-rich arenes s. C.L. Dwyer, C.W. Holzapfel, Tetrahedron *54*, 7843-8 (1998).

*Zeolite (s.a. under NO)*       ←
**Sym. ureas from prim. amines**       $2\ RNH_2 \to RNHCONHR$

131.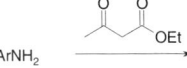

**Sym. N,N'-diarylureas.** 0.6 eq. Ethyl acetoacetate added dropwise during 1 min to a mixture of *p*-anisidine and zeolite HSZ-360 (0.05 g/mmol amine) in a hot oil bath (180°), and stirred efficiently for 5 h → N,N'-bis(4-methoxyphenyl)urea. Y 76% (selectivity 95%). In the absence of zeolite only *p*-methoxyacetanilide was isolated. This is an innovative phosgene- and solvent-free method which proceeds in good yield and with excellent selectivity. F.e.s. F. Bigi, G. Sartori et al., Chem. Commun. *1998*, 513-4.

*N,N'-Carbonyldiimidazole and N,N'-Thiocarbonyldiimidazole*       ←
**Ring closures with N,N'-carbonyl- and N,N'-thiocarbonyl-diimidazole**       ○
s. *21*, 393s*54*; 2*H*-1,2,4-benzothiadiazine-3(4*H*)-thione 1,1-dioxides and 3-(1-imidazolyl) derivs. s. P. de Tullio et al., Tetrahedron *54*, 4935-42 (1998); tetrahydro-1,3-oxazin-2-ones from 3-aminoalcohols s. P. Breuilles et al., Tetrahedron Lett. *36*, 8011-4 (1995); polymer-based synthesis of 3,5-disubst. hydantoins from α-aminocarboxylic acid amides s. A. Nefzi et al., Tetrahedron Lett. *39*, 8199-202 (1998).

*Tetramethyl(fluoro)formamidinium hexafluorophosphate/triethylamine*       ←
**Isothiocyanates from amines and carbon disulfide**       $NH_2 \to N{=}C{=}S$
with BOP cf. *31*, 336s*51*; rapidly with tetramethyl(fluoro)formamidinium hexafluorophosphate/$Et_3N$, also carboxylic acid hydrazides from carboxylic acids, s. U. Boas et al., Synth. Commun. *28*, 1223-31 (1998).

*Oxalyl chloride/N,N,N',N'-tetramethylethylenediamine*       $(COCl)_2$/TMEDA
**Sulfonylisocyanates from sulfonic acid amides**       $SO_2NH_2 \to SO_2N{=}C{=}O$
via sulfonyloxamyl chlorides cf. *20*, 395; one-pot procedure with $(COCl)_2$/TMEDA s. Russian patent SU-1504981 (Plants Chem. Protection Res. Inst.).

*Nitrogen monoxide/zeolites*       ←
**1,1-Nitroethylene derivs. from ethylene derivs.**       H → $NO_2$
with NO/$Al_2O_3$ cf. *51*, 135; with NO/zeolites s. R. Sreekumar et al., Tetrahedron Lett. *39*, 2695-6 (1998).

*Vanadyl trinitrate* $VO(NO_3)_3$
**Ar. mononitration under mild, non-acidic conditions**

132.

Toluene added rapidly to a preformed soln. of 0.67 eq. $VO(NO_3)_3$ in methylene chloride (ca. 12 wt%) *at room temp.,* and quenched with water after 3 min → nitrotoluene. Y >99% (50:47:3 mixture of *o:p:m* isomers). The procedure is simple, high-yielding, and applicable to a wide range of aromatics [although deactivated arenes, e.g. nitrotoluene, methyl benzoate, and benzoic acid, required a longer reaction period (several days)]. $VO(NO_3)_3$ (readily prepared on a large scale from $V_2O_5$ and $N_2O_5$) is a powerful nitrating agent, which is hydrolyzed in moist air but easy to handle as a soln. in methylene chloride at room temp. F.e.s. M.F.A. Dove, G. Pattenden et al., J. Chem. Soc. Perkin Trans. 1 *1998*, 1589-90.

*Methanesulfonyl azide/sodium hydride* $MeSO_2N_3/NaH$
**1,2,3-Triazoles by diazo group transfer**
5-amino-1,2,3-triazoles from amidines with $TsN_3$ cf. *25,* 250; 1,2,3-triazole-4-carbonyl compds. from enamines with $MeSO_2N_3/NaH$ s. G.A. Romeiro, V.F. Ferreira et al., Tetrahedron Lett. *38,* 5103-6 (1997).

*Trisyl azide s. under* $KN(SiMe_3)_2$ $ArSO_2N_3$

*Dichlorotris(triphenyphosphine)ruthenium(II)* $RuCl_2(PPh_3)_3$
**Ureas from amines and formamides** NH → NCON<

133. $Bu_2NH$ + $HCONHPh$ ⟶ $Bu_2NCONHPh$

**Dehydrogenative coupling.** A mixture of 0.48 g formanilide, 0.52 g dibutylamine, and 0.2 g $RuCl_2(PPh_3)_3$ in mesitylene heated with stirring under $N_2$ at 165°, and worked up after 20 h → N,N-dibutyl-N'-phenylurea. Y 90%. F.e. and catalysts, **also urethans from alcohols,** s. United States patent US-5686645 (Arco Chem Technology LP).

*Via intermediates* *v.i.*
**N-Formylation via oxidative cleavage of aldimines** s. *55,* 170 NH → NCHO

**Ureas from two different amines via *p*-nitrophenyl carbamates** ≥NCON≤
s. *52,* 141; ureapeptoids s. J.A.W. Kruijtzer et al., Tetrahedron Lett. *38,* 5335-8 (1997); polymer-based synthesis via supported phenyl carbamates cf. X. Xiao et al., J. Org. Chem. *62,* 6968-73 (1997).

# Oxygen↑ NC ↕ O

*Without additional reagents* *w.a.r.*
**N-Carbalkoxylation with polymer-based benzotriazol-1-yl carbonates** NH → NCOOR

134.

2.6 eqs. Benzyl chloroformate added to a suspension of polymer-based 1-hydroxybenzotriazole in methylene chloride, treated with 3.6 eqs. pyridine, the suspension rocked at 25° for 1 h, the polymer filtered off, washed and dried, suspended in methylene chloride, 1,5-diaminopentane (0.88 eq. of $NH_2$ groups based on the activated polymer) added, the suspension rocked at 25° for 5 h, the polymer filtered off, washed, and the filtrate worked up → N,N'-bis(benzyloxycarbonyl)-1,5-diaminopentane. Y 68%. High yields of Fmoc- and Cbz-protected prim. and sec. amines were obtained by this method in a high state of purity, but the yield of *t*-Boc derivs. was poor-to-fair. Work-up is simple, the polymer can be regenerated, and water may be used as co-solvent (notably for the protection of water-soluble amino acid derivs.). F.e.s. K.G. Dendrinos, A.G. Kalivretenos, J. Chem. Soc. Perkin Trans. 1 *1998,* 1463-4.

**Polymer-based synthesis of hydroxamic acids**  CONHOH
methods s. *47*, 293s*54*; from aliphatic polymer-based O-acyloximes via hydroxamic acid silyl esters, notably from substrates with acid-labile functions, cf. A. Golebiowski, S. Klopfenstein, Tetrahedron Lett. *39*, 3397-400 (1998); f. method for chiral Fmoc-protected α-aminohydroxamic acids s. S.L. Mellor, W.C. Chan, Chem. Commun. *1997,* 2005-6.

**Amidinoureas [guanylureas] from amines**  NH → NCONHC(NHR)=NCOOR'
and cyanoguanidine cf. *16*, 262; from N,N'-di(carbo-*tert*-butoxy)guanidines **via N-(N'-carbo-*tert*-butoxyamidino)ureas** s. H. Miel, S. Rault, Tetrahedron Lett. *39*, 1565-8 (1998).

**Polymer-based synthesis of N-heterocyclics from α,β-ethyleneketones**  ○
Pyrimidines - 3,4-Dihydro-2(1*H*)-pyrimidinones - Pyrazoles s. *55*, 327

*Microwaves (s.a. under KHSO$_5$, Hydrochlorides and MnO$_2$)*  ←
**Selective N-acylation**  NH → NAc
of cytidine cf. *22*, 365; N$^4$-acetylation and -benzoylation in DMF under microwave irradiation s. P. Nahar, Tetrahedron Lett. *38*, 7253-4 (1997).

**N-Acetylation of prim. ar. amines** s. *55*, 79

**Benzimidazoles from *o*-diamines and carboxylic acids**  ○
thermal conversion cf. *12*, 432s*15*; 5(6)-(1-adamantyl)benzimidazoles s. D.S. Zurabishvili et al., Khim. Geterotsikl. Soedin. *1997*, 1646-9 (Russ.); rapidly under microwave irradiation in the absence of solvent, also benzoxazoles from *o*-aminophenols, s. K. Bougrin et al., Tetrahedron *54*, 8055-64 (1998).

**Benzazoles from *o*-functionalized prim. ar. amines and carboxylic acids** s. *55*, 151

*Lithium s. under TiCl$_4$*  Li
*Sodium hydride/N-phenyltriflimide*  NaH/(CF$_3$SO$_2$)$_2$NPh
**Amino-N-heterocyclics from hydroxy- via triflyloxy-N-heterocyclics**  OH → NR$_2$

135.

**One-pot conversion.** 4-Hydroxyquinoline in anhydrous DMF added dropwise under argon to 1.2 eqs. NaH (60% mineral oil dispersion washed three times with *n*-hexane), warmed *to 40°,* stirred for 30 min, cooled, 1.2 eqs. N-phenyltriflimide added, stirred at room temp. for 1 h, treated with 2.2 eqs. piperidine, and stirred for a further 19 h at room temp. → product. Y 75%. Reaction is generally applicable to prim. and sec. aliphatic or aromatic amines. The procedure is milder than earlier routes and does not require forcing conditions or a catalyst (cf. *53*, 150). F.e. incl. 2-amino-pyridines and -quinolines, also from the intermediate triflates (or nonaflates) s. S. Cacchi et al., Synlett *1997*, 1400-2.

*Sodium bis(trimethylsilyl)amide*  NaN(SiMe$_3$)$_2$
**Ar. nitriles from arylcarboxylic acid esters**  COOR → CN
with Me$_2$AlNH$_2$ cf. *35*, 248; hydroxy- and methoxy-benzonitriles with NaN(SiMe$_3$)$_2$ s. J.R. Hwu et al., Synthesis *1998*, 329-32.

*Ethyldiisopropylamine*  i-Pr$_2$NEt
**Ring closures with α,β-acetyleneketones**  ○
s. *27*, 769s*31*; pyrimidin-4-yl-subst. α-aminoacids s. R.M. Adlington et al., Chem. Commun. *1997*, 1757-8; polymer-based synthesis of 2-(alkylthio)pyrimidine-4-carboxylic acids s. D. Obrecht et al., Helv. Chim. Acta *80*, 65-72 (1997).

*Pyridine/ethyldiisopropylamine*  C$_5$H$_5$N/i-Pr$_2$NEt
**Carboxylic acid amides from esters**  COOR → CON<
β-ketoamides with py cf. *12*, 453; polymer-based synthesis of a piperazine-2-carboxamide library with added *i*-Pr$_2$NEt using an aryl thioether linker s. J.G. Breitenbucher et al., Tetrahedron

Lett. *39*, 1295-8 (1998); tetrahydro-β-carboline-3-carboxamides s. P.P. Fantauzzi, K.M. Yager, ibid. 1291-4.

*4-Dimethylaminopyridine*                               *DMAP*
**1,3-Benzoxazine-2,4-diones from *o*-hydroxycarboxylic acid esters and isocyanates**    ○

136.

A mixture of phenyl salicylate, *n*-butyl isocyanate and 0.1 eq. DMAP in DMF heated at 80° for 4 h → 3-butyl-1,3-benzoxazine-2,4-dione. Y 88% (98% after 12 h at room temp. with added Et$_3$N). The conversion required several days without Et$_3$N or DMAP, and yields were poor. The method is simple and general, and startg. ms. are readily available. F.e. and with DMSO as solvent s. P. Boontheung, P. Perlmutter, Tetrahedron Lett. *39*, 2629-30 (1998).

*Zinc*                                              *Zn*
**Acyl hydroxamates from nitro compds. under mild conditions**      NO$_2$ → N(OAc)Ac

137.          PhNO$_2$    $\xrightarrow{}$    [ PhNO ]    $\xrightarrow{Ac_2O}$    PhN(Ac)(OAc)

4 eqs. Acetic anhydride and nitrobenzene added sequentially to 5 eqs. Zn powder in methylene chloride, stirred under N$_2$ (or argon) at room temp. for 50 min, and quenched with 10% NH$_4$Cl → N-(acetoxy)-N-phenylacetamide. Y 87%. F.e. and from the intermediate nitroso compds., also with retention of ar. chlorine, s. B.H. Kim et al., J. Chem. Res., Synop *1998*, 46-7.

*Zinc bromide s. under Me$_3$SiCN*                                   *ZnBr$_2$*

*Sodium tetrahydridoborate/sulfuric acid*                          *NaBH$_4$/H$_2$SO$_4$*
**2,3,4,5-Tetrahydropyridazines from hydrazines**                         ○
3-cyano derivs. from γ-diketones cf. *8*, 444; from 2,5-dialkoxytetrahydrofurans with NaBH$_4$/AcOH s. G. Verardo et al., Tetrahedron *53*, 3707-22 (1997).

*Trimethylaluminum*                                       *Me$_3$Al*
**Carboxylic acid amides from esters**                            COOR → CON<
s. *26*, 358s*33*; solution- and solid-phase peptide synthesis s. S.F. Martin et al., Tetrahedron Lett. *39*, 1517-20 (1998).

*Zeolite-Y*                                               ←
**N-Heterocyclics from diketones**                              ○
pyrroles and pyrazoles with montmorillonite cf. *41*, 336; with zeolite-Y s. R. Sreekumar, R. Padmakumar, Synth. Commun. *28*, 1661-5 (1998).

*Boron fluoride/magnesium sulfate*                            *BF$_3$/MgSO$_4$*
**N-Protected 5-oxazolidones from α-aminocarboxylic acids**
with SOCl$_2$/Ac$_2$O cf. *19*, 471; with BF$_3$/MgSO$_4$ or TsOH/SiO$_2$ s. M.A. Blaskovich, M. Kahn, Synthesis *1998*, 379-80.

*Scandium(III) triflate*                                      *Sc(OTf)$_3$*
**Ketimines from ketals and prim. amines**                    C(OR)$_2$ → C=NR'

138.          Ph$_2$C(OMe)$_2$    +    H$_2$NBn    →    Ph$_2$C=NBn

**Catalytic conversion.** A soln. of startg. ketal and benzylamine in toluene containing *5 mol%* Sc(OTf)$_3$ and 4 Å molecular sieves refluxed for 16 h under a Dean-Stark trap → product. Y 88%. Yields are significantly higher than those reported with TiCl$_4$ or other Lewis acids in stoichiometric amount. F.e., and N-condensed phthalimidines from *o*-(α,α-dialkoxy)carboxylic acid esters via cyclic N-acylimmonium ions, s. H. Heaney et al., Synlett *1998*, 640-2.

*N,N,N′,N′-Bis(tetramethylene)-O-(pentafluorophenyl)uronium* ←
  *hexafluorophosphate/diisopropylamine*
**Peptide synthesis** COOH → CON<
with uronium salts cf. *28*, 144s*49*; *47*, 303; solid-phase glycopeptide synthesis with N,N,N′,N′-bis(tetramethylene)-O-(pentafluorophenyl)uronium hexafluorophosphate s. J. Habermann, H. Kunz, Tetrahedron Lett. *39*, 265-8 (1998).

*Dicyclohexylcarbodiimide/polymer-based 1-hydroxybenzotriazole* ←
**N-Subst. carboxylic acid amides from carboxylic acids** s. *55*, 139

*Dicyclohexylcarbodiimide/ethyl 1-hydroxy-1,2,3-triazole-4-carboxylate* ←
**Peptide synthesis**
with DCCI/1-hydroxybenzotriazole cf. *22*, 394s*33*; with DCCI/ethyl 1-hydroxy-1,2,3-triazole-4-carboxylate for solid-phase synthesis with real-time monitoring s. L. Jiang et al., Tetrahedron *54*, 14233-54 (1998); study of undesirable interaction of 1-hydroxybenzotriazole, N-hydroxysuccinimide and other couplers with chloroalkane solvents in the presence of Et$_3$N s. J. Ji et al., Tetrahedron Lett. *39*, 6515-6 (1998).

*Polymer-based 1-ethyl-3-(3-dimethylaminopropyl)carbodiimide* ←
**2-Amino-4H-3,1-benzoxazin-4-ones** ◯
from *o*-ureidocarboxylic acids cf. *21*, 378s*38*; in one step from *o*-aminocarboxylic acids and isocyanates with polymer-based 1-ethyl-3-(3-dimethylaminopropyl)carbodiimide, automated solution-phase parallel synthesis, s. B.O. Buckman et al., Tetrahedron Lett. *39*, 1487-8 (1998).

*N,N′-Carbonyldiimidazole* ←
**N-Subst. carboxylic acid amides from carboxylic acids** COOH → CONHR
N,N′-diacylpolyamines s. *40*, 235; hippuric acid esters s. S.C. Conway, R.B. Perni, Synth. Commun. *28*, 1539-45 (1998).

*Polymer-based 1-hydroxybenzotriazole/pyridine* ←
**N-Subst. carboxylic acid amides from amines** (RCO)$_2$O → RCON<

139.   (CH$_3$CO)$_2$O + [P-benzotriazole-OH] → [P-benzotriazole-OCOCH$_3$] —H$_2$NCH$_2$CH$_2$CH$_2$OH→ CH$_3$CONHCH$_2$CH$_2$CH$_2$OH

**and carboxylic acid anhydrides.** A suspension of polymer-based 1-hydroxybenzotriazole [immobilized on dried Bio-Rad SM-2 macroporous polystyrene beads], 3 eqs. acetic anhydride, and 3.2 eqs. pyridine in methylene chloride rocked for 1 h at 25°, the polymer filtered off, washed, re-suspended in methylene chloride, 0.82 eqs. 3-aminopropan-1-ol added, and the suspension rocked again for 3.5 h at 25° → N-acetyl-3-aminopropan-1-ol. Y 99%. This is a simple, clean and efficient method from prim. and sec. amines. The reagent displays high reactivity, is recyclable, and can be used with a variety of solvents, incl. water, without swelling or contraction. F.e. **and from carboxylic acids** with DCC s. K. Dendrinos, A.G. Kalivretenos et al., Chem. Commun. *1998*, 499-500.

*Nitrobenzene* PhNO$_2$
**Benzimidazoles from o-diamines and aldehydes** ◯
s. *46*, 321; polymer-based synthesis s. Q. Sun, B. Yan, Bioorg. Med. Chem. Lett. *8*, 361-4 (1998).

*Acetic acid* AcOH
**5-Aminopyrazoles from α-cyanoketones**
s. *19*, 461s*26*; polymer-based synthesis s. R.D. Wilson et al., Tetrahedron Lett. *39*, 2827-30 (1998).

*Carbon tetrachloride s. under (RO)$_2$PH(O)* CCl$_4$

*Chiral 2-chloro-4,6-dimenthoxy-1,3,5-triazine* ←
**Peptide synthesis** COOH → CON<
with 2-chloro-4,6-dimethoxy-1,3,5-triazine cf. *41*, 344; asym. coupling with chiral 2-chloro-4,6-dimenthoxy- or 2,4-dichloro-6-menthoxy-1,3,5-triazine (cf. *37*, 330) s. Z.J. Kaminski et al., Synth. Commun. *28*, 2689-96 (1998).

*Tetramethyl(fluoro)formamidinium hexafluorophosphate/triethylamine* ←
**Carboxylic acid hydrazides from acids** s. *31*, 336s55    COOH → CONHN<

*N-Methyl-N-(trimethylsilyl)trifluoroacetamide*    $CF_3CON(Me)SiMe_3$
**N-Carbo-9-fluorenylmethoxylation of α-aminocarboxylic acids**    NH → NCOOR
with 9-fluorenylmethyl pentafluorophenyl carbonate cf. *11*, 283s*41*; with N-(9-fluorenylmethoxy-carbonyloxy)succinimide in the presence of $CF_3CON(Me)SiMe_3$ s. World Intellectual Property Organization patent WO-9741093 (Affymax Technologies NV).

*Trimethylsilyl cyanide/zinc bromide/tetra-*n*-butylammonium fluoride* ←
**Tert. isonitriles from alcohols**    OH → NC:

140.

3 eqs. Trimethylsilyl cyanide added to a soln. of startg. alcohol and 3 eqs. $ZnBr_2$ in dry dichloromethane under argon, stirred at ambient temp. for 18 h, 3 eqs. 1 *M* $Bu_4NF$ in THF added, and stirred for 10 min → product. Y 90% (by GLC). Formamides cf. *17*, 453s*52*. Reaction of tert. halides was much slower. The method is mild and good-yielding. F.e. and with $ZnCl_2$ or $ZnI_2$ s. Y. Kitano et al., Tetrahedron Lett. *39*, 1911-2 (1998).

*Titanium tetrachloride/lithium/trimethylsilyl chloride/cesium fluoride* ←
**Synthesis of N-heterocyclics with atmospheric nitrogen as nitrogen source**    ○

141.

**Pyrroles.** A soln. of {$TiCl_m[N(SiMe_3)_n]_o$} [prepared under dry air from 1.25 eqs. $TiCl_4$, 12.5 eqs. Li and 12.5 eqs. $Me_3SiCl$ in THF at room temp. over 24 h] added to a soln. of startg. triketone and 5 eqs. CsF in THF, and heated at reflux overnight → product. Y 56% (86% using molecular nitrogen). Other titanium complexes, such as $Ti(OPr-i)_4$, may be used, and a *catalytic* variant with 0.1 eq. $TiCl_4$ was also developed (Y 220% based on $TiCl_4$). F.e. and pyrroles from γ,δ-acetyleneketones, also **δ-enaminolactams** from δ-ketoacyl phosphonates, incl. a formal total synthesis of racemic lycopodine, s. M. Mori et al., Angew. Chem. Int. Ed. Engl. *37*, 636-7 (1998).

*Triphenylphosphine/diethyl azodicarboxylate*    $Ph_3P/RO_2CN=NCO_2R$
**Mitsunobu N-alkylation**    NH → NR
s. *28*, 753s*53*; of polymer-based N-benzylsulfonamides and release of sec. benzylamines s. C. Kay et al., Tetrahedron Lett. *38*, 6941-4 (1997); site-specific N-alkylation of peptides on a polymer-support s. J.F. Reichwein, R.M.J. Liskamp, ibid. *39*, 1243-6 (1998).

**Prim. amines from alcohols via N-subst. phthalimides**
s. *27*, 429; with a polymer-based phthalimide, selectivity, s. A.M. Aronov, M.H. Gelb, Tetrahedron Lett. *39*, 4947-50 (1998).

*Triphenylphosphine/diethyl azodicarboxylate/diphenyl phosphorazidate*
**Prim. amines from alcohols via azides**
**One-pot conversion with inversion of configuration**  ← OH → NH$_2$

142.

The Mitsunobu and Staudinger reactions have been coupled in a one-pot conversion of alcohols to prim. amines. E: Equivalent amounts of triphenylphosphine and diethyl azodicarboxylate added to a soln. of startg. alcohol in THF, a soln. of 1 eq. diphenyl phosphorazidate in the same solvent added dropwise over 30 min, after 24 h at room temp. a further 1 eq. triphenylphosphine and diethyl azodicarboxylate added, followed after 4 h by a further 1 eq. triphenylphosphine and water, and stirred at room temp. for 4 days → (3β,5β,7α,12α)-3-amino-7,12-dihydroxycholan-24-oic acid benzyl ester. Y 40%. F.e.s. P.L. Anelli et al., Synth. Commun. 28, 109-17 (1998).

*Benzotriazolyloxytris(pyrrolidino)phosphonium hexafluorophosphate/ethyldiisopropylamine* ←
**N-Subst. carboxylic acid amides from carboxylic acids**  COOH → CONHR
s. 28, 144s50; polymer-based synthesis of the taxoid side-chain using radiofrequency encoded combinatorial chemistry s. X.-Y. Xiao et al., J. Org. Chem. 62, 6029-33 (1997).

*Benzotriazolyloxytris(pyrrolidino)phosphonium hexafluorophosphate/*
  *ethyldiisopropylamine/p-toluenesulfonic acid*  ←
**Phthalimides from phthalic acid monoesters and prim. amines**
**via phthalamic acid esters**

143.

**One-pot procedure.** A soln. of 1.1 eqs. startg. monoester in THF and 1.5 eqs. *i*-Pr$_2$NEt added sequentially to a suspension of 1.1 eqs. benzotriazolyloxytris(pyrrolidino)phosphonium hexafluorophosphate in THF, the mixture stirred at room temp. for 40 min, added via cannula to a suspension of startg. prim. amine in THF, stirring continued for a further 2-3 h, a little *p*-TsOH added, and the mixture refluxed overnight → product. Y 82%. The method is mild, simple, direct and efficient. It also tolerates hydroxyl groups and ester functions on the amine, so that the procedure can be used for **selective protection of prim. amino groups**. F.e. and in the absence of *p*-TsOH, also with isolation of the intermediate amide esters, s. N. Aguilar et al., Synthesis *1998*, 313-6.

*7-Azabenzotriazolyloxytris(pyrrolidino)phosphonium hexafluorophosphate/*
  *ethyldiisopropylamine*  ←
**Peptide synthesis**
with benzotriazolyloxytris(pyrrolidino)phosphonium hexafluorophosphate cf. 28, 144s50; solid-phase synthesis with the 7-aza-analog s. F. Albericio et al., Tetrahedron Lett. 38, 4853-6 (1997).

*Diphenyl phosphorazidate s. under Ph$_3$P*   (PhO)$_2$P(O)N$_3$

*Phosphorous acid diesters/carbon tetrachloride/potassium carbonate/*
  *benzyltriethylammonium chloride*  ←
**N-Subst. carboxylic acid amides from carboxylic acids**
with (EtO)$_2$P(O)Br cf. 34, 358; with diethyl (or diphenyl) phosphite/CCl$_4$ in the presence of K$_2$CO$_3$ and a little BnEt$_3$NCl, also carboxylic acid esters from alcohols, s. Z.M. Jászay et al., Synth. Commun. 28, 2761-8 (1998).

*Diethyl thionophosphorochloridate/2-mercapto-1,3,4-oxadiazoles/triethylamine* ←
**N-Subst. carboxylic acid amides from carboxylic acids**
with (EtO)₂P(O)Cl/3,6-diethyl-2-hydroxypyrazine cf. *40*, 242; carboxylic acid anilides with (EtO)₂P(S)Cl/2-mercapto-1,3,4-oxadiazoles via *in situ*-generated 2-acylthio-1,3,4-oxadiazoles s. B.N. Goswami et al., J. Chem. Res., Synop *1998*, 268-9.

*2,4-Dinitrobenzenesulfonamide/triethylamine* $ArSO_2NH_2/Et_3N$
**Nitriles from carboxylic acids** $COOH \rightarrow CN$
**via carboxylic acid chlorides and N-acylsulfonic acid amides**
**One-pot conversion under mild conditions via Smiles rearrangement**

144.

6.2 eqs. Oxalyl chloride added to a mixture of startg. carboxylic acid in benzene, stirred at room temp. under N₂ for 6 h, evaporated *in vacuo,* the crude acyl chloride dissolved in THF, a soln. of 1.2 eqs. 2,4-dinitrobenzenesulfonamide and 16 eqs. Et₃N in dry THF added, and allowed to react under N₂ at room temp. for 72 h → [*sym*-(decyl)dibenzo-16-crown-5-oxy]acetonitrile. Y 50%. Reaction appears insensitive to structural variations; however, the yield of benzonitrile and heptanenitrile were disappointingly low. F.e.s. V.J. Huber, R.A. Bartsch, Tetrahedron *54*, 9281-8 (1998).

p-*Toluenesulfonic acid* TsOH
**Δ⁴-2-Oxazolone-4-carboxylic from α-keto-β-nosyloxycarboxylic acid esters** ○

145.

A mixture of startg. 3-nosyloxy-2-ketoester, methyl carbamate, and 10% TsOH in toluene refluxed for 15 h → product. Y 84%. There was no formation of the regioisomeric Δ⁴-2-oxazolone-5-carboxylic acid esters. The electron-withdrawing properties of the *p*-nitrobenzenesulfonate (nosylate) group increase the electrophilicity of the ketone group thereby facilitating attack by the carbamate. 3-Bromo-2-ketoesters failed to react. F.e. and conversion to α-amino-β-hydroxycarboxylic acid esters via N-acetylation and stereoselective hydrogenation s. R.V. Hoffman et al., Tetrahedron Lett. *39*, 1283-6 (1998).

*Potassium peroxymonosulfate/alumina/microwaves* ←
**Nitriles from aldehydes** $CHO \rightarrow CN$
**Microwave irradiation on a solid support in the absence of solvent**

146.

A mixture of 3,4,5-trimethoxybenzaldehyde, 1.1 eqs. NH₂OH·HCl, and 1 eq. Oxone-on-neutral alumina mixed on a vortex mixer, the solid placed in an alumina bath inside a commercial microwave oven (2450 MHz), and irradiated for 7 min → 3,4,5-trimethoxybenzonitrile. Y 95%. The method is generally applicable to aliphatic and aromatic aldehydes. It is also rapid, and environmentally friendly. F.e.s. D.S. Bose, A.V. Narsaiah, Tetrahedron Lett. *39*, 6533-4 (1998).

*Molybdenum imido complex*
**Nitriles from aldehydes**
and NH$_4$OH with (NH$_4$)$_6$Mo$_7$O$_{24}$·4H$_2$O/H$_2$O$_2$/Bu$_4$NI cf. *43*, 309; gas-phase conversion with NH$_3$ over a molybdenum imido complex s. German patent DE-19620815 (SKW Trostberg AG).

*Lithium perchlorate*                                                                              LiClO$_4$
**Polymer-based synthesis of 5-α-amino-2-oxazolidones from urethans via N-(2,3-epoxy)urethans**

147.

A suspension of startg. polymer-based urethan (obtained from the Wang resin and the appropriate isocyanate), 1 eq. LiI, and 10 eqs. glycidyl tosylate in dry N-methyl-2-pyrrolidone stirred for 10 min at room temp. under argon, 2 eqs. 1 *M* lithium bis(trimethylsilyl)amide in THF added dropwise, stirred overnight, the resin removed, washed and dried, suspended in dry THF with 5 eqs. LiClO$_4$, stirred at room temp. for 5 min, 5 eqs. pyrrolidine added, and stirring continued overnight → 3-phenyl-5-(pyrrolidinomethyl)-2-oxazolidone. Y 94% (based on the theoretical loading of the commercial resin; purity 98.4%). The procedure is compatible with cyano, methoxy, carbethoxy and nitro groups on the aromatic ring, and should, in principle, be workable with nucleophiles other than pyrrolidine. F.e.s. H.-P. Buchstaller, Tetrahedron *54*, 3465-70 (1998).

*Hydrochlorides/microwaves*
**1-Arylpiperazines from prim. ar. amines**
**Microwave irradiation in the absence of solvent**
from N,N-bis(2-chloroethyl)amine·HCl cf. *54*, 170; from diethanolamine·HCl s. Synth. Commun. *28*, 1175-8 (1998); f. method with SOCl$_2$/NaHCO$_3$ s. Japanese patent JP-09255671 (Konica Chem. KK).

*Hydrogen bromide/acetic acid*                                          HBr/AcOH
**Solid-phase peptide synthesis**                                         COOH → CON<
updates s. *19*, 33s*51, 52, 54*; peptide and glycopeptide synthesis by the Boc- and Fmoc-strategy using HYCRON as an allylic linker, readily removable under neutral conditions, s. O. Seitz, H. Kunz, J. Org. Chem. *62*, 813-26 (1997); synthesis and purification of hydrophobic peptides by a Fmoc 'solubilising tail' method s. C.T. Choma et al., Tetrahedron Lett. *39*, 2417-20 (1998); preservation of Fmoc protective groups under alkaline conditions with CaCl$_2$ s. R. Pascal, R. Sola, ibid. 5031-4; synthesis of peptide-oligonucleotide conjugates on a controlled pore glass support s. S. Peyrottes et al., Tetrahedron *54*, 12513-22 (1998); synthesis of N-linked peptides using a resin-bound Boc equivalent s. R. Léger et al., Tetrahedron Lett. *39*, 4171-4 (1998); synthesis of arginine-containing peptides by guanidine attachment to a sulfonyl linker s. H.M. Zhong et al., J. Org. Chem. *62*, 9326-30 (1997); monitoring solid-phase syntheses with an ion-selective electrode s. M. Pátek et al., Tetrahedron Lett. *39*, 753-6 (1998); inverse peptide ester synthesis using a 9-phenylfluoren-9-yl polystyrene-based resin [for immobilization of N- or O-nucleophiles] s. K.H. Bleicher, J.R. Wareing, ibid. 4587-90; peptide alcohols s. ibid. 4591-4; use of a polymer-supported benzyl chloroformate for attachment of N-nucleophiles cf. J.R. Hauske, P. Dorff, ibid. *36*, 1589-92 (1995); mild preparation of aminomethyl and 4-methylbenzhydrylamine polystyrene resins s. J.H. Adams et al., J. Org. Chem. *63*, 3706-16 (1998); of a 2-chlorotrityl chloride resin s. G. Orosz, L.P. Kiss, Tetrahedron Lett. *39*, 3241-2 (1998); of an inert PEG-based hydrophilic resin s. J. Buchardt, M. Meldal, ibid. 8695-8; functionalization of polystyrene-grafted polypropylene MicroTube™ reactors with chloromethyl groups for generating combinatorial libraries s. R. Li et al., ibid. 8581-4; automated synthesis of four soluble peptide libraries with a novel purification protocol s. R. Ramage et al., ibid. 8715-8; sequence determination of peptides generated in split syntheses by 'photolytic mass laddering' s. K. Burgess et al., J. Org. Chem. *62*, 5662-3 (1997).

*Manganese dioxide/silica gel/microwaves*
**Benzoxazoles from *o*-aminophenols and aldehydes** s. *55*, 151

---

*Nickel(II) chloride/sodium methoxide* $NiCl_2/NaOMe$
**Sym. cyclic tetrapeptides from unactivated dipeptide esters**

148.

**on a transition metal template.** Equivalent amounts of startg. dipeptide ester hydrochloride and $NiCl_2 \cdot 6H_2O$ in methanol treated dropwise with 6 eqs. methanolic NaOMe, heated to 65° for 24 h, 2 eqs. $[Ph_3P=N-PPh_3]^+Cl^-$ added, and the crystals collected → product. Y 96%. The neutral tetrapeptide was liberated from the nickel complex by dissolving the latter in methanol, and treating with HCl gas at room temp. for 15 min. The prerequisite for such a double head-to-tail condensation is that the dipeptide initially coordinates to the metal in a *trans*-fashion. The procedure does not require an activated or protected substrate, nor a coupling agent, and does not involve a high-dilution strategy. F.e. (incl. 12-, 14-, 16- and 18-membered cyclic tetrapeptides) and with $CuCl_2 \cdot 2H_2O$ or $Na_2[PdCl_4]$ s. K. Haas, W. Beck et al., Angew. Chem. Int. Ed. Engl. *37*, 1086-9 (1998).

---

*Palladous acetate/bis(di-tert-butylphosphino)methane/acetic acid*
**Urethans from nitro compds.** $NO_2 \rightarrow NHCOOR$
with $PdCl_2/FeCl_3$/py cf. *22*, 420s*47*; with $Pd(OAc)_2$/bis(di-*tert*-butylphosphino)methane/AcOH s. German patent DE-196218 (BASF AG); substituent effects and selectivity s. P. Wehman et al., Chem. Ber. *130*, 13-21 (1997).

---

*Palladium phosphine complexes*
**Palladium-catalyzed N-allylation** C=C-C-N<
s. *42*, 354s*49*; of benzylamine or phthalimide with cyclic acoxy-2-ethylenes s. N.S. Sirisoma, P.M. Woster, Tetrahedron Lett. *39*, 1489-92 (1998); synthesis of 2-α-functionalized 1,3-dienes from polymer-supported 2-α-acoxy-1,3-dienes with simultaneous cleavage of the support in the presence of $Pd(PPh_3)_4$ s. S.C. Schürer, S. Blechert, Synlett *1998*, 166-8.

---

*Bis(η³-allylpalladium chloride)/chiral 2-[o-(diphenylphosphino)phenyl]-*
*Δ²-oxazolines or N,N'-bis[o-(diphenylphosphino)benzoyl]-1,2-diamines*
*or bicyclic phosphorodiamidites*
**Asym. palladium-catalyzed N-allylation**
with chiral 1,3,2-diazaphospholidines as ligand s. Vol. **53** (p.83); with chiral bicyclic phosphorodiamidites cf. T. Constantieux et al., Synlett *1998*, 49-50; with a chiral indanol-based 2-[*o*-(diphenylphosphino)phenyl]-Δ²-oxazoline (cf. Vol. *54* (p.87)) s. A. Sudo, K. Saigo, J. Org. Chem. *62*, 5508-13 (1997); asym. N-allylation of α-amino esters with chiral N,N'-bis[*o*-(diphenylphosphino)-benzoyl]-1,2-diamines as ligand (method s. *50*, 195) s. B.M. Trost et al., Tetrahedron Lett. *39*, 1713-6 (1998).

# Nitrogen ↑   NC ↓↑ N

*Without additional reagents*   *w.a.r.*
**Kinetic resolution of amines via asym. N-acetylation**   NH → NAc

149.

1-(1-Naphthyl)ethylamine treated with 0.5 eq. 2-acetylamino-2'-diacetylamino-1,1'-binaphthyl in DMSO at room temp. for 21 h → (S)-product. Y 44% (e.e. 35%). This is the first report of such a kinetic-controlled N-acetylation under non-enzymatic conditions. F.e. and resolution of α-aminocarboxylic acid esters, also preparation and recovery of the chiral reagent s. K. Kondo et al., Synlett *1998*, 725-6.

*Microwaves s. under Ca(OCl)$_2$*   ←

*Ammonium hydroxide*   $NH_4OH$
**1,3,4-Oxadiazoles from tetrazoles and carboxylic acid derivs.**   ←
from acyl chlorides cf. *17*, 503; 2-organothio-1,3,4-oxadiazoles from 5-organothiotetrazoles and carboxylic acid anhydrides with $NH_4OH$ s. L.M. Alam, G.I. Koldobskii, Zh. Org. Khim. *33*, 1224-30 (1997) (Russ.).

*Silver benzoate/triethylamine*   $AgOCOPh/Et_3N$
**Hydroxamic acid esters**   $COCHN_2 → CH_2CONOR$
**from α-diazoketones by Wolff rearrangement**

150.

**N-Protected β-aminohydroxamic acid esters.** 1.5 eqs. N,O-Dimethylhydroxylamine hydrochloride in THF treated overnight with 2 eqs. Et$_3$N, the mixture filtered, and the filtrate treated with startg. diazoketone, 3 eqs. Et$_3$N and 0.15 eq. Ag-benzoate at -25° to room temp. for 2 h → product. Y 96%. Reaction is also applicable to Fmoc-protected amino acids. F.e.s. D. Limal et al., Tetrahedron Lett. *39*, 4239-42 (1998).

*Calcium hypochlorite/alumina/microwaves*   ←
**Benzazoles from *o*-functionalized prim. ar. amines**   ○
**Microwave irradiation on a solid support in the absence of solvent**

151.

**Benzimidazoles from aldoximes.** Freshly prepared Ca(OCl)$_2$-on-Al$_2$O$_3$ added with stirring to equivalent amounts of startg. aniline and aldoxime in THF (or acetone) at room temp., the solvent evaporated under reduced pressure, and the resulting solid subjected to microwave irradiation in a monomode Synthewave 402 Prolabo oven operating at 60 W for 4 min (final temp. 140°) → product. Y 87%. The procedure is rapid, and yields are ≥ 80% as opposed to ≤ 12% by the classical thermal route (cf. *12*, 467). Reaction is generally applicable to the preparation of benzimidazoles, **benzoxazoles, and benzothiazoles,** and is a useful alternative to the orthoester method (cf. *52*, 147s*53*). F.e. incl. condensation with aldehydes using $MnO_2$-on-silica as oxidant (cf. *19*, 674s*53*), also benzimidazoles and benzoxazoles from carboxylic acids, s. K. Bougrin et al., Tetrahedron *54*, 8055-64 (1998).

*Rhodium-carbon*     *Rh-C*
**Oxazolidines from 2-aminoalcohols and nitriles**
with asym. induction s. *55*, 152

*Palladium-carbon*     *Pd-C*
**Reductive N-alkylation of 2-aminoalcohols with nitriles via oxazolidines**     NH → NR

152.

**One-pot procedure.** A soln. of (-)-ephedrine and 10 eqs. acetonitrile in methanol containing 1.2 mol% Pd-on-carbon kept under a rubber balloon filled with $H_2$ at room temp. for 24 h → product. Y 95%. Reaction with benzyl and isopropyl cyanide required an elevated $H_2$ pressure (12 atm. in a stainless steel autoclave). F.e. and isolation of the intermediate oxazolidines s. F. Hénin et al., Tetrahedron Lett. *38*, 7187-90 (1997); oxazolidines with asym. induction using Rh-on-carbon cf. ibid. *39*, 2327-30 (1998).

**Sym. sec. amines from azides by reductive dimerization**     $2 RN_3 \rightarrow R_2NH$

153.

**N-Protected sym. sec. amines.** A soln. of (2R,5S)-5-(4-azidobut-1-yl)-3,6-diethoxy-2,5-dihydro-2-isopropyl-5-methylpyrazine in ethanol containing 5% Pd-on-charcoal purged with $N_2$, hydrogen bubbled through the mixture and kept under a $H_2$ balloon at atm. pressure overnight, the crude amine worked up, dissolved in dioxane, treated with ca. 1.25 eqs. benzyl chloroformate at 0°, followed by dropwise addition of ca. 1.5 eqs. 1 *M* $NaHCO_3$, and stirred for 2 h → product. Y 63%. F.e.s. M. Lange et al., Tetrahedron *54*, 5745-52 (1998).

# Halogen ↑     NC ↓↑ Hal

*Sodium hydride*     *NaH*
**N-Arylation with ($\eta^6$-fluoroarene)tricarbonylchromium(0) complexes**     NH → NAr
of piperazines with $K_2CO_3$ cf. *8*, 563s*53*; of indoles in the presence of NaH (cf. *43*, 749s*49*) s. S. Maiorana et al., Synlett *1998*, 735-7; solution-phase combinatorial synthesis of N-(nitroaryl)-piperazines from nitroaryl fluorides s. L. Neuville, J. Zhu, Tetrahedron Lett. *38*, 4091-4 (1997).

*Sodium hydroxide*     *NaOH*
**N-Acylation**     NH → NCOR
of α-aminocarboxylic acids s. *2*, 430; protection of amino groups as cyclohexanecarboxamides and cleavage of the protective group with anhydrous HF s. G. Mezo et al., Tetrahedron *54*, 6757-66 (1998); nitroarylcarboxylic acid amides in an aq. ketonic medium s. Great Britain patent GB-2316403 (Ciba Speciality Chem. Holding Inc.).

*Sodium hydroxide/potassium iodide*     *NaOH/KI*
**N-Alkylation**     NH → NR
s. *20*, 334; β-amino- from β-chloro-phosphonic acids s. X. Fu et al., Synth. Commun. *28*, 2659-64 (1998).

*Potassium* tert-*butoxide* KOBu-t
**Unsym. sec. amines from phthalimides and halides**
**via N-alkylation of N-subst.** *o*-**(tetrahydropyran-2-yloxymethyl)carboxylic acid amides**

154.

A soln. of N-methylphthalimide in 6:1:1 isopropanol/toluene/water treated with 3 eqs. NaBH$_4$ at 0° for 4 h → intermediate hydroxyamide (Y 88-96%), in methylene chloride treated with 5 eqs. dihydropyran and a little TsOH at room temp. for 2 h → intermediate THP ether (Y 100%), in DMF treated with 1.2 eqs. KOBu-*t*, and mixed with 1.2 eqs. benzyl chloride at 40° for 6 h → intermediate N-benzyl-N-methylamide (Y 82%), in 4:2:1 acetic acid/THF/water heated at 60° for 4 h → product (Y 77%). Significantly, release of the sec. amine takes place under mild conditions. F.e.s. T. Fichert, U. Massing, Tetrahedron Lett. *39*, 5017-8 (1998).

*Superoxide ion* $O_2^-$
**Reactions with electrochemically activated carbon dioxide** ←
2,4-oxazolidiones cf. *51*, 169; general and mild procedure for preparing simple urethans from amines and halides, incl. 3-acyl-2-oxazolidones, s. J. Org. Chem. *62*, 6754-9 (1997).

*Tetraethylammonium hydrogen carbonate* $Et_4NHCO_3$
**Urethans from amines and alkyl halides** NH → NCOOR

155. BnNH$_2$ + IEt $\xrightarrow{Et_4NHCO_3}$ BnNHCOOEt

**under mild conditions.** Benzylamine added to a stirred soln. of 1.5 eqs. tetraethylammonium hydrogen carbonate in *dry* acetonitrile, 5 eqs. ethyl iodide added after 1 h, and stirred overnight → product. Y 98%. The reagent is stable over several months (if kept under argon), easily prepared from commercially available Et$_4$NOH and CO$_2$, and is a safe alternative to phosgene. Reaction is applicable to prim. or sec. aromatic and aliphatic amines (incl. allyl- or benzylamines). Prim., sec. and benzylic halides gave good-to-high yields, whilst tert. halides failed to react. F.e. and **cyclic urethans** from halogenamines, also from tosylates, s. A. Inesi et al., J. Org. Chem. *63*, 1337-8 (1998).

*Sodium azide/clay-supported quaternary ammonium halide* ←
**Azides from bromides** Br → N$_3$
with NaN$_3$/β-cyclodextrin-epichlorhydrin copolymer cf. *42*, 490; with a clay-supported quaternary ammonium halide as surfactant under solid-liq. phase transfer catalysis s. R.S. Varma, K.P. Naicker, Tetrahedron Lett. *39*, 2915-8 (1998).

*Triethylamine* $Et_3N$
**Cyclic guanidines from chloroformamidinium salts and prim. amines** ○

156.

**Chiral 2-iminoimidazolidines.** A soln. of 2-chloro-1,3-dimethyl-2-imidazolinium chloride in methylene chloride added dropwise at room temp. to 1 eq. (1S)-1-(1-naphthyl)ethylamine and 2 eqs. Et$_3$N in the same solvent, and stirred at room temp. for 20 min → 1,3-dimethyl-2-[(1S)-1-(1-naphthyl)ethylimino]imidazolidine. Y 94%. F.e.s. T. Isobe et al., Tetrahedron:Asym. *9*, 1729-35 (1998).

*Copper/potassium carbonate* $Cu/K_2CO_3$
**Ullmann-Goldberg reaction** NH → NAr
in water cf. *45*, 231s*48*; N-phenylanthranilic acids *in DMF* s. R.F. Pellón et al., Tetrahedron Lett. *38*, 5107-10 (1997).

*Cuprous chloride or Copper(II)-exchanged zeolite* ←
**1-Sulfonylaziridines from ethylene derivs.** s. *55*, 159

*Calcium hydride* $CaH_2$
**N-Alkylation of isatins** NH → NR
with $K_2CO_3$ cf. *10,* 367s*36*; with alkyl iodides, bromides or chlorides in the presence of $CaH_2$ in undried DMF s. S.J. Garden et al., Synth. Commun. *28*, 1679-89 (1998).

*Zinc* Zn
**Carboxylic acid amides from carboxylic acid chlorides and amines** COCl → CON<

157. t-BuCOCl + $H_2$NCHCOOMe (CH$_2$CH$_2$Ph) ⟶ t-BuCOHNCHCOOMe (CH$_2$CH$_2$Ph)

**under mild, neutral conditions.** A mixture of pivaloyl chloride and 1 eq. activated Zn powder stirred in anhydrous toluene for 10 min at room temp., 1 eq. startg. amine in the same solvent added slowly, and stirred for 10 min → product. Y 96%. The procedure is remarkably fast, high-yielding, and generally applicable. There was no epimerization of α-aminocarboxylic acid esters, as may take place in the presence of base. Furthermore, acetonide, *tert*-butyldiphenylsilyl ethers, and carboxylic acid esters remained unaffected. F.e.s. H.M. Meshram, J.S. Yadav et al., Tetrahedron Lett. *39*, 4103-6 (1998); **urethans from chloroformic acid esters** and prim. amines s. ibid. 3259-62.

*Lithium azidohydridodiisobutylaluminate* $i$-$Bu_2AlH/LiN_3$
**Carboxylic acid azides from chlorides** s. *40*, 176s*55* COCl → $CON_3$

*Zeolites* s. under *Copper(II)* ←

*Diisopropylcarbodiimide* $i$-$PrN{=}C{=}NPr$-$i$
**Polymer-based synthesis of 2-piperazinone-5-acetic acid amides** ○
**from α-halogenocarboxylic acids and prim. amines**

158. [scheme: polymer-bound allylamine + bromoacetic acid → intermediate → with i-BuNH$_2$ → product; R = cycloheptyl]

Startg. polymer-based allylamine and bromoacetic acid allowed to react in the presence of diisopropylcarbodiimide (0.5 *M*, DMF, 2 x 30 min, room temp.), treated with a 2 *M* soln. of startg. prim. amine in DMSO for 2 h at room temp., and the resin cleaved with 95:5 trifluoroacetic acid/water for 20 min at room temp. → product. Y 63% (crude product lyophilized 3 times; purity 90%). A wide variety of unprotected amines may be used, but hindered amines gave products of lower purity (ca. 60%). F.e. and chiral compds., also combinatorial synthesis, s. D.A. Goff, Tetrahedron Lett. *39*, 1473-6 (1998); from Fmoc-amino acids s. ibid. *37*, 6247-50 (1996); polymer-based synthesis of **2-imidazolidone-4-acetic acid amides from isocyanates** s. ibid. *39*, 1477-80 (1998).

*1,1,3,3-Tetramethylguanidine* $(Me_2N)_2C{=}NH$
**Tert. from sec. amines and halides** NH → NR
with pyridine cf. *21*, 499; rapid microscale solution-phase parallel synthesis of a library of N-subst. piperazines and piperidines with 1,1,3,3-tetramethylguanidine as a readily removable, water-soluble base s. Y.F. Xie et al., Tetrahedron *54*, 4077-84 (1998).

*Titanium tetraisopropoxide* s. under $Pd_2(dba)_3$ $Ti(OPr$-$i)_4$

*Trimethylphenylammonium tribromide*  $PhMe_3NBr_3$
**1-Sulfonylaziridines from ethylene derivs. and N-chloro-N-sodiosulfonic acid amides**
**Stereospecific bromine-catalyzed conversion**

159.

A rare example of atom-transfer redox catalysis by a main group element [bromine] is reported in the aziridination of ethylene derivs. **E:** 10 Mol% trimethylphenylammonium tribromide added at 25° to a mixture of startg. olefin and 1.1 eqs. anhydrous Chloramine-T in acetonitrile, and stirred vigorously for 12 h → product. Y 89%. The procedure is inexpensive, applicable to a wide range of olefins (incl. allyl alcohols), and the crystalline products are readily isolated. Reaction is initiated by bromonium ion, which may also serve as a solid-liq. phase transfer catalyst aiding dissolution of Chloramine-T. F.e. incl. a large-scale (0.5 mol) method with commercial Chloramine-T trihydrate, and with other N-chloro-N-sodiosulfonamides s. J.U. Jeong, K.B. Sharpless et al., J. Am. Chem. Soc. *120*, 6844-5 (1998); 1-tosylaziridines with Bromamine-T (cf. *54*, 135) and 10 mol% CuCl or 5 mol% CuCl₂ cf. R. Vyas et al., Tetrahedron Lett. *39*, 4715-6 (1998); with PhI=NTs and copper(II)-exchanged zeolite (cf *46*, 355s*54*) s. European patent EP-831086 (Imperial Chem. Ind. plc).

*Bis(dibenzylideneacetone)palladium(0)/1,1′-bis(di-tert-butylphosphino)ferrocene/*  ←
  *sodium* tert-*butoxide*
**Ar. amines from halides**  NH → NAr
**Improved procedure**

160.

Sterically hindered, chelating tert. alkylphosphines as ligand effect a remarkable **rate acceleration in palladium-catalyzed N-arylation** of both prim. and sec. amines with ar. iodides, bromides *and with ar. chlorides* (the latter being unreactive under normal conditions, (cf. *51*, 171)). **E:** A 0.5 to 1 *M* soln. of *p*-chlorotoluene, 1.2 eqs. aniline, 1.2 eqs. NaOBu-*t*, and 3 mol% Pd(dba)₂/ 1,1′-bis(*tert*-butylphosphino)ferrocene in dioxane heated at 110° for 4 h → product. Y 93%. Reaction with ar. bromides or iodides can be undertaken *at room temp.*, while Pd(OAc)₂ is the catalyst of choice for N-arylation of sec. amines with ar. chlorides. Significant, also, is the fact that reaction is applicable to normally unreactive aryl tosylates. F.e.s. B.C. Hamann, J.F. Hartwig, J. Am. Chem. Soc. *120*, 7369-70 (1998).

*Tris(dibenzylideneacetone)dipalladium/2,2′-bis(diphenylphosphino)-*  ←
  *1,1′-binaphthyl/sodium* tert-*butoxide*
**Ar. amines from halides**
s. *52*, 171; ar. polyamines from ar. polybromides, selectivity, s. B. Witulski et al., Synlett *1998*, 504-6; N-arylation of piperazines with polysubst. ar. bromides or iodides with retention of contiguous chlorine atoms s. S. Morita et al., Tetrahedron *54*, 4811-8 (1998); s.a. G.J. Tanoury et al., Tetrahedron Lett. *39*, 6845-8 (1998).

**Preferential N-arylation**

161.

In the routine Pd-catalyzed N-arylation of amines (cf. *51*, 171) with aryl or heteroaryl halides, *prim*-amino groups are preferentially arylated in the presence of *sec*-amino groups. **E:** An evacuated mixture of 1.2 eqs. N-propylethylenediamine, 1.5 mol% $Pd_2(dba)_3$, 4.5 mol% BINAP, 1.1 eqs. NaOBu-$t$, and 2-bromotoluene purged with argon, diluted with toluene, degassed with argon for 5 min, and heated to 85° for 2 h → product. Y 81%. Selectivity for prim. amines over sec. amines was >99:1! With $K_2CO_3$/glycol at 140°, however, the sec-amino group was arylated preferentially. F.e. incl. arylation with N-subst. 2-chlorobenzimidazoles and 3-bromopyridine s. Y. Hong, C.H. Senanayake et al., Tetrahedron Lett. 39, 3121-4 (1998).

*Tris(dibenzylideneacetone)dipalladium/1,1′-bis(diphenylphosphino)ferrocene/*  ←
*sodium* tert-*butoxide/titanium tetraisopropoxide/lithium/trimethylsilyl chloride*
**Prim. ar. amines from ar. bromides and molecular nitrogen**  ArBr → $ArNH_2$

162.

A soln. of *p*-bromobiphenyl in toluene added *over 1 h* to a soln. of 2.5 mol% $Pd_2(dba)_3$, 7 mol% dppf, and 2.8 eqs. NaOBu-$t$ in the same solvent containing 2 eqs. 'Ti-N' complex (prepared from 2 eqs. Ti(OPr-$i$)$_4$, 20 eqs. Li, and 20 eqs. $Me_3SiCl$ in THF *under $N_2$* at room temp. for 4 h), and heated at 90° for 2 h → product. Y 77% (and 8% bis(4-biphenylyl)amine). The key step is the Ti→Pd transmetalation, followed by reductive elimination of Pd(0). Electron-donating groups in the ar. bromide accelerated the formation of unwanted diarylamine, while electron-withdrawing groups favoured formation of the desired prim. amine. F.e. incl. hindered products, **also from aryl triflates,** s. K. Hori, M. Mori, J. Am. Chem. Soc. 120, 7651-2 (1998).

*Dichloro[1,1′-bis(diphenylphosphino)ferrocene]palladium(II)/*  ←
*1,1′-bis(diphenylphosphino)ferrocene/sodium* tert-*butoxide*
**Prim. ar. amines from ar. halides**
via N-arylketimines cf. 53, 164; via sec. ar. allylamines or ar. diallylamines with Pd(dppf)Cl$_2$/ dppf/NaOBu-$t$ s. S. Jaime-Figueroa, D.G. Putman et al., Tetrahedron Lett. 39, 1313-6 (1998).

## Sulfur ↑                                                            NC ↓↑ S

*Without additional reagents*  w.a.r.
**Ureas from thiolcarbamic acid esters and amines**  >NCOSR → >NCON<
s. 9, 536; urea peptides s. M. Anbazhagan, S. Rajappa et al., Tetrahedron Lett. 39, 3609-12 (1998).

**Guanidines from isothioureas**  >NC(=NH)SR → >NC(=NH)N<
s. 5, 346; polymer-based synthesis from a supported Fmoc-protected amine via S-alkylation of a supported Fmoc-protected thiourea s. P.C. Kearney et al., Tetrahedron Lett. 39, 2663-6 (1998).

**Ring closures with N,N′-dicarbalkoxyisothioureas**  ○
2-carbalkoxyamino-$\Delta^2$-imidazolines cf. 39, 381; 2-carbalkoxyamino-4(3H)-pyrimidinone ring from *o*-aminocarboxylic acid esters s. A.J. Elliott et al., J. Org. Chem. 62, 8071-5 (1997).

*Cesium carbonate*  $Cs_2CO_3$
**N-Functionalized amines from 2,4-dinitrobenzenesulfonic acid amides**  ←

163.

**Ureas from hydroxamic acids via Lossen rearrangement.** 2 eqs. $Cs_2CO_3$ and 2 eqs. phenyl-hydroxamic acid added to a 1 *M* soln. of N-(*p*-methoxybenzyl)-2,4-dinitrobenzenesulfonamide in dry DMF under $N_2$, and the mixture stirred at room temp. for 4 h → N-(p-methoxybenzyl)-N'-phenylurea. Y 79%. The method offers a mild and simple alternative to the use of toxic phosgene or isocyanates. It is general for sec. or tert. N-alkyl- or N-aryl-2,4-dinitrobenzenesulfonamides, but methylhydroxamic acid and N-subst. hydroxamic acids failed to react. F.e., also carboxylic acid thioamides from Grignard compds. and $CS_2$, s. T. Messeri, N.C.O. Tomkinson et al., Tetrahedron Lett. *39*, 1673-6 (1998); carboxylic acid amides from thiolic acid esters s. ibid. 1669-72.

*Zinc salt/triethanolamine/triethylamine* ←
**Thioureas from amines** NH → NC(S)N<
and dithiocarbamates cf. *10*, 376; trisubst. thioureas from zinc dithiocarbamates in the presence of triethanolamine and $Et_3N$, also cyclic thioureas from diamines, s. K. Ramadas, N. Janarthanan, J. Chem. Res., Miniprint *1998*, 1101-8.

*1-Ethyl-3-(3-dimethylaminopropyl)carbodiimide hydrochloride* RN=C=NR
**Polymer-based synthesis of amidines** C(N<)=NR
**from carboxylic acid thioamides and amines**

164.

Ar = p-MeOC$_6$H$_4$

**α-Cyanoamidines.** A freshly prepared mixture of 1-ethyl-3-(3-dimethylaminopropyl) carbodiimide hydrochloride, DMF, and 4-methoxybenzylamine added to startg. polystyrene-Wang-supported thioamide, shaken for 24 h, filtered, the resin washed, suspended in 1:1 dichloromethane/trifluoroacetic acid, and shaken for 35 min → product. Y 71% (71% pure). There was no reaction with other carbodiimides. F.e. and with sec. or ar. amines s. F. Zaragoza, Tetrahedron Lett. *38*, 7291-4 (1997).

# Remaining Elements ↑ NC ↓↑ Rem

*Without additional reagents* w.a.r.
**Carbodiimides from phosphine imines** C=P< → N=C=N
and isocyanates cf. *34*, 420; *41*, 404; N-glycosylcarbodiimides from isothiocyanates s. J.M. García Fernández et al., Tetrahedron Lett. *38*, 4161-4 (1997).

**N-Heterocyclics from phosphine imines and heterocumulenes** ○
s. *44*, 362s*52*, *53*; 4-carbalkoxymethyl-3,4-dihydro-2(1H)-quinazolones from o-(phosphoranyl-ideneamino)cinnamic acid esters and isocyanates s. P. Molina et al., Synthesis *1998*, 283-7; 7,8-dihydropyrimido[4',5':4,5]thieno[2,3-c]pyridazines s. J.M. Quintela et al., Tetrahedron *54*, 8107-22 (1998).

*Sodium bis(trimethylsilyl)amide* NaN(SiMe$_3$)$_2$
**N-Acyl- from N-silyl-carboxylic acid amides** CONHSi< → CONHCOR
**and carboxylic acid pentafluorophenyl esters**

165.

2 eqs. N-Trimethylsilylpivalamide in THF treated with 2 eqs. NaN(SiMe$_3$)$_2$ at -78°, startg. pentafluorophenyl ester added, and the mixture allowed to react at -78° to room temp. for 15 min → product. Y 59%. Yields were lower with unprotected amides, or with only 1 eq. of N-silyl amides. The method is mild, simple, and general for prim. or sec. amides, leaving acid- or base-sensitive

protective groups (Boc, Cbz, OTBS) and conjugated double bonds unaffected. F.e., also N-acylation of 2-pyrrolidone, and application to the synthesis of immunosuppressants microcolin A and B s. M.B. Andrus et al., Tetrahedron Lett. *39*, 5465-8 (1998).

*Cupric acetate s.a. under PhI(OAc)₂*  *Cu(OAc)₂*
*Cupric acetate/triethylamine or pyridine*  *Cu(OAc)₂/Et₃N or C₅H₅N*
**N- and O-Arylation with arylboronic acids under mild conditions**  NH → NAr

166.

**N-Arylation of amines.** A slurry of startg. amine, 2 eqs. *p*-fluorophenylboronic acid, 1 eq. Cu(OAc)₂, and 2 eqs. Et₃N in methylene chloride stirred at room temp. for 18 h → product. Y 93%. Yields were dependent on the choice of the base. F.e. incl. N-arylation of acylamines, lactams, phthalimide, ureas, sulfonic acid amides, and urethans, **also O-arylation of phenols**, and with pyridine as base s. D.M.T. Chan et al., Tetrahedron Lett. *39*, 2933-6 (1998); further studies on O-arylation of phenols, s. D.A. Evans et al., ibid. 2937-40; N-arylation of 5-membered hetarenes possessing two nitrogen atoms s. ibid. 2941-4.

*Phenyl iodosoacetate/cupric acetate*  *PhI(OAc)₂/Cu(OAc)₂*
**Sec. ar. amines from prim. amines and triarylbismuth compds.**  NH₂ → NHAr
from triarylbismuth diacetates with Cu(OAc)₂ cf. *40*, 286; from the same compds. generated *in situ* **from triarylbismuthines** with PhI(OAc)₂, sec. diarylamines, s. S. Combes, J.-P. Finet, Tetrahedron *54*, 4313-8 (1998); N-arylpiperazines s. E. Vassileva et al., Synth. Commun. *27*, 1669-75 (1997).

*Stannous chloride/n-butyllithium*  *SnCl₂/BuLi*
**Carbodiimides from isocyanates and aminosilanes**  N=C=O → N=C=NR

167.

2.57 M *n*-BuLi in hexanes added to a soln. of N-*tert*-butyltrimethylsilylamine in ether at 0°, warmed to room temp., stirred for 2 h, transferred via cannula to a suspension of 0.55 eq. SnCl₂ in ether at 0°, allowed to warm to room temp., stirred for a further 2 h, re-cooled to 0°, a soln. of 1.1 eqs. *tert*-butyl isocyanate in ether added, warmed to room temp., and stirred again for 12 h → 1,3-di-*tert*-butylcarbodiimide. Y 84% (pure). Reaction proceeds via metathesis with an *in situ*-generated tin(II) bisamide. For preparation of N-silylcarbodiimides, however, reaction must be undertaken with commercially available Sn[N(SiMe₃)₂]₂ (poor yields being obtained with the *in situ*-generated reagent). F.e.s. J.R. Babcock, L.R. Sita, J. Am. Chem. Soc. *120*, 5585-6 (1998).

*Stannic chloride or Trimethylsilyl triflate*  *SnCl₄ or Me₃SiOSO₂CF₃*
**Vorbrüggen nucleoside synthesis**  ←
updates s. *26*, 446s*51, 53*; 5-fluorouracils with 1,4-oxaheteroepane moieties s. J.A. Gómez et al., Tetrahedron *54*, 13295-312 (1998); α-2′-deoxyribonucleosides s. Z. Wang, C.J. Rizzo, Tetrahedron Lett. *38*, 8177-80 (1997); 5-alkylidenehydantoin nucleosides s. H.M. Abdel-Bary et al., Bull. Soc. Chim. France *132*, 149-55 (1995); 3′-aza-4′-thia-2′,3′-dideoxynucleosides s. P. Faury et al., ibid. *133*, 553-62 (1996); 2′,3′-ethylenenucleosides from 2,3-unsatd. thioglycosides with NBS s. K. Sujino et al., Tetrahedron Lett. *37*, 6133-6 (1996); 1,3-oxathiolane nucleosides with Me₃SiI s. N. Nguyen-Ba, B. Zacharie et al., Synlett *1998*, 759-62; Vorbrüggen synthesis with glycosyl phosphorodiamidates, protected 2′-deoxynucleosides, s. T. Iimori, S. Ikegami et al., Heterocycles *42*, 485-8 (1996).

*Bismuth tribromide*                                                                                                                      $BiBr_3$
**Bismuth(III)-catalyzed Vorbrüggen nucleoside synthesis**           ←

168.

A stirred soln. of 1,2,3,5-tetra-O-acetyl-β-D-ribofuranose and 5 mol% $BiBr_3$ in methylene chloride treated at 0° under $N_2$ with 4 eqs. $Me_3SiBr$, stirred at room temp. for 10 min, the solvent and excess of $Me_3SiBr$ evaporated under reduced pressure, the residue diluted with anhydrous acetonitrile, 1 eq. startg. silylated base (prepared by standard treatment of thymine with hexamethyldisilazane and a little $(NH_4)_2SO_4$ at 130°) added, stirred for 4 h at room temp., and poured into cold satd. aq. $NaHCO_3$ soln. → product. Y 80%. This one-pot conversion (via *in situ*-generation of the α-glycosyl bromide) is simple and non-toxic, and work-up and purification are straightforward. F.e. incl. purine nucleosides s. J.-Y. Winum et al., Synth. Commun. *28*, 603-6 (1998).

*Osmium tetroxide/dihydroquinidine* p-*chlorobenzoate/Chloramine-T*          ←
**α-(Tosylamino)ketones from enoxysilanes**                            $C{=}C(OSi{\leqslant}) \to C(NHTs)CO$
**Asym. conversion**

169.

A mixture of 2 mol% dihydroquinidine *p*-chlorobenzoate in 1:1 *tert*-butanol/water and 1 mol% 0.5 *M* $OsO_4$ in toluene stirred for 2 min, 2.5 eqs. Chloramine-T added, followed after 2 min by addition of cyclohexanone trimethylsilyl enol ether, and the mixture quenched with Na-metabisulfite after a further 15 min → 2-(N-tosylamino)cyclohexanone. Y 35% (e.e. 92%). The moderate yields are due to difficulties experienced in work-up. The absolute configuration was assigned on the basis that the ligand generally directs addition to the β-face of the alkenes in asym. Sharpless oxyamination. F.e. and with $(DHQD)_2$-PYR as ligand s. P. Phukan, A. Sudalai, Tetrahedron:Asym. *9*, 1001-5 (1998).

## Carbon ↑                                                                                                                                                                       NC ↓↑ C

*Without additional reagents*                                                                                                    *w.a.r.*
**N,N-Disubst. thionocarbamic acid esters from tert. amines** s. *55*, 19    $R_3N \to R_2NC(S)OR'$

**4,5-Dihydro-3(2H)-pyridazones from hydrazine**                                  ○
and 2-siloxycyclopropanecarboxylic acid esters cf. *40*, 220; and 5-β-keto-1,3-dioxane-4,6-diones, also one-pot preparation from Meldrum's acid, s. G. Tóth et al., Synth. Commun. *27*, 3513-23 (1997).

**N-Protected α-aminocarboxylic acid amides from 5-oxazolidones**                   C
s. *10*, 382; *13*, 516; polymer-based synthesis of Asn, Asp and Gln derivs. with monitoring by single bead FT-IR microspectroscopy s. R.E. Marti et al., J. Org. Chem. *62*, 5615-8 (1997).

*Sodium hydroxide/benzyltriethylammonium chloride*                      $NaOH/BnEt_3NCl$
**Sec. amines from N-subst. trifluoroacetamides**                              $NCOCF_3 \to NR$
with NaOH cf. *25*, 330; nitro-subst. sec. ar. amines with NaOH and $BnEt_3NCl$ as phase transfer catalyst s. S.A. Brown, C.J. Rizzo, Synth. Commun. *26*, 4065-80 (1996).

*Potassium fluoride/triethylamine*                                                    $KF/Et_3N$
**Carbo-*tert*-butoxyamines from carbo-9-fluorenylmethoxyamines**     $NCOOR \to NCOOR'$
s. *48*, 381; α-(carbo-*tert*-butoxyamino)carboxylic acids from polymer-based α-(carbo-9-fluorenylmethoxyamino)carboxylic acid esters, also dipeptide derivs., s. R.L.E. Furlán, E.G. Mata, Tetrahedron Lett. *39*, 6421-2 (1998).

m-*Chloroperoxybenzoic acid/ammonium ferrous sulfate*
**N-Formylation of α-aminocarboxylic acid esters
via α-(alkylideneamino)- and α-(oxaziridin-2-yl)-carboxylic acid esters**

NH → NCHO

170.

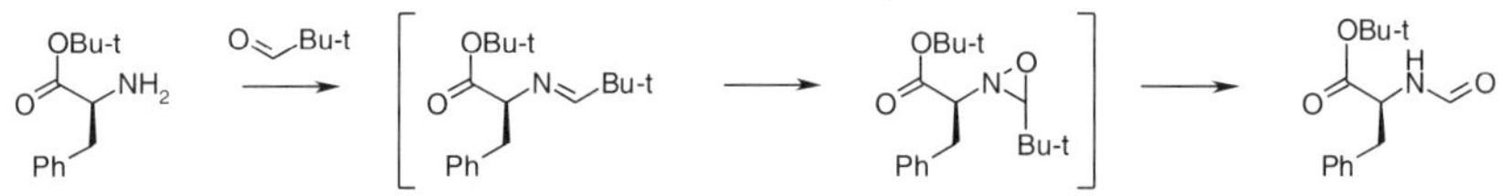

**One-pot procedure.** 1 eq. Et$_3$N and 1.09 eq. pivalaldehyde added sequentially to a soln. of (S)-phenylalanine *tert*-butyl ester hydrochloride in methylene chloride containing 3 Å molecular sieves at room temp. under argon, the mixture stirred for 40 h, 1 eq. *m*-CPBA added portionwise at 0°, stirred at 0° for 20 min then at room temp. for 1 h, a soln. of 1 eq. ammonium ferrous sulfate hexahydrate (Möhr's salt) in 2.5:1 methanol/water added, and stirring continued for a further 15 h → (S)-N-formyl-L-phenylalanine *tert*-butyl ester. Y 77% (96% overall with isolation of the intermediates). The method does not require any standard formylating agent and proceeds **without racemization**. It is, however, limited to aminoesters with an unfunctionalized chain. F.e. and with isolation of the intermediates, and preferential formylation of prim. over sec. amines, s. T. Giard et al., Synthesis *1998*, 297-300.

*Bis(trichloromethyl) carbonate*
**Carbamyl chlorides from tert. benzylamines**

$(Cl_3CO)_2O$
R$_2$NBn → R$_2$NCOCl

171.

[ + PhCH$_2$Cl ]

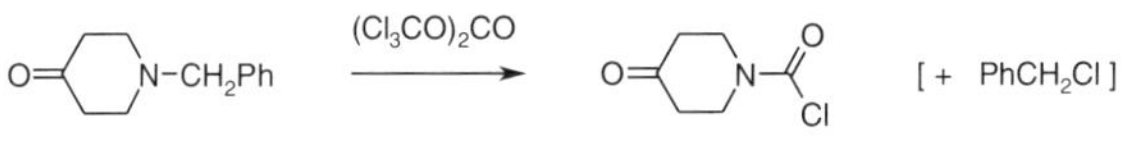

A soln. of 1-benzyl-4-piperidone in dichloromethane added to a soln. of 0.33 eqs. triphosgene in dichloromethane at 0° under inert atmosphere, allowed to warm to room temp., and stirred until reaction complete by TLC (7 h) → product. Y 90%. The method is mild and compatible with various functional groups (ketone, ester, amide, 1,3-enyne); however, tert. ar. benzylamines were unreactive. F.e.s. C. Jorand-Lebrun et al., Synth. Commun. *28*, 1189-95 (1998).

*Tetrakis(triphenylphosphine)palladium(0)/phenylsilane*
**Solid-phase peptide synthesis**
via *in situ*-N-decarballyloxylation s. *29*, 28s54

Pd(PPh$_3$)$_4$/PhSiH$_3$
NCOOR → NCOR

## Elimination ⇑

## Hydrogen ↑

NC ⇑ H

*Bismuth(III) nitrate*
*Ruthenium trichloride/oxygen/acetic acid*
**Pyridines from 1,4-dihydropyridines**

Bi(NO$_3$)$_3$
RuCl$_3$/O$_2$/AcOH

172.

**Pyridine-3,5-dicarboxylic acid esters.** A little RuCl$_3$ added to a soln. of startg. 1,4-dihydropyridine in glacial acetic acid, and the mixture stirred at room temp. for 30 min under O$_2$ → product. Y 75%. The method is catalytic, clean, mild, and free from by-products. Phenols, phenolethers, olefins, and aromatic nitro compds. were unaffected. F.e.s. S.H. Mashraqui, M.A. Karnik, Tetrahedron Lett. *39*, 4895-8 (1998); with Bi(NO$_3$)$_3$ cf. Synthesis *1998*, 713-4.

## Oxygen ↑ NC ⇑ O

*Sodium hydride/sodium trihydridocyanoborate*   NaH/NaBH₃CN
**Quinoline ring from β-aryl-O-(2,4-dinitrophenyl)oximes**
with dehydrogenation to 8-hydroxyquinolines s. *50*, 254s*53*; with reduction to 8-hydroxy-1,2,3,4-tetrahydroquinolines using NaBH₃CN s. A. Ono, K. Narasaka et al., Chem. Lett. *1998*, 437-8.

*Triethylamine or Ethyldiisopropylamine*   Et₃N or i-Pr₂NEt
**Polymer-based synthesis of hydantoins**
from α-(carbalkoxyamino)carboxamides cf. *31*, 452s*53*; from N-phenoxycarbonyl derivs. with i-Pr₂NEt s. X. Xiao et al., J. Org. Chem. *62*, 6968-73 (1997); from α-ureidocarboxylic acid esters, 1-(2-thiazolyl)hydantoins, s. J. Stadlwieser et al., Angew. Chem. Int. Ed. Engl. *37*, 1402-4 (1998).

*Piperidine*   R₂NH
**2,5-Piperazinediones from dipeptide esters**
with NH₃ cf. *19*, 559; polymer-based synthesis using a 'backbone amide linker' from N-Fmoc-protected dipeptide esters with piperidine s. M. del Fresno et al., Tetrahedron Lett. *39*, 2639-42 (1998).

*Zinc s.a. under TiCl₄*   Zn

*Zinc/hydrogen chloride*   Zn/HCl
**Reductive ring closures of nitronitriles**
indoles from α-(o-nitroaryl)nitriles with 30% Pd-on-carbon cf. *14*, 564; 2-iminoindolines with Zn/HCl s. European patent EP-826668 (L'Oreal SA).

*Formic acid*   HCOOH
**Ring closures via cyclic N-acylimmonium salts**
review s. *38*, 982s*41*; stereospecific polymer-based synthesis of condensed 4-acyl-2-piperazinones s. T. Vojkovský et al., J. Org. Chem. *63*, 3162-3 (1998).

*tert-Butyldimethylsilyl chloride/imidazole*   ←
**Nitriles from aldoximes**   CH=NOH → CN
via O-silylation with Me₃SiI/(Me₂Si)₂NH cf. *35*, 311s*39*; with t-BuMe₂SiCl/imidazole s. M. Ortiz-Marciales et al., Synth. Commun. *28*, 2807-11 (1998).

*Titanium tetrachloride/zinc*   TiCl₄/Zn
**2-Aminoquinolines from β-cyano-o-nitrostyrenes**
with SnCl₂/NaBH₄/HCl cf. *2*, 649s*53*; with TiCl₄/Zn s. L. Zhou et al., Synthesis *1998*, 851-4.

*Triphenylphosphine/diethyl azodicarboxylate*   Ph₃P/EtO₂CN=NCO₂Et
**N-Protected 2-vinylaziridines from 4-amino-2-ethylenealcohols**

**Chiral compds.** Startg. protected aminoalcohol (enantiomerically pure) and 2 eqs. triphenylphosphine in freshly distilled THF treated dropwise at 0° with 1.5 eqs. DEAD under N₂, and the soln. stirred under N₂ for 3-6 h → product. Y 70%. This method permits the preparation of functionalized aziridines while avoiding protection-deprotection steps. F.e. incl. N-benzoyl derivs. s. H.F. Olivo et al., Synlett *1998*, 247-8.

*Methyl(carboxysulfamyl)triethylammonium hydroxide inner salt*
**Isonitriles from formamides**  NHCHO → NC:   ←

174.  Me₂C=CHCH₂CH₂C(Me)CH=CH₂ (NHCHO) ⟶ Me₂C=CHCH₂CH₂C(Me)CH=CH₂ (NC)

1.5 eqs. Burgess' reagent added in one portion to a soln. of startg. formamide in dry dichloromethane, and heated at reflux under N₂ for 80 min → product. Y 88%. Halide-sensitive trimethylsilyl ethers were unaffected. F.e. incl. peptidyl isonitriles and glycoside derivs. with unprotected hydroxyl groups s. S.M. Creedon et al., J. Chem. Soc. Perkin Trans. 1 *1998*, 1015-7.

### Nitrogen ↑  NC ⇑ N

*Dimethyldioxirane*  ←
**Nitriles from hydrazones**  CH=N-N< → CN
with *m*-chloroperoxybenzoic acid cf. *22*, 408s*44*; cleanly and rapidly with dimethyldioxirane s. A. Altamura, R. Curci et al., Tetrahedron Lett. *39*, 2009-12 (1998).

### Halogen ↑  NC ⇑ Hal

*Irradiation*  ⫽
**N-Condensed cyclimmonium salts by cycloquaternization**  ○
s. *27*, 527; azonia derivs. of benzo[*c*]phenanthrene and helicenes s. S. Arai et al., J. Chem. Soc. Perkin Trans. I *1998*, 1561-7; pyrido[1,2-*a*:3,4-*b'*]diindoles by thermal cyclization s. O.S. Radchenko et al., Tetrahedron Lett. *38*, 5339-42 (1997).

### Remaining Elements ↑  NC ⇑ Rem

*Potassium* tert-*butoxide*  KOBu-t
**Indoles from *o*-(silylethynyl)amines**  ○
with CuI/CaCO₃ cf. *39*, 433; oxy-functionalized indoles from N-carbo-*tert*-butoxy derivs. with KOBu-*t* s. Y. Kondo et al., J. Org. Chem. *62*, 6507-11 (1997).

# Formation of Hal-S Bond

## Exchange  ⇵

### Hydrogen ↑  HalS ⇵ H

*Carbon tetrachloride*  CCl₄
**Sulfenyl chlorides from mercaptans** s. *55*, 54  SH → SCl

# Formation of Hal-Rem Bond

## Exchange  ⇵

### Halogen ↑  HalRem ⇵ Hal

*Sodium hexafluorosilicate*  Na₂SiF₆
**Replacement of P-chlorine by fluorine**  P-Cl → P-F
with AsF₃ cf. *19*, 589s*37*; phosphonic acid difluorides with Na₂SiF₆ s. O. Farooq, J. Chem. Soc. Perkin Trans. I *1998*, 839-40.

# Formation of Hal-C Bond

## Uptake ⇓

### Addition to Oxygen and Carbon      HalC ⇓ OC

*Tris(2,2,6,6-tetramethyl-3,5-heptanedionato)europium(III)*      *Eu(III)*
**2-Acoxyhalides from epoxides**      ∇o∕ → C(Hal)C(OAc)
with AlCl₃ cf. *20*, 175s29; 2-acoxy-chlorides and -bromides with tris(2,2,6,6-tetramethyl-3,5-heptanedionato)europium(III) or the yttrium analog s. Y. Taniguchi, Y. Fujiwara et al., Tetrahedron Lett. *39*, 4559-60 (1998).

*Graphite*      $C_8$
**Acoxyhalides from cyclic ethers** s. *55*, 105

*Macrocyclic crown dilactams*      ←
**1,2-Halogenhydrins from epoxides**      ∇o∕ → C(Hal)C(OH)
Regio- and stereo-specific ring opening under mild conditions

175.

**1,2-Iodohydrins.** 1-Octene oxide in methylene chloride added to a stirred soln. of 10 mol% 1,15-diaza-3,4:12,13-dibenzo-16-(thiocarbonyl)-5,8,11-trioxacyclohexadecane-2,15-dione in the same solvent at room temp., treated dropwise with 1 eq. I₂ in methylene chloride during 15 min, refluxed for 16 h, and quenched with 10% aq. Na₂S₂O₃ and water → 1-iodo-2-octanol. Y 90%. Reaction was considerably longer (or failed completely) in the absence of the crown ether. The latter facilitates generation of a halogen nucleophile (via a charge-transfer complex), which attacks the epoxide with high regioselectivity (>95%) at the least substituted site. The catalyst may be simply regenerated (in as little as 0.05 mol% for styrene oxide) for reuse through several catalytic cycles with no loss of activity. Ring opening is also stereospecific as demonstrated by the *anti*-cleavage of cyclohexene oxide. F.e. incl. **1,2-bromhydrins** (with Br₂), and comparison of crown ethers s. H. Sharghi et al., J. Org. Chem. *63*, 1455-61 (1998).

*Chiral zirconium(IV) aminoalkoxides/allyl bromide*      ←
**2-Siloxybromides from epoxides with desymmetrization**      ∇o∕ → C(Br)C(OSi≼)

176.

A mixture of startg. epoxide, 1.25 eqs. trimethylsilyl azide, and 20 eqs. allyl bromide in chlorobenzene allowed to react at 25° for 48 h in the presence of 5 mol% chiral zirconium(IV) aminoalkoxide (prepared from Zr(OBu-*t*)₄ and (S,S,S)-tri-2-propanolamine) → product. Y 81% (e.e. 95%). The mechanism of the reaction involves coordination of *two* metal centres, one of which activates the epoxide and the other activates the azido function of the intermediate siloxyazide prior to azide-bromine exchange with allyl bromide. Ether and ester groups remained unaffected.

Isolation of the intermediate siloxyazides s. 47, 232. F.e. and conversion to **chiral *cis*-2-amino-alcohols,** s. W.A. Nugent, J. Am. Chem. Soc. *120*, 7139-40 (1998).

## Addition to Nitrogen and Carbon          HalC ⇓ NC

*Magnesium bromide*                                                                             $MgBr_2$
**2-Carbo-*tert*-butoxyamino-3-siloxybromides**                                                 C
**from 1-carbo-*tert*-butoxy-2-(siloxymethyl)aziridines**
**Regio- and stereo-specific halogenative ring opening under mild conditions**

177.

2 eqs. $MgBr_2 \cdot Et_2O$ added to a soln. of startg. chiral N-Boc-aziridine in ether, and the mixture stirred at room temp. for 4 h → product. Y quantitative (>99% major regioisomer). The method is simple, general and high-yielding. The regioselectivity was not affected, even by a bulky substituent at the C-3 position. F.e. and conversion to 2-amino- or 2-carbalkoxyamino-1,3-bromohydrins s. G. Righi et al., Tetrahedron Lett. *39*, 2385-8 (1998).

*Potassium peroxymonosulfate/sodium chloride*                                                   $KHSO_5/NaCl$
**1,1-Nitrochlorides from oximes**                                                              C=NOH → C(Cl)NO$_2$
with NaOCl cf. *5*, 381; via 1,1-nitrosochlorides (*in situ*) with Oxone/NaCl s. P. Ceccherelli, M. Curini et al., Tetrahedron Lett. *39*, 4385-6 (1998).

## Addition to Carbon-Carbon Bonds          HalC ⇓ CC

*Sodium bromide/sodium perborate/acetic acid*                                                   $NaBr/NaBO_3/AcOH$
**1,2-Dibromides from ethylene derivs.**                                                        C=C → C(Br)C(Br)

178.

2.2 eqs. NaBr added to a mixture of 1.1 eqs. $NaBO_3 \cdot 4H_2O$ and cyclohexene in glacial acetic acid, and stirred for 2 h → 1,2-dibromocyclohexane. Y 87%. While the use of $Br_2$ (in combination with a variety of solvents/oxidants) has its drawbacks in terms of its corrosive nature and environmental concerns, $NaBO_3 \cdot 4H_2O$ is stable, inexpensive and easy to handle. F.e. incl. α,β-dibromo- from α,β-ethylene-carboxylic acids or esters s. G.W. Kabalka et al., Synth. Commun. *28*, 925-9 (1998).

*Potassium iodide/sodium nitrate/acetic acid*                                                   $KI/NaNO_3/AcOH$
**(E)-α,β-Ethylene-β-nitroiodides from acetylene derivs.**                                      C(I)=C(NO$_2$)
**Regio- and stereo-specific conversion**

179.

1.5 eqs. KI added to a soln. of phenylacetylene and 3 eqs. $NaNO_3$ in acetic acid at 85°, the mixture stirred at 85° for 3 h, then poured into water → α-iodo-β-nitrostyrene. Y 67% (83% E-isomer). Reaction is applicable to both internal and terminal alkynes. F.e. and with $I_2/NaNO_3$ in lower yield but higher stereoselectivity s. M.S. Yusubov, V.D. Filimonov et al., Synth. Commun. *28*, 833-6 (1998).

*Sodium perborate s. under NaBr*                                                                $NaBO_3$
m-*Chloroperoxybenzoic acid s. under HCl*                                                       $ArCOO_2H$

*Phenyl iodosoacetate/quaternary phosphonium or ammonium halides* ←
**1,2-Acoxyhalides from ethylene derivs.**   $C=C \rightarrow C(OAc)C(Hal)$
**Regio- and stereo-specific conversion under mild conditions**

180.

**Acyl 2-iodo-2-deoxyglycosides.** 3 eqs. PhI(OAc)$_2$ and 3 eqs. Ph$_3$MePI in dichloromethane stirred for 15 min at room temp., startg. glycal added to the formed diacetoxyiodine(I) species, and the mixture stirred for 72 h → product. Y 78% ($\alpha$:$\beta$ 3:1). The novel phosphonium iodine(I) species serves as an acetyl hypoiodite equivalent and can be isolated before use. 1,2-*trans*-Adducts were obtained exclusively with a preference for $\alpha$-glycosyl acetates. F.e., solvents and phosphonium salts, and with added trimethylsilyl triflate s. A. Kirschning et al., Chem. Commun. *1998*, 33-4; bromo-analogs with Et$_4$NBr s. Synlett *1998*, 195-7.

p-*Methyliodobenzene difluoride/triethylamine pentakis(hydrogen fluoride)*   ArIF$_2$/Et$_3$N·5HF
**1,2-Difluorides from terminal ethylene derivs.**   $C=C \rightarrow C(F)C(F)$

181.        MeO$_2$C(CH$_2$)$_8$CH=CH$_2$   ⟶   MeO$_2$C(CH$_2$)$_8$CH(F)CH$_2$F

1.3 eqs. *p*-Methyliodobenzene difluoride in 5:3 Et$_3$N·5HF/dichloromethane added to a soln. of methyl 10-undecenoate in dichloromethane at -78° under N$_2$ in a Teflon vessel, the mixture stirred at 0° for 2 h, then poured into aq. NaHCO$_3$ → methyl 10,11-difluoroundecanoate. Y 68%. *p*-Methyliodobenzene difluoride is readily prepared without the requirement of special equipment, and is a useful alternative to F$_2$. No reaction occurred in the absence of Et$_3$N·5HF or commercially available Et$_3$N·3HF. Terminal double bonds reacted in preference to conjugated ones, and a variety of functional groups (e.g. alcohols, esters, cyclic acetals and chlorides) remained unaffected. F.e. incl. cyclic analogs with *cis*-selectivity s. S. Hara, N. Yoneda et al., Synlett *1998*, 495-6; **1,1-difluorides** from cyclic ethylene derivs. **with isocyclic ring contraction** (cf. *32*, 469) s. Tetrahedron Lett. *39*, 2589-92 (1998).

*N-Chloromethyl-N'-fluoro-1,4-diazoniabicyclo[2.2.2]octane bis(fluoroborate)* ←
**2-Functionalized fluorides from ethylene derivs.**   $C=C \rightarrow C(X)C(F)$
s. *49*, 407; 1-functionalized 2-fluoro-2-deoxysugars from glycals via N-$\alpha$-(2-fluoro-2-deoxyglycosyl)-1,4-diazoniabicyclo[2.2.2]octane salts s. M. Albert et al., Tetrahedron *54*, 4839-48 (1998).

*Potassium peroxymonosulfate s. under HCl*   KHSO$_5$
*Triethylamine pentakis(hydrogen fluoride) s. under ArIF$_2$*   Et$_3$N·5HF

*Bis(collidine)iodine(I) perchlorate* ←
**2-Iodo-2-deoxyglycosides from glycals** ←
s. *45*, 285; combinatorial synthesis of 2,6-dideoxytrisaccharides s. M. Izumi, Y. Ichikawa, Tetrahedron Lett. *39*, 2079-82 (1998).

*Hydrogen chloride/*m-*chloroperoxybenzoic acid or potassium peroxymonosulfate* ←
**1,2-Acoxychlorides from ethylene derivs.**   $C=C \rightarrow C(OAc)C(Cl)$
1,2-formoxychlorides cf. *53*, 186; 1,2-acetoxychlorides, regioselectivity, s. Synth. Commun. *28*, 159-65 (1998).

*Manganese(III) acetoacetonate/alumina/sodium chlorite* ←
**1,2-Dichlorides from ethylene derivs.**   $C=C \rightarrow C(Cl)C(Cl)$
with MnO$_2$/AcCl/AcOH cf. *8*, 593s*52*; under mild heterogeneous conditions with Mn(acac)$_3$/wet alumina/NaClO$_2$ s. S. Yakabe et al., Synth. Commun. *28*, 1871-8 (1998).

*Tetradecyltrimethylammonium permanganate/*            $[C_{14}H_{29}Me_3N]MnO_4/Me_3SiCl$
*trimethylsilyl chloride*
**trans-1,2-Dichlorides from ethylene derivs.**            C=C → C(Cl)C(Cl)
with [BnEt$_3$N]MnO$_4$/(COCl)$_2$ cf. *46*, 437; with the more stable tetradecyltrimethylammonium permanganate/Me$_3$SiCl s. B.G. Hazra et al., J. Chem. Res., Synop *1998*, 8-9.

*Xenon fluorotriflate*            *FXeOTf*
**(E)-α,β-Ethylene-β-triflyloxyiodonium triflates**            C(OTf)=C-I$^+$R
**from terminal acetylene derivs.**
with PhIO/CF$_3$SO$_3$H cf. *49*, 399; regio- and stereo-specific conversion with PhI/FXeOTf s. T.M. Kasumov et al., Tetrahedron *53*, 13139-48 (1997).

*Ferric sulfate or Hydrogen tetrabromoferrate*            $Fe_2(SO_4)_3$ or $HFeBr_4$
**Iron(III)-catalyzed hydrohalogenation**            C=C → CHC(Hal)
hydrochlorination using FeCl$_3$ in 1,2-dichloroethane cf. *22*, 557; **hydrobromination** using Fe$_2$(SO$_4$)$_3$ with 47% aq. HBr/cyclopentane s. European patent EP-826655 (BASF AG); by concentrating aq. solns. of HBr as reaction progresses cf. EP-826656 (BASF AG); with complex metal salts of the type H$^+_n$[MX$_{3+n}$]$^{n-}$ (M = Fe, Ru, or Al; X = Cl or Br), e.g. HFeBr$_4$ in carbon tetrachloride, cf. A.R. Suárez et al., Tetrahedron *54*, 7375-86 (1998).

# Exchange ⇅

# Hydrogen ↑            HalC ⇅ H

*Electrolysis/tetraethylammonium fluoride tetrakis(hydrogen fluoride)*            $⁁/Et_4NF·4HF$
**Anodic α-fluorination of thioethers**            H → F
1,1-fluorothioethers with Et$_4$NF·3HF cf. *42*, 462s*54*; of benzo-condensed α-(arylthio)lactams s. Y. Hou et al., J. Org. Chem. *62*, 8773-6 (1997); 1,1,1-difluorothioethers with Et$_4$NF·4HF s. A. Konno, T. Fuchigami, ibid. 8579-81; anodic fluorination of flavones s. Synlett *1998*, 973-4.

tert-*Butyllithium*            t-*BuLi*
*o*-**Metalation of arylphosphine oxides**            ←

182.

1.09 eqs. 1.4 M *t*-BuLi added dropwise to a soln. of di-*tert*-butylphenylphosphine oxide in dry THF below -70°, stirred for 80 min, treated with a soln. of I$_2$ in THF via cannula, allowed to warm to room temp. over 8-10 h, and excess of iodine removed with aq. Na$_2$S$_2$O$_3$ → product. Y 76%. F.e. and electrophiles, also prepn. of the startg. phosphine oxides from ar. bromides, s. M. Gray, V. Snieckus et al., Synlett *1998*, 422-4.

*Cupric chloride/mercuric chloride/iodine*            $CuCl_2/HgCl_2/I_2$
**2-Chlorination of 1,4-naphthoquinones**            H → Cl
with chlorine monoxide cf. *11*, 618s*49*; with CuCl$_2$/HgCl$_2$/I$_2$ s. P.C. Thapliyal, Synth. Commun. *28*, 1123-6 (1998).

*Poly[styrene(iodosoacetate)]*
**Ar. iodination**            H → I
with PhI(OCOCF$_3$)$_2$ cf. *48*, 439s*51*; with readily removable poly[styrene(iodosoacetate)], also α-arylcarboxylic acid esters from acylophenones via 1,2-aryl migration (cf. *41*, 132), s. H. Togo et al., Synlett *1998*, 534-6.

*1-Tosyloxy-1,2-benziodoxol-3(1H)-one*
**Ar. iodination**    H → I

183.

1,3,5-Triisopropylbenzene in acetonitrile treated with 1.2 eqs. 1-tosyloxy-1,2-benziodoxol-3(1*H*)-one and 0.6 eq. I$_2$, and stirred overnight (ca. 16 h) in the dark at room temp. → product. Y 87% (78% in methanol; 36% in ethyl acetate). The method is simple and high yielding, and the reagent is of low toxicity. The reaction is believed to proceed via a cationic iodonium species. F.e. incl. iodination of heteroaromatics and di- or poly-iodination, **also ar. chlorination and bromination** (with added LiCl and LiBr, respectively), s. T. Muraki et al., Synlett *1998*, 286-8.

*Cyanogen bromide/triethylamine*    BrCN/Et$_3$N
**C-α-Halogenation of sulfones**    H → Hal
with tetrahalogenomethanes cf. *36*, 211; 2α-bromocephalosporin 1,1-dioxides with BrCN/Et$_3$N s. T.E. Gunda, G.N. Szöke, Synth. Commun. *27*, 3395-403 (1997).

*N-Bromosuccinimide*    NBS
**Ar. bromination**    H → Br
s. *14*, 597; of polymethoxyarenes in dichloromethane at room temp., mono- and di-bromination, s. J.L. Bloomer, W. Zheng, Synth. Commun. *28*, 2087-95 (1998).

*1,3-Dichloro-5,5-dimethylhydantoin/potassium iodide/potassium hydroxide*    ←
**α,β-Acetylenehalides from terminal acetylene derivs.**    H → Hal
with NaOCl/KI cf. *13*, 573; with 1,3-dichloro-5,5-dimethylhydantoin/KI/KOH and f. halogenating agents, (α,β-acetylenehalogen)hydrins, s. World Intellectual Property Organization patent WO-9747575 (Lonza Inc.).

*N,N'-Difluoro-2,2'-bipyridinium bis(fluoroborate)*    ←
**Fluorination with N,N'-difluoro-2,2'-bipyridinium bis(fluoroborate)**    ←

184.

Inexpensive, crystalline, non-hygroscopic, easy-to-handle N,N'-difluoro-2,2'-bipyridinium bis(fluoroborate) is a useful altenative to Selectfluor (cf. *47*, 462s*49*) for the fluorination of a wide range of substrates (diketones, ketoesters, ketones, activated aromatics, styrenes, enolesters, and enoxysilanes). E: 0.5 eq. N,N'-Difluoro-2,2'-bipyridinium bis(fluoroborate) added under N$_2$ to a stirred soln. of 2-acetylcyclohexanone in acetonitrile, and refluxed for 3 h → 2-acetyl-2-fluorocyclohexanone. Y 71% (82% with 0.1 eq. added NaOTf). Both fluorine atoms of the reagent are available. F.e. and reagents s. T. Umemoto et al., J. Org. Chem. *63*, 3379-85 (1998).

*Ozone/sodium acetate/acetic acid*    O$_3$/NaOAc/AcOH
**Oxidative ar. bromination**    H → Br
with 30% aq. H$_2$O$_2$/HBr cf. *3*, 440; with O$_3$/HBr *in non-aq.* (buffered acetic) media s. World Intellectual Property Organization patent WO-9808785 (Hoechst Research & Technology Deut GMBH & Co.).

*Chiral N-fluorosultams*    ←
**Asym. α-fluorination of ketones**    H → F
with (S)-N-fluoro-N-(1-phenylethyl)-*p*-toluenesulfonamide cf. *47*, 435s*53*; with chiral N-fluorosultams s. F.A. Davis et al., J. Org. Chem. *63*, 2273-80 (1998).

*Sulfuric acid* $H_2SO_4$
**α-Bromination of ketones** H → Br
in concd. $H_2SO_4$ s. *13*, 215; aminoaryl dibromomethyl ketones, and partial debromination with $(EtO)_2P(O)H/Et_3N$ (cf. *48*, 68), s. Z. Diwu et al., Tetrahedron Lett. *39*, 4987-90 (1998).

*Sodium tungstate/hydrogen peroxide/potassium iodide/sulfuric acid* ←
**Biomimetic ar. halogenation** H → I
ar. bromination cf. *50*, 272s*51*; ar. monoiodination of carboxylic acid anilides with KI, also with Na-perborate as reoxidant, s. P. Beinker, J.R. Hanson et al., J. Chem. Res., Synop *1998*, 204-5.

*Tetra*-n-*butylammonium chloride* $Bu_4NCl$
**α,α′,β-Trihalogenoketones from ketones** H → Hal

185.

$Cl_2$ added (under the liquid surface) at a rate of 0.25 g/min to a mixture of 9.39 g 2-methylpentan-3-one and 2.52 g $Bu_4NCl$ under argon (exothermic to 60°), and heated at 60-70° with continued addition of $Cl_2$ for 2 h → 1,2,4-trichloro-2-methylpentan-3-one. Selectivity 96.9%. Impurities were <5% in most instances. F.e. and with $Pr_3N·HCl$ s. United States patent US-5703248 (J.S. Rommel).

*Pyridinium hydrobromide perbromide* $C_5H_5NHBr_3$
**Ar. bromination** H → Br
monobromination of ar. amines s. *48*, 447; of phenolethers in ether/AcOH/water, also dibromination in aq. AcOH, s. W.P. Reeves et al., Synth. Commun. *28*, 499-505 (1998).

*Manganese(III) acetoacetonate/alumina/sodium chlorite* ←
**α-Chloroketones from ketones** H → Cl
with $MnO_2/AcCl/AcOH$ cf. *31*, 163s*52*; $C_{21}$-chlorination of 20-oxosteroids s. P. Borah et al., J. Chem. Res., Synop *1998*, 236-7; with $Mn(acac)_3/NaClO_2$ and moist alumina s. S. Yakabe et al., Synth. Commun. *28*, 131-8 (1998).

*Manganese(III) acetoacetonate/sodium chlorite/sodium bromide/montmorillonite or silica* ←
***p*-Halogenation of phenolethers** H → Hal
*p*-chlorination with $Mn(acac)_3/NaClO_2/Al_2O_3$ cf. *54*, 192; *p*-bromination, incl. monobromination of polymethoxyarenes, with $Mn(acac)_3/NaClO_2/NaBr$ and moist silica gel s. M. Hirano, T. Morimoto et al., Synth. Commun. *28*, 1463-70 (1998); with moist montmorillonite K 10 cf. ibid. 669-76.

*Palladous acetate/lithium bromide/lithium acetate/p-benzoquinone/acetic acid* ←
**δ-Bromo-δ,ε-ethylene-γ-lactones from γ-allenecarboxylic acids** O
**Regio- and stereo-specific bromolactonization**

186.

A 0.55 *M* soln. of startg. allene in acetic acid added during 18 h to a stirred soln. of 5 mol% $Pd(OAc)_2$, 5 eqs. LiBr, 1.5 eqs. LiOAc, and 2.5 eqs. *p*-benzoquinone in the same solvent at 40°, and stirring continued for a further 48 h → product. Y 70% (76% Z-isomer). F.e. and method s. C. Jonasson, J.-E. Bäckvall, Tetrahedron Lett. *39*, 3601-4 (1998).

# Oxygen ↑ HalC ↓↑ O

*N,N-Diethyl-1,1,2,3,3,3-hexafluoropropylamine/triethylamine tris(hydrogen fluoride)* ←
**Replacement of hydroxyl groups by fluorine** OH → F
with DAST cf. *30*, 365s*52*; *31*, 501s*51*; benzyl fluorides with N,N-diethyl-1,1,2,3,3,3-hexafluoro-

propylamine/triethylamine tris(hydrogen fluoride) s. World Intellectual Property Organization patent WO-9732835 (Daikin Ind. Ltd.).

*Titanium tetraisopropoxide/isopropylmagnesium chloride*
**β,γ-Acetylenehalides from 2-acetylenephosphoric acid esters**
with chirality transfer s. *55*, 347

$Ti(OPr\text{-}i)_4/i\text{-}PrMgCl$
C≡C-C(Hal)

*Phosphorus oxide chloride/dimethylformamide/triethylamine*
**1-Chlorenamines from carboxylic acid amides**
via chlorimidium salts with COCl$_2$ cf. *25*, 398; with less toxic POCl$_3$/DMF/Et$_3$N, also 1-bromenamines with POBr$_3$, s. L. Ghosez et al., Tetrahedron *54*, 9207-22 (1998).

←
CHCON< → C≡C(Cl)N<

*Bismuth(III) chloride*
**Chlorides from alcohols**
with Me$_3$SiCl and 5 mol% BiCl$_3$ cf. *50*, 292; rapid and simple procedure from sec. and tert. alcohols with *1 eq*. BiCl$_3$ under heterogeneous conditions s. B. Boyer et al., Synth. Commun. *28*, 1737-41 (1998).

$BiCl_3$
OH → Cl

*Tellurium dioxide/trimethylsilyl chloride*
**Chlorides from alcohols**
with SeO$_2$/Me$_3$SiCl cf. *44*, 431; rapid, general procedure (except with tert. alcohols) with TeO$_2$ and Me$_3$SiCl (or MeSiCl$_3$ or SiCl$_4$) s. D.S. Ha, G.S. Chai, Bull. Korean Chem. Soc. *18*, 1045-7 (1997).

$TeO_2/Me_3SiCl$

## Nitrogen ↑      HalC ↓↑ N

*N-Iodosuccinimide*
**8-Iodochromans from 1-amino-7-γ-hydroxybenzotriazoles**
**Benzynes as intermediates**

NIS
C O

187.

A soln. of startg. benzotriazole in methylene chloride treated with N-iodosuccinimide at 20° for 30 min → product. Y 86%. There was no 7-membered ring formation. F.e., and **8-iodo-3-chromenes** from styryl analogs s. D.W. Knight, P.B. Little, Tetrahedron Lett. *39*, 5105-8 (1998).

*Nitrogen dioxide/sodium iodide*
**Ar. iodides from prim. ar. amines under mild, neutral, non-aq. conditions**

$NO_2/NaI$
NH$_2$ → I

188.

2.2 eqs. Liq. NO$_2$ introduced over 5 min into a stirred soln. of startg. aniline in acetonitrile at -20° (*caution:* use of a fume cupboard is imperative), 1.5 eqs. powdered NaI added in one portion (slight evolution of gas), and the mixture stirred for 10 min → product. Y 98%. The method is fast and particularly useful for less basic anilines possessing electron-withdrawing substituents. Significantly, the use of strong acids, such as H$_2$SO$_4$ or HCl (for classical diazotization), is not required. Aromatic chlorides, iodides, ethers, and nitro compds. remained unaffected. F.e.s. H. Suzuki, N. Nonoyama, Tetrahedron Lett. *39*, 4533-6 (1998).

*tert-Butyl nitrite/silicon tetrafluoride*
**Ar. halides from amines by aprotic diazotization**
with *t*-BuONO/CuHal$_2$ cf. *22*, 580s*32*; ar. fluorides with *t*-BuONO/SiF$_4$ for acid-sensitive substrates s. M. Tamura et al., Eur. J. Org. Chem. *1998*, 725-7; with KHF$_2$/SiF$_4$ cf. J. Fluorine Chem. *78*, 95-6 (1996).

*t-BuONO/SiF$_4$*
ArNH$_2$ → ArF

## Halogen ↑          HalC ↓↑ Hal

*Potassium fluoride/18-crown-6 polyether*      *KF/crown*
**Replacement of chlorine by fluorine in a perfluorocarbon medium**     Cl → F

189.

Perfluoroperhydrophenanthrene (b.p. 215°) serves as a useful 'bulking agent' to minimize the problem of solvent recovery in halogen exchange. E: A mixture of pentachloropyridine, 8 eqs. KF, 10 mol% 18-crown-6, and perfluoroperhydrophenanthrene heated at 190° with stirring for 4 h, cooled, filtered, and the fluorocarbon layer extracted with toluene → 3,5-dichloro-2,4,6-trifluoropyridine. Y 65%. The inert, non-hazardous, fluorocarbon can be readily recovered and recycled. Furthermore, less solvent is required by comparison with earlier procedures, and the method is suitable for large-scale conversions. F.e. and methods s. R.D. Chambers, A.R. Edwards, J. Chem. Soc. Perkin Trans. 1 *1997*, 3623-7.

*Fluoride ion*                   $F^-$
**Replacement of ar. chlorine by fluorine**
with KF cf. *12*, 619; large-scale procedure in non-toxic phosphol-ane or -ene oxides with various fluoride ion sources, also replacement of ar. bromine, s. German patent DE-19608791 (Hoechst AG); halogen-exchange with polyacrylate-supported HF, as a safe, easy-to-handle, storable source of fluoride ion s. World Intellectual Property Organization patent WO-9732907 (Allied-Signal Inc.).

## Sulfur ↑          HalC ↓↑ S

*Lithium bromide/sulfuric acid*      $LiBr/H_2SO_4$
**Epoxides from cyclic glycol sulfates via regiospecific formation of 1,2-bromhydrins**
**Retention of configuration**

190.

**Chiral glycidic acid esters.** Anhydrous LiBr added to a soln. of startg. cyclic glycol sulfate (obtained in two steps from ethyl (2R,3R)-2,3-dihydroxyoctadecanoate) in dry THF, the mixture stirred under $N_2$ until reaction complete, solvent removed *in vacuo*, ether and 20% aq. $H_2SO_4$ added to the residue, and the mixture stirred vigorously for 4 h 5 crude intermediate bromohydrin, in methanol treated with anhydrous $K_2CO_3$, the mixture stirred at -23° under $N_2$ for 3.5-4 h, then quenched sequentially with satd. aq. $NH_4Cl$ and water 5 product. Y 93% (e.e. 97%). Reaction takes place with overall retention of configuration. The method is simple, mild, high-yielding, and compatible with acid-sensitive functions such as PMP- and TBDPS-ethers. F.e. incl. 2,3-epoxy-4-siloxyethers s. L. He et al., Tetrahedron Lett. *39*, 2071-4 (1998).

## Remaining Elements ↑          HalC ↓↑ Rem

*Without additional reagents*         *w.a.r.*
**α-Fluoroketones from enoxysilanes** s. *46*, 456s55     C=C(OSi≤) → C(F)CO

*N-Halogenosuccinimides*  *NIS or NBS*
**Ar. halides from arylboronic acids under mild conditions**  $B(OH)_2 \rightarrow Hal$

191.   Br—⟨C₆H₄⟩—B(OH)₂  →(NIS)  Br—⟨C₆H₄⟩—I

**Ar. iodides.** 1.5 eqs. NIS added to a soln. of *p*-bromophenylboronic acid in acetonitrile, and the mixture stirred at 81° for 6 h protected from air and light → *p*-(bromo)iodobenzene. Y 88%. The method avoids the use of highly reactive halogens, strong oxidizing agents or toxic heavy metals. Chlorine, bromine and methoxy, formyl, vinyl or methyl groups on the aromatic ring remained unaffected, but yields were low from 3-nitrophenylboronic acid. F.e. incl. iodothiophenes, also with NaI/NCS, and ar. bromides with NBS, s. C. Thiebes et al., Synlett *1998*, 141-2.

## Carbon ↑  HalC ↓↑ C

*Without additional reagents*  *w.a.r.*
**α-Fluoroketones from enolesters**  $C=C(OAc) \rightarrow C(F)CO$
with 1-fluoro-1,4-diazoniabicyclo[2.2.2]octanes cf. *47*, 462; with $F_2/N_2$ (1:9) in dry acetonitrile, also from enoxysilanes (cf. *46*, 456) s. World Intellectual Property Organization patent WO-9746508 (F2 Chem. Ltd.).

*Samarium diiodide/air*  $SmI_2/air$
**4-Iodobutyl glycosides from trichloroacetimidoyl glycosides**  ←

192.  [reaction scheme showing glucopyranosyl trichloroacetimidate converting via SmI₂/O₂ through oxocarbenium intermediates to 4-iodobutyl glycoside]

**Stereospecific conversion** A soln. of tetra-O-acetyl-α-D-glucopyranosyl trichloroacetimidate and 2 eqs. methanol in THF treated with 1 eq. '$(SmI_2)_2O$' (obtained by air oxidation of $SmI_2$) at room temp. for 5 h → product. Y 85%. The stereochemistry is explained by the neighbouring group participation of the $O^2$-acetyl group with the developing oxocarbenium ion. The mannosyl analog, however, gave predominantly the corresponding α-glycosyl iodide. The products are considered as potential building blocks for the preparation of glycoconjugates. F.e.s. M. Adinolfi, A. Iadonisi et al., Tetrahedron Lett. *39*, 5605-8 (1998).

# Formation of S-S Bond

## Exchange  ↓↑

## Hydrogen ↑  SS ↓↑ H

*Cupric nitrate*  $Cu(NO_3)_2$
*Cupric nitrate·dinitrogen tetroxide*  $Cu(NO_3)_2·N_2O_4$
**Sym. disulfides from mercaptans**  $2\,RSH \rightarrow RSSR$
with $Fe(NO_3)_3$-clay cf. *4*, 274s38; with $Cu(NO_3)_2·3H_2O$ s. H. Firouzabadi et al., Synth. Commun. *28*, 1179-87 (1998); with $Cu(NO_3)_2·N_2O_4$ cf. ibid. 367-75.

*Enzymes*  ←
**Sym. disulfides from mercaptans**
with yeast cf. *47*, 468; general method with horseradish peroxidase or mushroom tyrosinase s. M. Sridhar et al., Synth. Commun. *28*, 1499-502 (1998).

*Bis(tetra-n-butylammonium) hexasulfide* $(Bu_4N)_2S_6$
**Cyclic polysulfides from mercaptans**
with $H_2S/NH_3$ cf. *22*, 587s*44*; cyclic peptide derivs. with bis(tetra-*n*-butylammonium) hexasulfide s. D.A. Erlanson, J.A. Wells, Tetrahedron Lett. *39*, 6799-802 (1998).

# Formation of S-Rem Bond

## Uptake ⇓

## Addition to Remaining Elements SRem ⇓ Rem

*Bis(thionocarbethoxy) tetrasulfide* $EtOC(S)SSSSC(S)OEt$
**Thionophosphoric acid esters and diesters by P-thionation** ⪈P → ⪈PS
oligonucleoside thionophosphates with dibenzoyl tetrasulfide cf. *45,* 303s*47-50*; solid-phase procedure with bis(thionocarbethoxy) tetrasulfide s. Z. Zhang et al., Tetrahedron Lett. *39*, 2467-70 (1998); f. details s. World Intellectual Property Organization patent WO-9808809 (Hybridon Inc.); 2′-deoxyribonucleoside phosphorodithioates, method s. A. Okruszek et al., J. Org. Chem. *62*, 2269-72 (1997).

# Formation of S-C Bond

## Uptake ⇓

## Addition to Hydrogen and Carbon SC ⇓ HC

*Dimethylformamide* $Me_2NCHO$
**α-Sulfonation of carboxylic acid esters** H → $SO_3H$
in $CCl_4$ cf. *23*, 577; with added Lewis base, e.g. DMF, or inorganic sulfur compds. s. Japanese patents JP-09216861, JP-09216862, JP-09216863 (Lion Corp.).

## Addition to Oxygen and Carbon SC ⇓ OC

*Microwaves s. under NaOH* ←

*Sodium hydroxide/polyethylene glycol/microwaves* ←
**2-Hydroxythioethers from epoxides** ▽$_O$ → C(OH)C(SR)
with Na⁺ cf. *2*, 532; phase transfer catalysis with NaOH/polyethylene glycol under microwave irradiation s. J.-X. Wang et al., J. Chem. Res., Synop *1998*, 216-7.

*Sodium salt/polysorbate-80* ←
**β-Hydroxysulfones from epoxides** ▽$_O$ → $C(OH)C(SO_2R)$
with PEG 4000 as phase transfer catalyst cf. *50*, 302; with polysorbate-80 s. Indian J. Chem. *35B*, 67-8 (1996).

*1,8-Diazabicyclo[5.4.0]undec-7-ene*                                           *DBU*
**2-Siloxymercaptans from epoxides**                      $\triangledown_O \rightarrow C(OSi\leqslant)C(SH)$
**Regiospecific ring opening**

193.

Styrene oxide added dropwise to an equimolar mixture of triisopropylsilanethiol and DBU in dry THF at 25° under $N_2$, and stirred for 12 h → product. Y 85%. The method is operationally simple with excellent regioselectivity, the (R)-substrate reacting **with retention of chirality**. Use of toxic and unpleasant $H_2S$ is avoided. F.e. incl. ring opening of disubst. epoxides, and desilylation s. J.C. Justo de Pomar, J.A. Soderquist, Tetrahedron Lett. *39*, 4409-12 (1998).

*Samarium diiodide*                                                             $SmI_2$
**2-Hydroxythioethers from epoxides** s. *50*, 335s55            $\triangledown_O \rightarrow C(OH)C(SAr)$

## Addition to Carbon-Carbon Bonds          SC ⇓ CC

*Without additional reagents*                                    *w.a.r.*
**Regio- and stereo-specific hetero-Diels-Alder reaction**
**with** *in situ***-generated α-iminosulfines**

194.

**4-Acoxy-3,4-dihydro-2*H*-1,4-thiazine 1-oxides.** A soln. of startg. sulfine precursor and 2 eqs. startg. *electron-rich* alkene in chloroform heated at 60° for 9 h → product. Y 55% (*cis/trans* >98:2). There was no relationship between the geometry of the startg. sulfoxide and that of the product. F.e.s. G. Capozzi, S. Menichetti et al., Synthesis *1998*, 915-8.

*Irradiation s. under PhSeSePh*                                  ⫽

*Ammonium ceric nitrate/ammonium thiocyanate*     $(NH_4)_2Ce(NO_3)_6/NH_4SCN$
**1,2-Di(thiocyanates) from ethylene derivs.**             C═C → C(SCN)C(SCN)
with $Br_2/Pb(SCN)_2$ cf. *18*, 647; more cleanly with $(NH_4)_2Ce(NO_3)_6/NH_4SCN$ s. V. Nair, L.G. Nair, Tetrahedron Lett. *39*, 4585-6 (1998); with $PhI(OAc)_2/Me_3SiNCS$ s. M. Bruno et al., ibid. 3847-8.

*Lanthanum(III) trisodium tris[(R)-1,1'-bi-2-naphthoxide]*                  ←
**Catalytic asym. Michael addition of mercaptans to α,β-ethyleneketones**    C═C → CHC(SR)

195.

A soln. of startg. enone in 60:1 toluene/THF treated with 1 eq. 4-*tert*-butylthiophenol and 10 mol% lanthanum(III) trisodium tris[(R)-1,1'-bi-2-naphthoxide] at -40° for 20 min → adduct. Y

93% (e.e. 84%). This is the most efficient catalytic asym. Michael addition of a mercaptan to a cyclic enone yet reported. The Na-naphthoxide residue functions as a Bronsted base to activate the thiol, and the central metal functions as a Lewis acid to control the face selectivity as well as activating the carbonyl group. F.e. incl. addition of benzyl mercaptans s. E. Emori, M. Shibasaki et al., J. Am. Chem. Soc. *120*, 4043-4 (1998).

**Catalytic asym. Michael addition of mercaptans to α,β-ethylenethiolic acid esters** CHC(SR)

196.

**via asym. protonation.** A soln. of startg. thiolic acid ester (0.5 mmol scale) in methylene chloride treated with 4-*tert*-butylthiophenol and 20 mol% lanthanum(III) trisodium tris[(R)-1,1'-bi-2-naphthoxide] at -78° for 2 h → product. Y 93% (e.e. 90%). High levels of enantioselectivity are a consequence of the highly efficient catalytic asym. protonation of the intermediate enolate by an *acidic* (phenolic) form of the chiral complex, produced in a catalytic cycle by initial deprotonation of the mercaptan by one of the Na-binolate residues (the central metal functioning as a Lewis acid to activate the carbonyl group). Enantioselectivity was lower from the corresponding enoates. F.e. and with the Sm(III) complex, also large-scale procedure (1 g level) with 2 mol% catalyst, s. E. Emori, M. Shibasaki et al., J. Am. Chem. Soc. *120*, 4043-4 (1998).

*Sultenes/trifluoroacetic acid*
**Thiiranes from ethylene derivs. by sulfur atom transfer with sultenes**

197.

A soln. of 5 eqs. norbornene and startg. sultene (prepared by refluxing fluorenethione S-oxide and *trans*-cyclooctene in deuteriochloroform containing $K_2CO_3$ for 16 h) in deuteriochloroform allowed to react at 20° for 30 min in the presence of a little trifluoroacetic acid → product. Y >95% by $^1$H NMR (based on 85% conversion). The stereochemistry of the olefin is retained (*trans*-cyclooctene giving the *trans*-fused thiirane). The sulfur transfer is thought to occur via initial attack of the olefin on the protonated sultene to give a hydroxythiiranium ion, which expels the thiirane on formation of the oxetane ring. However, reaction failed with less reactive olefins, e.g. cyclohexene. Interestingly, the preparation of the reagent illustrates the first example of a sulfine reacting as a 1,3-dipole with a carbon-carbon multiple bond. F.e.s. W. Adam, S. Weinkötz, J. Am. Chem. Soc. *120*, 4861-2 (1998).

*Diphenyl diselenide/irradiation*  PhSeSePh/⊕
**2,3-Ene-1,4-di(thioethers) from 1,3-dienes** s. *47*, 568s55  PhS-C-C=C-C-SPh

*Phenyl iodosoacetate/trimethylsilyl isothiocyanate*  $PhI(OAc)_2/Me_3SiNCS$
**1,2-Di(thiocyanates) from ethylene derivs.** s. *18*, 647s55  C=C → C(SCN)C(SCN)

*Titanium tetrachloride/zinc*                           $TiCl_4/Zn$
**β-(Arylthio)carboxylic**                       C=C → CHC(SAr)
**from α,β-ethylenecarboxylic acid esters and arenesulfonyl chlorides**

198.        $PhSO_2Cl$ + $CH_2$=CHCOOMe  ⟶  $PhSCH_2CH_2COOMe$

A mixture of 4 eqs. Zn-dust and 2 eqs. $TiCl_4$ in THF refluxed under argon for 2 h, cooled to room temp., a soln. of benzenesulfonyl chloride and 1.5 eqs. methyl acrylate in THF added dropwise over 30 min, stirred at 50° for 20 h, cooled to room temp., then quenched with 10% HCl → product. Y 91%. The method avoids the use of foul-smelling mercaptans and the generation of thiolates in basic media. F.e.s. D. Shi et al., Synth. Commun. *28*, 1073-8 (1998).

*Trifluoromethanesulfonic anhydride*                    $(CF_3SO_2)_2O$
**1,2-Di(sulfonium salts) from ethylene derivs.**        C=C → C(S⁺R$_2$)C(S⁺R$_2$)

199.

**Stereospecific conversion.** Trifluoromethanesulfonic anhydride added to a well-stirred soln. of 1 eq. dimethyl sulfoxide in methylene chloride at -40°, 1 eq. dimethyl sulfide in the same anhydrous solvent added dropwise, allowed to warm to -20°, a soln. of 1 eq. indene in the same solvent added dropwise, and worked up when TLC indicated completion of reaction (1-5 h) → *trans*-[1-(dimethylsulfonio)-2,3-dihydro-1*H*-inden-2-yl](dimethyl)sulfonium bistrifluoromethanesulfonate. Y 85%. Reaction is limited to aryl-conjugated ethylene derivs. F.e. and **2-ene-1,4-di(sulfonium salts)** from 1,3-dienes s. V.G. Nenajdenko et al., Tetrahedron *54*, 5353-62 (1998).

*Acetonitrile(pentacarbonyl)tungsten*                    $W(CO)_5(MeCN)$
**3,6-Dihydro-1,2-dithiins from 2-vinylthiiranes**

200.

A soln. of startg. vinylthiirane and a little $W(CO)_5(MeCN)$ in dideuteriodichloromethane shaken in an NMR tube (with $C_6Me_6$ as internal standard) at 25° for 24 h → product. Y 82% (catalytic turnover 15/h). A methyl group on the vinyl function increases the reaction rate, but substitution of the thiirane ring has the reverse effect. An intermediate thiirane-$W(CO)_5$ complex is thought to be involved. F.e.s. R.D. Adams et al., J. Am. Chem. Soc. *120*, 1922-3 (1998).

*Cobalt(II) Schiff base complex/phenylsilane*                ←
**Thioethers from ethylene derivs.**               C=C → CHC(SR)
radical addition cf. *41*, 546; *anti*-Michael addition to α-methylenecarbonyl compds. via hydrocobaltation with a cobalt(II) Schiff base complex/$PhSiH_3$ s. C.L. Friend, N.S. Simpkins et al., Tetrahedron *54*, 2801-8 (1998).

---

# Rearrangement                             ∩

# Hydrogen/Carbon Type              SC ∩ HC

*Tetra-n-butylammonium fluoride*                          $Bu_4NF$
**1,2-Migration of sulfonyl groups**                         ←
2-azulenyl sulfones with 96% $H_2SO_4$ cf. *16*, 644s*32*; 1,2-disulfonylcyclopropanes with $Bu_4NF$ s. M. Yoshimatsu et al., Tetrahedron Lett. *39*, 1781-2 (1998).

## Oxygen/Sulfur Type   SC ∩ OS

*Palladous acetate/1,6-bis(diphenylphosphino)hexane*   $Pd(OAc)_2/dpph$
α-**Allenesulfones from terminal sulfinyloxy-2-acetylenes**   $C{=}C{=}C(SO_2R)$
**with asym. induction**

201.

Startg. chiral sulfinate (e.e. 87%) and 0.075 eq. 1,6-bis(diphenylphosphino)hexane in THF treated with 0.05 eq. Pd(OAc)$_2$ at room temp. for 18 h → (S)-product. Y 74% (stereospecificity 80%). This is the first example of the synthesis of chiral allenes from propargyl alcohol derivs. bearing chiral leaving groups. The presence of a phosphine ligand improved asym. induction, 1,6-bis(diphenylphosphino)hexane being the most effective. The reaction is believed to proceed via coordination of both the acetylene group and the sulfinate S-atom to the Pd-atom leading to formation of a σ-allenylpalladium complex, followed by intramolecular sulfonylation with retention of configuration. F.e.s. K. Hiroi et al., Chem. Lett. *1998*, 553-4.

## Exchange   ↕

### Hydrogen ↑   SC ↕ H

*Sulfur/hydrogen bromide*   $S_8$/HBr
**2-Mercaptobenzothiazoles from ar. amines**   ○
from dimethylaniline with S$_8$ cf. *8*, 656; from prim. ar. amines with S$_8$/CS$_2$/HBr s. World Intellectual Property Organization patent WO-9746544 (Akzo Nobel NV).

*12-Tungstophosphoric acid/phosphoric acid*   ←
**Sym. diaryl sulfones from arenes**   $2\,ArH \to Ar_2SO_2$
with SbF$_5$/HSO$_3$F cf. *48*, 489; rapidly and economically with 12-tungstophosphoric acid/phosphoric acid s. Japanese patent JP-10017542 (New Japan Chem. Co. Ltd.).

### Oxygen ↑   SC ↕ O

*Microwaves s. under Ca(OCl)$_2$*   ←

*Kaolinitic clay*   ←
**Reactions of mercaptans on kaolinic clay**   ←

202.

β-**Ketothiolic from** β-**ketocarboxylic acid esters.** A mixture of startg. β-ketoester, 1.1 eqs. 4-chlorobenzenethiol, and 20% (w/w) natural kaolinitic clay (from Kerala, India) in toluene refluxed for 6 h under Dean-Stark conditions → product. Y 75%. This is the first report of catalytic transthiolesterification of β-ketoesters. With dithiols the keto group reacted selectively to give the corresponding cyclic mercaptal, while diols gave the hydroxyalkyl ester. The success of the reaction was attributed to the formation of a stable enolate complex with surface aluminum ions which activate the acyl oxygen bond towards attack by the incoming nucleophile. F.e. and preferential transesterification s. D.E. Ponde et al., J. Org. Chem. *63*, 1058-63 (1998); **cyclic mercaptals from acetals** (with retention of keto groups) and from oximes, tosylhydrazones and enamines s. G.K. Jnaneshwara et al., J. Chem. Soc. Perkin Trans. I *1998*, 965-8.

*Boron fluoride* $BF_3$
**Thioglycosides from acyl glycosides** OAc → SR
with $ZnCl_2$ cf. *20*, 447; phenyl β-thioglycosides with $BF_3$-etherate s. United States patent US-5693770 (Transcell Technologies Inc.).

*Trifluoroacetic acid* $CF_3COOH$
**Unsym. mercaptals from aldehydes** CHO → CH(SR)(SR')

203.

Trifluoroacetic acid (1 ml/mmol aldehyde; 1 part) added to a suspension of *p*-chlorobenzaldehyde, 1.1 eqs. benzyl mercaptan, and 2 eqs. 4-mercaptopyridine in 1,2-dichloroethane (4 parts) at 0°, the mixture allowed to warm to room temp., and stirred at 25° for 16 h before being poured slowly into vigorously stirred ice-cold 10% aq. $NaHCO_3$ → 4-[[(4-chlorophenyl)[(phenylmethyl)-thio]methyl]thio]pyridine. Y 81%. The nature of the aldehyde and the solvent does not appear to affect the yield; however, the condensation may be faster and the yield higher when a strong Lewis acid (e.g. $BF_3$-etherate) is used as catalyst (with or without TFA as co-solvent/co-catalyst). If the mixture is not allowed to warm to room temp. but is quenched at 0°, even after a few hours, the major product is the kinetically favoured dibenzyl dithioacetal. F.e.s. J.Y. Gauthier et al., Synlett *1998*, 289-91.

*2,4-Bis(p-methoxyphenyl)-1,3,2,4-dithiadiphosphetane-2,4-disulfide* ←
**3,6-Dihydro-2H-1,3,4-thiadiazines from thioketones** ○
s. *37*, 507; f. method from α-diketone monohydrazones with 2,4-bis(*p*-methoxyphenyl)-1,3,2,4-dithiadiphosphetane-2,4-disulfide cf. J.-D. Charrier et al., Tetrahedron:Asym. *9*, 1531-7 (1998).

*Tungsten hexachloride* $WCl_6$
**Cyclic mercaptals from acetals under mild conditions** $C(OMe)_2 → C(SR)_2$

204.

4 Mol% $WCl_6$ added to a soln. of startg. acetal and 1.1 eqs. ethanedithiol in dry dichloromethane at 0-5°, and stirred for 2 h → product. Y 96%. Under these conditions, functional groups such as alkenes, esters and *tert*-butyldimethylsilyl ethers were tolerated. The method is mild, high-yielding, and is applicable to the chemoselective formation of cyclic mercaptals **from oxo compds.** (aldehydes reacting faster than ketones, and cyclic ketones faster than methyl ketones, while aryl ketones remained inert). F.e.s. H. Firouzabadi et al., Synlett *1998*, 739-40.

*Calcium hypochlorite/alumina/microwaves* ←
**Benzothiazoles from *o*-aminomercaptans** ○
under microwave irradiation on a solid support without solvent s. *55*, 151

*Ruthenium trichloride/ammonium thiocyanate* $RuCl_3/NH_4SCN$
**Thiiranes from epoxides**

205.

**with inversion of configuration.** 2 Mol% anhydrous $RuCl_3$ added to a mixture of (R)-styrene oxide and 3 eqs. $NH_4SCN$ in acetonitrile at 0°, and stirred until reaction complete → (S)-styrene sulfide. Y 93% (optical purity 78%). The procedure is convenient, simple, relatively short and mild, and can be performed with a wide range of epoxides. F.e. from racemic substrates s. N. Iranpoor, F. Kazemi, Tetrahedron *53*, 11377-82 (1997).

## Nitrogen ↑      SC ↓↑ N

*Potassium salt*      $K^+$
**Displacement of nitrogen from diazonium fluoroborates with S-nucleophiles**      $N_2^+ \to S-$
xanthates cf. *43*, 498; S-aryl O,O-dialkyl dithiophosphates s. B.D. Grishchuk et al., Khim. Farm. Zh. *32*, No.5, 33-4 (1998) (Russ.).

*Magnesium*      *Mg*
**Asym. synthesis of N-tosylsulfilimines from Grignard compds.**      $RMgBr \to RS(=NTs)R'$

206.

Startg. (4S)-4-benzyl-2-oxazolidone (enantiopure) treated with 2 eqs. phenylmagnesium bromide in THF at -78° for 1 h → product. Y 91% (e.e. 94%). The startg. sulfilimines were prepared from the corresponding 3-alkylthio-2-oxazolidones by reaction with Chloramine-T in the presence of a little hexadecyltributylphosphonium bromide. The displacement reaction occurred with good chemical yields even with bulky reagents such as cyclohexyl- or 2-naphthyl-magnesium bromide; however, there was no reaction with *tert*-butylmagnesium bromide, even using a 4-fold excess and for longer reaction time (8 h at 25°). There was no racemization of the recovered chiral auxiliary. F.e. and enantiomers s. G. Celentano, N. Gaggero et al., Chem. Commun. *1998*, 701-2.

*Kaolinitic clay*      ←
**Cyclic mercaptals from oximes, tosylhydrazones or enamines** s. *55*, 202      $C(SR)_2$

## Halogen ↑      SC ↓↑ Hal

*Potassium hydroxide/hydrazine*      $KOH/N_2H_4$
**Thioethers from mercaptans and halides**      $Hal \to SR$

207.

BuSH —KOH→ [ BuSK ] —MeI→ BuSMe

EtSSEt ···KOH···► [ EtSK ] ···$BrCH_2CH=CH_2$···► $EtSCH_2CH=CH_2$ (97%)

**under mild conditions.** 1 eq. Startg. mercaptan added gradually to a stirred soln. of KOH *in hydrazine hydrate,* cooled to room temp., methyl iodide added dropwise, stirred for a further 1 h, and worked up → product. Y 82%. Hydrazine hydrate serves as both medium and reductant. The products are easily separated, and there was no oxidation of the mercaptan to the disulfide (an inert atmosphere not being required). F.e., **also from disulfides** with 2 eqs. KOH or via isothiouronium salts, s. E.N. Deryagina et al., Zh. Obshch. Khim. *67*, 866-9 (1997) (Russ.).

*Lithium bis(trimethylsilyl)amide*      $LiN(SiMe_3)_2$
**Sulfones from sulfonic acid fluorides**      $SO_2F \to SO_2R$
s. *34*, 547s*49*; α-sulfonylation of phosphonic acid esters with $LiN(SiMe_3)_2$ as base, also one-pot preparation of α,β-ethylenesulfones, s. W.B. Jang et al., Synth. Commun. *28*, 1253-6 (1998).

*Potassium thiocyanate*      KSCN
**2-Aminothiazoles from 2-ketothiocyanates**      ○
s. *9*, 408; one-pot procedure from α-halogenoketones and prim. amines s. J.G. Schantl, I.M. Lagoja, Synth. Commun. *28*, 1451-62 (1998).

*Amberlyst A 26*      ←
**Sym. acyl disulfides from carboxylic acid chlorides**      $2\,RCOCl \to RCOSSCOR$
with $Na_2S_2$/polyethylene glycol-400 cf. *5*, 452s*51*; with $S_8$/Amberlyst A 26 (OH⁻ form) in dry benzene s. B. Tamami, A.R. Kiasat, Synth. Commun. *28*, 1275-80 (1998).

*Thioureas/triethylamine*      $(>\!N)_2CS/Et_3N$
**Isothiocyanates from hydroximinochlorides**      $RC(Cl)\!=\!NOH \rightarrow RN\!=\!C\!=\!S$

208.

The Dondoni isothiocyanate synthesis from nitrile oxides (*28*, 527) has been adapted in one pot from the precursor hydroximinochlorides and thioureas *without* isolation of the unstable intermediate 1,4,2-oxathiazoles. **E:** 1 eq. Et$_3$N in THF added dropwise at room temp. to a stirred mixture of 1 eq. startg. hydroximinochloride and 1 eq. startg. thiourea in the same solvent, and worked up after <30 min → 2,6-dichlorophenyl isothiocyanate (Y 86%) and N-phenyl-N′-(2,6-dichlorophenyl)urea. F.e.s. K.S. Jung, J.N. Kim et al., Synth. Commun. *28*, 1879-84 (1998).

*Hydrazine s. under KOH*      $N_2H_4$

*Trimethyl phosphite/triethylamine*      $(MeO)_3P/Et_3N$
**Trihalogenomethyl sulfones from alcohols**      $OH \rightarrow SO_2CHal_3$

209.

**Trichloromethyl sulfones.** Equivalent amounts of Et$_3$N and trimethyl phosphite added gradually and simultaneously via syringe to equivalent amounts of startg. alcohol and trichloromethanesulfonyl chloride in dry methylene chloride *at -20°* (cf. *42*, 87), stirred for 15 min, the cooling bath removed, and stirring continued at room temp. for 30 min → 9-fluorenyl trichloromethyl sulfone. Y 88%. Excess of phosphite must be avoided in order to prevent decomposition of the intermediate ester. Aliphatic prim. alcohols failed to react. F.e. incl. a benzyl triflone s. S. Braverman, Y. Zafrani, Tetrahedron *54*, 1901-12 (1998).

*Activated nickel*      Ni
**Sulfones from sulfonic acid chlorides and halides**      $SO_2Cl \rightarrow SO_2R$

210.      p-MeC$_6$H$_4$SO$_2$Cl    +    BrBn    ⟶    p-MeC$_6$H$_4$SO$_2$Bn

**Aryl benzyl sulfones.** A suspension of 2 eqs. potassium in dry toluene sonicated at room temp. for 5 min under N$_2$, 1 eq. anhydrous NiCl$_2$ added, sonication continued for a further 0.5 h, the black slurry quenched with ethanol, volatiles removed, 1.1 eqs. *p*-toluenesulfonyl chloride in DMF added, stirred for 0.5 h, warmed to 90°, benzyl bromide added dropwise, and kept at the same temp. for 1.5 h → benzyl *p*-tolyl sulfone. Y 76%. The method is mild, short, and clean. F.e. incl. allyl benzyl sulfones s. H. Li, Y. Shi et al., Synth. Commun. *28*, 409-15 (1998).

*Tris(dibenzylideneacetone)dipalladium/1,1′-bis(diphenylphosphino)ferrocene/*      ←
*ethyldiisopropylamine*
**Polymer-based synthesis of ar. thioethers**      $ArI \rightarrow ArSR$
**from ar. iodides and mercaptans**

211.

Dimethylacetamide, 0.8 eq. dppf, 0.2 eq. Pd$_2$(dba)$_3$, and 8 eqs. *i*-Pr$_2$NEt added to startg. resin-supported iodide, the suspension degassed for 20 min, 4 eqs. 3-phenylpropyl mercaptan added, shaken for 24 h at 60°, the resin removed, washed, and dried, suspended in dioxane, treated with 6 eqs. methanolic NaOMe, and shaken for 24 h at room temp. → product. Y 96%. F.e. and polymer-based Suzuki and Stille coupling s. S. Wendeborn, A. De Mesmaeker et al., Synlett *1998*, 671-5.

## Sulfur ↑         SC ↓↑ S

*Microwaves s. under K⁺*      ←

*Potassium hydroxide/hydrazine*      $KOH/N_2H_4$
**Thioethers from disulfides and halides** s. *55*, 207      RSSR → RSR′

*Potassium salt/microwaves*      ←
**Ar. trifluoromethyl thioethers from diaryl disulfides**      ArSSAr → ArSCF$_3$
and CF$_3$COOK s. *41*, 748s52; under microwave enhancement, and further nucleophilic polyfluoroalkylations, s. French patent FR-2751959 (Rhone-Poulenc Chim.); preparation of CF$_3$S(O)OH from SO$_2$ s. FR-2751961.

*Indium/sodium salt or Samarium/sodium salt*      In/Na⁺ or Sm/Na⁺
**2-Ketothioethers from α-bromoketones and thiosulfuric acid S-monoesters**   SSO$_3$Na → SR

212.     PhCH$_2$SSO$_2$ONa   +   BrCH$_2$COPh   ⟶   PhCH$_2$SCH$_2$COPh

**in aq. media.** A mixture of startg. thiosulfate, 1.25 eqs. α-bromoacetophenone, and 1 eq. In (cut in small grains) in 20:1 THF/water stirred at room temp. for 2 h, then under slight reflux until the soln. became turbid (18 h) → product. Y 80%. There was no disulfide formation. The procedure is mild, simple, moderate-to-good yielding, and based on inexpensive substrates. F.e.s. Z. Zhan et al., J. Chem. Res., Synop *1998*, 130-1; **allyl thioethers** from allyl bromide with Sm s. ibid. 148-9; with In cf. Synth. Commun. *28*, 493-7 (1998).

## Carbon ↑         SC ↓↑ C

*Potassium* tert-*butoxide*      KOBu-t
**2-Aminothioethers from 2-oxazolidones and mercaptans**      C
**Regiospecific conversion**

213.

**with retention of chirality.** A soln. of startg. chiral 2-oxazolidone, 2 eqs. thiophenol, and 1 eq. KOBu-*t* in *tert*-butanol refluxed until reaction complete (typically 6 h) → product. Y 89%. 2-Oxazolidones are useful alternatives to more toxic aziridines (cf. *8*, 643). F.e., **also 5,6-dihydro-4H-1,4-thiazin-3(2H)-ones** with ethyl thioglycolate in refluxing PrOH/PrONa, s. H. Ishibashi et al., Synlett *1997*, 915-6.

*Samarium diiodide*      SmI$_2$
**Generation and reactions of samarium(III) arylmercaptides from ar. thiocyanates**    ←
ar. thioethers cf. *50*, 335; 2-hydroxythioethers from epoxides, regioselectivity, s. Synth. Commun. *28*, 913-23 (1998).

## Elimination ⇑

### Oxygen ↑     SC ⇑ O

*Calcium chloride/triethylamine*     $CaCl_2/Et_3N$
**Δ³-Cephems from 4-disulfido-2-azetidinones**
s. *39*, 545; 3-organothio-Δ³-cephems from 1-(2-triflyloxyvinyl)-2-azetidinon-4-yl disulfides, and 3-functionalized Δ³-cephems from 4-sulfonylthio derivs. (cf. *31*, 576s*48*), s. H. Tanaka, S. Torii et al., Bull. Chem. Soc. Japan *69*, 3651-8 (1996); details s. J. Org. Chem. *62*, 3610-7 (1997).

p-*Toluenesulfonyl chloride/pyridine*     $TsCl/C_5H_5N$
**4-Ethylene-3-hydroxythioethers from 2,4-dihydroxythioethers**     ←
with 1,4-arylthio group migration s. *55*, 214

### Remaining Elements ↑     SC ⇑ Rem

*Sodium tetrahydridoborate*     $NaBH_4$
**Thiiranes from α-(phosphorylthio)ketones**     COC-SPO(OR)₂ → ▽ₛ
*in situ*-preparation s. *47*, 981; isolation of thiiranes, also one-pot conversion from enoxysilanes, and subsequent desulfurization to ethylene derivs. s. Synthesis *1997*, 1134-6.

### Carbon ↑     SC ⇑ C

p-*Toluenesulfonyl chloride/pyridine*     $TsCl/C_5H_5N$
**3-Hydroxytetrahydrothiophenes from 2,4-dihydroxythioethers**

214.

Startg. benzyl *anti,anti*-dihydroxythioether treated with TsCl in pyridine, followed by aq. HCl work-up → product. Y 93% (100% *anti,syn*-selectivity). The reaction occurs with **retention of configuration** at three stereogenic centres, and is insensitive to the substitution at the thioether centre and to the developing stereochemistry within the sulfonium salt. In the case of *alkyl* thioether derivs. **4-ethylene-3-hydroxythioethers** were formed in quantitative yield with 1,4-alkylthio group migration. F.e. incl. sec. and prim. benzyl thioether derivs. s. J. Eames, S. Warren et al., Tetrahedron Lett. *39*, 1247-50 (1998); ar. 4-ethylene-3-hydroxythioethers with 1,4-arylthio group migration s. ibid. *37*, 1117-20 (1996).

# Formation of Rem-Rem Bond

## Exchange ⇕

### Carbon ↑     RemRem ⇕ C

*Samarium diiodide*     $SmI_2$
**Sym. diselenides from selenocyanates**     2 RSeCN → (RSe)₂
with NaBH₄ cf. *22*, 655s*53*; with SmI₂, sym. dioxodiselenides and selectivity, s. P. Salama, C. Bernard, Tetrahedron Lett. *39*, 745-8 (1998).

# Formation of Rem-C Bond

## Uptake ⇓

### Addition to Oxygen and Carbon                                    RemC ⇓ OC

*Lithium dimethyl(silyl)zincates/dilithium dimethyl(cyano)cuprate*  $Me_2(Si\leqslant)ZnLi/Me_2Cu(CN)Li_2$
**2-Hydroxysilanes from epoxides**                                   $\diagdown_o\diagup \rightarrow C(OH)C(Si\leqslant)$
and 1,4-addition to 3-ethyleneepoxides s. *55*, 215

*Boron fluoride*                                                     $BF_3$
**2-Hydroxyselenides from epoxides**                                 $\diagdown_o\diagup \rightarrow C(OH)C(SeR)$
with PhSeSePh/NaOH/Bu₃P cf. *47*, 555; with PhSeSnBu₃/BF₃-etherate, chemo-, regio- and stereo-selectivity, s. Y. Nishiyama et al., Chem. Lett. *1998*, 159-60.

*Titanium tetraisopropoxide/(1S,2S)-trans-1,2-cyclohexanediol*       ←
**Asym. synthesis of α-hydroxyphosphonic acid esters from aldehydes**    $CH(OH)PO(OR)_2$
with lanthanum(III) trilithium tris((R)-1,1'-bi-2-naphthoxide) cf. *49*, 510s*53*; with Ti(OPr-i)₄/(1S,2S)-*trans*-1,2-cyclohexanediol and comparison of chiral diols s. M.D. Groaning et al., Tetrahedron Lett. *39*, 5485-8 (1998).

### Addition to Carbon-Carbon Bonds                                  RemC ⇓ CC

*Lithium organo(stannyl)cuprates/cuprous cyanide*                    ←
**Regiospecific 1,4-stannylcupration**                               $C\equiv C \rightarrow CH=C(Sn\leqslant)$
**of electron-deficient acetylene derivs.**
with higher-order Li-trimethylstannylcuprates cf. *46*, 533s*47*; (E)-α,β-ethylene-β-stannyl-carboxylic acids with lithium organo(stannyl)cuprates/CuCN, also regiospecific iododestannylation, s. J. Thibonnet et al., Tetrahedron Lett. *39*, 4277-80 (1998).

*Silver trifluoromethanesulfonate*                                   *AgOTf*
**2-Azidoselenides from ethylene derivs.**                           $C=C \rightarrow C(N_3)C(SeR)$
with NaN₃/PhSeCl cf. *43*, 515; with AgOTf/PhSeCl, regio- and stereo-specific conversion, s. M. Tiecco et al., Synth. Commun. *28*, 2167-79 (1998).

*Silver trifluoromethanesulfonate/bromine*                           *AgOTf/Br₂*
**Regiospecific asym. oxyselenation**                                $C=C \rightarrow C(OR)C(SeR')$
s. *49*, 515s*54*; with camphor-based selenenyl triflates s. T.G. Back, S. Nan, J. Chem. Soc. Perkin Trans. I *1998*, 3123-4; with (NH₄)₂S₂O₈/CF₃SO₃H cf. M. Tiecco et al., Tetrahedron Lett. *39*, 2809-12 (1998).

*Lithium dimethyl(silyl)zincates/dilithium dimethyl(cyano)cuprate/scandium(III) triflate*   ←
**Cuprate-catalyzed syntheses with lithium dimethyl(silyl)zincates**    ←

215.

**Co-catalyzed 1,4-addition.** A soln. of dimethylzinc in toluene added to a soln. of phenyldimethylsilyllithium in THF at -78°, treated with *3 mol%* Me₂Cu(CN)Li₂ (0.0024 *M* in Cu) and 5 mol% Sc(OTf)₃, isophorone added, and worked up after *5 min* → product. Y 81%. Yields were high in the absence of rare earth catalyst, but reaction was considerably longer (2.5 h). This is a significant improvement on syntheses with (PhMeSi)₂Cu(CN)Li₂ (from CuCN and *2 eqs.* phenyldimethylsilyllithium), from which only one silyl group is transferrable and for which 1 eq. of Cu(I) is required. Furthermore, the latter procedure fails with highly hindered substrates. F.e. incl. 1,4-addition to enals, trapping of the intermediate Zn-enolates with electrophiles, 1,2-silylzincation of alkynes, addition to epoxides, and 1,4-addition to 3-ethyleneepoxides, s. B.H. Lipshutz et al., J. Am. Chem. Soc. *120*, 4021-2 (1998).

*Tris(pentafluorophenyl)borane/triethylsilane* $Ar_3B/Et_3SiH$
**Enestannanes from acetylene derivs.** $C{\equiv}C \rightarrow CH{=}C(Sn{\leqslant})$
**Regio- and stereo-specific conversion with *in situ*-generated tri-*n*-butyltin hydride**

216.

under Lewis acid catalysis. 1.5 eqs. Tri-*n*-butyltin chloride, 1 eq. Et$_3$SiH, and oct-1-yne added consecutively to 0.1 eq. tris(pentafluorophenyl)borane in dry toluene at 0° under argon, the mixture stirred for 40 min at this temp., allowed to warm to room temp., stirred for 3 h, and quenched with 0.5 eq. Et$_3$N → product. Y 78% (*cis/trans* >95:5). Tri-*n*-butyltin hydride is thus generated *in situ* from stable inexpensive reagents, and there was no competing hydrosilylation. β-Hydrostannylation products were formed exclusively from alk-1-ynes with *cis*-stereoselectivity. F.e. incl. hydrostannylation of phenylallene and styrene, and with ZrCl$_4$, s. V. Gevorgyan et al., Chem. Commun. *1998*, 37-8.

*Scandium(III) triflate* s. under Li-dimethyl(silyl)zincates $Sc(OTf)_3$

*Phenyl iodosoacetate* $PhI(OAc)_2$
**Regiospecific oxyselenation of ethylene derivs.** $C{=}C \rightarrow C(O\text{-})C(SeR)$
2-acoxyselenides with (PhSeO)$_2$O cf. *29*, 180s*47*; with PhI(OAc)$_2$, also 2-hydroxyselenides in acetonitrile/water, and intramolecular oxyselenation, s . M. Tingoli et al., Synth. Commun. *28*, 1769-78 (1998).

*Chlorobis(cyclopentadienyl)hydridozirconium* $Cp_2Zr(H)Cl$
**Functionalized ethylene from acetylene derivs.** $C{\equiv}C \rightarrow CH{=}C(X)$
**via regio- and stereo-specific hydrozirconation**
(E)-enetellurides cf. *50*, 343s*51*; (E)-1-(organoseleno)enetellurides from 1-acetylene-1-selenides, and ketene telluroacetals and 1-iodoenetellurides from 1-acetylene-1-tellurides, s. M.J. Dabdoub et al., Tetrahedron *54*, 2371-400 (1998).

*Ammonium persulfate/trifluoromethanesulfonic acid* $(NH_4)_2S_2O_8/CF_3SO_3H$
**Regiospecific asym. oxyselenation** s. *49*, 515s*55* $C{=}C \rightarrow C(OR)C(SeR')$

*Dichloro[1,2-bis(diphenylphosphino)ethane]nickel(II)* $NiCl_2(dppe)$
**Regiospecific nickel(II)-catalyzed hydroboration** ←
of 1-acetylene-1-thioethers cf. *48*, 547; of 1,3-dienes, and f. catalysts, s. M. Zaidlewicz, J. Meller, Tetrahedron Lett. *38*, 7279-82 (1997).

*Iodotris(triphenylphosphine)rhodium(I)* $RhI(PPh_3)_3$
**Regio- and geo-specific hydrosilylation of terminal acetylene derivs.** $C{\equiv}C \rightarrow CH{=}C(Si{\leqslant})$
(E)-isomers from terminal alkynes with Rh(cod)$_2$BF$_4$/2 PPh$_3$ cf. *15*, 494s*51*; (E)-(Si-alkoxy)-enesilanes with RhI(PPh$_3$)$_3$, and (Z)-isomers on inverse addition, s. A. Mori et al., Chem. Lett. *1998*, 443-4.

*cis-Dimethylbis[dimethyl(phenyl)phosphine]palladium/diphenylphosphinic acid* ←
**α,β-Ethylenephosphine oxides from acetylene derivs.** $C{\equiv}C \rightarrow CH{=}C\text{-}P(O)R_2$
**Reversal of regioselectivity**

217.

**α-Methylenephosphine oxides.** A soln. of diphenylphosphine oxide, 1 eq. 1-octyne, 5 mol% Ph$_2$P(O)OH and 3 mol% *cis*-[PdMe$_2$(PPhMe$_2$)$_2$] in dry benzene heated at 70° for 4 h under argon

→ adduct. Y 92% (95:5 mixture of α/β-regioisomers, isolated in 80% and 4% yield, respectively, by TLC). By comparison with *51*, 239s*52*, addition of just a trace of Ph$_2$P(O)OH switches the regioselectivity in favour of the α-adduct (88% of the β-adduct being formed in the absence of the acid for the example described), as well as enhancing the catalytic activity (especially with sterically less demanding and more basic phosphine ligands). The method is applicable to a variety of aliphatic and aromatic terminal alkynes. (Trimethylsilyl)acetylene, however, gave the β-adduct (63%; single *trans*-isomer). The reaction was very clean, and olefin, amino, cyano and hydroxyl groups were tolerated. F.e. incl. bis(α-methylenephosphine oxides), and reaction of sym. internal acetylenes s. L.-B. Han et al., Angew. Chem. Int. Ed. Engl. *37*, 94-6 (1998).

## Rearrangement

### Carbon/Carbon Type

tert-*Dodecanethiol/di*-tert-*butyl hyponitrite*
**Regiospecific thiyl-mediated intramolecular hydrosilylation**

t-$C_{12}H_{25}SH/HN(OBu$-t$)_2$

RemC ⋂ CC

218.

The intramolecular variant of thiyl-mediated hydrosilylation (*50*, 341) is reported. **E:** 2.5 Mol% tert-dodecanethiol and 2.5 mol% di-*tert*-butyl hyponitrite (as radical initiator) added to a soln. of diphenyl(2-methylbut-3-en-2-yloxy)silane in hexane under argon, stirred at 60° for 1 h, further amounts (2.5 mol% each) of the two reagents added, and stirring continued for 2 h → 2,2-diphenyl-5,5-dimethyl-1-oxa-2-silacyclopentane. Y 88%. Yields were higher with triorganosilyl mercaptans as mediator, but AIBN was a poor initiator. F.e. and ring closures of homoallyloxy- and bishomoallyloxy-silanes s. Y. Cai, B.P. Roberts, J. Chem. Soc. Perkin Trans. 1 *1998*, 467-75.

## Exchange

### Oxygen ↑

RemC ↓↑ O

*Dichlorobis(triphenylphosphine)palladium(II)/1,3-bis(diphenylphosphino)propane/ ethyldiisopropylamine*
**Arylphosphine oxides from aryl triflates**
and phosphinous acids with Pd(OAc)$_2$/dppb/*i*-Pr$_2$NEt cf. *38*, 584s*54*; from Ph$_2$P(O)H or Et$_2$P(O)H generated *in situ* from Ph$_2$PH or Et$_2$PH with PdCl$_2$(PPh$_3$)$_2$/dppp under O$_2$ s. G. Martorell, J.M. Saá et al., J. Org. Chem. *63*, 3463-7 (1998).

ArOTf → ArP(O)Ph$_2$

### Nitrogen ↑

RemC ↓↑ N

*Organolithium compds.*
**Tert. phosphines from phosphinous acid amides** s. *55*, 224

RLi
>P-N< → >P-R

### Halogen ↑

RemC ↓↑ Hal

*Irradiation* s. under *R$_2$Zn*

*Electrolysis/nickel(II) chloride/2,2'-bipyridyl*
**Sym. phosphine oxides from halides**

⌇/NiCl$_2$/bipy
3 RHal → R$_3$PO

219.

3 PhBr + P$_4$ —[ Ni(0) ]→ Ph$_3$PO

A soln. of bromobenzene, ca. 20 mol% 2,2'-bipyridyl, and ca. 6 mol% NiCl$_2$ in acetonitrile containing 0.25 eq. white phosphorus electrolyzed in an undivided cell fitted with a Pt cylinder as cathode and an Al anode at 50° until 6.2 F/mol (of P$_4$) passed with a current density of 0.5 A/dm$^2$ → triphenylphosphine oxide. Y 79%. This is the first synthesis involving formation of a carbon-phosphorus bond from white phosphorus. F.e. incl. trialkylphosphine oxides s. Y.G. Budnikova et al., Mendeleev Commun. *1997*, 67-8.

n-*Butyllithium/(-)-sparteine*
**Deprotonation of sec. phosphine-borane complexes with dynamic kinetic resolution**  ←

220.

**Chiral tert. phosphine-borane complexes.** 1 eq. 2.4 *M* n-BuLi in hexane added to a soln. of racemic *tert*-butylphenylphosphine-borane and 1.3 eqs. (-)-sparteine in ether at -78° under argon, allowed to warm to room temp., 1.3 eqs. 2-methoxybenzyl chloride added, allowed to warm to -20° very slowly over 2-3 h, stirred at the same temp. for a total of 24 h, and worked up with 5% aq. H$_2$SO$_4$ → (R)-P-(2-methoxyphenylmethyl)-P-*tert*-butylphenylphosphine-borane. Y 80% (e.e. 95%). The borane protective group can be easily removed, preferably by heating with neat pyrrolidine at room temp. to 35° for 24 h. F.e. incl. chiral bis(tert. phosphine-borane complexes) s. B. Wolfe, T. Livinghouse, J. Am. Chem. Soc. *120*, 5116-7 (1998).

tert-*Butyllithium*                                                                                                                    t-*BuLi*
**Asym. synthesis of ferrocenes**                                                                                                     ←
s. *49*, 536s*54*; chiral *o*-subst. ferrocenyl ketones via asym. *o*-metalation of hydrazone derivs. s. D. Enders et al., Synlett *1997*, 1462-4; chiral *o*-subst. ferrocenecarboxaldehydes s. X. Lu, G. Chen, Tetrahedron *54*, 12539-46 (1998); cf. O. Riant et al., J. Org. Chem. *62*, 6733-45 (1997); also chiral 2,2'-disubst. 1,1'-ferrocenedicarboxaldehydes s. G. Iftime et al., Angew. Chem. Int. Ed. Engl. *37*, 1698-701 (1998).

**(poly-Si)-Heterocyclics from bis(chlorosilanes)**                                                                                    ○

221.

A soln. of bis[bis(methylthio)methyl]dimethylsilane in THF treated with 2.2 eqs. 1.51 *M* t-BuLi in pentane at -40°, cooled to -78° after 3 h, treated with 1.2 eqs. startg. bis(chlorosilane) in THF, allowed to warm to room temp., and quenched with satd. aq. NH$_4$Cl → intermediate (Y 67%), heated with Bu$_3$SnH and a little AIBN at 120° → product (Y 64%). F.e. incl. reaction with dichlorosilanes to give 1,3-disilacyclobutanes s. M. Shimizu et al., Tetrahedron Lett. *39*, 3193-6 (1998); 1,4-silacyclohexanes s. ibid. 3197-200.

tert-*Butyllithium/N,N,N',N'-tetramethylethylenediamine*                                                                              t-*BuLi/TMEDA*
**Ring closures via intramolecular carbolithiation of vinyllithium compds.**

222.

**3-α,4-α-Disubst. Δ$^3$-pyrrolines.** A soln. of N,N-bis(2-bromoallyl)amine in ether treated at -78° with *4 eqs.* t-BuLi, 4 eqs. TMEDA added, the cooling bath removed, the mixture allowed to stand at 20°, and the intermediate dilithio deriv. quenched with trimethylsilyl chloride → product. Y 82%. The same dilithio derivs. were also formed with 3% CuCN (in place of TMEDA) via intramolecular carbocupration in a catalytic cycle. F.e. and electrophiles, **also 2,3-α-disubst. indoles** from 2-bromo-N-(2-bromoallyl)anilines via 2-lithiation of the intermediate 3-lithiomethylindoles, **and 3-α-subst. indoles** by quenching the latter with electrophiles, s. J. Barluenga et al., J. Am. Chem. Soc. *120*, 4865-6 (1998).

*Sodium hydrogen selenide/tetra-n-butylammonium hydrogen sulfate*     $NaHSe/Bu_4NHSO_4$
*Sodium hydrogen telluride*     $NaTeH$
**(Z)-3-(Alkylidene)selenophthalides from *o*-acetylenecarboxylic acid chlorides**     ○

223.

**Phase transfer catalysis.** Startg. crude acyl chloride in toluene added slowly to 2.2 eqs. NaHSe in water under argon at room temp., treated with a little $Bu_4NHSO_4$, and vigorously stirred for 6-12 h → product. Y 78%. There was no formation of 2-benzoselenopyran derivs. F.e. and **(Z)-3-(alkylidene)tellurophthalides** with NaHTe s. H. Sashida, A. Kawamukai, J. Heterocycl. Chem. *35*, 165-7 (1998); selenochromones and tellurochromones from *o*-bromoaryl α,β-acetyleneketones s. Synlett *1998*, 745-7.

*Magnesium*     $Mg$
**Synthesis of mixed tert. phosphines from amino(chloro)phosphines**     $>P\text{-}Cl \to >P\text{-}R$
**via phosphinous acid amides**

224.

Chloro(N-methylanilino)phenylphosphine in THF at 0° treated with 1.5 eqs. *o*-tolylmagnesium bromide under $N_2$, the mixture stirred at room temp. (20°) until reaction complete (by $^1H$ and $^{31}P$ NMR), cooled in ice, and neutralized slowly with $NH_4Cl$ (1 *M*) → intermediate phosphinous amide (Y 96%), in THF at 0° treated with 1.5 eqs. MeLi under $N_2$, the mixture warmed to room temp., and stirred until reaction complete by NMR → product (Y 93%). This is a general and efficient method (which should be suitable for solid phase parallel synthesis) for introduction of alkyl, vinyl and aryl substituents. It exploits the different leaving group abilities of chloride *vs.* amide and the differential reactivities of organolithium *vs.* organomagnesium reagents. This transformation could also be effected in one-pot by sequential treatment of dichloro(phenyl)phosphine (the precursor to the amino(chloro)phosphine) with LiNMePh, *o*-tolylmagnesium bromide and MeLi (Y 59%). F.e.s. S. Singh, K.M. Nicholas, Chem. Commun. *1998*, 149-50.

*Magnesium/zinc chloride*     $Mg/ZnCl_2$
*Zinc/hexamethylphosphoramide*     $Zn/HMPA$
**α-(Organoseleno)carbonyl compds. from α-bromocarbonyl compds.**     $Br \to SeR$

225.

**via chlorozinc selenolates.** 1 eq. Anhydrous $ZnCl_2$ and THF added to a soln. of phenylmagnesium bromide in THF at 0°, the mixture stirred at room temp. for 30 min, 1 eq. selenium added, boiled with stirring until disappearance of the metal, 1 eq. ethyl bromoacetate and HMPA added, the mixture stirred at 60° for 20 h, then treated with dil. HCl → ethyl (phenylseleno)acetate. Y 80%. The method is simple, mild, generally applicable to alkyl and ar. bromides, and starting materials are readily available. F.e.s. X. Huang, X.-H. Xu, Synth. Commun. *28*, 807-11 (1998); ar. 2-ethyleneselenides from β,γ-ethylenebromides and diaryliodonium salts via bromozinc 2-ethyleneselenolates (with Zn/HMPA) s. ibid. 801-5.

*Dialkylzinc/irradiation* $R_2Zn/⚡$
**Photo-induced synthesis of functionalized organozinc compds.** ←

226.

**Functionalized diorganozinc compds.** A soln. of startg. iodide and *1 eq.* Et$_2$Zn in methylene chloride-d$_2$ irradiated in a Pyrex tube (≥280 nm) with a 275 W GE sunlamp for 3 h at 23° → product. Y 90% (<10% without irradiation). The method is generally applicable to reaction of dialkylzinc with prim. or sec. iodides, and a variety of functional groups (e.g. COOR, CONR$_2$, BnO, TIPSO) were unaffected. The procedure avoids the use of an excess of dialkylzinc and/or a transition metal catalyst. The more reactive diisopropylzinc led to higher yields. The corresponding **sym. diorganozinc compds.** were obtained from the iodide with 0.5 eq. dialkylzinc, and **organozinc iodides** from alkyl iodides and EtZnI (or preferably *i*-PrZnI). F.e.s. A.B. Charette et al., J. Am. Chem. Soc. *120*, 5114-5 (1998).

*Nickel(II) chloride s. under* ↯ $NiCl_2$

*Tris(dibenzylideneacetone)dipalladium/triphenylphosphine/triethylamine* ←
**Arylphosphonic acid esters from ar. halides** Hal → PO(OR)$_2$
under Pd-catalysis s. *38*, 584s*51*; phosphonyl-N-hetarenes from bromo-N-hetarenes s. J. Park, P.H. Lee, Bull. Korean Chem. Soc. *18*, 1130-2 (1997).

*Tris(dibenzylideneacetone)dipalladium/tri-o-tolylphosphine/ethyldiisopropylamine* ←
**Arylsilanes from ar. iodides and organosilicon hydrides** ArI → ArSi≤

227. PhI + HSi(OEt)$_3$ ⟶ PhSi(OEt)$_3$

**Trialkoxy(aryl)silanes.** Iodobenzene, 3.06 eqs. ethyldiisopropylamine, and 1.5 eqs. triethoxysilane added to 0.6 mol% Pd$_2$(dba)$_3$·CHCl$_3$ and 6 mol% tri-*o*-tolylphosphine in N-methyl-2-pyrrolidone under argon, and stirred for 1 h at room temp. → triethoxyphenylsilane. Y 72%. This is the first report of the highly selective Pd-catalyzed formation of arylsilanes from organosilicon hydrides, reaction taking place via oxidative addition of Pd(0) to the Si-H bond rather than the aryl iodide bond. An amide solvent (DMF, NMP, DMAc) appears essential. Furthermore, the presence of an electron-withdrawing group on the aromatic ring disfavours reaction, and ar. bromides generally afford low yields. F.e. incl. coupling with hetaryl iodides s. M. Murata, Y. Masuda et al., J. Org. Chem. *62*, 8569-71 (1997).

## Sulfur ↑ RemC ↓↑ S

*Titanocene dichloride/magnesium/triethyl phosphite* ←
**Silanes from mercaptals and organosilicon hydrides** C(SR)$_2$ → CHSi≤

228. PhCH$_2$CH$_2$CH(SPh)$_2$ —[ Cp$_2$TiP(OEt)$_3$ ]$_2$→ [ PhCH$_2$CH$_2$CH=TiCp$_2$ ] —HSiMe$_2$Ph→ PhCH$_2$CH$_2$CH$_2$SiMe$_2$Ph

THF and 4.4 eqs. triethyl phosphite added to a stirred mixture of 2.6 eqs. Mg-turnings, 2.2 eqs. Cp$_2$TiCl$_2$ and 4 Å molecular sieves at room temp. under argon, 1.1 eqs. dimethylphenylsilane in THF added after 3 h, stirred for 10 min, startg. mercaptal in THF added, and stirring continued at room temp. for a further 1.5 h → product. Y 89%. F.e., **also germanes** with triethylgermane, and **(E)-2-ethylene-silanes, -germanes, or -stannanes from** α,β-ethylenemercaptals or ene-1,3-di(thioethers) (with retention of geochemistry), s. T. Takeda et al., Tetrahedron Lett. *39*, 3533-6 (1998).

# Remaining Elements ↑          RemC ↓↑ Rem

*Irradiation*          ⫽
**Radical addition of dichalcogenide mixtures to carbon-carbon multiple bonds**     ←
2-(arylthio)selenides cf. 47, 568; 2-(arylthio)eneselenides from acetylene derivs., regioselectivity, and radical ring closure, s. J. Org. Chem. 63, 881-4 (1998); 2,3-ene-1,4-di(thioethers) from 1,3-dienes with $(PhS)_2$ and $(PhSe)_2$ as polymerization inhibitor s. Tetrahedron Lett. 39, 1577-8 (1998).

*Boron fluoride or Iodosobenzene*          $BF_3$ or *PhIO*
**Synthesis of bismuthonium salts**          $R_4Bi^+$
review s. 52, 239s52; f. method **from arylstannanes** with $Ph_3BiF_2/Me_3SiCN$ in the presence of $BF_3$ cf. Chem. Lett. 1998, 127-8; tetraarylbismuthonium salts from two triarylbismuthine molecules with PhIO s. H. Suzuki et al., J. Chem. Soc. Perkin Trans. I 1997, 1609-16.

*Samarium diiodide*          $SmI_2$
**Selenides from silyl selenides under neutral conditions**      $RSeSi\leqslant \rightarrow RSeR'$

229.      $PhSeSiMe_3 \xrightarrow{SmI_2} [\ PhSeSmI_2\ ] \xrightarrow{ClBn} PhSeBn$

**Ar. selenides.** A soln. of startg. silyl selenide in THF added via syringe to a soln. of 2.2 eqs. $SmI_2$ in the same solvent at reflux under $N_2$, 1 eq. benzyl chloride added via syringe after 3 h, and stirred at reflux for a further 3 h → product. Y 84%. The procedure is simple, mild and neutral. F.e.s. S. Zhang, Y. Zhang, J. Chem. Res., Synop 1998, 350-1.

*Phenyl iodosoacetate*          $PhI(OAc)_2$
**Intramolecular oxyselenation** s. 29, 180s55      ○

*Hexamethyldisilazane*          $(Me_3Si)_2NH$
**1,4-Dien-1-ylmercury compds. from 1-silyl-2,n-enynes**
with isocyclic ring closure s. 55, 279

*Tin*          *Sn*
**2-Ethyleneselenides from β,γ-ethylenebromides and diselenides**     Br → SeR
in aq. ethanol with In cf. 52, 237; in aq. THF with Sn powder, also propargyl selenides, s. J. Chem. Res., Synop 1998, 150-1.

*Bromine/silver trifluoromethanesulfonate*          $Br_2/AgOTf$
**Asym. intramolecular oxyselenation**     ○
s. 51, 258; details and asym. intramolecular aminoselenation s. Eur. J. Org. Chem. 1998, 1361-9; intermolecular process s. 49, 515s55.

*Bromine/silver trifluoromethanesulfonate/collidine*     ←
**Asym. intramolecular carboselenation of ethylenearenes**

230.

**Chiral 2-(arylseleno)tetralins.** 1.05 eqs. 1 M $Br_2$ in carbon tetrachloride added to a soln. of startg. chiral diselenide in dichloromethane at -78°, after 5 min the mixture treated with 2.1 eqs. 2 M AgOTf in methanol, a soln. of 2 eqs. startg. ethylenearene in dichloromethane introduced slowly after a further 5 min, stirring continued at -78° for 30 min, allowed to warm to 0°, stirred for 30 min, then neutralized with 2.8 eqs. *sym*-collidine → product. Y 70% (d.e. 98%). When treated with strong acid [liberated $CF_3SO_3H$ in this instance], the intermediate 2-alkoxyselenides cyclize to **seleniranium ions** prior to ring closure. F.e. incl. **1-α- and 2-(arylseleno)indans**, and 2-step procedure (with isolation of the intermediate alkoxyselenides and their cyclization with $BF_3$-etherate) s. R. Déziel et al., Tetrahedron Lett. 39, 5493-6 (1998).

*Tetrakis(triphenylphosphine)palladium(0)* Pd(PPh$_3$)$_4$
**Selenol- and tellurol-carbonic from chloroformic acid esters** ←
s. *53*, 252; f. details s. J. Org. Chem. *63*, 5713-5 (1998).

## Carbon ↑ RemC ↓↑ C

*Irradiation* ⫽
**Phosphonic acids from carboxylic acids** COON≤ → PO(OH)$_2$
via 1-acoxy-2-pyridinethiones cf. *49*, 557; modified procedure (with SO$_2$) for sensitive natural products, e.g. linoleic acid, and stabilization of white phosphorus solns. with TEMPO, s. Tetrahedron *54*, 12475-96 (1998).

# Formation of C-C Bond

## Uptake ⇓

### Addition to Hydrogen and Carbon CC ⇓ HC

*Phenylsodium/diisopropylamine* PhNa/*i*-Pr$_2$NH
**Benzylsodium compds. from alkylarenes** ←
with K/Na$_2$O cf. *10*, 511; with PhNa/*i*-Pr$_2$NH (cf. *8*, 697), also benzylpotassium compds., s. World Intellectual Property Organization patent WO-9745433 (CI Kasei Co. Ltd.).

*Sodium salt/N,N-dimethylacetamide* Na$^+$/MeCONMe$_2$
**Kolbe synthesis of *o*-hydroxycarboxylic acids** H → COOH
with alkali salts cf. *7*, 678; with Na$^+$/N,N-dimethylacetamide or urethans as auxiliary s. Japanese patent JP-10059897 (Mitsui Petrochem Ind. Co. Ltd.).

### Addition to Oxygen and Carbon CC ⇓ OC

*Electrolysis* ↯
**Cathodic synthesis of alcohols from oxo compds. and trialkylboranes** CO → C(OH)R

231.  Me$_2$CO + Et$_3$B ⟶ Me$_2$C(OH)Et

**under mild conditions.** A stirred soln. of triethylborane (1 *M* in THF), 1 eq. acetone, and 0.5 eq. tetrabutylammonium iodide in DMF electrolyzed under N$_2$ at room temp. in an undivided cell fitted with a Pt cathode and a sacrificial Cu anode at -3.2 V for 9 h → 2-methyl-2-butanol. Y 68%. Reaction is generally applicable to the addition of hindered or unhindered trialkylboranes to ar. or aliphatic oxo compds. However, only one of the alkyl groups of the trialkylborane is transferrable. F.e.s. J.H. Choi, J.S. Kim et al., Tetrahedron Lett. *39*, 4835-8 (1998).

*Microwaves s. under Montmorillonite* ←

*Lithium/naphthalene or 4,4'-di-*tert-*butylbiphenyl* ←
**Synthesis of alcohols from oxo compds.**
and chlorides s. *47*, 576s52; 3-methylene-1,5-diols from 2-chloro-3-(2-methoxyethoxy)propene as a 2-methylenepropane-1,3-dicarbanion equivalent, sequential trapping with electrophiles, and conversion to 2,8-dioxabicyclo[3.3.0]octanes s. Tetrahedron Lett. *39*, 3303-6 (1998); 4-functionalized 2-ethylenealcohols from γ-functionalized α,β-ethylenechlorides s. Tetrahedron *54*, 6177-84 (1998).

*Lithium/polymer-based naphthalene*
**Heterogeneous reductive lithiation** CO → C(OH)R

232.

Startg. chloride treated with excess of Li-powder and 10 mol% polymer-based naphthalene (prepared by polymerizing 2-vinylnaphthalene in the presence of styrene and divinylbenzene) in THF at -90 to -78° for 1 h, treated with cyclohexanone, allowed to warm to 20°, and hydrolyzed → product. Y 90%. The polymer-based naphthalene can be easily recovered and reused without loss of any activity. F.e. **and double Barbier-type reaction** s. C. Gómez et al., Tetrahedron Lett. *39*, 1397-400 (1998).

*Potassium tert-butoxide/modified hydrotalcite*
**Hydrotalcites as solid base**
s. *49*, 589s*51*; heterogeneous aldol condensation with *t*-BuOK-modified hydrotalcite (cf. *43*, 556) s. B.M. Choudary et al., Tetrahedron Lett. *39*, 3555-8 (1998).

*Organolithium compds.* RLi
**Asym. synthesis of amines from oxazolidines** C
chiral prim. amines s. *46*, 601; chiral α-(trifluoromethyl)amines with retention of configuration using organolithium compds. s. A. Ishii et al., Tetrahedron Lett. *39*, 1199-202 (1998); chiral 1-β-hydroxy-2-piperidones from 7-oxa-1-azabicyclo[4.3.0]nonan-2-ones with dilithium dialkyl-(cyano)cuprates s. M. Amat et al., Tetrahedron:Asym. *7*, 977-80 (1996).

*n-Butyllithium* BuLi
**2-Acetylenealcohols from terminal acetylene derivs.** CO → C(OH)C≡CR
s. *24*, 663s*53*; chiral 2-acetylene-2'-aminoalcohols with asym. induction, and conversion to chiral γ-hydroxycarboxylic acid derivs. via Claisen rearrangement and ozonolysis s. J. Clayden et al., Tetrahedron:Asym. *9*, 1427-40 (1998).

*n-Butyllithium/(1S,2S)-1,2-dimethoxy-1,2-diphenylethane* ←
**β-Hydroxyphosphonic acid esters from ketones** CO → C(OH)C-PO(OR)$_2$
Asym. aldol condensation s. *55*, 464

*n-Butyllithium/hexamethylphosphoramide* BuLi/HMPA
**Synthesis of alkoxysilanes from epoxides** C
γ-siloxycarboxamides with LDA cf. *34*, 607; 5-siloxyenesilanes and conversion to 4'-hydroxy-5-siloxyenesilanes with aldehydes s. K. Takaku et al., Tetrahedron Lett. *39*, 2575-8 (1998).

*Lithium diisopropylamide* i-Pr$_2$NLi
**Asym. acetate aldol condensation** CHO → CH(OH)C-CO

233.

**β-Hydroxycarboxylic acids from aldehydes with two extra C-atoms**. Startg. chiral α-siloxy-ketone [prepared by addition of Li-acetylide to (1R)-(+)-camphor, followed by standard hydration and silylation with N-trimethylsilyl-2-oxazolidone] treated with 1.2 eqs. LDA in THF at -78° for 0.5 h, a precooled (-78°) soln. of pivalaldehyde in THF added, allowed to react for 6 h, then treated with 1 *M* HCl/MeOH (or 2 eqs. Bu$_4$NF in THF at room temp. for 5 min) → adduct (Y 70%; d.r. >98:2), treated with NaIO$_4$ in 2:1 MeOH/water at room temp. or reflux for 12-48 h → product (with 85-90% recovery of camphor). This is the first methyl ketone enolate strategy that allows recovery of the chiral controller. It is general for aromatic, α,β-unsatd., and linear or branched aliphatic aldehydes, and the diastereomeric excesses are excellent. F.e., also **β-siloxyketones**

(with organocerium compds.) and **β-siloxyaldehydes** (with BH$_3$·THF), s. C. Palomo et al., Angew. Chem. Int. Ed. Engl. *37*, 180-2 (1998).

**Asym. synthesis of α-amino-β-hydroxycarboxylic acid esters**     CHO → CH(OH)C-CO
review s. *38*, 632s*54*; *anti*-isomers by aldol condensation with chiral N-(carbalkoxymethyl)-oxazolidines using LDA as base s. E.J. Iwanowicz et al., Synlett *1998*, 664-6.

**γ-Hydroxynitriles from epoxides and nitriles**     ▽o∕ → C(OH)C-C(CN)
s. *29*, 959s*48*; chemo-, regio- and stereo-selectivity s. S.K. Taylor et al., Synth. Commun. *28*, 1691-701 (1998).

*Lithium diisopropylamide/trimethyl borate*     i-*Pr$_2$NLi/(MeO)$_3$B*
**Synthesis of β-aminocarboxylic acid esters via aldol condensation** ←
s. *25*, 487s*49*; aldol condensation of β-(dibenzylamino)carboxylic acid esters with glyoxylic acid esters, asym. induction, s. D. Ma, J. Jiang, Tetrahedron:Asym. *9*, 575-9 (1998).

*Lithium diisopropylamide/aluminum tris(2,6-diphenylphenoxide)*     i-*Pr$_2$NLi/Al(OAr)$_3$*
**Vinylogous aldol condensation**
**of α,β-ethyleneoxo compds. with aldehydes**     CHO → CH(OH)C-C=C-CO

234.

with retention of configuration. 1 eq. Crotonaldehyde and 1 eq. pentanal added sequentially to a soln. of 2.2 eqs. Al-tris(2,6-diphenylphenoxide) in toluene at -78° under argon, the mixture deprotonated with 1.2 eqs. LDA in THF, stirred for 15 min, and quenched with aq. NH$_4$Cl → product. Y 83%. Deprotonation and subsequent addition take place exclusively at the *γ-position* of the unsatd. aldehyde, the bulky Lewis acid inhibiting attack at the α-position of the satd. aldehyde. It is essential to pre-complex *both* aldehyde components in order to prevent self-dimerization of the enal. 2-Cyclohexenones reacted similarly at the γ-site (the α'-site being shielded by the Lewis acid). F.e. and preferential benzylic deprotonation of *p*-methylacetophenone, s. S. Saito, H. Yamamoto et al., J. Am. Chem. Soc. *120*, 813-4 (1998).

*Potassium diisopropylamide*     i-*Pr$_2$NK*
**α-Lateral metalation of N-heterocyclics** ←
of pyridines with LDA cf. *28*, 732; 2-α-metalation of pyridines with *i*-Pr$_2$NK or K- or Na-tetramethylpiperidide s. E. Pasquinet, P. Rocca et al., Tetrahedron *54*, 8771-82 (1998).

*Triethylamine*     Et$_3$N
**C-α-Bis(hydroxymethylation)**     CH$_2$ → C(CH$_2$OH)$_2$
of aldehydes with K$_2$CO$_3$ cf. *17*, 735; improved procedure with Et$_3$N s. Japanese patent JP-09295956 (Mitsubishi Chem. Corp.); bis(hydroxymethylation) of β-dicarbonyl compds. with Et$_3$N or pyridine s. A. Guzaev, H. Lönnberg, Synthesis *1997*, 1281-4.

*Lithium dialkylcuprates/boron fluoride*     LiCuR$_2$/BF$_3$
**Synthesis of protected 1,1-hydroxystannanes from cyclic 1-stannylacetals** ←

235.

with asym. induction. 6 eqs. MeLi soln. added dropwise at -30° to a suspension of 3 eqs. CuI in ether (in a dry Schlenk tube), stirred for 30 min, cooled to -78°, 3 eqs. BF$_3$-etherate added, stirring continued for 5 min, startg. stannylacetal added via syringe, stirred for a further 2 h at -60°, and quenched with satd. aq. NH$_4$Cl → intermediate (Y 92%; d.r. 85/15), subjected to Swern oxidation at -60° in the normal way → 4-(1-tributylstannylethoxy)pentan-2-one (Y 72%; d.r. >99:1 after liquid chromatography), in methanol treated with K$_2$CO$_3$, and stirred at 15° for 4 h → (S)-1-(tributylstannyl)ethanol (isolated as the methoxymethyl ether: Y 68%; e.e. 98.6%). The stereochemistry was predominantly inverted with Me$_3$Al or organoaluminum chlorides in place of cuprates. F.e.s. J.-C. Cintrat, J.-P. Quintard et al., Tetrahedron *53*, 7615-28 (1997).

*Cupric trifluoromethanesulfonate* $Cu(OTf)_2$
**α-Siloxynitriles from oxo compds.** $CO \rightarrow C(OSi\leqslant)CN$
from ketones with $ZnI_2$ cf. *36*, 766; also from aldehydes with $Cu(OTf)_2$, and asym. variant, s. P. Saravanan et al., Tetrahedron Lett. *39*, 3823-4 (1998).

*Cuprous iodide/triethylamine* $CuI/Et_3N$
**Δ²-Oxazolines from isonitriles**
and aldehydes with $Et_3N$ cf. *25*, 484s*31*; from prochiral ketones, systematic study of transition metal/base-catalyzed synthesis (e.g. with $CuI/Et_3N$), stereochemistry, scope and limitations for preparing β,β-disubst. β-hydroxy-α-amino acids s. V.A. Soloshonok et al., J. Org. Chem. *62*, 3470-9 (1997).

*Magnesium* $Mg$
**Synthesis of alcohols from oxo compds. with asym. induction** $CO \rightarrow C(OH)R$
by Grignard addition s. *9*, 741s*54*; chiral 2,3-epoxy-*tert*-alcohols from α,β-epoxyketones s. A.T. Gillmore et al., Tetrahedron Lett. *39*, 3315-8 (1998); Grignard addition to aldehydoalkyl glycosides s. T. Yoshida et al., ibid. 4305-8; to α-spiroketones condensed at the 2-position of 1,3-oxathiolane, tetrahydrofuran or tetrahydrothiophene ring s. M. Dimitroff, A.G. Fallis, ibid. 2527-30, 2531-4; chiral α-amino-β-hydroxycarboxylic acids via Grignard addition to N-protected α-amino-β-ketoorthocarboxylic acid esters s. M.A. Blaskovich et al., J. Org. Chem. *63*, 3631-46 (1998); chiral α-hydroxyacetals s. K.M. Akhoon, D.C. Myles, ibid. *62*, 6041-5 (1997); Grignard addition to chiral O-protected polyhydroxyketones s. J. Mulzer et al., ibid. 3938-43.

*Magnesium/zinc iodide/trimethylsilyl cyanide/sodium tetrahydridoborate* ←
**2-Aminoalcohols from aldehydes via α-siloxynitriles** $CHO \rightarrow CH(OH)CH(NH_2)R$

236.

**One-pot procedure.** *trans*-Cinnamaldehyde added dropwise under $N_2$ to a stirred mixture of 1 eq. trimethylsilyl cyanide and a little $ZnI_2$ over 10 min, heated at 75° for 8 h, cooled to -50°, 1.46 eqs. freshly prepared benzylmagnesium chloride added over 10 min, warmed to ambient temp., stirred for 4 h, recooled to 0°, ca. 1 eq. $NaBH_4$ in methanol added over 30 min, acidified with 3 *M* aq. HCl to pH 2 when effervescence had stopped, and stirred for a further 3 h → 1,5-diphenyl-3-hydroxy-4-aminopent-1-ene. Y 76%. F.e.s. J. Howarth et al., Synth. Commun. *28*, 2751-9 (1998).

*Magnesium/diethylaluminum chloride* $Mg/Et_2AlCl$
**2-(Homoallylamino)alcohols from oxazolidines**
with allylmagnesium chloride/$CeCl_3$ cf. *46*, 601; with allylmagnesium bromide/$Et_2AlCl$ or $Et_3Al$, bridged N-heterocyclic derivs. via bridgehead cyclimmonium salts, s. N. Yamazaki et al., J. Org. Chem. *62*, 8280-1 (1997).

*Zinc/ammonium chloride* $Zn/NH_4Cl$
**Pinacolization in aq. media** $C(OH)C(OH)$
with Zn/NaOH cf. *30*, 561s*52*; with $Zn/NH_4Cl$ s. L. Wang et al., J. Chem. Res., Synop *1998*, 336-7; with In in 1:1 aq. *t*-BuOH under ultrasonication cf. H.J. Lim, Y. Kim et al., Tetrahedron Lett. *39*, 4367-8 (1998).

*Dialkylzinc/chiral 2-aminoalcohols or bicyclic phosphonic acid diamide* ←
**Asym. synthesis of sec. alcohols from aldehydes** $CHO \rightarrow CH(OH)R$
s. *42*, 616s*51-54*; with fine-tunable, functionalized chiral 2-aminoalcohols, optimization, s. A. Vidal-Ferran et al., J. Org. Chem. *62*, 4970-82 (1997); with D-mannitol-based 2-aminoalcohols s. B.T. Cho, Y.S. Chun, Tetrahedron:Asym. *9*, 1489-92 (1998); with chiral aziridinylcarbinols, details, s. D. Tanner et al., Tetrahedron *54*, 14213-32 (1998); with a chiral bicyclic phosphonic acid diamide cf. J.-M. Brunel et al., Tetrahedron Lett. *39*, 2961-4 (1998).

*Dialkylzinc/(R)-3,3'-bis[2,5-di(hexyloxy)phenyl]-1,1'-bi-2-naphthol*  CHO → CH(OH)R
**Asym. synthesis of sec. alcohols from aldehydes**

237.
Ph-CHO + Et$_2$Zn → Ph-CH(OH)Et    Ar = 2,5-di(OC$_6$H$_{13}$-n)phenyl

A monomeric form of the chiral poly(naphthol) ligands (*53*, 266) is the most efficient (in terms of yield and enantioselectivity) and generally applicable catalyst yet reported for asym. addition of diethylzinc to aldehydes (method s. *42*, 616s*53*). **E:** A soln. of 2 eqs. Et$_2$Zn and 5 mol% chiral binaphthol in toluene stirred under N$_2$ in a Schlenk flask for ca. 15 min at room temp., cooled to 0°, benzaldehyde added dropwise, and quenched with 1 *N* HCl after 4 h (at 0°) → (R)-1-phenylpropanol. Y 95% (e.e. >99%). Reaction is applicable to *p*-, *o*-, and *m*-subst. ar. aldehydes, linear or branched aliphatic aldehydes, and aryl- or alkyl-substituted enals. Furthermore, no Ti(IV) catalyst is required (cf. *44*, 565). F.e.s. W.-S. Huang et al., J. Org. Chem. *63*, 1364-5 (1998).

*Dialkylzinc/chiral poly(1,1'-bi-2-naphthols)*  ←
**Asym. synthesis of sec. alcohols from aldehydes**
s. *53*, 266; improved procedure with terphenyl-linked poly(1,1'-bi-naphthols) s. J. Org. Chem. *63*, 2798-9 (1998).

*Dialkylzinc/titanium tetraisopropoxide/chiral 1,2-di(sulfonylamino)cyclohexanes*  ←
**Asym. synthesis of sec. alcohols from aldehydes**
s. *44*, 565s*54*; with pre-formed, crystalline bis(sulfonamido)titanium(IV) dialkoxides s. S. Pritchett et al., J. Am. Chem. Soc. *120*, 6423-4 (1998); f. ligands s. Tetrahedron Lett. *39*, 5941-2 (1998); s.a. J. Qiu et al., J. Org. Chem. *62*, 2665-8 (1997).

*Dialkylzinc/titanium tetraisopropoxide/chiral γ-hydroxysulfonamides/calcium hydride*  ←
**Asym. synthesis of tert. alcohols from ketones** s *55*, 239    R$_2$CO → R$_2$C(OH)R'

*Dialkylzinc/vanadium tetrachloride*    R$_2$Zn/VCl$_4$
**Synthesis of alcohols from oxo compds.**    CO → C(OH)R

238.    PhCHO + Et$_2$Zn ⟶ PhCH(OH)Et

Dialkylzincs, which are normally inert towards oxo compds., can be activated for 1,2-addition by *1 eq.* VCl$_4$ or VCl$_3$(THF)$_3$. **E:** Diethylzinc in hexane added *at -78°* to a suspension of 1 eq. VCl$_4$ in THF, stirred for 1 h, 1 eq. benzaldehyde in THF added, warmed to 0° gradually, the resulting purple soln. stirred for 5 h, and treated with 1 *N* HCl → 1-phenylpropan-1-ol. Y 97% (94% with VCl$_3$(THF)$_3$). A reactive heteropolymetallic complex comprising dialkylzinc and the vanadium reagent in a higher valency state is thought to be formed prior to addition. At reflux, however, a vanadium(II) species is formed, which induces the expected pinacol coupling, while reaction with *2 eqs.* dialkylzinc at 0° to reflux facilitates deoxygenative coupling to the hydrocarbon. Reaction is generally applicable to addition of Et$_2$Zn or Me$_2$Zn to aliphatic, ar. and α,β-unsatd aldehydes; reaction with ketones requires a higher temp. (20°), so that in competition experiments with a mixture of aldehyde and ketone, the latter remains unaffected at 0°. F.e.s. Y. Kataoka, K. Tani et al., J. Org. Chem. *62*, 8540-3 (1997).

*Diethylzinc/tetrakis(triphenylphosphine)palladium(0)*    Et$_2$Zn/Pd(PPh$_3$)$_4$
**Regiospecific synthesis of 3-ethylenealcohols from acoxy-2-ethylenes**    CH(OH)C-C=C
and aldehydes via palladium π-allyl complexes and allylzincs with Zn/Pd(PPh$_3$)$_4$ cf. *43*, 699; via 2-subst. allylzincs with Et$_2$Zn/Pd(PPh$_3$)$_4$, stereoselectivity, s. M. Shimizu et al., Tetrahedron Lett. *39*, 609-12 (1998).

*Diarylzinc/(-)-3-*exo-*(dimethylamino)isoborneol/methanol*
**Asym. synthesis of tert. alcohols from ketones**     $R_2CO \rightarrow R_2C(OH)R'$ ←

239.

**Chiral tert. benzylalcohols.** The first example of catalytic asym. addition of an organometallic to a ketone is reported. **E:** A soln. of 3.5 eqs. diphenylzinc and 15 mol% (-)-3-*exo*-(dimethylamino)isoborneol in toluene stirred for 5 min at room temp., 1.6 eqs. methanol added dropwise by syringe, followed after 10 min by a soln. of 2-propionaphthone (also by syringe), stirred for 48 h at room temp. with exposure to air, and treated with 1 N HCl → (+)-1-(2-naphthyl)-1-phenylpropanol. Y 80% (e.e. 86%). The yield was poor in the absence of methanol due to the predominant formation of a dimeric product. With alkyl aryl ketones, the yield and enantioselectivity increased with the bulk of the alkyl group, and the enantioselectivity was slightly lower from dialkyl ketones. F.e.s. P.I. Dosa, G.C. Fu, J. Am. Chem. Soc. *120*, 445-6 (1998); with dialkylzinc/Ti(OPr-*i*)$_4$/CaH$_2$ in the presence of chiral γ-hydroxysulfonamides cf. D.J. Ramón, M. Yus, Tetrahedron Lett. *39*, 1239-42 (1998).

*Magnesium iodide*     $MgI_2$
**Chelation-controlled aldol-type condensation**     CHO → CH(OSi≼)C-COOR
**with protected α-amino-β-hydroxyaldehydes with double asym. induction**

240.

A soln. of startg. chiral aldehyde in methylene chloride added at 0° to 1.1 eqs. 97% anhydrous MgI$_2$ suspended in the same solvent, stirred for 20 min, cooled to -10°, 1.5 eqs. startg. silyl enol ether added dropwise over 15 min, allowed to warm to 0° over 30 min, stirred for a further 1.5 h, quenched with half-satd. aq. NaHCO$_3$ in ether, worked up, and the residual oil treated with 0.4 eqs. K$_2$CO$_3$ in methanol at 23° with stirring for 20 h → product. Y 77%. The *anti*-selectivity is explained by the intermediate formation of a IMg⁺ chelate involving the benzylic nitrogen and the formyl group, which stabilizes synclinal approach of the silyl enol ether to the aldehyde. This is the first efficient double-face selective Mukaiyama-type aldol condensation. F.e.s. E.J. Corey et al., J. Am. Chem. Soc. *120*, 2330-6 (1998).

*Indium*     *In*
**Pinacolization in aq. media** s. *30*, 561s*55*     C(OH)C(OH)

*Indium/hydrogen chloride*     *In/HCl*
**2-Allenealcohols from aldehydes and β,γ-acetylenebromides**     C(OH)C=C=C
in aq. media s. *40*, 567s*50*; with added HCl, regio- and stereo-selectivity, s. Chem. Commun. *1998*, 449-50.

*Trimethylaluminum/(R)-1,1'-bi-2-naphthol*     $Me_3Al/(R)$-*BINOL*
*cis-Δ²-***Oxazoline-4-carboxylic acid esters**     ←
**from 5-alkoxyoxazoles and aldehydes**
**Catalytic asym. conversion**

241.

31.5 Mol% 1.05 *M* Me$_3$Al in hexane added to a soln. of 30 mol% (R)-BINOL in acetonitrile, the mixture stirred at room temp. for 1 h, cooled to -20°, a soln. of 5-methoxy-2-(*o*-methoxyphenyl)-

oxazole and 10 eqs. benzaldehyde in the same solvent added dropwise, stirring continued at 5° for 27 h, then quenched with satd. aq. NaHCO$_3$ → (4S,5S)-product. Y 92% (85% cis-isomer; e.e. 84%). This is the first example of a catalytic, asym., cis-selective preparation of Δ$^2$-oxazoline-4-carboxylates using a chiral catalyst. Poor results were obtained with cinnamaldehyde and 2-thiophenecarboxaldehyde. F.e.s. H. Suga et al., Tetrahedron Lett. *39*, 869-72 (1998); preparation of trialkylalanes from halides with Al,Mg alloy s. Japanese patent JP-09077774 (Mitsui Toatsu Chem. Inc.).

*Dialkylborinyl triflate/tert. amine*      $R_2BOTf/R_3N$
**Asym. aldol condensation with carboxylic acid esters**      C(OH)C-COOR
via boron ester enolates s. *51*, 275; effect of the dialkylborinyl triflate/tert. amine combination on *syn-* versus *anti*-selectivity s. Tetrahedron Lett. *39*, 1873-6 (1998).

*Di-n-butylborinyl triflate/triethylamine*      $Bu_2BOTf/Et_3N$
**Polymer-based asym. aldol condensation with 3-acyl-2-oxazolidones**    CO → C(OH)C-CO
s. *38*, 632s*54*; s.a. C.W. Phoon, C. Abell, Tetrahedron Lett. *39*, 2655-8 (1998).

*Aluminum tris(2,6-diphenylphenoxide) s. under i-Pr$_2$NLi*      $Ar(OAr)_3$

*2,7-Dimethyl-1,8-biphenylenedioxybis(dialkylaluminums)*      ←
**Synthesis of sec. alcohols from aldehydes**      CHO → CH(OH)R

242.    Ph-CHO + [Me$_2$AlO-(2,7-dimethylbiphenylene)-OAlMe$_2$] ⟶ PhCH(OH)Me

By comparison with the sluggish addition of Me$_3$Al and (2,6-dimethylphenoxy)dimethylaluminum (DDA) to aldehydes, reaction with *bidentate* 2,7-dimethyl-1,8-biphenylenedioxybis(dialkylaluminums) is considerably enhanced as a result of the facile formation of a cyclic 6-membered transition state via an initially formed 1:1 coordination complex. **E:** 2 eqs. 2 *M* Me$_3$Al in hexane added at room temp. under argon to a degassed suspension of 2,7-dimethyl-1,8-biphenylenediol in dry methylene chloride, stirred for 30 min, cooled to -78°, benzaldehyde added dropwise, allowed to warm to *-20°*, stirring continued for 4 h, and poured into ice-cooled 1 *N* HCl → 1-phenylethanol. Y 84% (no reaction with DDA). Reaction takes place even more smoothly (at -78° to -40°) with the *amphiphilic* mono-ate complex formed from 2,7-dimethyl-1,8-biphenylenedioxy(dimethylaluminum) and 1 eq. MeLi. F.e.s. T. Ooi, M. Takahashi, K. Maruoka, Angew. Chem. Int. Ed. Engl. *37*, 835-7 (1998).

*Montmorillonite K 10*      ←
**α-Siloxynitriles from aldehydes under heterogeneous catalysis**    CHO → CH(OSi≼)CN
with Fe(III)-exchanged montmorillonite cf. *49*, 589; with montmorillonite K 10 from ar. or aliphatic aldehydes s. R. Somanathan et al., Synth. Commun. *28*, 2043-8 (1998).

*Montmorillonite K 10/microwaves*      ←
**Sym. 1,2-disiloxy compds. from oxo compds.**    2 CO → C(OSi≼)C(OSi≼)
**under microwave irradiation on a solid support in the absence of solvent**

243.    2 PhCHO + 2 Me$_3$SiCl ⟶ PhCH(OSiMe$_3$)CH(OSiMe$_3$)Ph

Benzaldehyde, 1.1 eqs. trimethylsilyl chloride, and ca. 1 g montmorillonite K 10 clay in a Teflon container irradiated in a microwave oven for 1.5-2 min → product. Y 85% (*dl/meso* ratio 0.62). This is a mild, effective, environmentally friendly and practical method for coupling aldehydes and ketones under solvent-free conditions. Aromatic aldehydes and ketones were reduced in good yield, but aliphatic ketones produced coupling products in lower yields. F.e.s. M. Bolourtchian et al., Synth. Commun. *28*, 2017-20 (1998).

*Hydrotalcites s. under KOBu-t*      ←

*Boron fluoride*     $BF_3$
**Syntheses via acylzirconocene chlorides as acyl carbanion equivalents**    ←

244.

**α-Hydroxyketones from aldehydes**. 4 eqs. 1-Octene added to a suspension of 2 eqs. $Cp_2Zr(H)Cl$ in methylene chloride, stirred for 30 min at room temp., then again for 2 h under an atmosphere of CO, benzaldehyde and 2 eqs. $BF_3$-etherate added at -20°, stirred at 0° for 1 h, and quenched with aq. $NaHCO_3$ → 1-hydroxy-1-phenyl-2-decanone. Y 79%. Neither ketones nor acyl chlorides reacted with the generated acylzirconocene chloride, and reaction was impeded with pivalaldehyde for steric reasons; treatment with $ZnCl_2$ in place of $BF_3$-etherate gave the corresponding aldehydes. F.e. and regio- and stereo-selectivity, **also (E)-α,β-ethylene-α′-hydroxyketones** from acetylene derivs. via α,β-ethyleneacylzirconocene chlorides, s. S. Harada et al., Angew. Chem. Int. Ed. Engl. *37*, 1696-8 (1998).

*Indium(III) fluoride/trimethylsilyl cyanide*     $InF_3/Me_3SiCN$
**Cyanohydrins from aldehydes in aqueous medium**     CHO → CH(OH)CN

245.     $CH_2=CHCHO + Me_3SiCN \longrightarrow CH_2=CHCH(OH)CN$

2 eqs. Trimethylsilyl cyanide added to a mixture of acrolein and 0.3 eq. $InF_3$ in water, and stirred vigorously overnight at room temp. → product. Y 75%. The method is clean, extremely mild, high-yielding, and chemoselective (ketones remaining unaffected), and $InF_3$ is commercially available and stable in water. The procedure is also generally applicable to aliphatic, ar. and α,β-unsatd. aldehydes. F.e.s. T.-P. Loh et al., Synlett *1998*, 369-70.

*Samarium/diethylaluminum iodide*     $Sm/Et_2AlI$
*Samarium diiodide/alcohols*     $SmI_2/ROH$
**Sym. glycols from oxo compds.**     C(OH)C(OH)
with $SmI_2$/LiCl cf. *53*, 22s54 and with $SmI_2$/Ti(OPr-*i*)$_4$ cf. *43*, 571s52; from aryl ketones with Sm/Et$_2$AlI s. Y. Nishiyama, Tetrahedron Lett. *39*, 3705-8 (1998); chiral polyoxy-functionalized cyclopentane-1,2-diols by one-pot Swern oxidation-intramolecular pinacolization with $SmI_2$/*t*-BuOH s. M. Adinolfi et al., ibid. 2021-4; chiral decalin ring by hydroxyl-directed intramolecular pinacolization with $SmI_2$/MeOH, and reversal of stereoselectivity with added HMPA, s. M. Kawatsura et al., Synlett *1997*, 479-80.

*Chiral lanthanum(III) 1,1′-bi-2-naphthoxides*     ←
**Cyanohydrins from aldehydes by asym. hydrocyanation**     CHO → CH(OH)CN
with Ti(OPr-*i*)$_4$/(R)-BINOL cf. *43*, 576s54; with chiral lanthanum(III) 1,1′-bi-2-naphthoxides s. C. Qian et al., J. Chem. Soc. Perkin Trans. I *1998*, 2131-2.

*Scandium(III) triflate*     $Sc(OTf)_3$
**Catalytic ene reaction**     CO → C(OH)C-C=C
using Yb(OTf)$_3$ cf. *54*, 261; with unactivated ethylene derivs. using Sc(OTf)$_3$, and *in situ* trapping of the product by O-acetylation s. V.K. Aggarwal et al., Tetrahedron Lett. *39*, 1997-2000 (1998); ene reaction of trifluoroacetaldehyde with dienes using Zn(OTf)$_2$ s. E. Hayashi et al., Bull. Chem. Soc. Japan *67*, 3040-3 (1994).

*Samarium trichloride/chiral bis(phosphorodiamidates)*     ←
**α-Siloxynitriles from aldehydes - Asym. conversion**     CHO → CH(OSi≤)CN

246.

Freshly distilled benzaldehyde (1 mmol) and 1.5-2 eqs. trimethylsilyl cyanide added sequentially to a suspension of *0.2 mol%* dry $SmCl_3$ and *0.6 mol%* (2S,2′S,4S,4′S,5R,5R′)-N,N′-bis(3,4-

dimethyl-2-oxo-5-phenyl-1,3,2-oxazaphospholan-2-yl)ethane-1,2-diamine [prepared easily from (1R,2S)-(-)-ephedrine, POCl$_3$ and ethylenediamine] in toluene at -78° under N$_2$, and the heterogeneous mixture stirred for 24 h while maintaining the temp. at -10 to -20° → product. Y 99% (e.e. ca. 80%). Significantly, the chiral auxiliary can be used in minute amount, and is readily retrievable. Other Lewis acids, e.g. SmI$_3$, LaCl$_3$ and Sc(OTf)$_3$, were also effective, but Sm(OPr-$i$)$_3$ or Ti(OPr-$i$)$_4$ were inefficient in terms of conversion or enantioselectivity. F.e.s. W.-B. Yang, J.-M. Fang, J. Org. Chem. *63*, 1356-9 (1998).

*Oxynitrilase* ←
**Cyanohydrins from aldehydes by asym. hydrocyanation**   CHO → CH(OH)CN
s. *22*, 693s53; in a micro-aq. organic phase (diisopropyl ether or ethyl acetate) cf. S. Han et al., Tetrahedron:Asym. *9*, 1835-8 (1998).

*Titanium tetraisopropoxide s.a. under R$_2$Zn*   Ti(OPr-i)$_4$
*Titanium tetraisopropoxide/isopropylmagnesium chloride*   Ti(OPr-i)$_4$/i-PrMgCl
**Regio- and stereo-specific synthesis of 3-ethylenealcohols**   CO → C(OH)C-C=C
from 2-ethylenecarbonic acid esters s. *51*, 281s52; chiral N-protected 2-vinyl-3-aminoalcohols s. X. Teng et al., Tetrahedron Lett. *38*, 8977-80 (1997).

**3-Acetylenealcohols from 2-acetylenephosphoric acid esters**   CHO → CH(OH)C-C≡C
and aldehydes with asym. induction s. *55*, 347

*Titanium tetraisopropoxide/chiral Schiff base* ←
**δ-Hydroxy-β-ketocarboxylic acid esters from aldehydes**   C(OH)C-CO-C-COOR
asym. synthesis with at least 50 mol% Ti(IV)-Schiff base complex cf. *49*, 595; *catalytic* version with 20 mol% Schiff base s. N. Oguni et al., Synlett *1998*, 601-2.

*Chiral titanium(IV)-1,1'-bi-2-naphthol complex* ←
**Asym. ene reaction**   CO → C(OH)C-C=C
s. *44*, 568s51; with α,β-unsatd. aldehydes and methyl glyoxylate s. K. Mikami et al., Tetrahedron Lett. *37*, 8515-8 (1996).

*Germanium diiodide/potassium*   GeI$_2$/K
**Stereospecific germanium-mediated Reformatskii synthesis**   CHO → CH(OH)C-CO
**under mild conditions**

247.

**with asym. induction.** 4 eqs. Freshly-cut K-metal added to a suspension of 2.2 eqs. GeI$_2$ [predried at 100° for 1 h under reduced pressure] in THF contained in a flame-dried flask under argon, the mixture stirred vigorously under reflux for 2 h, the resulting black suspension of activated germanium metal allowed to cool to room temp., 2 eqs. startg. chiral oxazolidone in THF and 1 eq. benzaldehyde in THF added successively dropwise, and stirred at room temp. for 18 h → adduct (Y 94% based on the aldehyde; *syn*:*anti* 99:1; 4R,5S:4S:5R 99:1) and debrominated acyl-oxazolidone (Y 22% based on the bromo-deriv.). A single recrystallization afforded diastereo-merically pure adducts (Y 83% for the example above). A drawback of the method is the need to use 2 eqs. of chiral substrate to achieve superior reaction rate, yield and diastereoselectivity. F.e. incl. stereospecific Reformatskii synthesis with α-brominated ketones s. H. Kagoshima et al., J. Org. Chem. *63*, 691-7 (1998).

*Titanium tetrachloride*   TiCl$_4$
**Regio- and stereo-specific Lewis acid-catalyzed aldol condensation**   CHO → CH(OH)C-CO
**with unsym. ketones**

248.

Aldol condensation with unsym. ketones takes place at the *more hindered* α-site in the presence of TiCl$_4$ *in catalytic* amount. **E:** 0.1 eq. TiCl$_4$ added dropwise to a soln. of benzaldehyde and

2-butanone in anhydrous toluene *at room temp.* under argon in an inert atmosphere, and stirred for 16 h → product. Y 83% (97:3 mixture of regioisomers; *syn:anti* 95:5). Significantly, *no base is required*, and prior conversion of the ketone to an active enol deriv. is not necessary. F.e.s. R. Mahrwald, B. Gündogan, J. Am. Chem. Soc. *120*, 413-4 (1998).

*Bis(pentafluorophenyl)tin dibromide* $(C_6F_5)_2SnBr_2$
**Parallel differentiated recognition of ketones and acetals** ←
and of ketones and aldehydes s. *55*, 446

*Chromium(III) chloride/manganese/dichlorodimethylsilane* ←
**Catalytic pinacolization** C(OH)C(OH)
of ar. aldehydes with $Cp_2TiCl_2/Zn/Me_3SiCl/MgBr_2$ cf. *52*, 268; also of ar. ketones with $CrCl_3$ (or $Cp_2Cr$) in the presence of Mn and $Me_2SiCl_2$ s. A. Svatos, W. Boland, Synlett *1998*, 549-51.

*Lithium trialkylmanganates* $R_3MnLi$
**3-Ethylenealcohols from aldehydes** CHO → CH(OH)C-C=C
and allyl chloride with Mn/Cu cf. *52*, 273s54; with allylmanganese(II) compds. generated from 1,3-dibromopropene and Li-trialkylmanganates, regio- and stereo-selectivity, s. H. Kakiya, K. Oshima et al., Chem. Lett. *1998*, 73-4.

*Tetrakis(trimethylphosphine)cobalt(0)* $[Co(PMe_3)_4]$
**Reformatskii-type synthesis of β-hydroxyphosphonic acid esters** CH(OH)C-PO(OR)$_2$
**from α-halogenophosphonic acid esters and oxo compds.**

249.        PhCHO + ICH$_2$PO(OEt)$_2$  ⟶  PhCH(OH)CH$_2$PO(OEt)$_2$

A soln. of 3 eqs. diethyl iodomethylphosphonate and 1 eq. benzaldehyde in THF added dropwise to a soln. of 3 eqs. [Co(PMe$_3$)$_4$] in the same solvent at room temp., and worked-up when reaction complete by TLC → product. Y 81%. The method is mild, neutral, and does not require freshly dried solvents. The yield depends on the nature of halogenophosphonate and carbonyl compd., and on the amount of Co-phosphine complex. F.e. and with the corresponding Ph$_3$P complex s. F. Orsini, Tetrahedron Lett. *39*, 1425-8 (1998).

*Acetoacetonato(dicarbonyl)rhodium(I)/(R,R)-2,2"-bis[(S)-1-(diphenylphosphino)-* ←
*ethyl]-1,1"-biferrocene*
**α-Cyano-β-hydroxycarboxylic acid esters from aldehydes** CHO → CH(OH)C(CN)COOR
**Asym. aldol condensation**

250.

0.01 eq. Rh(acac)(CO)$_2$ and 0.011 eq. (R,R)-2,2"-bis[(S)-1-(diphenylphosphino)ethyl]-1,1"-biferrocene in dibutyl ether stirred at room temp. for 10 min, startg. 2-cyanopropionate followed by 1.34 eqs. aq. paraformaldehyde (freshly prepared as a clear soln. by refluxing a suspension of paraformaldehyde in water for 1 h) added at -10°, and the mixture stirred at this temp. for 24 h → product. Y 86% (e.e. 93%). The enantioselectivity is very dependent on the solvent used, dibutyl ether giving the best result. A bulky ester group on the 2-cyanopropionate was also essential to attain high enantioselectivity (Y 67%, e.e. 35% for the methyl ester). Electron-withdrawing groups on the P-aromatic group of the *trans*-chelating ligand gave lower enantioselectivity and reactivity, while electron-donating groups gave slightly higher selectivity; however, dialkylphosphino analogs showed much lower selectivity. F.e.s. R. Kuwano et al., Chem. Commun. *1998*, 71-2.

*Tetrakis(triphenylphosphine)palladium(0) s. under Et$_2$Zn* Pd(PPh$_3$)$_4$

*[(1R,1'R)-2,6-Bis[1-(diphenylphosphino)ethyl]phenyl]chloropalladium(II)* ←
**Asym. synthesis of Δ$^2$-oxazolines from isonitriles and aldehydes** ○
with chiral cationic arylpalladium(II) bis(Δ$^2$-oxazoline) complexes cf. *42*, 612s54; with [(1R,1'R)-2,6-bis[1-(diphenylphosphino)ethyl]phenyl]chloropalladium(II) s. J.M. Longmire et al., Organometallics *17*, 4374-9 (1998).

*Ethylenebis(triphenylphosphine)platinum* $Pt(CH_2{=}CH_2)(PPh_3)_2$
**Regio- and stereo-specific synthesis of γ'-siloxy-γ,δ-ethyleneboronic acid esters** ←
**from 1,3-dienes and aldehydes**

251.

**via silaboration.** A soln. of startg. diene, silylboronate, and *1.5 eqs.* benzaldehyde in octane heated at 120° with 2 mol% $Pt(CH_2{=}CH_2)(PPh_3)_2$ until reaction complete → product. Y 79% (99:1 mixture of diastereoisomers). Reaction takes place via oxidative addition of Pt to the B-Si bond, followed by regioselective insertion of the least substituted ethylene group into the generated Pt-B bond to give an intermediate **4-boryl-2-ethyleneplatinum complex** which reacts with the aldehyde at the γ-position. Significantly, 1,4-silaboration takes place in the absence of the aldehyde. Reaction is efficient with both aliphatic and ar. aldehydes. F.e.s. M. Suginome, Y. Ito et al., J. Am. Chem. Soc. *120*, 4248-9 (1998).

## Addition to Nitrogen and Carbon            CC ⇓ NC

*Without additional reagents*                                                    w.a.r.
**β-Ketothiolactams from lactams via α,β-ethylene-β-siloxy-α-(silyl)thiolactams**
**Ring expansion by two C-atoms**

252.

A mixture of bis(trimethylsilyl)thioketene and N-methyl-2-pyrrolidone allowed to react at room temp. → intermediate adduct (Y 56%), in methanol containing 0.01 wt% HCl allowed to stand for a further 4 h → N-methyl-3-oxo-ε-thiocaprolactam. Y 54% overall. F.e.s. Japanese patent JP-10045719 (Agency of Industrial Science & Technology); also **β-oxocarboxylic acid thioamides** s. T. Tsuchiya et al., Chem. Commun. *1996*, 1621-2.

*n-Butyllithium*                                                                 *BuLi*
**α-Phosphonylamidines from phosphonic acid esters** s. *55*, 369     $H \rightarrow C(NR_2){=}NH$

*Magnesium*                                                                      *Mg*
**Asym. synthesis of hydroxylamines from nitrones**         $C{=}N(O)R \rightarrow C(R')N(OH)R$
s. *11*, 752s52; addition of Grignards or organolithiums to erythrulose-derived cyclic nitrones s. J.A. Marco et al., Tetrahedron Lett. *39*, 3237-40 (1998).

**Asym. synthesis of prim. amines**                     $C{=}NN{<} \rightarrow C(R)NHN{<}$
from aldehyde hydrazones with RLi cf. *42*, 621; chiral α-subst. benzylamines with Grignards s. P. Bataille et al., Tetrahedron:Asym. *9*, 2181-92 (1998).

*Magnesium/magnesium halides*                                       *$Mg/MgBr_2$ or $MgI_2$*
**Asym. synthesis of sec. amines from chiral azomethines**     $C{=}NR \rightarrow C(R')NHR$
s. *39*, 612; effect of $MgBr_2$ or $MgI_2$ on diastereoselective addition to acyclic ketimines, and conversion to chiral α,α-disubst. prim. amines s. D.M. Spero, S.R. Kapadia, J. Org. Chem. *62*, 5537-41 (1997).

*Zinc*                                                                           *Zn*
**Blaise reaction**                                                  $C(NH_2){=}C{-}COOR$
under ultrasonication s. *52*, 278; β-amino-α,β-ethylene-γ-siloxycarboxylic acid esters with retention

of chirality, also conversion to rac. β-amino-γ-lactones, s. J. Syed et al., Tetrahedron:Asym. *9*, 805-15 (1998); racemization-free conversion to β-keto-γ-lactones [tetronic acids] s. ibid. 817-25.

*Zinc/sodium hydroxide*                                             *Zn/NaOH*
**Sym. 1,2-diamines from aldimines**              2 CH=NR → CH(NHR)CH(NHR)
macrocyclic 1,2-diamines with $Zn/MeSO_3H$ cf. *47*, 614; with Zn in 10% NaOH, stereoselective intermolecular coupling, s. M.P. Dutta et al., Synlett *1998*, 857-8.

*Magnesium bromide/ethyldiisopropylamine*                     $MgBr_2/i\text{-}Pr_2NEt$
**Synthesis of sulfonylamines from N-sulfonylimines**      $C=NSO_2R → C(R)NHSO_2R$
with asym. induction using organolithium compds. cf. *49*, 606; chiral 1-(β-sulfonylaminoacyl)-pyrazoles from 1-acylpyrazoles s. C. Kashima et al., J. Heterocycl. Chem. *34*, 1559-65 (1997).

*Chiral aluminum salen complex*                                              ←
**α-(Trifluoroacetylamino)nitriles from aldimines**                CH=NR → CH(CN)NHR
**Asym. Strecker synthesis**

253.

The first instance of an asym. Strecker synthesis catalyzed by a *main* group salen metal complex is reported. **E:** 1.2 eqs. 0.85 *M* HCN in toluene added with stirring at -70° to 5 mol% chiral Al salen complex in the same solvent, after 5 min the mixture treated via syringe in one portion with startg. imine, followed after a further 15 h with 1.5 eqs. trifluoroacetic anhydride, and allowed to warm to room temp. → (S)-product. Y 91% (e.e. 95%). The catalyst can be prepared easily on a large scale and appears to have an indefinite shelf-life even at room temp. Enantioselectivity was lower from aliphatic and cycloaliphatic aldimines, but the nature of the N-substituent had little effect. F.e. and conversion to chiral α-aminocarboxylic acid esters (with retention of chirality), s. M.S. Sigman, E.N. Jacobsen, J. Am. Chem. Soc. *120*, 5315-6 (1998); parallel screening of a library of chiral N-(2-thioureidocyclohexyl)-*o*-hydroxyaldimines (*without* a central metal) for asym. Strecker synthesis s. ibid. 4901-2.

*Boron fluoride*                                                                      $BF_3$
**Pyrrolo[1,2-*a*]quinoxalines**
by Bischler-Napieralski ring closure cf. *25*, 662; 4-α-hydroxypyrrolo[1,2-*a*]quinoxalines from N-(*o*-isocyanoaryl)pyrroles and oxo compds. with $BF_3$ s. K. Kobayashi et al., Chem. Lett. *1998*, 551-2.

**trans-3,4-Dihydroisocarbostyril-4-carboxylic acids from homophthalic anhydrides**   ←
and azomethines without reagent cf. *32*, 617; improved method with $BF_3$-etherate, also one-pot procedure from aldehydes for *in situ*-generation of azomethines (with $Na_2SO_4$), s. N. Yu, J.-C. Gesquiere et al., Tetrahedron Lett. *39*, 829-32 (1998).

*Samarium*                                                                                            *Sm*
**β,γ-Ethylenecarboxylic acid amides from isocyanates**      $NCO → NHCOCH_2CH=CH_2$
**Synthesis with addition of three C-atoms**

254.

2.2 eqs. Sm and 2.5 eqs. allyl bromide stirred at room temp. under $N_2$, the resulting purple mixture stirred for a further 1 h until homogeneous, phenyl isocyanate added, and stirring continued at room temp. until reaction complete → product. Y 86%. The procedure is simple, rapid, and mild (neutral). F.e., also **β,γ-ethylenecarboxylic acid thioamides from isothiocyanates,** s. M. Yu et al., J. Chem. Res., Synop *1998*, 256-7.

*Samarium diiodide/magnesium/ytterbium(III) triflate*      $SmI_2/Mg/Yb(OTf)_3$
**Sym. 1,2-diamines from azomethines** s. *43*, 584s55      2 C=NR → C(NHR)C(NHR)

*Chiral N-(2-thioureidocyclohexyl)-o-hydroxyaldimines*      ←
**Asym. Strecker synthesis** s. *55*, 253      CH=NR → CH(CN)NHR

*Bis(cyclopentadienyl)phenyltitanium(III)*      $Cp_2TiPh$
**Radical ring closures of cyanoketones** s. *55*, 482      ○

*Titanium trichloride/lithium*      $TiCl_3/Li$
**Sym. 1,2-diamines from azomethines**      2 C=NR → C(NHR)C(NHR)
from aldimines with $Cp_2TiCl_2$/Sm cf. *43*, 584s*53*; from ar. or aliphatic aldimines with $TiCl_3$/Li s. S. Talukdar, A. Banerji, J. Org. Chem. *63*, 3468-70 (1998); also from ketimines with $SmI_2$ *(0.2 eq.)* in the presence of Mg (excess) and 1 eq. $Yb(OTf)_3$ (cf. *43*, 584s*46*), also with asym. induction, s. R. Annunziata et al., Tetrahedron Lett. *39*, 3333-6 (1998).

*Lithium perchlorate*      $LiClO_4$
*Bis(benzonitrile)dichloropalladium(II)*      $(PhCN)_2PdCl_2$
**2-Iminopyrrolidines from aziridines and ketenimines**      ○

255.

Equimolar amounts of (S)-1-*tert*-butyl-2-phenylaziridine (e.e. 93%) and startg. ketenimine in THF added to 5 mol% $LiClO_4$ in the same solvent, and allowed to react at room temp. for 5 h → (R)-product. Y 76% (e.e. 83%). Reactivity depends on the electronic nature of the substituent on the aziridine ring (e.g. with an ester group at the $C_2$-position a higher temp. (50°) and longer reaction period (18 h) was required). The method is mild, regioselective, and proceeds with retention of chirality. F.e., also with $(PhCN)_2PdCl_2$ as catalyst in lower yield but with less racemization, s. H. Maas et al., J. Org. Chem. *63*, 17-20 (1998).

*Iridium hydride complexes*      ←
**(Z)-β-Amino-α,β-ethylenenitriles from two different nitrile molecules**      $C(CN)=C(NH_2)$

256.

**under mild, neutral conditions.** A mixture of startg. α-cyanoketone, 2 eqs. methoxyacetonitrile, and 3 mol% $IrH(CO)(PPh_3)_3$ in dry THF stirred at 120° for 12 h under argon → product. Y 96%. Reaction, which proceeds chemo-, regio- and stereo-selectively, involves initial oxidative addition of a low-valent iridium species into the α-C-H bond of the cyanoketone, followed by addition across the CN triple bond of the second nitrile molecule, itself activated by the same catalyst. The more basic $IrH_5(i-Pr_3P)_2$ was used for activation of unfunctionalized nitriles (e.g. acetonitrile). $RuH_2(PPh_3)_4$ was ineffective. F.e. incl. **cyclic β-amino-α,β-ethylenenitriles from dinitriles,** and dimerization of ethyl cyanoacetate s. H. Takaya et al., J. Am. Chem. Soc. *120*, 4244-5 (1998).

## Addition to Remaining Elements and Carbon     CC ⇓ RemC

*Lithium organo(cyano)cuprates*      $RCu(CN)Li$
**Selenolic acid esters from organolithium compds.** s. *55*, 382      RLi → RC(O)SeR'

## Addition to Carbon-Carbon Bonds                                  CC ⇓ CC

*Without additional reagents*                                                      w.a.r.
**Diels-Alder reaction with 2-amino-1,3-dienes with asym. induction**
s. *49*, 622; asym. cycloaddition to nitroalkenes and conversion to chiral 4-nitrocyclohexanones, also Michael addition with (Z)-2-amino-1,3-dienes, f. details s. J. Org. Chem. *62*, 6746-53 (1997).

**Diels-Alder reaction with 2-pyridones**
s. *34*, 627s*48*; with bulky 1-(arylsulfonyl)-2-pyridones, prevention of N→O-sulfonyl group migration, s. K. Afarinkia, F. Mahmood, Tetrahedron Lett. *39*, 493-6 (1998).

**Regio- and stereo-specific 1,3-dipolar cycloaddition**
with nitrile oxides s. *16*, 888s*54*; **polymer-based 1,3-dipolar cycloaddition** with nitrile oxides and supported alkynes or alkenes, also parallel solution-phase synthesis, s. E.J. Kantorowski, M.J. Kurth, J. Org. Chem. *62*, 6797-803 (1997); also with polymer-based nitrile oxides cf. J.-F. Cheng, A.M.M. Mjalli, Tetrahedron Lett. *39*, 939-42 (1998); preparation of a small library of isoxazoles and isoxazolines from a supported nitrile oxide cf. B.B. Shankar et al., ibid. 2447-8; polymer-based synthesis of 5-(Δ$^2$-isoxazolin-5-ylmethyl)hydantoins s. K.-H. Park et al., Chem. Commun. *1998*, 1679-80.

**1,3-Dipolar cycloaddition with isoquinolinium N-imides**
s. *22*, 708; 1,2,3,10b tetrahydropyrazolo[5,1-*a*]isoquinolines s R. Huisgen, R. Temme. Eur. J. Org. Chem. *1998*, 387-401.

**1-Alkoxypyrrolidine-3-carboxylic acid esters**
**from 2-alkylidenecyclopropanone ketals and alkoximes**

257.

[3+2]-Cycloaddition with trimethylenemethane equivalents (cf. *48*, 638) has been adapted with alkoximes in place of electron-deficient olefins. **E:** A soln. of startg. cyclopropanone ketal and 0.83 eq. *anti*-glyoxylic acid *tert*-butyl ester O-benzyloxime in acetonitrile-d$_3$ heated in a sealed NMR tube at 100° for 17 h, treated with 1 *N* 10% HCl in THF, and stirred for 5 min → 1-benzyloxy-*cis*-4-(2,2-dimethyl-3-hydroxypropoxycarbonyl)-*cis*-5-isopropyl-*r*-2-*tert*-butoxycarbonylpyrrolidine. Y 79% (>97% *cis* after GLC). Reaction was smooth with alkoximes derived from ar. or heteroar. aldehydes, but aliphatic derivs. were poor substrates, even under high pressure (10 kbar). F.e.s. S. Yamago, E. Nakamura et al., J. Org. Chem. *63*, 1694-703 (1998).

**3-Component synthesis of 3-alkoxy-2,9-dioxa-1-azabicyclo[4.3.0]nonanes**
**via regiospecific asym. hetero-Diels-Alder reaction-1,3-dipolar cycloaddition**

258.

**Carbohydrate derivs.** Startg. carbohydrate-derived nitroalkene allowed to react with excesses of ethyl vinyl ether and methyl vinyl ketone in ethanol at room temp. for 5-7 days → product. Y 70% (diastereomerically pure after flash chromatography and crystallization). Selective

6-membered ring opening was achieved under mild conditions by refluxing in 1:1 ethanol/water. This provides a route to richly functionalized nitrogen-containing polycyclics from an acyclic precursor, and to homologated carbohydrates. F.e.s. M. Avalos et al., Chem. Commun. *1998*, 459-60.

*Irradiation (s.a. under Benzophenone and Azodiisobutyronitrile)*
**Synthesis of enetellurides from acetylene derivs.** s. *55*, 490         $C \equiv C \rightarrow C(TeR) = C(R')$
**6-Acyl-*p*-quinone methids from *p*-quinones and acetylene derivs.**

259.

**Regiospecific conversion.** A 0.1 $M$ soln. of 3,5-dimethyl-1-(phenylethynyl)benzene and 2,6-dichlorobenzoquinone in methylene chloride irradiated under argon in a quartz cuvette with focused light from a 500 W medium-pressure Hg-lamp (filtered through an aq. IR filter and an ESCO 410 nm filter) for 22 h → product (as a 10:1 mixture of regioisomers). Y 88% (62% conversion). Addition to unsym. acetylenes proceeded with remarkable selectivity in favour of the more substituted benzylidene group and the least substituted benzoyl group. Products arise via Paterno-Büchi reaction, formation of cyclobutene derivs. by cycloaddition to the quinone ring not taking place. F.e. with regioselectivity up to 25:1 s. E. Bosch et al., J. Am. Chem. Soc. *120*, 386-95 (1998).

*Electrolysis*
**1,4-Addition with electrochemically-generated carbanions**         $C = C \rightarrow CHC(R)$
s. *39*, 578s*47, 49*; addition to *p*-quinone monoketals s. S. Torii et al., Synlett *1998*, 599-600.

*Electrolysis/nickel(II) complex*         ⚡/Ni(II)
**Electrochemical 1,4-addition of halides**
s. *47*, 450s*51*; 1,4-addition to α-methylene-γ-lactones in the presence of a nickel(II) perchlorate complex s. S. Ozaki et al., Chem. Pharm. Bull. *45*, 198-201 (1997).

*Microwaves (s.a. under Piperidine and CeCl₃)*         ←
**Diels-Alder reaction with microwave enhancement**         ○
s. *41*, 199s*42*; with fluorinated dienophiles, e.g. 1,2-difluoro-1-chlorovinyl phenyl sulfone, s. M. Sridhar et al., Tetrahedron Lett. *39*, 6529-32 (1998).

*Organolithium compds.*         RLi
**1,4-Addition of organolithium compds. to α,β-ethylenecarboxylic acids**         $C = C \rightarrow CHC(R)$

260.

2.2 eqs. *n*-BuLi (1.6 $M$ in hexanes) in dry THF under argon cooled to -78°, (E)-2-butenoic acid in THF added slowly, the mixture stirred at -78° for 1 h, 4 eqs. trifluoroacetic acid in THF added, and the soln. allowed to warm slowly to room temp. with stirring → 3-methylheptanoic acid. Y 80%. Initial deprotonation of the acid reduced, but did not completely suppress, the reactivity of the carbonyl group towards 1,2-addition. Reaction with PhLi proceeded sluggishly, and MeLi failed to react. F.e.s. B. Plunian et al., Chem. Commun. *1998*, 81-2.

*Organolithium compds./chiral diamines*         ←
**Asym. 1,4-addition to α,β-ethylenecarboxylic acid esters**
s. *54*, 281; asym. addition of aryllithiums to *tert*-butyl esters in the presence of (-)-sparteine s. F. Xu et al., Tetrahedron:Asym. *9*, 1651-5 (1998).

n-*Butyllithium* BuLi
**3-Component synthesis of α-(arylthiomethyl)-β-hydroxycarboxylic acid esters** ←
**by stereospecific Michael addition-aldol condensation**

261.
Ph-CHO + CH$_2$=CH-CO$_2$Bu-t + PhSH →[n-BuLi] [PhSLi] → Ph-CH(OH)-CH(SPh)-CO$_2$Bu-t

Startg. acrylate added to Li-thiophenolate (formed as a white precipitate on treatment of thiophenol with *n*-BuLi at -78° in methylene chloride), treated with benzaldehyde at the same temp., and the homogeneous, pale-yellow soln. kept at -50° for 7 h → product. Y 80% (*syn:anti* 92:8). Reaction was applicable to aliphatic, ar., and α,β-ethylenic aldehydes, but stereoselectivity was low with methyl or ethyl acrylate. Phenoxide was too unreactive to promote reaction, but lithium phenylselenolate (from diphenyl diselenide and MeLi) gave the corresponding **α-(arylselenomethyl)-β-hydroxycarboxylic acid esters**. F.e.s. A. Kamimura et al., Chem. Commun. *1998*, 1095-6.

*Potassium carbonate* $K_2CO_3$
**Michael addition** C≡C → CH=C(R)
s. *47*, 631; of cyclic β-ketoesters to α,β-acetylenecarbonyl compds. in acetone with 10 mol% $K_2CO_3$ s. M. Miesch et al., Tetrahedron Lett. *39*, 6873-6 (1998).

**ω,ω-Bis(hydroxymethyl)-ω-nitrocarboxylic acids from cyclic α-nitroketones** C

262.
2-nitrocyclohexanone + CH$_2$O → HO-C(CH$_2$OH)$_2$-cyclohexane-NO$_2$ derivative

3 eqs. 30% Aq. formaldehyde and 2-nitrocyclohexanone added to 2 eqs. $K_2CO_3$ in water, and stirred overnight at room temp. → product. Y 75%. F.e. and reduction to ω-amino-derivs. s. R. Ballini et al., Synlett *1997*, 1389-90.

*Piperidine/microwaves* ←
**2-Amino-3-cyano-5-nitrocyclohexene-1,3-dicarboxylic acid esters** ○
**from two α-cyano-α,β-ethylenecarboxylic acid ester molecules**

263.
2 Ph-C(CN)=CH-CO$_2$Me + MeNO$_2$ → cyclohexene product

Startg. alkene, 0.6 eq. nitromethane, and *0.04 eq.* piperidine in a quartz tube irradiated in a Synthewave 402 Prolabo microwave reactor (2.45 GHz) at 90° for 11 min → product. Y 70%. No solvent was required and no cyclopropane formation was observed. Reaction is highly diastereoselective (producing only two isomers), and is believed to proceed via **double Michael addition**, followed by Thorpe-type ring closure onto the nitrile. F.e. and with decarbomethoxylation using *0.5 eq.* piperidine s. D. Michaud, F. Texier-Boullet et al., Chem. Commun. *1997*, 1613-4.

*Cinchona alkaloids* ←
**Asym. Diels-Alder reaction with 2-pyrones**
with Ti(OPr-*i*)$_4$/(R)-1,1'-bi-2-naphthol cf. *36*, 667s*51*; asym. cycloaddition of 3-hydroxy-2-pyrone to chiral N-acryloyl-2-oxazolidones in the presence of cinchona alkaloids s. H. Okamura et al., Tetrahedron Lett. *39*, 1211-4 (1998).

*Dilithium dialkyl(cyano)cuprates/n-butyllithium/trimethylsilyl chloride* ←
**1,4-Addition to α,β-ethylenecarboxylic acids** C=C → CHC(R)
with Li-dialkylcuprates/BF$_3$ cf. *34*, 649; with R$_2$Cu(CN)Li$_2$ via *in situ*-generated silyl esters (with *n*-BuLi/Me$_3$SiCl) s. J.A. Vroman et al., Synth. Commun. *28*, 1555-62 (1998).

*Chiral lithium organo(α-sulfoximinyl)cuprates* ←
**Asym. 1,4-addition** s. *55*, 368

*Cupric acetoacetonate s. under Dicyclohexylborane*     $Cu(acac)_2$
*Cuprous acetate s. under Dicyclohexylborane*     $CuOAc$
*Copper(II) Schiff base complex*
**5-Alkoxy-2(3H)-furanones from 1,2-bisketenes**

264.

A soln. of startg. bisketene, ca. 1 eq. ethanol, and 3 mol% copper(II) Schiff base complex in toluene stirred for 12 h at room temp. → product. Y 95%. The process is highly selective, and a wide range of alcohols (prim., sec., and tert.), as well as phenols, may be used. Other metal complexes, however, were without effect, and there was no asym. induction with chiral catalysts. F.e.s. M.M. Dejmek, R. Selke, Angew. Chem. Int. Ed. Engl. 37, 1540-2 (1998).

*Chiral copper(II) α-aminocarboxylic acid complex*
**Lewis acid-catalyzed asym. Diels-Alder reaction in water**

265.

A soln. of 17.5 mol% L-abrine and 17.5 mol% NaOH in water added to a soln. of 10 mol% $Cu(NO_3)_2$ in water, the pH adjusted to 6-6.5, cooled to 0°, a soln. of startg. enone in the minimum of ethanol added together with 2 eqs. cyclopentadiene, and stirred for 48 h at 0° → product. Y 94% (e.e. 74%; abs. configuration not determined). This is the first example of a water-enhanced Lewis acid-catalyzed asym. Diels-Alder reaction. However, the amino acid must possess an aryl group, suggesting that arene-arene interactions with the enone (known to be favoured in aq. media) are important for the face selectivity. The e.e. values in acetonitrile, THF, ethanol, and chloroform were in the range 17-44%. Details and complexes s. S. Otto et al., J. Am. Chem. Soc. 120, 4238-9 (1998).

*Cupric trifluoromethanesulfonate s.a. under $R_2Zn$*     $Cu(OTf)_2$
*Cupric trifluoromethanesulfonate/chiral bis($\Delta^2$-oxazolines)*
**Asym. Diels-Alder reaction**
s. 46, 662s48; comparison of ligands s. I.W. Davies et al., Tetrahedron Lett. 38, 1145-8 (1997).
**2,3-Dihydro-4-pyrones from oxo compds.**
**Asym. hetero-Diels-Alder reaction**
from aldehydes s. 46, 662s52; chiral 2,3-dihydro-4-pyrone-2-carbonyl compds. from α-ketocarbonyl compds. s. M. Johannsen et al., Chem. Commun. 1997, 2169-70.
**2-Alkoxy-3,4-dihydro-2H-pyran-6-phosphonic**
**from α,β-ethyleneacylphosphonic acid esters and enolethers**
**Asym. hetero-Diels-Alder reaction**

266.

Startg. acylphosphonate and 3 eqs ethyl vinyl ether added sequentially to a 0.02 M soln. of 0.1 eq. chiral copper(II) bis($\Delta^2$-oxazoline) complex in methylene chloride at -78°, and worked up after 48 h → product. Y 89% (*endo/exo* 99:1; e.e. 99%). The high reactivity of the substrate and the stereoselectivity are explained by prior coordination of copper to both the carbonyl and phosphoryl oxygen of the phosphonate. As little as 0.2 mol% catalyst is sufficient over a broad temperature range. This represents the first example of cyclopentadiene behaving *as a dienophile* in a hetero-Diels-Alder reaction with an unsatd. carbonyl compd. F.e. incl. addition to cyclic enolethers, and catalysts, also conversion to **chiral δ-aldehydocarboxylic acid esters**, s. D.A. Evans, J.S. Johnson, J. Am. Chem. Soc. *120*, 4895-6 (1998).

| | |
|---|---:|
| *Cuprous chloride s. under Cp$_2$Zr(H)Cl* | CuCl |
| *Cuprous iodide s. under Mg* | CuI |
| *Copper(I) salt/trimethylamine hydrochloride* | Cu(I)/Me$_3$N·HCl |
| **(Z)-β-Arylseleno-α,β-ethyleneketones** | C(SeAr)=C-CO |
| **from selenolic acid aryl esters and cuprous acetylides** | |

267.

Ph—≡—Cu + PhSeCOAr → [Ph—≡—COAr + PhSeCu] → Ph\C=C/COAr with PhSe
Ar = p-ClC$_6$H$_4$

An equimolar mixture of startg. selenocarboxylate and cuprous phenylacetylide in dry DMF heated at 80-100° for 8-24 h under N$_2$, cooled to room temp., 1 eq. Me$_3$N·HCl added, and heated at 50-60° for 4 h → product. Y 93%. The method is highly regio- and stereo-selective. When the reaction was conducted in the presence of free base (Et$_3$N), only α,β-acetyleneketones were obtained, suggesting that acid is required to give the addition product. F.e. and from terminal acetylene derivs. with 25 mol% CuCl or CuI s. C.-Q. Zhao et al., Tetrahedron Lett. *39*, 1933-6 (1998); tellurium analogs s. J. Org. Chem. *63*, 4170-1 (1998).

| | |
|---|---:|
| *Magnesium/cuprous bromide-dimethyl sulfide/boron fluoride* | ← |
| *Magnesium/cuprous iodide* | Mg/CuI |
| **Asym. 1,4-addition to α,β-ethylenecarboxylic acid amides** | C=C → CHC(R) |

with Grignards s. *37*, 658; asym. addition of alkylmagnesium halides to unsatd. amides based on (R)-N-(2-fluorobenzyl)-2-aminobutanol s. E. Brown et al., J. Chem. Res., Synop *1997*, 348-9; with (R)-2-alkylaminobutan-1-ol as inexpensive chiral auxiliary s. ibid. *1996*, 224-5; asym. addition of homoallyl- and vinyl-magnesium halides s. Tetrahedron:Asym. *9*, 1605-14 (1998); asym. addition to 1-(α,β-ethyleneacyl)pyrazoles with added CuI s. C. Kashima et al., J. Heterocycl. Chem. *35*, 503-11 (1998); asym. addition of Yamamoto organocopper reagents to 3-(α,β-ethyleneacyl)-2-oxazolidones s. D.R. Williams et al., Tetrahedron Lett. *39*, 8593-6 (1998).

| | |
|---|---:|
| *Magnesium/manganese(II) chloride* | Mg/MnCl$_2$ |
| **Synthesis of ethylene from acetylene derivs.** | C≡C → CH=C(R) |

with Grignard compds. and a little CuI cf. *31*, 641; regio- and stereo-specific synthesis of β-subst. *o*-hydroxystyrenes with a little MnCl$_2$ s. S. Nishimae, K. Oshima et al., Chem. Lett. *1998*, 785-6.

| | |
|---|---:|
| *Magnesium/dichlorobis(triphenylphosphine)nickel(II)/* | ← |
| *(S,S)-1,2-bis(diphenylphosphino)ethane/triphenylphosphine* | |
| **Nickel-catalyzed asym. 1,4-addition to α,β-ethyleneacetals** | C=C → CHC(R) |
| **Effect of a second phosphine ligand on enantioselectivity** | |

268.

[cyclohexene with MeO, OMe] + n-BuMgCl + Me-C(PPh$_2$)-Me(PPh$_2$) / (PPh$_3$)$_2$NiCl$_2$/PPh$_3$ → [cyclohexanone with Bu-n]

A soln. of startg. acetal in THF treated with 3 eqs. *n*-butylmagnesium chloride, 5 mol% NiCl$_2$(PPh$_3$)$_2$, 5 mol% (S,S)-Chiraphos, and *10 mol% triphenylphosphine* at 22° for 15 h → product. Y 85% (e.e. 85%). Enantioselectivity was significantly lower without addition of the second phosphine. F.e. and isolation of **chiral enolethers** (by subsequent treatment with NaHCO$_3$), also comparison with other monodentate tert. phosphines, s. E. Gomez-Bengoa, A.H. Hoveyda et al., J. Am. Chem. Soc. *120*, 7649-50 (1998).

*Zinc s. under NiBr$_2$*                                                                                                   Zn

*Ethylmagnesium bromide s. under Et₂Zn and Cp₂ZrCl₂*      EtMgBr

*Dialkylzinc/cupric trifluoromethanesulfonate/chiral 1,1'-bi-2-naphthol ←
or octahydro-1,1'-bi-2-naphthol phosphoramidites*
**Asym. 1,4-addition with dialkylzincs**     C=C → CHC(R)
to enones s. *52*, 297; enhanced enantioselectivity with (S)-5,5',6,6',7,7',8,8'-octahydro-1,1'-bi-2-naphthol phosphoramidite s. F.-Y. Zhang, A.S.C. Chan, Tetrahedron:Asym. *9*, 1179-82 (1998); asym. 1,4-addition to 1,1-nitroethylene derivs. s. N. Sewald, V. Wendisch, ibid., 1341-4.

*Diethylzinc/chlorotitanium triisopropoxide/ethylmagnesium bromide* ←
**(η²-Olefin)titanium(II)-catalyzed intramolecular carbozincation of enynes** ○

269.

0.1 eq. 0.5 *M* ClTi(OPr-*i*)₃ in hexanes and 0.2 eq. 3 *M* ethylmagnesium bromide in ether added sequentially to a soln. of 1-phenyl-6-hepten-1-yne and 1 eq. 1 *M* Et₂Zn (in hexanes) in 5:3 ether/hexanes, kept at 23° for 3.5 h, cooled to -78°, 2.5 eqs. I₂ in THF added, warmed to 23°, stirred overnight, and partitioned between ether and 3 *N* aq. HCl → product. Y 59%. With methoxymethyl bromide as electrophile, the corresponding **fused vinylcyclopropanes** were obtained. This is the first *catalytic* synthesis involving an (η²-olefin)titanium(II) complex. Monoynes, however, reacted more slowly. F.e. with proton, iodine or MeOCH₂Br as electrophile s. J.-L. Montchamp, E. Negishi, J. Am. Chem. Soc. *120*, 5345-6 (1998).

*Bromomagnesium triorganozincates/nickel(II)acetoacetonate*     R₃ZnMgBr/Ni(acac)₂
**1,4-Addition to α,β-ethylenesulfoxides with asym. induction**     C=C → CHC(R)

270.

Bromomagnesium triphenylzincate (prepared *in THF* at 0 to 23° from 2 eqs. ZnCl₂ and 6 eqs. phenylmagnesium bromide) added to a soln. of startg. olefin and 5-7 mol% Ni(acac)₂ *at -25°*, the deep burgundy soln. stirred for 4 h, quenched with NH₄Cl, and the pH adjusted to 10 with NH₄OH → product. Y >90% (e.e. 92%). Reaction with more familiar organometallics gave lower yields, or failed to take place. The solvent, reaction temp., and order of addition of the reactants is critical. However, vinyl- and alkynyl-zincates were unreactive. F.e. and addition of Li-triorganozincates s. I.N. Houpis, A. Molina et al., Tetrahedron Lett. *38*, 7131-4 (1997).

*Magnesium triflate or perchlorate/chiral Δ²-oxazolines* ←
**Asym. Diels-Alder reaction** ○
with chiral 2-(*o*-sulfonylaminophenyl)-Δ²-oxazolines s. *46*, 662s*51*; details s. J. Org. Chem. *62*, 7937-41 (1997); with Mg(ClO₄)₂ or Mg(OTf)₂ and chiral bis(Δ²-oxazolines), effect of ligand on face-selective *endo*-addition s. Tetrahedron *54*, 6099-110 (1998); with Mg(OTf)₂ and readily recoverable chiral 2,2-bis[4-(2-naphthyl)oxazolin-2-yl]propane s. S. Crosignani et al., ibid. 15721-30.

*Magnesium bromide*     MgBr₂
**Chelation-controlled 1,3-dipolar cycloaddition with nitrile oxides**
s. *47*, 640s*50*; regio- and stereo-specific cycloaddition to *syn-* or *anti*-2-(α,β-ethyleneacyl)-1,3-dithiane 1-oxides, reversal of stereoselectivity by Lewis acids (ZnI₂, MgBr₂), s. P.C. Bulman Page et al., Tetrahedron *53*, 7365-70 (1997).

*Zinc halides*                                        $ZnHal_2$
**Diels-Alder reaction with *p*-quinones with asym. induction**      ○
with sulfinyl-*p*-quinones s. *21*, 725s*51*; with bornene-fused substrates, reversal of face-selectivity in the presence of $ZnBr_2$, s. J. Org. Chem. *62*, 976-81 (1997); with menthyl *p*-quinone-2-carboxylates in the presence of $ZnCl_2$ or $ZnBr_2$ s. M.A. Brimble et al., Tetrahedron *54*, 5363-74 (1998).

*Borane-iodine/sodium hydroxide*                    $BH_3$-$I_2$/NaOH
**Stereospecific synthesis of ethylene from acetylene derivs.**   C≡C → CH=C(R)
and *in situ*-generated dialkylboranes s. *23*, 703; (Z)-ene-1,2-di(selenides) from 1,2-bis(organoseleno)ethynes s. D.-Y. Yang, X. Huang, Synlett *1997*, 891-2.

*Anion exchanger-supported tetrahydridoborate/nickel acetate*           ←
**Heterogeneous radical 1,4-addition of iodides**          C=C → CHC(R)
with polymer-based organotin hydrides cf. *48*, 675; 1,4-addition to enones, enoates and α,β-ethylenenitriles with anion exchanger-supported tetrahydridoborate and a little $Ni(OAc)_2$ ['nickel boride-on-borohydride exchange resin'] s. T.B. Sim, N.M. Yoon et al., J. Org. Chem. *62*, 2357-61 (1997).

*Dicyclohexylborane/cuprous acetate/cupric acetoacetonate*           ←
**C-Alkylation of terminal acetylene derivs. with ethylene derivs.**   C≡CH → C≡CR
**via hydroboration**

271.

A soln. of hex-1-ene in THF treated with 1 eq. dicyclohexylborane at 0° for 2 h, 1 eq. hex-1-yne, 2 eqs. CuOAc·$H_2O$ and 0.25 eqs. Cu(acac)$_2$ in dimethylacetamide (containing a small amount of water) added at the same temp., and kept at 20° for 18 h → product. Y 76%. A variety of functional groups (ketones, nitriles, esters, alcohols) were unaffected. F.e., also **(E)-1,3-enynes via hydroboration of acetylene derivs.** (with bis(1,2-dimethylpropyl)borane), s. Y. Masuda et al., Chem. Commun. *1998*, 807-8.

*9-Borabicyclo[3.3.1]nonane/organolithium compds./acetic acid*          ←
**Regiospecific synthesis of (E,E)-1-aryltelluro-1,3-dienes**    CH=CHCH=C(TeAr)
**from acetylene derivs. and lithium acetylides**

272.

0.5 *M* 9-Borabicyclo[3.3.1]nonane added to a soln. of 1.2 eqs. 1-hexyne in THF at room temp. under $N_2$, the mixture stirred for 1 h, cooled to -78°, a soln. of 1-hexynyllithium added by the double-ended needle technique, 1 eq. phenyltellurenyl iodide (prepared *in situ* by the addition of $I_2$ to diphenyl ditelluride) added, warmed to room temp., stirred for an additional 1 h, treated with glacial AcOH, and stirring continued at room temp. for 3 h → (1E,3E)-product. Y 85%. The procedure is general, simple and efficient. Acoxy groups remained unaffected. F.e., also 1-subst. enetellurides with $Et_3B$ (via preferential migration of ethyl), s. J.W. Sung, D.Y. Oh et al., Synth. Commun. *28*, 2635-40 (1998).

*Diisobutylaluminum hydride/hexamethylphosphoramide/di-n-butylborinyl triflate*    ←
**2-Ethylenealcohols from acetylene derivs. and oxo compds.**       C(OH)C=C
with *i*-$Bu_2AlH$ cf. *28*, 652; 1-subst. (Z)-2-ethylenealcohols with *i*-$Bu_2AlH$/HMPA/$Bu_2BOTf$, regioselectivity, s. G. Li et al., Tetrahedron Lett. *39*, 4607-10 (1998).

*Trialkylalanes* $R_3Al$
**1,4-Addition with trialkylalanes** $C{=}C \rightarrow CHC(R)$
s. *43*, 825s*48, 49*; addition to *p*-sulfinylmethyl-*p*-hemiquinols with asym. induction, regioselectivity, s. M.C. Carreño et al., J. Org. Chem. *63*, 3687-93 (1998).

*Trialkylalanes/dimethylaluminum chloride* $R_3Al/Me_2AlCl$
**Catalyzed 1,4-addition of trialkylalanes to α,β-ethyleneketones**
s. *49*, 652s*50*; to steroidal enones, preferential conversion, s. German patent DE-19626400 (Schering AG).

*Triethylaluminum* s. under $Cp_2ZrCl_2$ $Et_3Al$
*Di-n-butylborinyl triflate* s. under i-$Bu_2AlH$ $Bu_2BOSO_2CF_3$

*Lithium aluminum bis[(R,R)-1,1'-bi-2-naphthoxide]/sodium* tert-*butoxide* ←
**Asym. Michael addition of phosphonic acid esters to α,β-ethyleneketones**

273.

The first example of a catalytic asym. Michael addition of a Horner-type reagent to an enone is reported, the regio- and enantio-selectivity being perfectly controlled by a heteropolymetallic multifunctional complex. **E:** A soln. of 2-cyclopentenone and methyl dimethoxyphosphonylacetate in THF treated with 10 mol% lithium aluminum bis[(R,R)-1,1'-bi-2-naphthoxide] ((R)-ALB) and 9 mol% NaOBu-*t at room temp.* for 72 h → product. Y 95% (e.e. 95%). It is thought that an equilibrium exists between the tetracoordinate (R)-ALB and a hexacoordinate complex involving the Na⁺ cation, the actual catalytic species probably being a self-assembled tetracoordinate complex involving (R)-ALB and the alkoxide (or the Na-enolate formed from the ester). Horner coupling of the phosphonate with the keto group of the enone does not take place under these conditions. F.e.s. T. Arai, M. Shibasaki et al., J. Am. Chem. Soc. *120*, 441-2 (1998).

*Montmorillonite K 10* ←
**Stereospecific Diels-Alder reaction with α,β-ethylenecarbonyl compds.** ○
with Fe(III)-doped montmorillonite K 10 cf. *36*, 674s*39*; with montmorillonite K 10 itself (containing a small amount of water), in the absence of solvent s. M. Avalos et al., Tetrahedron Lett. *39*, 2013-6 (1998).

*Boron fluoride* $BF_3$
**Chemistry of thiophene 1-oxides** ←
review s. *29*, 591s*53*; Diels-Alder reaction of *in situ*-generated thiophene 1-oxides, diastereoselectivity, s. Y. Li et al., J. Org. Chem. *62*, 7926-36 (1997).

**4-Alkoxy-1,2,3,4-tetrahydroquinolines from N-arylaldimines** s. *53*, 301s*55* ○

*Boron fluoride/ethyldiisopropylamine* $BF_3/i-Pr_2NEt$
**3,6-Dihydro-2H-pyrans from unactivated 1,3-dienes and aldehydes**
with Sc(III)-perfluorooctanesulfonate cf. *53*, 303; under co-catalysis with a Lewis acid and a base (e.g. $BF_3$-etherate/*i*-$Pr_2NEt$) s. European patent EP-834509 (Kao Corp.).

*Boron fluoride/chiral 2-aminoalcohols* ←
**Asym. Diels-Alder reaction**
with enals s. *44*, 611s*47*; using chiral 2-azetidinylcarbinols as ligand s. W.A.J. Starmans et al., Tetrahedron *54*, 4991-5004 (1998).

*Dimethylaluminum chloride (s.a. under $R_3Al$)* $Me_2AlCl$
**Stereospecific Lewis acid-catalyzed Diels-Alder reaction**
using $AlCl_3$ cf. *22*, 721; with 2-α-silyl-1,3-dienes using $AlCl_3$ or, preferably, $Me_2AlCl$, and subsequent Sakurai-Hosomi reaction, s. M.G. Organ et al., J. Org. Chem. *62*, 5254-66 (1997).

### 4-Siloxy-3,6-dihydro-2H-pyrans from 2-siloxy-1,3-dienes and aldehydes
### Regio- and stereo-specific hetero-Diels-Alder reaction

274.

Ph-CH=CH-CHO + Me-C(OSiPr-i$_3$)=CH-CH=CH$_2$ → (2R*,3R*)-3-methyl-2(E)-cinnamyl-4-triisopropylsilyloxy-2,3-dihydropyran

0.14 eq. Dimethylaluminum chloride added to a stirred soln. of *trans*-cinnamaldehyde and 1.09 eqs. 3-triisopropylsilyloxy-1,3-pentadiene in dry toluene (freshly distilled from CaH$_2$) at -40° under argon, and the mixture stirred for ca. 3.5 h → (2R*,3R*)-3-methyl-2(E)-cinnamyl-4-triisopropylsilyloxy-2,3-dihydropyran. Y 93% (>19:1 mixture of diastereomers). The stability of the triisopropylsilyloxy-1,3-dienes towards acidic hydrolysis appears to be a significant advantage over their trimethylsilyloxy-counterparts, and results in efficient isolation and enhanced stability of the product, as well as improved diastereoselectivity. F.e. and methods, also with BF$_3$-etherate as the Lewis acid in comparable yield and stereoselectivity, and oxidative O-desilylation to 2,3-dihydro-4-pyrones, s. P.A. Evans, J.D. Nelson, J. Org. Chem. *61*, 7600-2 (1996); with 2-(*tert*-butyldimethylsiloxy)-1,3-dienes (using BF$_3$-etherate) cf. M.T. Mujica et al., Tetrahedron *52*, 2167-76 (1996).

*Diethylaluminum chloride*      *Et$_2$AlCl*
**[2+2]-Cycloaddition with allenes**
2-alkylthio-2-α-silyl(methylene)cyclobutanes cf. *24*, 694s*49*; 2-alkoxy-derivs. and conversion to 1,2-di(methylene)cyclobutanes s. Chem. Lett. *1998*, 331-2.

**Asym. Diels-Alder reaction with 3-(α,β-ethyleneacyl)-2-oxazolidones**
s. *36*, 667s*54*; polymer-based asym. Diels-Alder reaction s. J.D. Winkler, W. McCoull, Tetrahedron Lett. *39*, 4935-6 (1998).

*Indium trichloride*      *InCl$_3$*
**1,2,3,4-Tetrahydroquinolines from N-arylaldimines and ethylene derivs.**
s. *53*, 301; f. 3,4-fused derivs. from cyclic ethylene derivs. s. Tetrahedron Lett. *39*, 3225-8 (1998); 4-alkoxy-2-(trifluoromethyl)-1,2,3,4-tetrahydroquinolines from enolethers with BF$_3$ s. B. Crousse et al., ibid. 5765-8.

*Samarium/trimethylsilyl chloride*      *Sm/Me$_3$SiCl*
*Samarium diiodide*      *SmI$_2$*
**1-Amino-5-cyanocyclopentenes from two α,β-ethylenenitrile molecules**
Regio- and stereo-specific cyclodimerization s. *55*, 284

*Ytterbium(III) triflate*      *Yb(OTf)$_3$*
**Isoxazolidines from ethylene derivs. and nitrones**
**Stereospecific 1,3-dipolar cycloaddition**
*endo*-selectivity with added molecular sieves cf. *54*, 296; effect of solvent (toluene *versus* acetonitrile) and bidentate ligand (2-oxazolidone, 2-pyrrolidone, and succinimide) on *endo-* versus *exo*-selectivity, s. S. Minakata, M. Komatsu et al., Tetrahedron Lett. *39*, 5205-8 (1998).

*Europium(III) β-diketones*      *Eu(III)*
**2-Alkoxy-3,4-dihydro-2H-pyrans from α,β-ethyleneketones**
with asym. induction s. *20*, 294s*52*; chiral 2,4-dideoxysugar lactones s. G. Dujardin et al., Synthesis *1998*, 763-70; carbohydrate-based 2-spiro-3,4-dihydro-2H-pyrans from carbohydrate cyclic ketene acetals s. S.C. Johnson et al., Chem. Commun. *1998*, 1019-20; stereospecific addition of cyclic enoxysilanes to enones (with Eu(fod)$_3$ or SnCl$_4$) s. G. Dujardin et al., Tetrahedron Lett. *39*, 8647-50 (1998).

*Samarium diiodide/hexamethylphosphoramide*      *SmI$_2$/HMPA*
**Regiospecific reductive dimerization of α,β-ethylenecarbonyl compds.** ←
sym. δ-dicarboxylic acid esters cf. *47*, 656; sym. 1,6-diketones s. A. Cabrera et al., Synth. Commun. *28*, 1103-8 (1998).

### Bicyclo[n.m.0]alkane-1,3-diols from diene-α,β-epoxyketones via regio- and stereo-specific serial radical ring closure

275.

36 eqs. HMPA added to 6 eqs. freshly prepared SmI$_2$ in THF, argon bubbled through the mixture for 10 min, a soln. of 5,6-epoxy-6-methyl-1,9-decadien-4-one and methanol added over 1 h, and worked up when reaction complete → *cis*-3,8-dimethylbicyclo[4.3.0]nonane-1,8-diol. Y 72% (5.25:1 mixture of diastereoisomers). F.e. and with isolation of the intermediate 1-alkenyl-cycloalkane-1,3-diols, **also 1-oxaspiro[5.4]decan-7-ol-2-ones** by radical ring closure-lactonization, s. G.A. Molander, C. del Pozo Losada, Tetrahedron *54*, 5819-32 (1998); **cyclic 1,3-diols from ethylene-α,β-epoxyketones** s. J. Org. Chem. *62*, 2935 (1997).

*Cerium(III) chloride/microwaves*
**Michael addition under microwave irradiation**     C=C → CHC(R)
with EuCl$_3$ cf. *52*, 303; addition of β-dicarbonyl compds. to α,β-ethyleneketones in the absence of solvent with CeCl$_3$ s. A. Boruah, J.S. Sandhu et al., Synth. Commun. *28*, 653-8 (1998).

*1,4-Cyclohexadiene/triethylamine*
**Double ring closure via Myers-type 1,4-radicals**
s. *51*, 312; also f. methods of generating the intermediate enyne-allenes by sigmatropic rearrangement s. J. Org. Chem. *62*, 603-26 (1997).

*Benzophenone/irradiation*     Ph$_2$CO/⚡
**Asym. radical addition of alcohols to carbon-carbon double bonds**
s. *35*, 474s*54*; asym. addition to chiral 4-methylene-5-oxazolidones and conversion to chiral α-acylamino-γ-lactones s. S.G. Pyne, K. Schafer, Tetrahedron *54*, 5709-20 (1998).

### Sym. 1,5-cyclooctadienes from cyclobutenes

276.

A soln. of 3.5 g dimethyl 3-(1-methylethyl)cyclobutene-1,2-dicarboxylate and a little benzophenone (0.5 g) in acetonitrile irradiated with a 100 W high-pressure Hg-lamp at room temp. for 6 h, the mixture distilled *in vacuo*, the residue taken up in xylene, and refluxed at 150° for 48 h → 1.2 g product. F.e.s. Japanese patent JP-09278711 (Nissan Chem. Ind. Ltd.).

*Azodiisobutyronitrile*     RN=NR
**Thiyl radical-induced regio- and stereo-specific ring closures**
of unsatd. aldehyde N-derivs. s. *54*, 299; of oxygen- and nitrogen-tethered ethylene-alkoximes and -hydrazones, and conversion to rigid cyclic β-aminocarboxylic acids, s. O. Miyata et al., Synlett *1998*, 271-2.

*Azodiisobutyronitrile/irradiation*     RN=NR/⚡
**Radical ring closures of dienes with bisfunctionalization**
s. *49*, 669; 3-α-arylseleno-4-α-tosylpyrrolidines from quaternary N,N-di(allyl)ammonium salts, stereoselectivity, s. M.P. Bertrand et al., Synlett *1997*, 1420-2; f. effects of N-quaternization in the presence of Lewis acid (BF$_3$, AlMe$_3$ or BH$_3$) s. Tetrahedron *54*, 12829-40 (1998).

*Acetic acid*     AcOH
**Naphthalenes from *o*-α-hydroxyacetals via isobenzofurans**
with dimethyl acetylenedicarboxylate cf. *36*, 669; with activated ethylene derivs. s. M. Sugahara, T. Ukita et al., Tetrahedron Lett. *39*, 1377-80 (1998).

*Triphenylsilane/triphenylsilanethiol/di*-tert-*butyl hyponitrite*
**Radical addition to electron-rich ethylene derivs.**      C=C → CHC(R)
**under polarity-reversal catalysis**

277.  MeO$_2$C-CH(Cl)-CO$_2$Me + CH$_2$=C(OAc)Me ⟶ MeO$_2$C-CH(CO$_2$Me)-CH$_2$-C(OAc)(Me)$_2$

**Functionalized malonic acid esters.** A soln. of isopropenyl acetate, 1.3 eqs. triphenylsilane, 1.5 eqs. dimethyl chloromalonate, and a little di-*tert*-butyl hyponitrite and triphenylsilanethiol stirred at 60° under dry argon for 2 h → product. Y 88%. The silane-thiol couple serves as a useful alternative to toxic organotin hydrides (as used in the Giese procedure). F.e. incl. addition of methyl bromoacetate, **also asym. radical 1,4-addition** with a 1-thiosugar as the thiol component, s. H.-S. Dang et al., Chem. Commun. *1998*, 1413-4.

*1,1,2,2-Tetraphenyldisilane/azodiisobutyronitrile*      Ph$_2$Si(H)Si(H)Ph$_2$/RN=NR
**Radical reactions with 1,1,2,2-tetraphenyldisilane**
**as a stable alternative to tris(trimethylsilyl)silane**

278.  1-adamantyl-Br + CH$_2$=CH-SO$_2$Ph ⟶ (via Ph$_2$Si(H)-Si(H)Ph$_2$) 1-adamantyl-CH$_2$CH$_2$-SO$_2$Ph

**1,4-Addition.** A mixture of 1-adamantyl bromide, 3 eqs. phenyl vinyl sulfone, 2.5 eqs. 1,1,2,2-tetraphenyldisilane and 0.5 eq. AIBN *in ethanol* refluxed for 14 h → product. Y 88%. The reagent is crystalline, eco-friendly, highly efficient, and stable under aerobic conditions. Only one of the two hydrogen atoms is available so that >1 eq. of the reagent is required to afford good yields. F.e., also replacement of bromine by hydrogen (with AIBN or Et$_3$B as initiator), and *o*-alkylation of cyclimmonium salts with halides, s. O. Yamazaki et al., Tetrahedron Lett. *39*, 1921-4 (1998).

*Hexamethyldisilazane*      (Me$_3$Si)$_2$NH
**Regio- and stereo-specific intramolecular vinylmercuration**
**of acetylene derivs. with 2-ethylenesilanes**

279.  (E,Z)-1-(trimethylsilyl)-3-methyl-2-octen-7-yne + HgCl$_2$ ⟶ [cyclization intermediate] ⟶ [(E)-(2-methyl-2-vinylcyclopentylidene)methyl]mercuric chloride

1.1 eqs. HgCl$_2$ added to a stirred soln. of (E,Z)-1-(trimethylsilyl)-3-methyl-2-octen-7-yne and 0.2 eq. hexamethyldisilazane in methylene chloride at room temp., and worked up after 14 h → [(E)-(2-methyl-2-vinylcyclopentylidene)methyl]mercuric chloride. Y 56%. The predominant *anti*-selectivity in all instances (except with silyl-substituted acetylene derivs.) is the result of *trans*-addition of the nucleophilic β-carbon of the allylsilane to the Hg(II)-complexed alkyne group. The *exo*-product is exclusively formed from trimethylene-tethered substrates, while the tetramethylene homolog afforded the cyclohexane system in low yield, and formation of cycloheptanoids failed. The disilazane aids suspension of the mercury salt and serves as an acid scavenger. Other mercury(II) halides failed to induce reaction. F.e. and tetrahydrofuran ring from propargyl derivs. s. H. Huang, C.J. Forsyth, J. Org. Chem. *62*, 8595-9 (1997).

*Chlorobis(cyclopentadienyl)hydridozirconium/cuprous chloride*      Cp$_2$Zr(H)Cl/CuCl
**Sym. 1,3-dienes from two terminal acetylene deriv. molecules**      HC≡C-C≡CH
with *i*-Bu$_2$AlH/CuCl cf. *34*, 648; chiral sym. (E,E)-1,4-dialkoxy-1,3-butadienes with Cp$_2$Zr(H)Cl/CuCl s. M. Virgili, A. Pericàs et al., Tetrahedron Lett. *38*, 6921-4 (1997).

*Chlorobis(cyclopentadienyl)hydridozirconium/tetrakis(triphenylphosphine)palladium(0)*
**(E)-Styrenes**  $C{\equiv}CH \rightarrow CH{=}CH(Ar)$
**from terminal acetylene derivs. and diaryliodonium salts**
**via regio- and stereo-specific hydrozirconation**

280.

1-Heptyne added to a soln. of 1 eq. $Cp_2Zr(H)Cl$ in THF at room temp., the mixture stirred for 2 h, 1 eq. diphenyliodonium iodide and 5 mol% $Pd(PPh_3)_4$ in THF added, stirring continued at room temp. for 1-1.5 h, then treated with satd. aq. $NaHCO_3 \rightarrow$ (E)-1-phenyl-1-heptene. Y 98%. F.e.s. X. Huang, A.-M. Sun, *Synth. Commun.* **28**, 773-8 (1998).

*Zirconocene dichloride/n-butyllithium*  $Cp_2ZrCl_2/BuLi$
**Ring closures of enynes via zirconacyclopentenes**
s. *42*, 679s*50*; ring closure of α,ω-di(boronyl)enynes s. G. Desurmont et al., *J. Org. Chem.* **62**, 8907-9 (1997).

**Ring closures of azaen-ynes and -ediynes**
**via bicyclic zirconacyclo-pentenes and -pentadienes**
s. *50*, 428; 3-alkylidene-, 4-alkylidene- and 3,4-di(alkylidene)-piperidines s. *Synthesis 1998*, 557-68.

*Zirconocene dichloride/ethylmagnesium bromide/iodine*  $Cp_2ZrCl_2/EtMgBr/I_2$
**2-Cyclopentenones from acetylene derivs.**
**Zirconocene-mediated Pauson-Khand reaction**

281.

**2,3-Disubst. 2-cyclopentenones.** 2.4 eqs. 0.92 M Ethylmagnesium bromide in THF added to a soln. of 1.2 eqs. $Cp_2ZrCl_2$ in the same solvent contained in a Schlenk tube under $N_2$ at -78°, stirred for 1 h, 3-hexyne added, stirring continued at room temp. for 1 h, recooled to -78°, CO introduced slowly into the soln. for 3 h with stirring, and quenched with 1.8 eqs. $I_2 \rightarrow$ 2,3-diethylcyclopent-2-enone. Y 71%. 1,3-Diynes and 1,3-enynes reacted similarly to give the corresponding 2-alk-1-ynyl- and 2-vinyl-derivs. regioselectively. F.e. incl. 2-silyl- and 2-aryl-derivs., also in the presence of ethylene gas at atm. pressure, s. T. Takahashi et al., *Tetrahedron* **53**, 9123-34 (1997).

*Zirconocene dichloride/triethylaluminum*  $Cp_2ZrCl_2/Et_3Al$
**Zirconium-catalyzed syntheses via aluminacyclopent-2-enes**

282.

**2-Cyclopentenone ring from enynes.** 2.5 eqs. 1.9 M $Et_3Al$ in toluene added at 23° to a suspension of 12.5 mol% $Cp_2ZrCl_2$ in the same solvent, after 5 min 7-(trimethylsilyl)-1-hepten-6-yne added, stirred for 65 h, cooled to 0°, *carbon dioxide* slowly bubbled into the mixture via a 17 gauge needle, diluted with methylene chloride, and poured into 3 N HCl and ether at 0° → 2-(trimethylsilyl)-bicyclo[3.3.0]oct-1(2)-en-3-one. Y 50%. Such cyclopentenone closure with $CO_2$ (rather than toxic CO) is unprecedented (there being no reaction with CO itself). F.e. and isolated 2-cyclopentenones (from acetylene derivs.), also **1-vinylbicyclo[n.1.0]alkanes** (from enynes) with methoxymethyl bromide, and **vinylcyclopropanes** (from acetylene derivs.), s. E. Negishi et al., *Tetrahedron Lett.* **39**, 2503-6 (1998).

*Chlorotitanium triisopropoxide s. under Et$_2$Zn*      *ClTi(OPr-i)$_3$*
*Dichlorotitanium diisopropoxide/trialkylboranes*      *Cl$_2$Ti(OPr-i)$_2$/R$_3$B*
**Lewis acid-catalyzed asym. radical 1,4-addition**      C=C → CHC(R)
to chiral 2-sulfinyl-2-cyclopentenones s. *49*, 661; details s. J. Org. Chem. *62*, 7794-800 (1997); addition to a chiral α-(1-hydroxyethyl)vinyl sulfoxide, f. methods with or without Lewis acid, s. Tetrahedron Lett. *39*, 5553-6 (1998).

*Dichlorotitanium diisopropoxide/chiral α,α,α',α'-tetraaryl-1,3-dioxolane-4,5-dimethanol* ←
**Asym. 1,3-dipolar cycloaddition of nitrones**      ○
with 3-(α,β-ethyleneacyl)-2-oxazolidones cf. *51*, 317; improved *exo*-selectivity and enantio-selectivity with N-(α,β-ethyleneacyl)succinimides s. K.B. Jensen et al., J. Org. Chem. *62*, 2471-7 (1997).

*Trichlorotitanium isopropoxide/ethyldiisopropylamine*      *Cl$_3$TiOPr-i/i-Pr$_2$NEt*
**Asym. Michael addition with 3-acyl-2-oxazolidones**      C=C → CHC(R)
s. *47*, 664; polymer-based conversion s. C.W. Phoon, C. Abell, Tetrahedron Lett. *39*, 2655-8 (1998).

*Titanium tetrachloride*      *TiCl$_4$*
**Regio- and stereo-specific Diels-Alder reaction with α,β-etheneselenolic acid esters**      ○

283.

A soln. of startg. selenolic acid ester and 3-5 eqs. isoprene in methylene chloride treated with 1.1 eqs. TiCl$_4$ at -60° to room temp. for 2-18 h → product. Y 77% (regiochemically pure). Cyclo-addition with these esters **and with α,β-ethylenethiolic acid esters** is much more facile than with the corresponding enoates. F.e. incl. cycloaddition with 2-trimethylsiloxy-1,3-butadiene and cyclopentadiene, and Lewis acids s. C.-H. Byeon, D.J. Hart et al., Synlett *1998*, 596-8.

**Asym. Diels-Alder reaction with N-(α,β-ethyleneacyl)sultams**
s. *44*, 594s52; with N,N'-fumaroylbis[(2R)-bornane-10,2-sultam] s. Helv. Chim. Acta *81*, 324-9 (1998).

*Titanium tetrachloride/zinc*      *TiCl$_4$/Zn*
**1-Amino-5-cyanocyclopentenes from two α,β-ethylenenitrile molecules**
**Regio- and stereo-specific reductive cyclodimerization**

284.

2 eqs. TiCl$_4$ added dropwise via syringe to a stirred suspension of 4 eqs. Zn-powder in freshly distilled, dry THF at room temp. under N$_2$, the mixture refluxed for 2 h, cooled to room temp., a soln. of startg. nitrile in THF added dropwise over ca. 20 min, stirring continued at room temp. under N$_2$ for 1.5 h, solvent removed *in vacuo*, and the residue quenched with 3% HCl → product. Y 81%. Phenols, phenolethers, MOM-ethers, esters, and aromatic chlorides and bromides were not reduced, but aromatic nitro groups afforded the corresponding prim. amines. F.e.s. L. Zhou et al., Synthesis *1998*, 851-4; with SmI$_2$ cf. Tetrahedron Lett. *38*, 8063-6 (1997); from arylidene-malononitriles with SmI$_2$/Me$_3$SiCl cf. L. Wang, Y. Zhang, Tetrahedron *54*, 11129-40 (1998); in satd. aq. THF s. Tetrahedron Lett. *39*, 5257-60 (1998).

*Tri-n-butyltin hydride/azodiisobutyronitrile*      *Bu$_3$SnH/RN=NR*
**Radical 1,4-addition with xanthates**      C=C → CHC(R)
s. *39*, 646; 10-subst. taxoids s. K. Nakayama, T. Soga et al., Bioorg. Med. Chem. Lett. *8*, 427-32 (1998).

*Bismuth trichloride*      *BiCl$_3$*
**3,6-Dihydro-2$H$-pyrans from unactivated 1,3-dienes and oxo compds.** s. *53*, 303s55    ○

*Sodium dithionite/sodium hydrogen carbonate* $\quad Na_2S_2O_4/NaHCO_3$
**Addition of perfluoroalkyl iodides to allyl glycosides** s. *55*, 5 $\quad\leftarrow$

*Lithium trifluoromethanesulfonate* $\quad LiOSO_2CF_3$
**Regio- and stereo-specific Diels-Alder reaction with ($\eta^2$-styrene)osmium complexes** ○

285.

$\eta^2$**-Osmium-complexed 1,2,3,8a-tetrahydronaphthalene-1-carbonyl compds.** Excess of acrolein and $LiOSO_2CF_3$ in acetonitrile added to $[Os(NH_3)_5(2,3-\eta^2-4-methoxystyrene)](OTf)_2$, stirred for ca. 12 h, added with stirring to ether, and the precipitate collected → $[Os(NH_3)_5(3,4-\eta^2-8-formyl-2-methoxy-6,7,8,8a-tetrahydronaphthalene)](OTf)_2$. Y 97% (single diastereoisomer). Diels-Alder reaction with uncomplexed styrenes normally requires forcing conditions, and fails with such reactive dienophiles as enals. The osmium residue serves a triple role: to activate the aromatic system regiospecifically (by π-back bonding and partially localizing the aromatic π-system); to direct the dienophile from the opposite face; and to stabilize the resulting triene system so that further cycloaddition is prevented. F.e.s. S.P. Kolis, W.D. Harman et al., J. Am. Chem. Soc. *120*, 2218-26 (1998).

*tert-Butyldimethylsilyl triflate* $\quad t$-$BuMe_2SiOTf$
**Michael-type addition of pyrroles and indoles** s. *20*, 601s55

*Molybdenum hexacarbonyl/dimethyl sulfoxide* $\quad Mo(CO)_6/DMSO$
**Intramolecular Pauson-Khand-type reaction with allenes** ○
s. *46*, 661s50; regioselectivity s. K.M. Brummond, H. Wan, Tetrahedron Lett. *39*, 931-4 (1998); effect of allene substitution on π-bond selectivity s. J. Org. Chem. *63*, 6535-45 (1998).

*Chromous chloride* $\quad CrCl_2$
**Regio- and stereo-specific 3-component synthesis of 3-ethylenealcohols** $\quad\leftarrow$
**from 1,3-dienes, aldehydes and iodides**

286.

A soln. of nonanal, 3 eqs. isoprene, and 3 eqs. isopropyl iodide in DMF added at 25° to a mixture of 6 eqs. $CrCl_2$ in dry $O_2$-free DMF at 25°, stirred for 8 h, and poured into water → (3R*,4S*)-3-isobutyl-3-methyl-1-dodecen-4-ol. Y 70%, d.r. >98:2 (and 21% 3-isobutyl-2-methyl-1-dodecen-4-ol, *anti:syn* 67:33). The method is applicable to sec. or tert. iodides. F.e.s. K. Takai et al., Angew. Chem. Int. Ed. Engl. *37*, 152-5 (1998).

*Chromous chloride/lithium iodide/N,N,N',N'-tetramethylethylenediamine* $\quad\leftarrow$
**1,4-Addition of α-borylalkyl radicals** $\quad C{=}C \to CHC(R)$
**to terminal electron-deficient ethylene derivs.**

287.

3-Phenylpropyl acrylate and 2 eqs. pinacol 1-chloropentylboronate in dry DMF added at 25° to 4 eqs. $CrCl_2$, 4 eqs. LiI, and 8 eqs. TMEDA in DMF, and the mixture stirred at 25° for 8 h → product. Y 92%. Primary α-halogenoboronic acid esters were not reduced under these mild conditions, and primary alkyl chloride and ester substituents were unaffected. Radical trapping with butyl vinyl ether, allyl phenyl sulfide, or allyltributylstannane resulted in complex mixtures, but acrylonitrile and phenyl vinyl sulfone gave the desired products. When the reaction was conducted without addition of LiI, most of the acrylate was recovered, and addition of TMEDA enhanced the reducing power of the chromium(II) ion. The α-borylalkyl radicals are equivalent to α-hydroxyalkyl radicals since oxidative cleavage occurs readily. F.e.s. K. Takai et al., Synlett *1998*, 253-4; **radical 1,4-addition of aryl iodides** to α,β-unsatd. phosphonates, esters and nitriles with $CrCl_2/H_2NCH_2CH_2NH_2$ s. H.I. Tashtoush, R. Sustmann, Chem. Ber. *126*, 1759-61 (1993).

*Lithium perchlorate*      $LiClO_4$
**Diels-Alder reaction with 1-alkoxy-3-sulfinyl-1,3-dienes with asym. induction**
s. *36*, 667s*49*; asym. cycloaddition to maleic acid derivs. s. M.C. Aversa et al., Tetrahedron:Asym. *9*, 1577-87 (1998); s.a. J. Org. Chem. *62*, 4376-84 (1997).

*Lithium perchlorate/triethylamine*      $LiClO_4/Et_3N$
**[3+2]-Cycloaddition with metalated azomethines**
with $LiBr/Et_3N$ cf. *43*, 611; 4-nitropyrrolidine-2-carboxylic acid esters from 1,1-nitroethylene derivs. with $LiClO_4/Et_3N$, stereoselectivity, s. M. Ayerbe, F.P. Cossío et al., J. Org. Chem. *63*, 1795-805 (1998).

*Manganese(II) chloride s. under Mg*      $MnCl_2$

*Iron/ferric chloride*      $Fe/FeCl_3$
**Addition of polyhalides to ethylene derivs.** ←
with Fe/CuBr cf. *18*, 776s*51*; addition of $CCl_4$ or α-polychlorocarboxylates to various taxogens with $Fe/FeCl_3$ s. F. Bellesia et al., Tetrahedron *54*, 7849-56 (1998).

*Ferric 2-ethylhexanoate*      $Fe(OCOR)_3$
**2-Alkoxy-3,4-dihydro-2H-pyrans from α,β-ethylenealdehydes and enolethers**
**Regio- and stereo-specific hetero-Diels-Alder reaction**

288.

Ethyl (E)-4-oxobutenoate, 6 eqs. *n*-butyl vinyl ether, and 0.1 eq. Fe(III)-2-ethylhexanoate in mineral spirits stirred at room temp. for 44 h → *cis*-product. Y 81% (97% d.e.). Ferric 2-ethylhexanoate is a novel, mild, and relatively inexpensive Lewis acid catalyst which can be precipitated from the reaction mixture by addition of 20% acetonitrile in water. Increasing the reaction temp. shortened the reaction time but reduced the diastereoselectivity (96% at 60°/18 h and 90% at 80°/20 h). A trace of $Et_3N$ improved the yields at elevated temp., but at levels greater than 1 wt% it poisoned the catalyst. Optimal yields were obtained using 0.20-0.25 eq. catalyst. The yield could also be increased by increasing the excess of vinyl ether from 6 to 10 eqs. F.e.s. D.B. Gorman, I.A. Tomlinson, Chem. Commun. *1998*, 25-6.

*Tetra-n-butylammonium tricarbonyl(nitrosyl)ferrate/ferrous chloride*    $Bu_4N[Fe(CO)_3NO]/FeCl_2$
**Cyclodimerization of 1,3-dienes**
without catalyst under forcing conditions cf. *23*, 687; 4-vinylcyclohexenes by catalytic cycloaddition with $Bu_4N[Fe(CO)_3NO]/FeCl_2$ s. Japanese patent JP-10001446 (Mitsubishi Chem. Corp.).

*Cobalt carbonyl/N-methylmorpholine N-oxide*      $Co_2(CO)_8/R_3NO$
**Asym. Pauson-Khand reaction**
with $Co_2(CO)_6$-complexed alkynyl ethers based on 10-(methylthio)isoborneol cf. *49*, 674; improved diastereoselectivity with the corresponding alkynyl thioethers s. E. Montenegro et al., Tetrahedron Lett. *39*, 335-8 (1998).

*Tetracobalt dodecacarbonyl*      $Co_4(CO)_{12}$
**Catalytic Pauson-Khand reaction**
with a little $Co(acac)_2/NaBH_4$ cf. *50*, 415s*51*; with a little $Co_4(CO)_{12}$ for inter- and intra-molecular conversions s. J.W. Kim, Y.K. Chung, Synthesis *1998*, 142-4.

*(η⁴-Cycloocta-1,5-diene)(η⁵-4-hydroxybutyrylcyclopentadienyl)cobalt(I)*
**Benzene ring by trimerization of acetylene derivs. under mild conditions in aq. media**

289.

A soln. of startg. alkyne treated with 2.5 mol% water-soluble cobalt(I) complex in 60% water/methanol until reaction complete → product. Y 44% (unoptimized; single regioisomer). The success of the reaction is reliant on the choice of catalyst: the acyl residue on the cyclopentadienyl ring enhances the catalytic activity; the hydroxyl group facilitates water solubility; and the cyclo-octadiene ring serves as a control element in directing the alkyne residues to the coordination sphere of the central metal. Significantly, protection of alkyne functional groups (hydroxyl, amino, carboxyl, and keto) is not required. F.e. and regioselectivity s. M.S. Sigman et al., J. Am. Chem. Soc. *120*, 5130-1 (1998).

*Bis(1,5-cyclooctadiene)nickel(0)/triphenylphosphine* $Ni(cod)_2/Ph_3P$
**Regio- and stereo-specific synthesis of siloxy-3-ethylenes** CH-C≡C-C-CH(OSi≤)R
from 1,3-dienes and aldehydes s. *55*, 290

*Nickel(II) acetoacetonate s.a. under Bromomagnesium triorganozincates* $Ni(acac)_2$

*Nickel(II) acetoacetonate/triethylborane* $Ni(acac)_2/Et_3B$
**Regio- and stereo-specific synthesis of 4-ethylenealcohols** CHO → CH(OH)C-CH-C≡C
from 1,3-dienes and aldehydes

290.

A mixture of 4 eqs. isoprene, benzaldehyde, 10 mol% Ni(acac)₂, and *2.4 eqs*. Et₃B (1 *M* in hexane) in dry THF stirred at room temp. under N₂ for 35 h → 3-methyl-1-phenyl-4-pentenol. Y 90% (*syn:anti* 1:15). Only one regioisomer is formed, the terminus bearing the higher electron density undergoing addition in a nucleophilic fashion with Et₃B serving as reducing agent. Significantly, reaction is mild, economical, high-yielding, simple, devoid of oligomerization, requires as little as 1 mol% catalyst (with a catalytic turnover of >80), and proceeds with 1,2-, 1,3- and 1,2,3-diastereoselectivity (to give a single diastereoisomer in several instances). F.e.s. M. Kimura, Y. Tamaru et al., J. Am. Chem. Soc. *120*, 4033-4 (1998); **siloxy-3-ethylenes** (cf. *50*, 417) with Ni(cod)₂/Ph₃P/Et₃SiH, selectivity, s. M. Takimoto, M. Mori, Tetrahedron Lett. *39*, 4543-6 (1998).

*Dichlorobis(triphenylphosphine)nickel(II) s. under Mg* $NiCl_2(PPh_3)_2$

*Nickel(II) bromide/triphenylphosphine/zinc* $NiBr_2/Ph_3P/Zn$
**2,5(Z),8-Triene-1,10-diones** CO-C≡C-C-C≡C-C-C≡C-CO
from 1,3-dienes and two α,β-ethylene-β-iodoketone molecules

291.

Acetone added via syringe to 10 mol% NiBr₂, 10 mol% Ph₃P, and 1.25 eqs. Zn powder under N₂, followed by 3-iodo-2-cyclohexenone and 3 eqs. 2,3-dimethyl-1,3-butadiene, and stirred at 80° for 2 h → 2,3-dimethyl-1,4-bis(3-oxo-1-cyclohexen-1-yl)-2-butene. Y 82%. *cis*-β-Iodoacrylates with cyclic 1,3-dienes gave a mixture of 1,2- and 1,4-adducts. The mechanism of the reaction differs from that of Pd-catalyzed 1,4-diacetoxylation and 1,4-acetoxychlorination (cf. *44*, 131s*47*), the key step being the slow metalation of the iodoenone with Zn powder, followed by a catalytic cycle involving a nickel π-allyl species. F.e.s. D.-C. Jou, C.-H. Cheng et al., Tetrahedron *54*, 1041-52 (1998).

*Triruthenium dodecacarbonyl* $\qquad Ru_3(CO)_{12}$
**4,5-Fused 2(5H)-furanones from acetylenealdehydes**
**Oxa-Pauson-Khand reaction**

292.

A soln. of startg. ynal in toluene heated at 160° for 20 h under 10 atm. CO in the presence of 2 mol% $Ru_3(CO)_{12}$ → product. Y 62%. This is the first catalytic transformation of this type, as well as the first γ-lactone synthesis by [2+2+1]-cyclocoupling. The terminus of the acetylene group can be substituted by alkyl, aryl, vinyl, silyl or alkynyl groups. However, substrates with a terminally unsubstituted acetylene function failed to react. A mechanism involving oxidative addition of ruthenium to the C-H bond of the aldehyde is invoked. F.e. incl. ring closure of O- and N-tethered ynals s. N. Chatani, S. Murai et al., J. Am. Chem. Soc. *120*, 5335-6 (1998).

*Ruthenium carbene complex* $\qquad \leftarrow$
**1,3-Dienes by ene-yne metathesis** $\qquad C\equiv C \rightarrow C(=C)C\equiv C$
s. *54*, 320; polymer based metathesis with supported propargyl esters, and conversion to 2-α-functionalized 1,3-dienes, s. S.C. Schürer, S. Blechert, Synlett *1998*, 166-8.

*Ruthenium vinylidene complexes* $\qquad \leftarrow$
**Regio- and stereo-specific ring opening metathesis** $\qquad C$
with Ru-carbene complexes cf. *51*, 327s53; polymerization of norbornenes with ruthenium vinylidene complexes s. H. Katayama, F. Ozawa, Chem. Lett. *1998*, 67-8.

*Hexadecacarbonylhexarhodium/triethylamine* $\qquad Rh_6(CO)_{16}/Et_3N$
**3-Isochromanones from o-(hydroxymethyl)arylacetylenes**
**Cyclocarbonylation**

293.

A mixture of 2-(1-hexynyl)benzyl alcohol, 15 eqs. $Et_3N$, 4 eqs. water, and 0.1 mol% $Rh_6(CO)_{16}$ in dioxane stirred at 175° for 5 h under 100 atm. CO → 4-pentyl-3-isochromanone. Y 72%. The tert. amine is essential as initiator. F.e.s. E. Yoneda, S. Takahashi et al., Tetrahedron Lett. *39*, 5061-4 (1998).

*(1,5-Cyclooctadiene)rhodium(I) tetraphenylborate* $\qquad Rh(cod)BPh_4$
**(Z)-α,β-Ethylene-β-silylaldimines** $\qquad C(Si\leqslant)=C\text{-}CH=NR$
**from acetylene derivs., prim. amines, and organosilicon hydrides**
**4-Component synthesis via regio- and stereo-specific silylformylation**

294.

A mixture of hex-1-yne, 1.04 eqs. triethylsilane, 1.04 eqs. *p*-methoxyaniline, and ca. 1 mol% (1,5-cyclooctadiene)rhodium(I) tetraphenylborate in dry toluene flushed with argon in an autoclave, pressurized to 50 atm. with CO, and stirred at 60° for 22 h → (1E,3Z)-N-(*p*-methoxyphenyl)-3-butyl-4-triethylsilyl-1-aza-1,3-butadiene. Y 94% (Z/E >20/1). Side reactions were more prominent with [RhCl(cod)]$_2$. 2-Pyrrolidones were obtained in low yield (14-37%) by using $H_2$ in place of organosilicon hydrides. F.e. and conversion to **4-silyl-1,4-dihydropyridines** with acetylene derivs. via hetero-Diels-Alder reaction s. L. Bärfacker et al., Tetrahedron *54*, 4493-506 (1998).

*Acetoacetonato(dicarbonyl)rhodium(I)/2,2'-bis[(dibenzo[d,f][1,2,3]dioxaphosphepin-6-yl)oxy]-3,3'-di-tert-butyl-5,5'-dimethoxy-1,1'-biphenyl*
**Ring closures of protected unsatd. amines via hydroformylation**
s. *46*, 669s*54*; γ-(2-hydroxy-1-tosylpiperidin-6-yl)aldehydes from 4-tosylamino-1,6-dienes via regiospecific double hydroformylation with Rh(acac)(CO)$_2$/BIPHEPHOS s. I. Ojima et al., Tetrahedron Lett. *39*, 4599-602 (1998).

*Rhodium phosphine or phosphite complexes*
**Hydroformylation**     C=C → CHC(CHO)
developments s. *4*, 667s*54*; with Rh(acac)(CO)$_2$ and phosphorins ['phosphabenzenes'] or acyclic alkylidenephosphines cf. German patent DE-19621967 (BASF AG); with a combination of triarylphosphine and bis(triaryl phosphite) as ligand cf. European patent EP-839787 (DSM NV); hydroformylation of hex-1-ene in supercritical CO$_2$ catalyzed by rhodium trialkylphosphine complexes s. I. Bach, D.J. Cole-Hamilton, Chem. Commun. *1998*, 1463-4; hydroformylation of C-vinyl glycosides with asym. induction (without phosphine ligand) s. T. Takahashi et al., Synlett *1998*, 381-2.

*Polymer-based chiral rhodium(I) phosphine-phosphite complexes*
**Asym. hydroformylation in a highly cross-linked chiral polymer matrix**

295.

Highly cross-linked, polymer-immobilized, chiral rhodium(I) phosphine-phosphite complexes are as efficient as their homogeneous counterparts (cf. *49*, 683) in asym. hydroformylation, and can be readily removed and reused *without* loss of activity. **E:** A soln. of styrene in benzene heated at 60° for 12 h with 0.05 mol% chiral polymer-based rhodium(I) complex (prepared by co-polymerizing vinyl-BINAPHOS with divinylbenzenes, dispersing in benzene with Rh(acac)(CO)$_2$, and drying *in vacuo*) under 20 atm. 1:2 CO/H$_2$ → product (2-phenylpropanal: 3-phenylpropanal 84:16). Conversion >99%; e.e. of (R)-2-phenylpropanal 89%. The regioisomeric ratio was 89:11 with Rh(acac)$_2$ under homogeneous conditions (e.e. 92%). The readily removable catalyst settles at the bottom of the pressure bottle, and the products can be removed from the soln. by a syringe. Diffusion of the substrate in the polymer matrix is rapid. F.e. and catalysts s. K. Nozaki et al., J. Am. Chem. Soc. *120*, 4051-2 (1998).

*Dicarbonyl(chloro)rhodium(I) dimer*     [RhCl(CO)$_2$]$_2$
**Rhodium-catalyzed intramolecular Pauson-Khand reaction**
**3,4-Fused 2-cyclopentenones**

296.

A soln. of diethyl 8-nonen-3-yne-6,6-dicarboxylate in di-*n*-butyl ether added to a soln. of 1 mol% [RhCl(CO)$_2$]$_2$ in the same solvent under *1 atm.* of CO, and the mixture heated at 130° (oil-bath temp.) for 18 h → diethyl 8-ethyl-7-oxobicyclo[3.3.0]oct-8(1)-ene-3,3-dicarboxylate. Y 91%. The method, which illustrates the first example of a Rh-catalyzed Pauson-Khand reaction, compares well with the prior art. It is experimentally simple, and does not require an autoclave. F.e. incl. double ring closures of allyl propargyl ethers or N-tosylamines s. Y. Koga et al., Chem. Lett. *1998*, 249-50.

*Chloro(cyclooctadiene)rhodium(I) dimer* [Rh(cod)Cl]$_2$
**Sym. sec. and tert. amines from two ethylene deriv. molecules** (CH-C-CH$_2$)$_2$N(H,R)
via hydroformylation s. 55, 356

*Bis(dibenzylideneacetone)palladium(0)/(S)-1,1′-bi-2-naphthol/sodium salt* ←
**Asym. synthesis of ethylene derivs. from allenes** C=C=C → C=C-C(R)
**by carbopalladation-carbanion capture**
**Palladium π-allyl complexes as intermediates**

297.

A soln. of startg. racemic allene, 1.5 eqs. iodobenzene, and 1.3 eqs. dimethyl sodiomalonate in DMSO treated with 4 mol% Pd(dba)$_2$ and 4 mol% (S)-BINOL at 40° for 24 h → (S)-product. Y 42% (e.e. 96%). F.e. and chiral phosphine ligands, also from the chiral allene with 100% asym. induction, s. K. Hiroi et al., Chem. Lett. *1998*, 397-8.

*Tetrakis(triphenylphosphine)palladium(0) s.a. under Cp$_2$Zr(H)Cl* Pd(PPh$_3$)$_4$
*Tetrakis(triphenylphosphine)palladium(0)/acetic acid* Pd(PPh$_3$)$_4$/AcOH
**α,β-Ethylenecarboxylic acid derivs. from allenes** C=C=C → CH-C=C-CO(N<,OR)
**Regio- and stereo-specific carbonylation via acylpalladation**

298.

**α,β-Ethylenecarboxylic acid amides.** A degassed soln. of pyrrolidine, 5 mol% Pd(PPh$_3$)$_4$, and 5 mol% acetic acid in dry THF treated with 1.2 eqs. startg. allene under 1 atm. CO, and heated to 110° for 1 h (final pressure 5 atm.) → (E)-N-[2-methyl-3-(3′-pyridyl)acryloyl]pyrrolidine. Y 60%. Reaction is generally applicable to prim., sec. and heterocyclic amines, and is thought to involve catalysis with an *in situ*-generated hydridopalladium(II) species. F.e., **also α,β-ethylenecarboxylic acid aryl and oxime esters** [with phenols and oximes, respectively], s. R. Grigg et al., Tetrahedron 54, 3885-94 (1998).

*Cationic methyl(phenanthroline)palladium(II) complex* ←
**Regio- and stereo-specific ring closure-hydrosilylation of 1,6-dienes** ○

299.

**(Cyclopentylmethyl)silanes.** Cationic, electrophilic methyl(phenanthroline)palladium(II) complexes are useful alternatives to air- and moisture-sensitive, and oxophilic lanthanide [d$^0$-metallocene] catalysts for tandem ring closure-hydrosilylation of 1,6-dienes (cf. 50, 402). E: Trimethylsilane bubbled through a soln. of startg. diene and 5 mol% methyl(phenanthroline)-palladium(II) tetraarylborate at 0° for 5 min → product. Y 80% (55:1 mixture of stereoisomers).

The catalyst is resistant to oxidative addition and facilitates both β-migratory insertion of olefins and hydrosilylation, suggesting that the initial Si-H bond cleavage occurs via a σ-bond metathesis. The protocol requires *gem*-disubstitution at the 4-position of the diene. F.e. incl. a 3-silylmethyl-pyrrolidine from a diallylamine s. R.A. Widenhoefer, M.A. DeCarli, J. Am. Chem. Soc. *120*, 3805-6 (1998).

*Bis(π-allylpalladium chloride)/N-[2-(diphenylphosphino)benzylidene]-2-phenylethylamine* ←
**Regio- and stereo-specific synthesis of 1-stannyl-1,3-enynes**     C(Sn≤)=C-C≡C
**from acetylene derivs. and acetylenestannanes**

300.

A mixture of ethyl 2-butynoate and 0.33 eq. startg. acetylenestannane in THF heated at 90° for 90 h in the presence of 0.8 mol% [PdCl(π-C₃H₅)]₂ and 1.6 mol% N-[2-(diphenylphosphino)-benzylidene]-2-phenylethylamine → product. Y 57% (>99% major regioisomer). Reaction proceeds via oxidative addition of Pd(0) to the Sn-C bond, followed by regiospecific addition of the resulting complex across the acetylene bond, then reductive elimination of the catalyst. For addition to α,β-acetylene-ketones and -esters, the alkynyl residue of the acetylenestannane adds in Michael fashion under electronic control, whereas arylacetylenes afford the opposite regioisomer as a result of steric control. F.e.s. E. Shirakawa et al., J. Am. Chem. Soc. *120*, 2975-6 (1998).

*Via intermediates*     *v.i.*
**2,3-Condensed 5-hydroxycyclopentadienes from diynes via acylmanganation**     ○

301.

A stirred soln. of startg. diyne in ether treated with 1 eq. MeMn(CO)₅ in the same solvent at room temp., and worked up after 12 h → intermediate Mn-complex (Y 50%), in THF treated with 2.5 eqs. trimethylamine N-oxide at room temp., stirred for 12 h, treated with 1-2 drops of water, and stirring continued for 2 h → product (Y 83%). The purpose of the N-oxide is to convert the intermediate complex to a reactive 16-electron species with a free coordination site to facilitate bonding of manganese with the free acetylene group. Heteroatoms in the tether are tolerated, and reaction is applicable to both terminal and internal alkyne groups. F.e.s. S.H. Hong, Y.K. Chung, Tetrahedron Lett. *39*, 4843-6 (1998).

## Rearrangement

## Hydrogen/Carbon Type     CC ∩ HC

*Irradiation (s.a. under Ph₂CO)*
**γ-Diketones from α,β-ethylene-β'-hydroxyketones**     COC-C-CO

302.

**Photochemical rearrangement.** A 0.01 *M* soln. of startg. ethyleneketone in benzene irradiated with a high-pressure Hg-lamp for 6 h → product. Y 53% (> 92% conversion). The intermediate 1,3-diyl is formed by an unusual intramolecular 1,4-hydrogen abstraction, assisted by the allylic hydroxyl group, followed by a cyclopropanol ring closure-opening sequence. The substrates are simply obtained from enones and aldehydes (Baylis-Hilmann reaction), so that the overall conversion amounts to **1,4-addition with an acyl carbanion equivalent.** F.e. incl. a γ-ketoaldehyde in low yield from a silyl-protected substrate, s. S. Matsumoto et al., J. Am. Chem. Soc. *120*, 4015-6 (1998).

*Sodium hydride*  NaH
**Stereospecific intramolecular Michael addition**  ○
s. *33*, 662s*52*; N-condensed phthalimidines with sulfones as nucleophile s. F.A. Luzzio, D.P. Zacherl, Tetrahedron Lett. *39*, 2285-8 (1998); intramolecular addition to carvone with asym. induction (with DBU) s. M.D. Bachi et al., ibid. 3035-8.

*Potassium* tert-*butoxide*  KOBu-t
**Anionic cycloisomerization of acetylene derivs.**
Δ²-pyrroline-4-carbonitriles with LDA cf. *51*, 337; 4-benzylcarbostyrils with KOBu-*t* s. A. Arcadi, S. Cacchi et al., Synlett *1998*, 446-8.

tert-*Butyllithium/zinc bromide/*n-*butyllithium*  t-BuLi/ZnBr₂/BuLi
**Regio- and stereo-specific ring closures of ethylenehydrazones via intramolecular olefin-aldol condensation**
**Zinc azaenolates as intermediates**

303.

1 eq. 1.76 *M* t-BuLi in pentane added to a soln. of 8-methyl-1-nonen-7-one N,N-dimethylhydrazone in ether at -78°, the mixture warmed to 0°, treated after 4 h with 1 eq. 0.33 *M* ZnBr₂ in ether, cooled to -78°, allowed to react for 1 h, 1 eq. 1.6 *M* n-BuLi in hexane added, the mixture allowed to react at 20-25° for 25 h, then quenched with a 1/15 *N* phosphate buffer → product. Y 90% (88% *cis*-isomer). Reaction proceeds via a 5- or 6-*exo*-trig cyclization, 6-*endo*- and 7-*exo*-cyclization being unfavourable. The method is simple and conditions are mild. F.e. incl. an α-spiro-δ-lactam, and further functionalization by anion capture, s. E. Nakamura et al., Tetrahedron Lett. *39*, 2157-8 (1998).

*Lithium diisopropylamide/zinc bromide*  i-Pr₂NLi/ZnBr₂
**Stereospecific cycloisomerization of unsatd. α-aminocarboxylic acid esters via zinc ester enolates**
3-subst. prolinates cf. *52*, 321; s.a. Tetrahedron Lett. *38*, 85-8 (1997); piperidine-2-carboxylic from α-(bishomoallylamino)carboxylic acid esters s. E. Lorthiois et al., J. Org. Chem. *63*, 566-74 (1998).

*1,8-Diazabicyclo[5.4.0]undec-7-ene*  DBU
**β,γ-Ethylene- from α,β-ethylene-carboxylic acid esters**  C=C-CHCOOR
with LDA/HMPA cf. *29*, 810; 6,7-dihydro-2(3*H*)- from 6,7-dihydro-2(5*H*)-oxepinones with DBU (cf. *41*, 500) s. D.A. Jeyaraj, V.K. Yadav et al., J. Org. Chem. *63*, 287-94 (1998).

*Zinc bromide (s.a. under* t-*BuLi and* i-*Pr₂NLi)*  ZnBr₂
**Lewis acid-catalyzed intramolecular ene reaction**  ○
of 1,6-dienes with ZnCl₂ cf. *36*, 682s*46*; of 3-siloxy-1,6-dienes with perfect control of stereochemistry over 3 contiguous C-atoms (using ZnBr₂) s. J. Org. Chem. *62*, 6006-11 (1997).

*Benzophenone/irradiation*  Ph₂CO/*hν*
**4-Vinyl-3-isochromanones from 5-vinyl-3-oxatricyclo[4.4.0.0¹,⁵]deca-7,9-dien-4-ones**  ←

304.

1 eq. Benzophenone and startg. vinylnorcaradiene deriv. in benzene irradiated with a 400 W high-pressure mercury lamp for 70 min → 4-(2-methylprop-1-enyl)isochroman-3-one. Y 83%.

Irradiation of the startg. diene without the sensitizer resulted in a complex mixture from which two compounds were isolated in low yield, neither of which was the isochroman-3-one deriv. The triplet excited state of the 1,3-diene moiety is thought to be responsible for the photorearrangement. F.e.s. S. Kohmoto et al., Chem. Commun. *1997*, 1973-4.

*Achiral or chiral nickel(II) phosphine complexes/lithium hydridotriethylborate* ←
**O-Vinyl from O-allyl derivs.** RO-C≡C-CH
with Ni(dppe)Cl$_2$/*i*-PrMgBr/Me$_3$SiCl cf. *34*, 668s*52*; (Z)-isomers with Ni(dppb)Cl$_2$/LiBHEt$_3$ s. A. Wille et al., Synthesis *1998*, 305-8; chiral 1,3-dioxins and 4,5-dihydro-1,3-dioxepins **with asym. induction** using chiral dihalogenonickel(II) phosphine complexes cf. Tetrahedron:Asym. *9*, 1103-6 (1998).

*Palladous acetate/triphenylphosphine/triethylamine* $Pd(OAc)_2/Ph_3P/Et_3N$
**Regio- and stereo-specific cycloisomerization of bis(1,3-dienes)** ○
s. *47*, 687; of bis(1,3-dienes) possessing a terminal carbalkoxy group **with deconjugation**, also effect of added AcOH on (Z)/(E)-selectivity, s. Tetrahedron Lett. *39*, 5003-6 (1998).

*Tris(dibenzylideneacetone)dipalladium/tri-*o*-tolylphosphine/acetic acid* ←
**Cycloisomerization of enynes**
s. *41*, 671; *44*, 648; *42*, 683; chiral 5- and 6-membered isocyclic α-aminocarboxylic acids, effect of catalyst on regioselectivity, and by intramolecular Heck vinylation (cf. *43*, 965s*49*), s. B. Møller, K. Undheim, Tetrahedron *54*, 5789-804 (1998).

*Tris(dibenzylideneacetone)dipalladium/1,1'-bis(diphenylphosphino)ferrocene* $Pd_2(dba)_3/dppf$
**1,3-Dienes from allenes** s. *55*, 73 CHC≡C=C → C=C-CH=C

## Oxygen/Carbon Type CC ∩ OC

*Without additional reagents* w.a.r.
**Claisen rearrangement of allyl enolethers** ←
s. *27*, 738; γ,δ-ethylene-α-fluorocarboxylic acids s. F. Tellier et al., Tetrahedron Lett. *39*, 5041-4 (1998).

n-*Butyllithium* BuLi
**Wittig rearrangement of benzyl ethers** ←
with PhLi cf. *7*, 746; generation of lithiated benzyl ethers from 1,1-benzyloxystannanes with *n*-BuLi, chelation effects on inversion *vs.*retention of configuration, s. R.E. Maleczka, Jr., F. Geng, J. Am. Chem. Soc. *120*, 8551-2 (1998).

tert-*Butyllithium/cuprous cyanide/lithium bromide* t-BuLi/CuCN/LiBr
*o*-**Allylphenols from** *o*-**allyloxyhalides via copper(II) π-allyl complexes** ←
**Regio- and stereo-specific abnormal Claisen rearrangement**

305.

A soln. of startg. *o*-allyloxybromide in ether treated with *2 eqs.* *t*-BuLi at -78°, 0.5 eq. CuCN and 1 eq. LiBr added at the same temp., allowed to warm to 20°, and the mixture hydrolyzed → product. Y 77%. The stereochemistry of the double bond is completely retained, reaction taking place by 1,3→O-C-allyl shift, rather than the more familiar [3.3]-sigmatropic rearrangement (with no evidence of *para*-rearrangement). The process is thought to involve oxidative addition of an intermediate higher-order cuprate, generating a π-allyl species which then undergoes reductive elimination. F.e. and regiospecific intramolecular carbocupration of an isolated alkene group s. J. Barluenga et al., Tetrahedron Lett. *38*, 6103-6 (1997).

*Lithium diisopropylamide/trimethylsilyl chloride* i-$Pr_2NLi/Me_3SiCl$
**Claisen rearrangement of allyl esters** ←
*à la* Ireland s. *28*, 683s*53*; 3-subst. 2-allylsuccinic acid monoesters with asym. induction s. L.M. Pratt et al., Synlett *1998*, 531-3.

*Lithium (S,S)-N,N'-bis((R)-1-phenylethyl)-1,2-ethanediamide/lithium chloride* ←
**Asym. Wittig rearrangement of allyl benzyl ethers** ←
with BuLi/chiral 2-aminoethers cf. *53*, 336; of Cr(CO)$_3$-complexed allyl benzyl ethers with Li-(S,S)-N,N'-bis((R)-1-phenylethyl)-1,2-ethanediamide/LiCl s. S.E. Gibson et al., Chem. Commun. *1998*, 123-4.

*Lithium bis(trimethylsilyl)amide/zinc chloride* $LiN(SiMe_3)_2/ZnCl_2$
**Stereospecific chelation-controlled Claisen rearrangement** ←
s. *49*, 703s*54*; N-protected 2-amino-4-en-6-ynecarboxylic acid esters s. F.L. Zumpe, U. Kazmaier, Synlett *1998*, 434-6; with asym. induction s. Tetrahedron Lett. *39*, 817-8 (1998).

*Cuprous cyanide s. under* t-*BuLi* *CuCN*

*Zinc iodide* $ZnI_2$
**6-Hydroxyfulvenes from 7-oxabicyclo[2.2.1]hepta-2,5-dienes** ←

306.

**6-Aryl-6-hydroxyfulvenes.** A soln. of startg. 7-oxabicyclo[2.2.1]heptadiene in methylene chloride treated with 4 eqs. ZnI$_2$ at room temp. for 48 h → product. Y 100%. There was no formation of the isomeric 6-hydroxy-3-arylfulvenes, indicating that the O-C$_4$ bond is cleaved regiospecifically. The nature of the Lewis acid has a profound effect on the reaction, ZnBr$_2$ affording the expected *p*-hydroxybiphenyls. F.e.s. A. Maggiani et al., Tetrahedron Lett. *39*, 4485-8 (1998).

*Aluminum isopropoxide* $Al(OPr\text{-}i)_3$
**1,3-Diols from 2,3-epoxyalcohols with stereospecific isocyclic ring expansion** C○

307.

**Spirocyclic 1,3-diols.** Startg. epoxyalcohol treated with excess of Al(OPr-*i*)$_3$ in THF or isopropanol at reflux → *cis,trans*-product. Y 98% (isomeric ratio >99:1). The method is simple, efficient and highly stereoselective. F.e.s. Y.Q. Tu et al., Chem. Lett. *1998*, 285-6.

*Boron fluoride* $BF_3$
**Oxo compds. from epoxides with rearrangement** ←
s. *45*, 436s*54*; *23*, 735s*51*; cyclopentanones from 1-oxaspiro[2.3]hexanes (cf. *30*, 514s*42*, *43*) s. T. Fujiwara et al., Chem. Lett. *1998*, 741-2; diarylacetaldehydes with [(η$^5$-C$_5$H$_5$)Fe(CO)$_2$(THF)]$^+$ BF$_4^-$, preferential aryl migration, s. J. Picione, M.M. Hossain et al., Tetrahedron Lett. *39*, 2681-4 (1998).

*Methylaluminum dichloride* $MeAlCl_2$
**Stereospecific intramolecular carbonyl ene reaction** ○
s. *36*, 682s*39*; 4-hydroxy-2-methylenesilacyclohexanes (with MeAlCl$_2$) s. J. Robertson et al., Tetrahedron Lett. *39*, 669-72 (1998); open *vs.* closed transition states s. D.C. Braddock et al., Angew. Chem. Int. Ed. Engl. *37*, 1720-3 (1998).

*Samarium diiodide/hexamethylphosphoramide* $SmI_2/HMPA$
**Radical Wittig rearrangement** CH≡C-C-C(OH)
via 1,5-hydrogen transfer s. *55*, 484

### 1,2-Ene-3,n-diols from vinyloxyketones via stereospecific O→C-vinyl migration

308.

1.6 eqs. Samarium metal and 1.4 eqs. methylene iodide in dry THF stirred vigorously for 2 h under argon, ca. 12 eqs. HMPA added, followed by dropwise addition via cannula over 1 h of a 0.03 $M$ soln. of startg. vinyloxyketone in THF, and the mixture quenched with satd. aq. NaHCO$_3$ → 1-ethenyl-2-(2-hydroxyethyl)cycloheptanol. Y 71% (4:1 mixture of diastereomers). The procedure is complementary in many ways to nucleophilic alkenyl addition to oxo compds., stereoselectivity being higher in many instances. It avoids strongly basic, nucleophilic reaction conditions, and enolization of the carbonyl group is not a problem. Substituted enolethers afforded *trans*-alkenyl derivs. F.e.s. G.A. Molander, C.R. Harris, J. Org. Chem. *63*, 812-6 (1998).

*Trifluoroacetic acid* $\qquad$ $CF_3COOH$
### [1.3]-Sigmatropic rearrangement of allyl phenolethers
with montmorillonite cf. *46*, 686; rearrangement of 2-chloro- and 2-bromo-cyclohexenylmethyl aryl ethers with CF$_3$COOH s. N. Geetha, K.K. Balasubramanian, Tetrahedron Lett. *39*, 1417-20 (1998).

*Tri-n-butyltin hydride/azodiisobutyronitrile* $\qquad$ $Bu_3SnH/RN{=}NR$
### Radical-mediated Claisen rearrangement

309.

Unprecedented radical-mediated sigmatropic rearrangement is exemplified by the novel Claisen rearrangement **via allylic O-stannyl ketyls under mild conditions. E: γ,δ-Ethylene-α-hydroxy-ketones from α-allyloxy-α,β-ethyleneketones.** A soln. of startg. allyloxyketone in benzene treated with 1 eq. Bu$_3$SnH and 0.2 eq. AIBN, and refluxed for 3 h → product. Y 74%. The intermediate radical formed prior to H-atom quench can also be trapped with C-radicals (e.g. by *in situ*-**cross-coupling with stannanes**), while the tin(IV) enolate can be quenched with electrophiles other than proton (e.g. acetyl chloride). F.e. and diastereoselectivity, also with a *catalytic* amount of Bu$_3$SnH, s. E.J. Enholm et al., J. Am. Chem. Soc. *120*, 3807-8 (1998).

*Molybdenum hexacarbonyl* $\qquad$ $Mo(CO)_6$
### 2,2-Dimethylchromans from prenyl phenolethers
via thermal Claisen rearrangement cf. *25*, 533; under mild conditions with 40 mol% Mo(CO)$_6$ s. A.M. Bernard, P.P Piras et al., Synthesis *1998*, 256-8.

*Dicarbonyl($\eta^5$-cyclopentadienyl)(tetrahydrofuran)iron fluoroborate*
### Aldehydes from epoxides with preferential aryl shift s. *45*, 436s55

4
## Nitrogen/Carbon Type $\qquad$ CC ∩ NC

*Without additional reagents* $\qquad$ *w.a.r.*
### Intramolecular hetero-Diels-Alder reaction
with 2-ethylene-1,1-iminocyanides s. *49*, 713s*53*; tricyclic 2,3,4,5-tetrahydro-1*H*-1,4-benzo-diazepines s. Tetrahedron Lett. *39*, 4283-6 (1998).

### Synthesis of 4-thiazolidone 1,1-dioxides from 1,2-thiazetidin-3-one 1,1-dioxides

310.

2-[(Ethoxycarbonyl)methyl]-4,4-dimethyl-1,2-thiazetidin-3-one 1,1-dioxide in DMF added under $N_2$ at -20° to a suspension of 2 eqs. NaH in the same solvent, stirred at -20° for 10 min, 4 eqs. dimethyl sulfate added through a septum, slowly warmed to room temp., stirred for 24 h, cooled to 0°, ether added, and hydrolyzed with satd. NaCl (adjusted to pH 3-5 with HCl) → 2-(ethoxycarbonyl)-2,3,5,5-tetramethyl-1,3-thiazolidin-4-one 1,1-dioxide. Y 60%. At 0° in half the amount of DMF (without methylating agent), the corresponding **3-α-acylamino-4-thiazolidone 1,1-dioxides** were formed from two molecules of the substrate. F.e.s. D. Glasl et al., Helv. Chim. Acta **80**, 671-83 (1997).

### Ring closures of N-(o-alk-1-ynylaryl)ketenimines via 1,4-diradicals

311.

**5H-Benzo[b]carbazoles.** A soln. of startg. ketenimine in anhydrous benzene heated under reflux for 24 h, and the solvent allowed to evaporate slowly → 11-*tert*-butyl-6-phenyl-5H-benzo[b]-carbazole. Y 98%. A 2-step diradical mechanism, related to the Myers-type cyclization of enyne-allenes, is favoured over a concerted Diels-Alder mechanism which is unlikely in view of the sterically demanding *tert*-butyl group. F.e.s. C. Shi, K.K. Wang, J. Org. Chem. **63**, 3517-20 (1998).

*Methyllithium/N,N,N′,N′-tetramethylethylenediamine*   MeLi/TMEDA
**(E)-α,β-Ethylenesulfonic acid amides from 1,2-thiazetidine 1,1-dioxides**

312.

1.2 eqs. MeLi and TMEDA added dropwise to a soln. of 2-cyclohexyl-3-phenyl-1,2-thiazetidine 1,1-dioxide in THF at 0°, allowed to warm to room temp. over 1 h, and quenched with satd. aq. $NH_4Cl$ → (E)-N-cyclohexyl-2-phenylvinylsulfonamide. Y 84%. F.e. and with MeMgBr s. T. Iwama et al., Tetrahedron **54**, 5507-22 (1998).

*Lithium diethylamide*   LiNEt$_2$
**Aniline ring by cycloisomerization of nitriles**
with $H_2SO_4$ cf. *10*, 562; 9-aminophenanthrenes from o′-subst. o-cyanodiaryls via o′-lateral lithiation with LiNEt$_2$ s. L. Benesch, V. Snieckus et al., Tetrahedron Lett. **39**, 961-4 (1998).

*Lithium diisopropylamide/N,N′-dimethyl-N,N′-propyleneurea*   i-Pr$_2$NLi/DMPU
**α-(Carbalkoxyamino)ketones from N-acylurethans**   COC(NHCOOR)
**via 1,2-N→C-acyl group migration**

313.

A mixture of 3 eqs. *i*-Pr$_2$NH, 3 mol% N,N′-dimethyl-N,N′-propyleneurea and 3 eqs. *n*-BuLi (1.6 M in hexane) in THF stirred at -78° for 30 min, startg. urethan in THF added, stirred for a further

1 h, then quenched with aq. NH$_4$Cl → product. Y 81%. Interestingly, other strong bases such as KH, KN(SiMe$_3$)$_2$ or s-BuLi/sparteine were ineffective. The method is simple, efficient and general, leaving esters, methylenedioxy groups, and phenolethers unaffected. Migration of the pivaloyl group was sluggish and proceeded with low conversion. F.e. incl. amino acid derivs., and with retention of chirality leading to a quaternary centre next to the carbonyl group, s. O. Hara et al., Tetrahedron Lett. *39*, 5537-40 (1998).

*Aluminum chloride*      *AlCl$_3$*
**1,5-N→C-Acyl migration**      ←
s. *11*, 799; Fries-type rearrangement of 3-acyl-2(3*H*)-benzoxazolones s. H. Ucar et al., Tetrahedron *54*, 1763-72 (1998).

## Sulfur/Carbon Type      CC ∩ SC

*Lithium diisopropylamide/N,N'-dimethyl-N,N'-propyleneurea*      *i-Pr$_2$NLi/DMPU*
**5-Methylene-6-α-(alkylthio)-1,3-cyclohexadienes from benzylsulfonium salts**      ←
**via stereospecific thia-Sommelet rearrangement**

A soln. of startg. sulfonium salt treated with 1.05 eqs. LDA in 4:1 THF/N,N'-dimethyl-N,N'-propyleneurea *at -78°*, and allowed to warm to room temp. → product. Y 87% (diastereoselectivity >20:1). Reaction was complete within a few min. The *anti*-stereoselectivity is interpreted in terms of an *endo* transition state. Diastereoselectivity was lower from acyclic sulfonium salts. F.e.s. R. Berger et al., J. Am. Chem. Soc. *120*, 841-2 (1998).

## Remaining Elements/Carbon Type      CC ∩ RemC

*Hafnium tetrachloride/trimethylsilyl chloride*      *HfCl$_4$/Me$_3$SiCl*
**Regiospecific intramolecular allylsilylation of acetylene derivs.**      ○

**3-Vinyl-1-silylcycloalkenes.** A mixture of 10 mol% HfCl$_4$ in methylene chloride stirred at room temp. for 10 min, cooled to 0°, treated with 50 mol% trimethylsilyl chloride and startg. enyne, stirred for 50 min, diluted with pentane, and quenched with diethylamine → product. Y 61%. This is the first example of an exclusive *endo-dig* carbocyclization, the key zwitterionic vinyl-hafnium carbocation being stabilized by electronic and steric effects. F.e. incl. cyclopentene and cycloheptene analogs s. K. Imamura, Y. Yamamoto et al., J. Am. Chem. Soc. *120*, 5339-40 (1998).

## Carbon/Carbon Type      CC ∩ CC

*Without additional reagents*      *w.a.r.*
**Regio- and stereo-specific intramolecular Diels-Alder reaction**      ○
s. *34*, 693s*54*; pinnatoxin A ring s. Y. Kishi et al., J. Am. Chem. Soc. *120*, 7647-8 (1998); racemic batrachotoxinin A ring s. ibid. 6627-8; (+)-himbeline and (+)-himbacine synthesis s. D.J. Hart et al., J. Org. Chem. *62*, 5023-33 (1997); intramolecular cycloaddition of 3-(tetrahydropyridinyl)-indoles to *Strycnos* alkaloid-type pentacyclics s. P. Gharagozloo et al., ibid. *63*, 1974-80 (1998); tigliane and daphnane diterpenoids s. P.C. Bulman Page et al., Tetrahedron Lett. *38*, 5395-8 (1997).

**Regiospecific double ring expansion of (cyclopropylalkylidene)cyclopropanes**
**Cyclopropyltrimethylenemethane 1,3-diradicals as intermediates**

316.

A variety of fused and bridged bicyclic 6-membered carbocyclics is available by a novel double cyclopropane ring expansion **under flash vacuum pyrolysis. E:** Startg. dicyclopropyl deriv. flash vacuum pyrolyzed at 0.01 Torr and 550° → product. Y 92%. There was no competing H-atom transfer, although a retro-ene reaction was observed in one instance. The method is also applicable to generating the taxoid **bicyclo[5.3.1]undec-10-ene ring**. F.e.s. H. Liu, T. Cohen et al., J. Am. Chem. Soc. *120*, 605-6 (1998).

*Irradiation*
**Intramolecular 1,3-dipolar cycloaddition with azomethinium ylids**
generated from aziridines s. *42*, 986s49; cycloaddition of chiral siloxy-tethered substrates with asym. induction s. P. Garner et al., J. Org. Chem. *62*, 493-8 (1997).

*Silver trifluoromethanesulfonate s. under RhCl(PPh$_3$)$_3$*  $AgOSO_2CF_3$
*Tris(triphenylphosphine)rhodium(I) fluoroborate*  $[Rh(PPh_3)_3]BF_4$
**3-Alkylidenecyclopentenes from allenylcyclopropanes**

317.

**Regiospecific ring expansion.** Startg. allenylcyclopropane (0.2 to 0.3 mmol scale) added to a soln. of 5 mol% [Rh(PPh$_3$)$_3$]BF$_4$ (prepared *in situ* from RhCl(PPh$_3$)$_3$ and AgBF$_4$) in benzene, and heated under reflux for 3 h → product. Y 98% (>99:1 mixture of regioisomers). The high regioselectivity is explained by the overwhelming steric repulsion between the alkyl substituent on the cyclopropane ring and the ligands of the catalyst in the initially formed allene-rhodium complex. 2-Phenyl-substituted allenylcyclopropanes, however, were cleaved in the presence of a *non-phosphine*-containing Rh(I) complex by the alternative, *ionic* mode, perhaps via a phenyl-stabilized carbocation. No conjugated dienes were formed as by-products. F.e. and catalysts s. M. Hayashi, K. Saigo et al., Angew. Chem. Int. Ed. Engl. *37*, 837-9 (1998).

*[1,2-Bis(diphenylphosphino)ethane]rhodium(I) hexafluoroantimonate*
**Stereospecific intramolecular Diels-Alder reaction with unactivated acetylene derivs.**
2,3-fused 1,4-cyclohexadienes under nickel catalysis cf. *45*, 439; under rhodium catalysis with [1,2-bis(diphenylphosphino)ethane]rhodium(I) hexafluoroantimonate s. S.R. Gilbertson, G.S. Hoge, Tetrahedron Lett. *39*, 2075-8 (1998).

*Chlorotris(triphenylphosphine)rhodium(I)/silver trifluoromethanesulfonate*
**Stereospecific intramolecular [5+2]-cycloaddition of ethylene derivs.**
**to vinylcyclopropanes**

318.

**Cycloheptene ring.** 10 Mol% RhCl(PPh$_3$)$_3$ and 10 mol% AgOTf added sequentially (in one portion) to a base-washed, oven-dried Schlenk flask under argon, O$_2$-free toluene added, stirred for 5 min at room temp., startg. cyclopropane in toluene added over 10 sec, and heated to 110° for 17 h → product. Y 86% (single stereoisomer). The remarkable stereoselectivity is consistent with the preferred formation of a *cis*-fused metallacyclopentane intermediate. Reaction takes place on the mg to g scale and at concentrations up to 1 $M$ with a catalyst loading of 0.1 to 10 mol%. A 4-membered and a 2-oxatrimethylene tether were tolerated, and the *gem*-bis(methoxy-carbonyl) group is not mandatory. However, there was no reaction with substrates having a substituent at the terminal carbon atom of the isolated alkene group. F.e.s. P.A. Wender et al., J. Am. Chem. Soc. *120*, 1940-1 (1998).

## Exchange ↕

## Hydrogen ↑ CC ↕ H

*Without additional reagents* w.a.r.
**α-(Carbalkoxyamino)carboxylic acid amides by Ugi 5-component condensation** ←

319.

Methanol saturated with $CO_2$ at 0° added to a neat mixture of isobutanol and 1.25 eqs. *n*-butyl-amine (final concentration ca. 0.1 $M$), 1 eq. 1-cyclohexenyl isocyanide added, and a slight positive pressure of $CO_2$ maintained while stirring for 18-24 h → product. Y 89%. For higher boiling or solid alcohols, the latter were used in a 10-fold excess with chloroform as solvent. Where yields were low, the bulk of the starting material could be recovered, and improved yields could be obtained by addition of 3 Å molecular sieves and applying a higher $CO_2$ pressure (23 p.s.i.). A mixture of products was obtained with COS in place of $CO_2$, **while α-aminocarboxylic acid thioamides** were formed predominantly with $CS_2$. F.e.s. T.A. Keating, R.W. Armstrong, J. Org. Chem. *63*, 867-71 (1998).

*Electrolysis*
**Diels-Alder reaction with *in situ*-generated quinones**
under electrolysis in micellar media s. *35*, 506s*53*; with a [poly-(tetrafluoroethylene)]-fiber-coated glassy carbon electrode in nitromethane containing $LiClO_4$, also **asym. cycloaddition** with chiral quinols, s. Tetrahedron Lett. *39*, 5527-30 (1998).

*Lithium diisopropylamide/1-cyanobenzotriazole* ←
**Replacement of hydrogen by cyano groups** H → CN
with LDA/*i*-Pr$_2$NCN cf. *39*, 673s*41*; arylmalononitriles from arylacetonitriles with LDA/1-cyano-benzotriazole, and prepn. of the reagent, s. T.V. Hughes et al., J. Org. Chem. *63*, 401-2 (1998); **N- and S-cyanation** s. A.R. Katritzky et al., Rev. Roum. Chim. *36*, 573-80 (1991).

*Lithium bis(trimethylsilyl)amide/phenyl iodosoacetate* $LiN(SiMe_3)_2/PhI(OAc)_2$
**Asym. oxidative dimerization of enolates** 2 RH → R-R
with LDA/Cu(II) cf. *4*, 685s*50*; of chiral 3-acyl-2-oxazolidones with $LiN(SiMe_3)_2/PhI(OAc)_2$ or $PhI(OCOCF_3)_2$ (cf. *4*, 685s*54*) s. J.W. Kim, K.H. Ahn et al., Synth. Commun. *28*, 1287-92 (1998).

*Sodium amide/potassium permanganate* $NaNH_2/KMnO_4$
**Oxidative nucleophilic substitution by carbanions** ArH → ArR
of Cr(CO)$_3$-complexed arenes with LDA/I$_2$ cf. *30*, 540; α-(*p*-nitroaryl)nitriles from ar. nitro compds. and nitriles with $NaNH_2/KMnO_4$ s. M. Makosza, K. Stalinski, Tetrahedron *54*, 8797-810 (1998).

*Di-μ-hydroxodicopper(II) complexes/hydrogen peroxide* ←
**Oxidative dimerization of phenols** 2 ArH → Ar-Ar
with CuCl/TMEDA/air cf. *31*, 719s*53*; with di-μ-hydroxodicopper(II) complexes/$H_2O_2$ s. M. Kodera et al., Chem. Lett. *1998*, 441-2; with MeBu$_3$N$^+$MnO$_4^-$ in *non-aq.* media cf. F.A. Marques et al., Tetrahedron Lett. *39*, 943-6 (1998).

*Aluminum chloride/oxalyl chloride* $AlCl_3/(COCl)_2$
**Friedel-Crafts carbamylation** $H \rightarrow CON{<}$

320.

69 ml Oxalyl chloride added to 108 g $AlCl_3$ in 1,2-dichloroethane at room temp., a soln. of 69.9 g 4-phenylcyclohexanone in the same solvent added dropwise at 5-15°, stirred at room temp. for 2 h, excess of oxalyl chloride removed by distillation, and 40% aq. dimethylamine added at 10-15° → 4-[4-(dimethylaminocarbonyl)phenyl]cyclohexanone. Y 97%. F.e.s. German patent DE-19704401 (Girindus Chem. Gmbh & Co. AG).

*Aluminum bromide s. under $CBr_4$* $AlBr_3$

*Ytterbium/hexamethylphosphoramide/1-naphthaldehyde/methyl iodide* ←
**Sym. 1,2-di(azomethines) from aldimines** $2\ CH{=}NR \rightarrow C({=}NR)C({=}NR)$

321.  $2\ \text{p-MeOC}_6H_4CH{=}NPh \longrightarrow \text{p-MeOC}_6H_4\overset{PhN}{\overset{\|}{C}}{-}\overset{NPh}{\overset{\|}{C}}C_6H_4OMe\text{-p}$

Tetrahydrofuran, HMPA (25 vol%), and methyl iodide added successively to a mixture of startg. aldimine and 0.5 eq. Yb under argon, stirred for 2 h at room temp., 1 eq. 1-naphthaldehyde (as H-acceptor) added, and stirring continued at room temp. for a further 2 h → product. Y 57%. There was no reaction in the absence of HMPA. Reaction is generally applicable to aromatic aldimines (electron-donating groups in the ring favouring reaction). This is the first example of a metal-mediated dehydrogenative coupling of aldimines. F.e.s. W.-S. Jin, Y. Fujiwara et al., Chem. Commun. *1998*, 1101-2.

*Phenyl iodosoacetate s. under $LiN(SiMe_3)_2$* $PhI(OAc)_2$

*Carbon tetrabromide/aluminum bromide* $CBr_4/AlBr_3$
**Alkylation of deactivated arenes with hydrocarbons** $H \rightarrow R$
**in the presence of an aprotic superacid**

322.

A mixture of ca. 6 eqs. $AlBr_3$, ca. 3 eqs. carbon tetrabromide, and dry methylene bromide stirred until homogeneous, cooled to -20°, the reaction vessel filled with dry propane, 1,2,4-trichlorobenzene in the same solvent added under a propane atmosphere, stirred at -20° for 30 min under a slight over-pressure of propane, and hydrolyzed with ice-water → product. Y 86%. The superacid is presumed to abstract hydride ion from the hydrocarbon, and the liberated carbonium ion reacts with the arene in the normal manner for electrophilic substitution. In certain instances, selective and effective mono- and di-alkylation can be achieved with both alkanes and cycloalkanes at -40 to 0°. F.e. and regioselectivity s. A.V. Orlinkov et al., Mendeleev Commun. *1997*, 61-3.

*Hydrogen peroxide s. under Cu(II) complexes* $H_2O_2$

*Manganese(III) acetate* $Mn(OAc)_3$
**γ-Lactones from ethylene derivs.**
s. *24*, 768; γ-aryl-α,β-dicarbalkoxy-derivs. with K-monomethyl malonate in acetic or formic acid, stereoselectivity, s. L. Lamarque et al., Tetrahedron Lett. *39*, 8283-4 (1998).

*Potassium permanganate s. under $NaNH_2$* $KMnO_4$

*Tri-n-butylmethylammonium permanganate*      $MeBu_3NMnO_4$
**Oxidative dimerization of phenols** s. *31*, 719s55      2 ArH → Ar-Ar

*Rhodium trichloride/triphenylphosphine/2-amino-4-picoline/alkenes*      ←
**Synthesis of aryl ketones**      $ArCH_2OH$ → ArCOC-CH
**from prim. benzylalcohols and terminal ethylene derivs.**

323.

Rh-catalyzed oxidation of alcohols (cf. *15*, 261s*41*) and regiospecific hydroacylation (cf. *52*, 319) have been combined to afford the first example of a direct ketone synthesis from a prim. alcohol and a 1-alkene. **E:** A mixture of benzyl alcohol, 1 eq. 2-amino-4-picoline, and 16.5 mol% $Ph_3P$ in *10 eqs.* 1-pentene stirred for several min in a screw-capped vial, treated with 3.3 mol% $RhCl_3·H_2O$, and stirred at 130° for 12 h → hexanophenone. Y 86%. Yields were low with aliphatic alcohols. There appear to be no limitations with respect to the 1-alkene. F.e.s. C.-H. Jun et al., Angew. Chem. Int. Ed. Engl. *37*, 145-7 (1998).

*Palladous acetate*      $Pd(OAc)_2$
**Carbonylation of hypervalent iodine compds.**      ←

324.

***p*-Iodocarboxylic acid esters.** 0.2 Mol% $Pd(OAc)_2$ added to a stirred soln. of Zefirov's reagent in DMF containing 1.2 eqs. methanol under an atmosphere of CO at room temp., and stirred for 30 min → methyl *p*-iodobenzoate. Y 91%. Interestingly, **arylcarboxylic acid esters** were obtained **from diaryliodonium *tosylates* or *fluoroborates*,** while the corresponding triflates or bromides reacted in the same way as Zefirov's reagent. F.e. incl. phenolesters from phenols, **also α,β-ethylenecarboxylic acid esters** from α,β-ethyleneiodonium fluoroborates, and selective conversion of unsym. diaryliodonium salts, s. S.-K. Kang et al., J. Chem. Soc. Perkin Trans. 1 *1998*, 841-2.

# Oxygen ↑      CC ↓↑ O

*Without additional reagents*      *w.a.r.*
**α-Keto-γ-lactones from α-ketocarboxylic acids and oxo compds.**
s. *17*, 821; α-keto-γ-spiro-γ-lactones from cyclic ketones (ninhydrin and alloxan) without reagent s. H.N. Song, J.N. Kim et al., Synth. Commun. *28*, 687-92 (1998).

**Ugi 4-component condensation**      ←
s. *17*, 809s*53*; chiral N-succinoyl-α-aminocarboxamides with methanolic *ammonia* as the amine component s. C.D. Floyd et al., Synlett *1998*, 637-9.

**1-Carbamyllactams by Ugi condensation**
s. *52*, 351s*54*; 5-carbamyl-2-pyrrolidones and 3-carbamylphthalimidines s. C. Hanusch-Kompa, I. Ugi, Tetrahedron Lett. *39*, 2725-8 (1998).

**Asym. synthesis of α-*prim*-amino-β-hydroxycarboxylic acids from aldehydes via 4,8-dioxa-1-azabicyclo[4.3.0]nonan-5-ones**

325.

3 eqs. Freshly distilled benzaldehyde added to a soln. of (5S)-5-phenyl-2-morpholone in dry toluene, and heated to reflux for 48 h under $N_2$ with stirring under a Soxhlet extractor →

(2S,6S,7R,9S)-2,7,9-triphenyl-4,8-dioxa-1-azabicyclo[4.3.0]nonan-5-one (Y 69%), suspended in 10% aq. methanol in a Fischer-Porter bottle, 1 eq. trifluoroacetic acid and 1 eq. (by mass) Pd(OH)$_2$/C added with stirring, the mixture degassed, kept under 5 atm. H$_2$ for 48 h with continued stirring, worked up, and purified on a Dowex anion exchange column → (2S,3R)-2-amino-3-hydroxy-3-phenylpropanoic acid (Y 65%; enantiopure). For products from aliphatic aldehydes, the intermediate was first cleaved with 1 M methanol HCl prior to hydrogenation. F.e.s. D. Alker, L.M. Harwood et al., Tetrahedron 54, 6089-98 (1998).

*Microwaves (s.a. under LiCl, Bentonite and Montmorillonite)*
**2-Aminopyridines from α,β-ethylenenitriles and ketones**

326.

**2-Amino-3-cyanopyridines.** A mixture of startg. malononitrile, 1 eq. acetophenone, 8 eqs. NH$_4$OAc, and *a small volume* of *o*-dichlorobenzene subjected to microwave irradiation *for 3 min* in a BMO-700 T domestic microwave oven at a power output of 275 W (2450 MHz) → product. Y 72% (52% with no solvent). Yields were higher than by the classical thermal route, and reaction times considerably shorter. F.e.s. S. Paul et al., J. Chem. Res., Synop 1998, 330-1.

*Lithium hydroxide/oxygen*   LiOH/O$_2$
**Polymer-based synthesis of α,β-ethyleneketones from aldehydes**   CHO → CH=C
**and subsequent ring closures**

327.

Ar = C$_6$H$_4$OMe-p

**Pyrimidines from amidines.** 20 eqs. Each of LiOH·H$_2$O and acetophenone added to the resin-based aldehyde in dry DME, shaken in a capped vial for 16 h at room temp., the resulting supported enone washed and dried, 10 eqs. startg. amidine in N,N-dimethylacetamide added, the suspension stirred vigorously at 100° overnight under air, the resin washed and dried, then cleaved with 20% trifluoroacetic acid in methylene chloride for 0.25 h → 4-[2-(4-methoxyphenyl)-6-phenylpyrimidin-4-yl]benzamide. Y 98% (after preparative HPLC). F.e. and ring closures, also isolation of enones by cleavage of the intermediate resin, and preparation of supported enones by **polymer-based Wittig synthesis**, s. A.L. Marzinzik, E.R. Felder, J. Org. Chem. 63, 723-7 (1998).

*Potassium hydroxide*   KOH
**1-Vinylpyrroles from (E)-oximes**
**Trofimov reaction**

328.

**2-(Pyridyl)-1-vinylpyrroles.** A mixture of startg. oxime and 1 eq. KOH in DMSO heated at 120° under acetylene in a rotating autoclave for 3 h (the acetylene pressure increasing from 16 atm. at room temp. to 25 atm. at 120°) → product. Y 65%. F.e. and pyridyl isomers s. O.V. Petrova, A.I. Mikhaleva et al., Mendeleev Commun. 1997, 162-3.

*Sodium hydride*   NaH
**Phenols from α,β-acetyleneketones**
with KOBu-*t* cf. 28, 730; under milder, less basic conditions with NaH, regioselectivity, s. A. Covarrubias-Zúñiga, Synth. Commun. 28, 1525-30 (1998).

*Potassium* tert-*butoxide/*p-*toluenesulfonic acid*　　　　　　　　　　　　　　　KOBu-t/TsOH
**4-Pyrones from β-alkoxy-α,β-ethyleneketones**

and acyl chlorides with LiN(SiMe$_3$)$_2$ cf. *36*, 819; 2-perfluoroalkyl-4-pyrones from perfluoro-
carboxylic acid esters with KOBu-*t*, also from α,β-epoxyketones, s. V.I. Tyvorskii et al., Tetrahedron
*54*, 2819-26 (1998).

*Organolithium compds.*　　　　　　　　　　　　　　　　　　　　　　　　　　　　　　RLi
**Stereospecific synthesis of β-arylseleno-β-carbalkoxy-γ-lactones from aldehydes
via 1,4-addition-aldol condensation-lactonization**

329.

1.1 eqs. Methyllithium added to a stirred soln. of dimethyl 2-(phenylseleno)fumarate in dry ether
at -70° under argon, allowed to react for 10 min, 1.2 eqs. startg. aldehyde in ether added, the
mixture stirred for 1 h at -70°, warmed to 0°, and water added → product. Y 71% (d.r. 93:7). The
method is applicable to alkyl, aryl or hetaryl aldehydes, so that there is flexibility with respect to
the substituent at C-5, characteristic of paraconic acids. F.e., also conversion to **4-carbalkoxy-
2(5H)-furanones** via selenoxide elimination, or β-carbalkoxy-γ-lactones by reductive deselenation
(with Bu$_3$SnH/AIBN), s. F. D'Onofrio, L. Parlanti et al., Chem. Commun. *1998*, 185-6.

n-*Butyllithium*　　　　　　　　　　　　　　　　　　　　　　　　　　　　　　　　　　BuLi
**Nitriles from halides or sulfonates**　　　　　　　　　　　　　　　　　　　OSO$_2$R → CH$_2$CN
**Synthesis with addition of two C-atoms**

330.　　　　　C$_{10}$H$_{21}$OSO$_2$Ph　　+　　[ LiCH$_2$CN ]　　⟶　　C$_{10}$H$_{21}$CH$_2$CN

**Improved procedure.** 2.4 *M* n-BuLi in hexanes added at -78° under N$_2$ to a soln. of acetonitrile
in dry THF, stirred at the same temp. for 1 h, the mixture *transferred via cannula over 20 min* to
a soln. of 0.4 eq. startg. sulfonate in dry THF at 0°, stirring continued for 15 min, and quenched
with water → product. Y 72%. Dialkylation of acetonitrile is minimized under these conditions.
F.e., method, and with halides as electrophile s. D.F. Taber, S. Kong, J. Org. Chem. *62*, 8575-6
(1997).

**Synthesis of 4-amino-1,4-dihydronaphthalene-1-carboxylic acid derivs.**　　　　　　　　←
**via stereospecific 1,6-addition-α-alkylation of 2-(1-naphthyl)-Δ$^2$-oxazolines**

331.

1.2-1.6 eqs. *n*-BuLi added dropwise to a stirred soln. of 1.2-1.6 eqs. diallylamine in THF at -5°,
stirring continued for 30 min, cooled to -78°, treated with HMPA, stirred for 5 min, a soln. of
startg. naphthalene in THF added, stirred at -65 to -55° for 6 h, re-cooled to -78°, 1.4-1.9 eqs.
methyl triflate added, stirred for 1 h, and allowed to warm to -10° over 3 h → intermediate adduct
(Y 92%; 83:17 mixture of 4β/4α-isomers), the major isomer isolated chromatographically, treated
with 1 *N* HCl at room temp. with stirring for ca. 6 h, and acetylated in the usual way (Ac$_2$O/NaOH)
→ product (Y 97%). F.e. and electrophiles s. M. Shimano, A. Matsuo, Tetrahedron *54*, 4787-810
(1998).

(E)-Ethylene derivs. from 1-subst. benzotriazoles ←
and oxo compds. cf. *52*, 249; f. method from carboxylic acid esters via 1-β-ketobenzotriazoles, chiral 3-aryl-2-ethyleneamines, s. J. Org. Chem. *63*, 3438-44 (1998).

n-*Butyllithium/potassium* tert-*butoxide*     BuLi/KOBu-t
**Benzylic metalation** ←
with n-amylsodium/TMEDA cf. *27*, 838; of propylbenzene with n-BuLi/KOBu-*t*, stilbenes from aryloxo compds., s. A. Thurner et al., J. Chem. Res., Synop *1998*, 158-9.

*Lithium bis(trimethylsilyl)amide/magnesium/lithium perchlorate* ←
**3-Component synthesis of prim. amines**     CHO → CH(NH$_2$)R

332. PhCHO $\xrightarrow{(Me_3Si)_2NLi}$ [ PhCH=NSiMe$_3$ ] $\xrightarrow{BrMgCH_2SiMe_3}$ PhCHCH$_2$SiMe$_3$ (NH$_2$)

The Ipaktschi 3-component synthesis (*50*, 551) has been adapted for prim. amines. **E: 2-*prim*-Aminosilanes.** 5 M LiClO$_4$ in ether and startg. aldehyde added via syringe to a stirred soln. of 1.65 eqs. Li-bis(trimethylsilyl)amide in the same solvent under argon, stirring continued for 30 min, 2 eqs. trimethylsilylmethylmagnesium bromide added, stirred for a further 30 min, and quenched with water → product. Y 75%. F.e. incl. silylethynylcarbinamines s. M.R. Saidi et al., Tetrahedron Lett. *38*, 8071-2 (1997).

*Lithium chloride/microwaves* ←
**Knoevenagel condensation under microwave irradiation**     CO → C=C
**in the absence of solvent**
s. *46*, 713s*51, 54*; in the presence of LiCl s. G. Sabitha et al., Chem. Lett. *1998*, 773-4.

*Cesium fluoride*     CsF
**1-Carbalkoxy-3-oxabicyclo[3.1.0]hexan-2-ones**
**from glycidyl sulfonates and malonic acid esters**
**Double ring closure with asym. induction**

333. [reaction scheme: glycidyl m-nosylate + dimethyl malonate → intermediate → bicyclic product]

A suspension of 1.1 eqs. dimethyl malonate and 5 eqs. CsF in acetonitrile stirred at room temp. for 30 min, (S)-glycidyl *m*-nosylate (e.e. 99%) added, and the mixture stirred at room temp. for 110 h → (1S,5R)-product. Y 63% (e.e. 94%). The reaction failed with epichlorohydrin. The method is simple, conditions are almost neutral, and enantioselectivity is high. F.e. and from (1R)-glycidyl sulfonates s. K. Kitaori, J. Otera et al., Synlett *1998*, 499-500; s.a. Japanese patent JP-10059955 (Daiso Co. Ltd.).

*Piperidine/acetic acid*     C$_5$H$_{11}$N/AcOH
**Polymer-based Knoevenagel condensation**     CO → C=C
s. *3*, 632s*54*; (E)-alkylidenemalonamic acids s. B.C. Hamper et al., Tetrahedron Lett. *39*, 2047-50 (1998).

*Triethylenediamine*     dabco
**Polymer-based synthesis of α-methylene-β-sulfonylaminocarboxylic acids** ←
**by Baylis-Hillman-type reaction**

334. [reaction scheme]     R = p-CF$_3$C$_6$H$_4$

4 eqs. 4-Trifluoromethylbenzaldehyde, 5 eqs. 4-methoxyphenylsulfonamide, and 0.4 eq. DABCO added to a suspension of polymer-bound acrylic acid (prepared from 2-chlorotrityl chloride

resin (1% divinylbenzene), acrylic acid and 1.5 eqs. Et₃N in 1:1 DMF/dichloromethane at 0° for 4 h) in dioxane, stirred at 70° for 16 h, and the resin cleaved with 95:5 dichloromethane/ trifluoroacetic acid for 30 min → product. Y 78%. F.e.s. H. Richter, G. Jung, Tetrahedron Lett. *39*, 2729-30 (1998).

*Cuprous chloride s. under BF₃*  CuCl

*Silver trifluoroacetate/stannic chloride*  $AgOCOCF_3/SnCl_4$
**C-Aryl glycosides from acyl glycosides**  OAc → Ar
or simple glycosides with AgClO₄/Me₃SiOTf cf. *44*, 802s*47*; with AgOCOCF₃/SnCl₄, stereoselectivity, s. T. Kuribayashi et al., Tetrahedron Lett. *39*, 4537-40 (1998); arylidenebis(C-glycosides) by condensation with a second molecule of acyl glycoside s. ibid. 4541-2.

*Magnesium (s.a. under LiN(SiMe₃)₂)*  Mg
**Cross-coupling of Grignard compds. with O-functions** s. under CC↓↑Hal  O- → R

*Zinc s. under BF₃ and PdCl₂(PPh₃)₂*  Zn
*Isopropylmagnesium chloride s. under Ti(OPr-i)₄*  i-PrMgCl

*Phenylboronic acid/acetic acid*  $PhB(OH)_2/AcOH$
**3-Chromenes from phenols and α,β-ethylenealdehydes**  ○
with Ti(OEt)₄ cf. *35*, 530; under mild conditions with PhB(OH)₂ in 1:7.4 glacial AcOH/toluene s. B.A. Chauder, V. Snieckus et al., Synthesis *1998*, 279-82.

*Thallic acetate/polyphosphoric acid*  $Tl(OAc)_3/PPA$
**Coumarins from α,β-acetylenecarboxylic acids and phenols**
4-Arylcoumarins s. *54*, 367s*55*

*Hydrotalcites*  ←
**Hydrotalcites as a mild, solid base**  ←

335.

**Heterogeneous aldol condensation.** A mixture of startg. aldehyde and 70 eqs. acetone heated with a little heat-activated hydrotalcite (Mg:Al 2.5) for 1 h → product. Y 96%. The base (which can be tuned by adjusting the Mg/Al ratio) exhibits a high catalytic activity under very mild conditions, and can be easily re-activated by heating. F.e. and **Knoevenagel condensation** s. M.L. Kantam, B.M. Choudary et al., Chem. Commun. *1998*, 1033-4; O-2-cyanoethylation of alcohols with acrylonitrile s. P.S. Kumbhar et al., ibid. 1091-2.

*Bentonite s. under NH₄NO₃*  ←

*Montmorillonite*  ←
**Pechmann-Duisberg coumarin synthesis under heterogeneous catalysis**  ○
with zeolites cf. *1*, 591s*51*; with montmorillonite or KSF clay s. T.-S. Li et al., J. Chem. Res., Synop *1998*, 38-9.

*Montmorillonite/sulfuric acid/microwaves*  ←
**3,4-Dihydrocoumarins from phenols and α,β-ethylenecarboxylic acids**
**Microwave irradiation on a solid support in the absence of solvent**

336.

Freshly distilled phenol and 1 eq. recrystallized *p*-methoxycinnamic acid in dichloromethane added with 1 drop of concd. H₂SO₄ to heat-activated montmorillonite K-10 clay, the solvent evaporated, the resulting free-flowing solid placed on a silica bath, and subjected to microwave irradiation at 640 W for 10 min → product. Y 82%. An open vessel is used so that the possibility of an explosion is minimized. F.e., **also coumarins from α,β-acetylenecarboxylic acids,** s. J. Singh et al., J. Chem. Res., Synop *1998*, 280-1.

*Boron fluoride s.a. under $Me_3SiOSO_2CF_3$* $BF_3$

*Boron fluoride/sodium sulfate* $BF_3/Na_2SO_4$
**trans-3,4-Dihydroisocarbostyril-4-carboxylic acids** ←
from homophthalic anhydrides and aldehydes s. *32*, 617s55

*Boron fluoride/cuprous chloride/acetic acid* $BF_3/CuCl/AcOH$
**Catalytic Biginelli synthesis of 3,4-dihydro-2(1H)-pyrimidinones** ○

337.

**4-Aryl-3,4-dihydro-2(1H)-pyrimidinone-5-carboxylic acid esters.** A mixture of startg. β-ketoester, 1 eq. startg. aldehyde, 1.5 eqs. urea, 1.3 eqs. $BF_3$-etherate, 0.1 eq. CuCl and 0.1 eq. glacial acetic acid in dry THF heated to reflux under $N_2$ (65°) for 8-18 h, cooled to room temp., and quenched with 10% $Na_2CO_3$ → 4-(3,4-difluorophenyl)-6-ethyl-5-methoxycarbonyl-3,4-dihydro-pyrimidin-2(1H)-one. Y 82%. The procedure is simple, generally applicable (regardless of the nature of the β-ketoester or aryl aldehyde), and significantly more efficient than Folker's modification (with catalytic $H_2SO_4$ in refluxing ethanol). $CuCl_2$, $Cu_2O$, $NiBr_2$ and $Pd(OAc)_2$ could be used in place of CuCl, and trifluoroacetic acid or methanol could be used as the proton source. However, other Lewis acids were less effective. F.e.s. E.H. Hu et al., J. Org. Chem. *63*, 3454-7 (1998); with polyphosphoric acid ester as catalyst cf. C.O. Kappe, S.F. Falsone, Synlett *1998*, 718-20.

*Boron fluoride/zinc* $BF_3/Zn$
**Methylene from oxo compds.** $CO → C=CH_2$

338.

0.1 eq. $BF_3·OEt_2$ in THF added under argon to 1 eq. Nysted reagent [cyclo-dibromodi-μ-methylene(μ-tetrahydrofuran)trizinc] in THF at 0°, the mixture stirred at this temp. for 5 min, benzaldehyde in THF added, and stirring continued for 2 h at 18° → styrene. Y 96%. The Nysted reagent is superior to Wittig reagents especially for reaction with easily enolizable carbonyl compds. Other Lewis acids mediated the reaction (e.g. $SnCl_4$, $Me_3SnCl$, and $SnCl_2$) but $BF_3·Et_2O$ gave the best yield. Aldehydes with an α-stereogenic center reacted with complete retention of configuration, while ketoaldehydes reacted **with retention of keto groups**. Ketones were methylenated, however, in the presence of $TiCl_4$, $TiCl_3$ or $TiCl_2/BF_3$. F.e.s. S. Matsubara et al., Synlett *1998*, 313-5.

*Aluminum chloride* $AlCl_3$
**Friedel-Crafts acylation without solvent** s. *55*, 394 H → Ac

*Indium(III) chloride s. under $Me_2Si(H)Cl$* $InCl_3$

*Samarium/samarium diiodide/hexamethylphosphoramide*
**2-Arylamines**
**from alkylarenes and hindered carboxylic acid amides**

ArCH → ArC-CH(N<)R  (←)

339.

10:1 Toluene/HMPA and startg. amide added to 0.5 eq. Sm and 2.2 eqs. SmI$_2$, refluxed for 15 h at 110°, and quenched with satd. NaHCO$_3$ → 1-(α-piperidinophenethyl)adamantane. Y 76%. There was no amide dimerization (as with unhindered amides). F.e., **also 1-amino-1-aryl-cyclopropanes** from arylcarboxylic acid amides and ethylene derivs., s. A. Ogawa, N. Sonoda et al., Tetrahedron *53*, 12895-902 (1997).

*Scandium(III) triflate*
**Friedel-Crafts alkylation**

$Sc(OTf)_3$
H → R

benzylation and allylation with alcohols cf. *49*, 763s52; details of this and diarylmethane formation (*31*, 753s52) s. J. Org. Chem. *62*, 6997-7005 (1997); *sec*-alkylation with sec. mesylates s. H. Kotsuki et al., Synlett *1998*, 255-6.

**Polymer-based synthesis of N-condensed 5-aminoimidazoles**
**from *o*-amino-N-heterocyclics, aldehydes and isonitriles**

340.

Startg. resin-bound aldehyde in 1:3 methanol/methylene chloride treated with 6.8 eqs. 2-aminopyridine and 5 mol% Sc(OTf)$_3$, after 1 h 7 eqs. benzyl isonitrile added, the suspension shaken for 48 h at room temp., the resin washed with methylene chloride, methanol and again with methylene chloride, and cleaved by two treatments with 1:1 trifluoroacetic acid/methylene chloride → product. Y 65% (92% purity). F.e.s. C. Blackburn, Tetrahedron Lett. *39*, 5469-72 (1998); **parallel solution-phase synthesis** of 3-aminoimidazo[1,2-*a*]-pyridines and -pyrazines with removal of by-products on a cation exchanger, also subsequent N-acylation with acyl chloride in the presence of polymer-based morpholine, s. ibid. 3635-8; solution-phase method with HClO$_4$ cf. H. Bienaymé, K. Bouzid, Angew. Chem. Int. Ed. Engl. *37*, 2234-7 (1998).

*Scandium(III) triflate/tri-n-butyltin cyanide/hydrogen chloride*
**α-Aminonitriles from aldehydes and amines**

CHO → CH(N<)CN  (←)

341.  PhCHO + H$_2$NCHPh$_2$  →(Bu$_3$SnCN)  PhCHNHCHPh$_2$ with CN substituent

**in aq. medium.** Startg. amine, 1.5 eqs. Bu$_3$SnCN, and 1 eq. benzaldehyde added successively to 10 mol% aq. Sc(OTf)$_3$, stirred at room temp. for 20 h, worked-up, the crude materials treated with 4:1 THF/1 *M* HCl at room temp. for 1 h, hexane and satd. aq. NaHCO$_3$ added, and the aq. layer worked up with ethyl acetate → product. Y 88%. Reaction is generally applicable to aliphatic, aromatic, heterocyclic and α,β-unsatd. aldehydes. The by-product, bis(tributyltin) oxide (which is readily converted to Bu$_3$SnCN), was recovered easily and quantitatively by eluting with methanol, while the catalyst was recovered from the original aq. layer, so that reaction takes place within a completely recyclable system. F.e. and in 1:1 acetonitrile/toluene s. S. Kobayashi et al., Chem. Commun. *1998*, 981-2; with LiClO$_4$/Me$_3$SiCN cf. A. Heydari et al., Tetrahedron Lett. *39*, 3049-50 (1998).

*Ytterbium(III) triflate*  
**Polymer-based 3-component synthesis of 1,2,3,4-tetrahydroquinolines**  $Yb(OTf)_3$

342.

Startg. polymer-supported aniline (based on the Wang resin) treated with a 0.5 $M$ soln. of benzaldehyde and a 0.5 $M$ soln. of cyclopentadiene in 2:1 acetonitrile/methylene chloride, 1% Yb(OTf)$_3$ in the same solvent mixture added, agitated by bubbling N$_2$ through the mixture for 24 h, the resin removed, washed and dried, and treated with 15% trifluoroacetic acid in methylene chloride → (3aR*,4S*,9bS*)-8-(2-benzamido-2-carboxyethyl)-4-phenyl-3a,4,5,9b-tetrahydro-3*H*-cyclopenta[*c*]quinoline. Y 83%. A **library of 1,2,3,4-tetrahydroquinolines** (50 compds.) was thus prepared in parallel (yields being highest from aldehydes with electron-withdrawing substituents). Polymerization of the olefin took place with trifluoroacetic acid as condensing agent. F.e.s. A.S. Kiselyov et al., Tetrahedron *54*, 5089-96 (1998).

*Samarium diiodide*  $SmI_2$  
**γ-Lactones from oxo compds. and α,β-ethylenecarboxylic acid esters**  
with asym. induction s. *41*, 723s*54*; from chiral Cr(CO)$_3$-complexed cyclic aryl ketones s. C.A. Merlic, J.C. Walsh, Tetrahedron Lett. *39*, 2083-6 (1998).

*Samarium diiodide/*tert-*butanol/(R)-2,2'-bis(diphenylphosphinyl)-1,1'-binaphthyl*  ←  
**Asym. synthesis of γ-lactones from α,β-ethylenecarboxylic acid esters and ketones**

343.

2 eqs. 0.05 $M$ SmI$_2$ in THF containing 2 eqs. (R)-2,2'-bis(diphenylphosphinyl)-1,1'-binaphthyl added to a soln. of acetophenone, 1 eq. methyl acrylate, and 2 eqs. *tert*-butanol in dry THF at -78° under argon, stirred for 20 min, warmed to room temp., and quenched with satd. NaHCO$_3$ → (S)-product. Y 46% (e.e. 67%; 74% at -105°). F.e.s. K. Mikami, M. Yamaoka, Tetrahedron Lett. *39*, 4501-4 (1998).

*Acetic acid*  *AcOH*  
**Polymer-based Mannich reaction**  CH → C-CH$_2$N<

344.

**3-(Aminomethyl)indoles.** A mixture of startg. Rink amide resin-supported indole, 1.5 eqs. pyrrolidine, and 1.5 eqs. formaldehyde in 1:4 acetic acid/dioxane allowed to react at 23° for 1.5 h, and the resin cleaved with 30% trifluoroacetic acid in methylene chloride → product. Y 93%

(100% purity). F.e. incl. Mannich reaction with benzylamine, also resin-based nucleophilic displacement of the amino group, s. H.-C. Zhang et al., Tetrahedron Lett. *39*, 4449-52 (1998).

*Trifluoroacetic acid*                                                                           $CF_3COOH$
**Pictet-Spengler ring closure**
s. *8*, 823s*52*; N-sulfonyl-1,2,3,4-tetrahydroisoquinolines s. L.K. Lukanov, A.P. Venkov, Synth. Commun. *28*, 2137-47 (1998); parallel synthesis on a hydroxyethyl-functionalized polystyrene support (cf. *8*, 823s*51*) s. A. van Loevezijn et al., Tetrahedron Lett. *39*, 4737-40 (1998); ring closure with a fluoride-removable serine-derived linker cf. Y.-L. Chou et al., ibid. 757-60; polymer-based synthesis of 1,2,3,4-tetrahydro-β-carboline-3-carboxamides s. P.P. Fantauzzi, K.M. Yager, ibid. 1291-4.

**1,2,3,4-Tetrahydroquinolines from prim. ar. amines, aldehydes and ethylene derivs.**
s. *52*, 363s*54*; synthesis of a library of polysubst. tetrahydroquinolines s. R. Baudelle et al., Tetrahedron *54*, 4125-40 (1998).

**3-Arylphthalides from *o*-aldehydocarboxylic acids and arenes**
with $MeSO_3H$ cf. *16*, 828s*31*; with $CF_3COOH$ s. M.V. Paradkar et al., J. Chem. Res., Synop *1998*, 332-3.

*Chloro(dimethyl)silane/indium(III) chloride*                         $Me_2Si(H)Cl/InCl_3$
**Reductive Friedel-Crafts alkylation with oxo compds. under mild conditions**     H → R

345.

2 eqs. Each of acetophenone and chloro(dimethyl)silane added to a mixture of 5 mol% $InCl_3$ in toluene at ambient temp., and heated at 60° for 1 h → product. Y 99% (*ortho:meta:para* 15:4:81). The method is applicable to alkylation of arenes (incl. deactivated arenes) with ar. ketones or aldehydes and with dialkyl ketones, but aliphatic aldehydes gave dialkyl ethers. This is the first report of a reductive Friedel-Crafts reaction using a hydrosilane as the reducing agent. The reaction is believed to occur via hydrosilylation of the oxo compd., followed by generation of a carbocation by desiloxylation, prior to electrophilic alkylation of the aromatic ring. Other hydrosilanes, e.g. $Et_3SiH$ or $MeSiCl_2H$, were not effective. F.e. and with $In(OTf)_3$ s. T. Miyai et al., Tetrahedron Lett. *39*, 6291-4 (1998); details s. Tetrahedron *55*, 1017-26 (1999).

*Dimethylphenylsilyllithium*                                                           $PhMe_2SiLi$
**α-*tert*-Aminoketones**                                                                    C(N<)=C(N<)
**from two N,N-disubst. carboxylic acid amide molecules**
**via sym. (Z)-ene-1,2-*tert*-diamines**

346.

Cyclohexanecarboxylic acid N,N-dimethylamide treated with 1.1 eqs. $PhMe_2SiLi$ in THF at -78 to -20° for 1 h, then quenched with aq. $NaHCO_3$ at -20° → intermediate (Z)-enediamine (Y 83%), heated with 3 *M* HCl at 70° for 18 h → product (Y 92%). Enediamines branched at the α-position were remarkably resistant to hydrolysis and were readily isolated. F.e. and **Z→E-isomerization** ($PtO_2$/MeOH/50°/15 min), also conversion to **sym. α-diketones** via 2,3-diamino-1,3-dienes, s. I. Fleming et al., Chem. Commun. *1998*, 711-2; mechanistic studies s. ibid. 713-4; **synthesis of tert. amines** in the presence of organolithium compds. s. ibid. 715-6; α-*tert*-aminoketones by electroreductive coupling via 2-*tert*-aminoenoxysilanes cf. S. Kashimura, T. Shono, Tetrahedron Lett. *39*, 6199-202 (1998).

*Titanium tetraisopropoxide/isopropylmagnesium chloride*     Ti(OPr-i)₄/i-PrMgCl
**Synthesis of acetylene derivs. from 2-acetylenealcohol O-derivs.**     C≡C-C-CH(OH)R
**via allenyltitanium(IV) complexes with transfer of chirality**

347.

**Chiral 3-acetylenealcohols.** A soln. of startg. propargyl phosphate (e.e. 96.7%) in ether treated with 1.5 eqs. Ti(OPr-i)₄ and 3 eqs. i-PrMgCl at -50° to -40° for 2 h under argon, and 0.8 eq. benzaldehyde added at -78° → product. Y 98% (*erythro:threo* 54:46; e.e. of the (1S,2R) and (1R,2R) diastereoisomers each being 94% after separation). The enantioselectivity is strongly dependent on the nature of the leaving group and on whether the propargyl deriv. is secondary or tertiary, reaction with phosphate derivs. proceeding with inversion of configuration, while reaction with carbonate derivs. proceed with retention of configuration. F.e. with >97% chirality transfer s. S. Okamoto et al., Tetrahedron Lett. *39*, 4551-4 (1998); asym. hydrolysis and deuterolysis, also prepn. of **chiral β,γ-acetylenehalides** s. ibid. 4555-8.

*Zirconocene dichloride/n-butyllithium/trimethylsilyl triflate*     ←
**Synthesis of 2-α-hydroxycyclopropanone ketals from oxo compds.**     ▽
**γ,γ-Dialkoxyallylzirconium complexes as intermediates**

348.

While γ,γ-dialkoxyallylzirconium complexes react with aldehydes at the γ-site in the absence of reagent (cf. *53*, 372), reaction in the presence of Lewis acid is dictated by the ketene acetal character so that aldol-type chemistry prevails at the β-site. **E:** A soln. of startg. γ,γ-dialkoxyallylzirconium complex (prepared *in situ* from triethyl orthoacrylate and 'Cp₂Zr' in toluene) mixed with 1.2 eqs. startg. aldehyde and 1.1 eqs. trimethylsilyl triflate for 2 h at -78° to room temp., and quenched with aq. NH₄Cl → product. Y 87%. The products can be hydrolyzed (with trifluoroacetic acid) to give **β,γ-ethylenecarboxylic acid esters** so that the startg. zirconium complexes serve as **homoenolate anion equivalents.** Reaction is applicable to both aliphatic and ar. aldehydes, as well as ketones. F.e. **and Michael-type addition** s. H. Ito, T. Taguchi et al., J. Am. Chem. Soc. *120*, 6623-4 (1998).

*Stannic chloride s. under AgOCOCF₃*     SnCl₄

*Ammonium nitrate/bentonite/microwaves*     ←
**Hantzsch pyridine synthesis under microwave irradiation**     ○
1,4-dihydropyridines in homogeneous media cf. *47*, 727s*53*; one-pot parallel combinatorial synthesis of a **pyridine library** with NH₄NO₃/bentonite s. I.C. Cotterill et al., Tetrahedron Lett. *39*, 1117-20 (1998); solid-phase synthesis of a 300-member combinatorial library of 1,4-dihydropyridines s. M.F. Gordeev et al., Bioorg. Med. Chem. *6*, 883-90 (1998).

*Triphenylphosphine*     Ph₃P
**Ring closures of acetylenedicarboxylic acid esters**
via intramolecular Wittig synthesis s. *54*, 367; dialkyl 2,5-dihydrofuran-2,3-dicarboxylates,

details, s. Tetrahedron *54*, 9169-74 (1998); 4-carbalkoxycoumarins from phenols s. I. Yavari et al., Tetrahedron Lett. *39*, 2391-2 (1998); coumarins from α,β-acetylenecarboxylic acids with Tl(OAc)₃/PPA, 4-aryl derivs., cf. K.M. Shamsuddin, M.J.A. Siddiqui, J. Chem. Res., Synop *1998*, 392-3.

| | |
|---|---|
| *Diethyl phosphorocyanidate/triethylamine* | $(EtO)_2P(O)CN/Et_3N$ |
| **Polymer-based C-acylation of active methylene groups with decarboxylative cleavage of the polymer support** | H → COR |

349.

α-**Cyanoketones**. Startg. polymer-based cyanoacetate (readily prepared from the Wang resin) and 10 eqs. benzoic acid dried *in vacuo* for 1 h, suspended in DMF containing 20 eqs. Et₃N, cooled to 0°, 10 eqs. diethyl phosphorocyanidate added slowly, kept at 0° for 30 min, shaken at room temp. for 14 h, the resin washed, re-suspended in 7:2:1 trifluoroacetic acid/methylene chloride/triethylsilane, and shaken for 1 h → benzoylacetonitrile. Y 80%. Poor yields were obtained with aliphatic acids, and other bases were ineffective. F.e.s. M.M. Sim et al., Tetrahedron Lett. *39*, 2195-8 (1998); **ar. β-aminoketones** from polymer-based 2-aroylacrylic esters via **Michael addition of amines**, and subsequent decarboxylative cleavage of the resin with acetic acid s. P. Garibay et al., ibid. 2207-10.

| | |
|---|---|
| *Polyphosphoric acid ester* | PPE |
| **Modified Biginelli synthesis of 3,4-dihydro-2(1*H*)-pyrimidinones** s. *55*, 337 | ○ |
| *Trimethylsilyl triflate s.a. under $Cp_2ZrCl_2$* | $Me_3SiOSO_2CF_3$ |
| *Trimethylsilyl triflate/pyridine/boron fluoride/1,8-diazabicyclo[5.4.0]undec-7-ene* | ← |
| **β′-Alkoxy-α,β-ethyleneoxo compds.** | H → C(OR)R′ |
| **from α,β-ethyleneoxo compds. and cyclic acetals** | |

from α,β-enones s. *47*, 745; also from enals and cyclic acetals with added BF₃-etherate s. F. Wang, R. Zibuck, Synlett *1998*, 245-6; with Me₂S in place of py cf. Chem. Commun. *1993*, 1188-9.

| | |
|---|---|
| *Trifluoromethanesulfonic acid* | $CF_3SO_3H$ |
| **β-Acylaminoaldehydes** | CH(NHCOR)C-CHO |
| **from two aldehyde molecules and prim. acylamines** | |

350.

Cyclohex-1-enylacetamide and 1 eq. paraldehyde in dichloromethane treated with 2% v/v trifluoromethanesulfonic acid, and the mixture stirred at 20° for 16 h → N-(4-oxobut-2-yl)cyclohex-1-enylacetamide. Y 51%. This reaction is believed to proceed via *in situ* formation of an acylimine from the amide and aldehyde, followed by 1,2-addition by the second aldehyde molecule. It is a one-pot process occurring **under mild conditions** at room temp., and no protection of the aldehyde is required. It is applicable to a variety of amides including β,γ-unsaturated, phenyl- or benzyl-amides. β-Acylaminoaldehydes are protected and relatively stable forms of β-aminoaldehydes which are generally difficult to isolate. F.e.s. C.M. Marson, A. Fallah, Chem. Commun. *1998*, 83-4.

*Silica-supported alkanesulfonic acids*
**Mesoporous silica-supported sulfonic acids as solid acid catalysts**

351.

Sulfonic acid-functionalized mesoporous silica (MCM or HMS) has been applied to reactions where zeolites have failed. **E: Sym. 1,1-bis(2-furyl)alkanes.** A mixture of 2-methylfuran and 2.5 eqs. acetone heated at 50° for 24 h in the presence of 10 wt% surface-coated MCM-supported sulfonic acid [prepared by partial hydration of MCM-41 by refluxing in water for 3 h, then refluxing with excess of 3-mercaptopropyltrimethoxysilane for 4 h, and oxidizing the mercapto groups with a three-fold excess of neutralised $H_2O_2$] → product. Conversion 85% (selectivity 96%). F. catalysts, also monoacylation of D-sorbitol with lauric acid (>95% selectivity) s. W.M. Van Rhijn et al., Chem. Commun. *1998*, 317-8; ar. alkylation with alcohols **in supercritical media** containing polysiloxane-based alkanesulfonic acids s. M.G. Hitzler et al., ibid. 359-60.

*Sulfuric acid* $H_2SO_4$
**1,1-Diarylalkanes from two arene molecules and oxo compds.** $CO \rightarrow CAr_2$
1,1-diaryl-2-acenaphthenones s. *2*, 680; 2,2-diarylindane-1,3-diones from ninhydrins s. H.N. Song, J.N. Kim et al., Synth. Commun. *28*, 1865-70 (1998).

*Chromous chloride/manganese/trimethylsilyl chloride/sodium iodide*
***anti*-Diol monoethers from acetals and aldehydes** $C{\equiv}C\text{-}CH(OR)CH(OH)R'$
**Catalytic Takai-Utimoto reaction**

352.

***anti*-3-Ene-1,2-diol 2-monoethers.** A mixture of *0.07 eq.* $CrCl_2$, 2.5 eqs. powdered Mn(0), and 0.2 eq. NaI in anhydrous THF stirred at room temp. for 20 min under argon, cooled to -30°, 2.3 eqs. startg. acetal and 1 eq. benzaldehyde added sequentially in portions, treated in one portion with 3.2 eqs. acid-free trimethylsilyl chloride in anhydrous THF, stirred at -30° for 30 h, quenched with 1 *M* aq. HCl, and warmed to room temp. → product. Y 77-88% (*anti:syn* 10.9-11.5:1). Reaction is generally applicable to ar., aliphatic and α,β-unsatd. aldehydes, and diastereoselectivity is usually higher than in the original non-catalytic procedure (cf. *44*, 719). However, only modest diastereoselectivity was recorded with α-functionalized aldehydes. F.e.s. R.K. Boeckman Jr., R.A. Hudack Jr., J. Org. Chem. *63*, 3524-5 (1998).

*Tricarbonyltris(propionitrile)molybdenum(0)/(R,R)-1,2-bis(picolinoylamino)cyclohexane*
**Regiospecific molybdenum-catalyzed asym. C-α-allylation** $H \rightarrow C\text{-}C{=}C$

353.

A 0.1 *M* soln. of startg. allyl carbonate and dimethyl sodio(methyl)malonate in THF allowed to react with 10 mol% $(EtCN)_3Mo(CO)_3$ and 15 mol% (R,R)-1,2-bis(picolinoylamino)cyclohexane at room temp. for 18 h → product. Y 54% (regioselectivity 99:1; e.e. 95%). Reaction takes place at the *more* substituted terminus of the allylic system (unlike the Pd-catalyzed conversion), possibly via an equilibrating π-allylmolybdenum complex. This is the first example of a practical catalytic system for molybdenum. Reaction is insensitive to temperatures up to 65°, suggesting that a fairly rigid chiral active site is formed. F.e. incl. reaction with 3-aryl- and 3-heteroaryl-allyl carbonates s. B.M. Trost, I. Hachiya, J. Am. Chem. Soc. *120*, 1104-5 (1998).

| | |
|---|---:|
| *Lithium perchlorate s.a. under LiN(SiMe₃)₂* | $LiClO_4$ |
| *Lithium perchlorate/trimethylsilyl cyanide* | $LiClO_4/Me_3SiCN$ |
| **α-Aminonitriles from aldehydes and amines** s. 55, 341 | $CHO \rightarrow CH(N{<}) CN$ |
| *Perchloric acid* | $HClO_4$ |
| **N-Condensed 5-aminoimidazoles** from *o*-amino-N-heterocyclics, aldehydes and isonitriles s. 55, 340 | ○ |
| *Tetra-*n-*butylammonium fluoride* | $Bu_4NF$ |
| **Trifluoromethyl ketones from carboxylic acid esters** | $COOR \rightarrow COCF_3$ |

354.

2.5 Mol% *anhydrous* Bu₄NF in THF added *at -78°* to a soln. of methyl benzoate and 1.25 eqs. trifluoromethyltrimethylsilane in dry toluene, allowed to warm to room temp. slowly, stirred for 18 h, and treated with 2 *M* HCl → product. Y 95%. Reaction is generally applicable to aromatic, aliphatic (notably enolizable), α,β-unsatd., and hindered esters. Anhydrous solvents/reagents are essential, and the low temp. is necessary to avoid double addition of the trifluoromethylating agent. The true catalyst is thought to be a deprotonated hemiacetal formed in a catalytic cycle. F.e.s. J. Wiedemann et al., Angew. Chem. Int. Ed. Engl. *37*, 820-1 (1998).

| | |
|---|---:|
| *Manganese s. under CrCl₂* | $Mn$ |
| *Ruthenium trichloride* | $RuCl_3$ |
| **α,β-Ethyleneketones from ketones and aldehydes via ruthenium(III)-catalyzed aldol condensation** | $COCH_2 \rightarrow COC{=}CHR$ |

355.

A mixture of ethyl methyl ketone and benzaldehyde heated with 2 mol% RuCl₃ in a sealed tube at 120° for 16 h → product. Y 90%. There was no self-condensation of the ketone. Isocyclic ketones, however, gave the corresponding **cyclic α,α'-di(alkylidene)ketones** with ar. aldehydes or cinnamaldehyde. F.e. and self-condensation of ketones and aldehydes s. N. Iranpoor, F. Kazemi, Tetrahedron *54*, 9475-80 (1998).

| | |
|---|---:|
| *Chloro(cyclooctadiene)rhodium(I) dimer* | $[Rh(cod)Cl]_2$ |
| **3-Component synthesis of tert. amines via hydroformylation-reductive N-alkylation** | $C{=}C \rightarrow CHC\text{-}CH_2N(R)CH_2R'$ |

356.

A 1:1:1 mixture of α-methylstyrene, *n*-butylamine, and isobutanal heated with 0.17 mol% [Rh(cod)Cl]₂ for 3 days at 135° in an autoclave under 60 atm. H₂ and 30 atm. CO → butyl(isobutyl)-(3-phenylbutyl)amine. Y 91%. Reaction is applicable to both aldehydes and ketones, and can be adapted to the synthesis of **cyclic tert. amines** from ethyleneketones as an intramolecular variant. F.e., **also sym. sec. and tert. amines** from two olefin molecules in the absence of oxo compd., s. T. Rische et al., Tetrahedron *54*, 2723-42 (1998).

*Chlorotris(triphenylphosphine)rhodium(I)/trimethyl or triphenyl phosphite/sodium hydride* ←
**α-Allylation of malonic acid esters with 2-ethylenecarbonic acid esters**     H → C-C=C
**Improved regioselectivity by *in situ* modification of Wilkinson's catalyst**

357.

30 Mol% triphenyl phosphite added to a soln. of 10 mol% Rh(PPh$_3$)$_3$Cl in dry THF, the mixture sonicated for 1-2 min, stirred at room temp. for 10 min, in a separate vessel 3 eqs. dimethyl malonate added dropwise via a tared syringe over ca. 5 min to a slurry of 2.9 eqs. NaH (60% w/w in mineral oil) in dry THF (*CAUTION*: evolution of H$_2$), startg. allyl carbonate added dropwise via a tared syringe to the modified Wilkinson's catalyst, the mixture added via a Teflon cannula to the Na-malonate soln., and heated at 30° for ca. 4 h → product. Y 77% (96% α-substitution). Regioselectivity was poor in the absence of the phosphite. This is the first example of Rh-catalyzed allylation with tert. carbonates leading to the formation of a **quaternary hydrocarbon group**. F.e. incl. activation of the catalyst with trimethyl phosphite, and allylation with sec. carbonates, s. P.A. Evans, J.D. Nelson, Tetrahedron Lett. *39*, 1725-8 (1998); with retention of chirality at the allylic site s. J. Am. Chem. Soc. *120*, 5581-2 (1998).

*Tetrakis(triphenylphosphine)palladium(0)/zinc cyanide*     Pd(PPh$_3$)$_4$/Zn(CN)$_2$
**Ar. nitriles from aryl triflates**     ArOTf → ArCN
s. *45*, 447s*51*; from hindered, electron-rich aryl triflates s. H. Kubota, K.C. Rice, Tetrahedron Lett. *39*, 2907-10 (1998).

*Tetrakis(triphenylphosphine)palladium(0)/triphenylphosphine*     Pd(PPh$_3$)$_4$/Ph$_3$P
**α-Allylation with acoxy-2-ethylenes**     H → C-C=C
s. *26*, 827s*46, 48, 49, 53*; 3-ethylene-1,1,1-tricarboxylic acid esters by allylation of triethyl methanetricarboxylate s. G. Cravotto, G. Palmisano et al., Tetrahedron *54*, 1639-46 (1998); heteroatom-directed, regiospecific allylation with ω-functionalized acoxy-2-ethylenes s. M.E. Krafft et al., J. Org. Chem. *63*, 1748-9 (1998); allylation with Baylis-Hillman acetates s. R. Kumareswaran, Y.D. Vankar, Synth. Commun. *28*, 2291-302 (1998); preparation of α-carbalkoxy-amino-γ,δ-ethylenecarboxylic acid esters s. D.A. Alonso et al., Tetrahedron Lett. *38*, 7943-6 (1997); C-β-vinyl glycosides s. V. Michelet et al., ibid. 7741-4; synthesis of α,β-ethylenesulfoxides **with asym. induction** s. K. Hiroi et al., Chem. Lett. *1995*, 1099-100; application to asym. synthesis of β-aryl-γ-lactones s. M. Braun et al., Synlett *1995*, 1174-6; regiospecific synthesis of 3,6-dihydro-2*H*-pyrans s. M.-R. Brescia et al., J. Org. Chem. *62*, 1257-63 (1997).

*Bis(π-allylpalladium chloride)/triphenylphosphine/lithium iodide/sodium salt*     ←
**Regio- and stereo-specific α-allylation with acoxy-2-ethylenes**
**Improved procedure**

358.

**α-Cinnamylation**. A mixture of 1-phenylprop-2-enyl acetate (or (E)-3-phenylprop-2-enyl acetate), 2 eqs. dimethyl methylmalonate Na-salt, 1 mol% [PdCl(π-C$_3$H$_5$)]$_2$, 2 mol% Ph$_3$P and *10 mol% LiI* in THF allowed to react at 0° under N$_2$ for 24 h → (E)-product. Y 99% (100% linear isomer). In the absence of LiI a 77:23 ratio of linear to branched isomer was obtained. As little as 2 mol% LiI may be used (Y 97%). The regioselectivity was not greatly improved by the addition of LiF, LiCl or LiBr, but high linear selectivity was observed in the presence of NaI, or with [PdI(π-C$_3$H$_5$)]$_2$ in the absence of additional iodide anion. Method s. *26*, 827s*53*. F.e. incl. reaction of methyl acetoacetate s. M. Kawatsura et al., Chem. Commun. *1998*, 217-8.

*Bis(allylpalladium chloride)/chiral bis(aziridines) or 2-α-hydroxy-6-(Δ²-*   ←
*oxazolin-2-yl)pyridines or 1-(2-methoxy-1-naphthyl)isoquinolines or phosphino-Δ²-*
*oxazolines or o-(phosphinoamino)aryl sulfoxides*
*Bis(η³-allylpalladium chloride)/chiral amphiphilic polymer-based triarylphosphines/*   ←
*potassium carbonate*
**Asym. α-allylation**                                                                    H → C-C=C
update s. *48*, 772s*54*; with chiral bi- or tri-cyclic 2-[*o*-(diphenylphosphino)phenyl]-Δ²-oxazolines as ligand s. B. Wiese, G. Helmchen, Tetrahedron Lett. *39*, 5727-30 (1998); substituent effects with monocyclic analogs s. S. Schaffner et al., Helv. Chim. Acta *81*, 1223-32 (1998); asym. synthesis of α- and β-amino acids s. J.F. Bower et al., J. Chem. Soc. Perkin Trans. I *1997*, 1411-20; asym. α-allylation with chiral 4-(diphenylphosphinomethyl)-Δ²-oxazolines as ligand s. K. Burgess, A.M. Porte, Tetrahedron:Asym. *9*, 2465-9 (1998); with C₁-symmetric 2-[4-(isopropyl)-Δ²-oxazolin-2-yl]-2'-diphenylphosphino-1,1'-binaphthyls s. T. Hayashi et al., ibid. 1779-87; s.a. I. Ikeda et al., Tetrahedron Lett. *39*, 4343-6 (1998); with chiral 2-α-hydroxy-6-(Δ²-oxazolin-2-yl)pyridines s. K. Nordström et al., J. Org. Chem. *62*, 1604-9 (1997); with chiral *o*-(phosphinoamino)aryl sulfoxides s. K. Hiroi, Y. Suzuki, Tetrahedron Lett. *39*, 6499-502 (1998); with axially chiral 1-(2-methoxy-1-naphthyl)isoquinoline or the 2-methylthio-analog s. G. Chelucci et al., ibid. *40*, 553-6 (1999); with C₂-symmetric bis(aziridines) s. D. Tanner et al., Tetrahedron *54*, 15731-8 (1998); parallel synthesis and optimization of chiral phosphino-Δ²-oxazolines via high-throughput catalytic screening s. A.M. Porte et al., J. Am. Chem. Soc. *120*, 9180-7 (1998); asym. α-allylation with chiral amphiphilic polymer-based 2-(diphenylphosphino)-1,1'-binaphthyls **in aq. media** containing K₂CO₃ (method s. *53*, 380) s. Tetrahedron Lett. *39*, 8303-6 (1998).

*Dichlorobis(triphenylphosphine)palladium(II)/zinc*                          $PdCl_2(PPh_3)_2/Zn$
**Sym. diaryls from aryl triflates**                                          2 ArOTf → Ar-Ar
under Ni- or Pd-catalysis with Zn or by cathodic reduction cf. *41*, 731s*48*; comparison of methods and scope s. J. Org. Chem. *62*, 261-74 (1997).

# Nitrogen ↑                                                                  CC ↓↑ N

*Without additional reagents*                                                           w.a.r.
**N,N-Disubst. dithiocarbamic acid benzyl esters**                          ArH → ArCH₂SC(S)N<
**from arenes and di-*tert*-aminomethanes**

359.

***p*-Hydroxybenzyl dithiocarbamates.** A 1:1:1 mixture of 2,6-xylenol, N,N,N',N'-tetramethylmethylenediamine, and CS₂ in 3:1 methanol/dioxane boiled for 40 min, and cooled to -5 to 0° → 3,5-dimethyl-4-hydroxybenzyl N,N-dimethyldithiocarbamate. Y 98.5%. F.e.s. Russian patent RU-2081110 (Tonar Res. Prodn. Firm).

**Pyridine ring from 1,2,4-triazines**                                                    ←
s. *26*, 833; *24*, 836; 4-stannylpyridines from ethynyltributylstannane (cf. *15*, 609s*53*) s. J. Sauer, D.K. Heldmann, Tetrahedron Lett. *39*, 2549-52 (1998).

**7-Subst. cycloheptatrienes from tropenium salts**                                       ←
from fluoroborate salts cf. *27*, 822; more conveniently from hexachlorophosphate chloride salts s. V.G. Noskov et al., Pharm. Chem. J. *31*, 494-6 (1997).

*Microwaves s. under AcOH*                                                                ←

*Lithium*                                                                                 Li
**Generation of organolithium compds. from 1-subst. benzotriazoles**                      ←
s. *54*, 382; syntheses with benzyl and vinyl α,α-dicarbanion equivalents s. J. Org. Chem. *62*, 4116-20 (1997).

*Lithium/1,2-dibromoethane*            $Li/BrCH_2CH_2Br$
**Bis(benzotriazol-1-yl)]methylarenes as benzyl α,α-dicarbanion equivalents** ←
**2-Aryl-1,3-diols from two oxo compd. molecules**

360.

0.6 eq. 1,2-Dibromoethane and THF added sequentially to 10 eqs. Li (30% dispersion in mineral oil; washed twice with dry THF under argon), the mixture cooled to -78°, a soln. of bis(benzotriazol-1-yl)methylbenzene and 2.4 eqs. 4-heptanone in THF added over 1 h, allowed to react at -78° for 3-4 h, then quenched with water → product. Y 76%. The startg. 1,1-bis(benzotriazoles) are readily prepared from the corresponding aromatic aldehydes, so that a rare **umpolung of aldehyde to 1,1-dicarbanion** can be achieved in a 2-step synthesis. F.e.s. A.R. Katritzky et al., Tetrahedron Lett. *39*, 2289-92 (1998).

*Sodium hydroxide*            NaOH
**Isoxazoles from aliphatic nitro compds.**     ○
and enamines cf. *29*, 786; from two [lower] nitroalkane molecules and ar. aldehydes, 3,5-disubst. 4-arylisoxazoles (with NaOH) s. W.M. Best et al., J. Chem. Res., Synop *1998*, 388-9.

n-*Butyllithium*            BuLi
**α,β-Acetylenealdehydes from terminal acetylene derivs.**    $C\equiv CH \rightarrow C\equiv C\text{-}CHO$

361.

1 eq. 1.53 *M* n-BuLi in hexanes added dropwise over ca. 2 min to a soln. of phenylacetylene in dry THF at -35 to -40° under $N_2$, treated with 2 eqs. anhydrous DMF in one portion, the cold bath removed, allowed to warm to room temp., aged for 30 min, and poured with vigorous stirring into a 2-phase mixture prepared from 4 eqs. 10% aq. $KH_2PO_4$ and *tert*-butyl methyl ether at 5° → product. Y 97%. The 'reverse' quench is essential. F.e.s. M. Journet, D. Cai et al., Tetrahedron Lett. *39*, 6427-8 (1998).

*Lithium diisopropylamide/hydrogen chloride*           $i\text{-}Pr_2NLi/HCl$
**Thiochromones from *o*-mercaptocarboxylic acid esters and acylhydrazones**    ○
**N,C-Dianions as intermediates**

362.

Startg. hydrazone in THF added to 4 eqs. LDA in the same solvent at 0° under $N_2$, ca. 1 eq. ethyl thiosalicylate in THF added after 45-60 min, stirred for 3 h (at 0° under $N_2$), treated with 3 *N* HCl, and stirred at reflux for 1 h → product. Y 94%. F.e.s. K.L. French, C.F. Beam et al., J. Heterocycl. Chem. *35*, 45-8 (1998).

*Cuprous trifluoromethanesulfonate*           $CuOSO_2CF_3$
**Regio- and stereo-specific 1,3-dipolar cycloaddition with carbonyl ylids**
and N-subst. maleimides s. *43*, 943s55

*Cuprous trifluoromethanesulfonate/chiral bis($\Delta^2$-oxazolines) or bis(phosphine imines)* ←
**Asym. cyclopropanation with diazo compds.**    ▽
s. *23*, 819s53; f. chiral bis($\Delta^2$-oxazolines) s. A.J. Rippert, Helv. Chim. Acta *81*, 676-87 (1998);

*Bromomagnesium diisopropylamide*  
**3-Ketothioethers from enamines and sulfoxides**  

i-$Pr_2NMgBr$  
C(N<)=C → COC-C(SR)

363.

3 eqs. Diisopropylamine added to a stirred soln. of 3 eqs. ethylmagnesium bromide in ether at 0°, stirred for 1 h at 0° then at room temp. for 15 min, the resulting turbid soln. re-cooled to 0°, startg. enamine and 1 eq. startg. sulfoxide added sequentially, allowed to warm to room temp., stirring continued overnight, and quenched with satd. aq. $NH_4Cl$ → 2-(phenylthiomethyl)cyclohexanone. Y 76%. Although yields were not very high, the method is advantageous in that the startg. materials are readily available, and manipulations are simple. F.e. incl. reaction with cyclic sulfoxides and methyl (methylthio)methyl sulfoxide s. K. Kobayashi et al., Tetrahedron 54, 2691-6 (1998).

*Boron fluoride/air*  
**Quinoline ring from 1-(arylaminomethyl)benzotriazoles**  

$BF_3/O_2$

1,2,3,4-tetrahydroquinolines from ethylene derivs. with $SnCl_4$ cf. 53, 386; quinolinium salts from acetylene derivs. with $BF_3$/air s. J. Heterocycl. Chem. 35, 467-70 (1998).

*Amberlite IRA-400*  
**α-Alkylidenation of active methylene groups with aldimines**  

$CH_2$ ← →  C=C

364.    PhCH=NPh + $CH_2(CN)_2$ ⟶ PhCH=C(CN)$_2$

**Arylidenemalononitriles.** Malononitrile in ethanol mixed with 1 eq. Amberlite IRA-400 (OH⁻ form) and 1 eq. benzylideneaniline for 4 h at reflux → product. Y 82%. Malononitrile exchanges with hydroxide ion to produce Amberlite IRA-400 ((NC)$_2$CH-form), and the supported carbanion then adds across the carbon-nitrogen double bond prior to elimination of aniline. F.e. and with cyanoacetic acid amide and esters s. D. Konwar et al., J. Chem. Res., Synop 1998, 342-3.

*Acetic acid*  
**Pyridine ring from enamines and β-ketoaldehyde equivalents**  

AcOH

s. 33, 758; 9, 807; from 2-β-ketooxazolidines with AcOH s. K. Singh et al., Tetrahedron 54, 935-42 (1998).

*Acetic acid/microwaves*  
**Fischer indole synthesis under microwave irradiation**  

←

in HCOOH cf. 45, 460s48; more rapidly in AcOH in an Erlenmeyer flask s. V. Sridar, Ind. J. Chem. 36B, 86-7 (1997).

*Bis(trichloromethyl) carbonate*  
**Vilsmeier-type formylation under mild conditions**  

$(Cl_3CO)_2CO$  
H → CHO

365.    $Me_2N$-⟨⟩  $(Cl_3CO)_2CO / Me_2NCHO$ ⟶  $Me_2N$-⟨⟩-CHO

5.9 g Bis(trichloromethyl) carbonate added to anhydrous DMF (15 ml), stirred at 20°, 4.9 g N,N-dimethylaniline added, and heated at 90-5° for 2 h → 4.9 g *p*-dimethylaminobenzaldehyde. The method avoids phosgene and the conventional S- and P-agents associated with the classical Vilsmeier formylation (cf. 1, 612; 2, 703). F.e. and with N-methylformanilide s. Japanese patent JP-10017520 (Nippon Kayaku KK).

*Stannous chloride s. under $RuCl_3$*  

$SnCl_2$

tert-*Butyldimethylsilyl triflate/triethylamine*      t-*BuMe$_2$SiOTf/Et$_3$N*
**Michael addition with enamines** ←
to enoates (with acidic hydrolysis) cf. *20*, 601; to enones with *t*-BuMe$_2$SiOTf/Et$_3$N (with basic hydrolysis), also Michael-type addition of pyrrole and indole, s. S. Kim et al., Bull. Korean Chem. Soc. *18*, 1043-5 (1997).

*Hydrochlorides* ←
**β-*tert*-Amino-α-methyleneketones from methyl ketones**     COCH$_3$ → COC(=CH$_2$)CH$_2$N<
with CH$_2$O/Me$_2$NH·HCl s. *19*, 854; *26*, 808; also with preformed dimethyl(methylene)ammonium chloride for *acid-labile* substrates, s. U. Girreser et al., Synlett *1998*, 715-7.

*Chiral ruthenium(II) porphyrin complex* ←
**Asym. cyclopropanation with diazo compds.** ▽
with chiral dirhodium(II) tetracarboxylates cf. *23*, 819s*51, 54*; with a chiral ruthenium(II) porphyrin complex for asym. cyclopropanation of styrene with ethyl diazoacetate s. M. Frauenkron, A. Berkessel, Tetrahedron Lett. *38*, 7175-6 (1997).

*Ruthenium trichloride/stannous chloride/triphenylphosphine* ←
**Indoles from ar. amines** ○
and triethanolamine with RuCl$_2$(PPh$_3$)$_3$ cf. *41*, 732s*51*; under co-catalysis with RuCl$_3$/SnCl$_2$/Ph$_3$P or FeCl$_3$ s. C.S. Cho et al., Chem. Commun. *1998*, 995-6.

*Rhodium(II) acetate*      *Rh$_2$(OAc)$_4$*
**Regio- and stereo-specific 1,3-dipolar cycloaddition with cyclic carbonyl ylids**
s. *43*, 943; 7-spiro-6,8-dioxabicyclo[3.2.1]octan-2-one ring from *o*-quinones s. V. Nair et al., Tetrahedron Lett. *39*, 5627-30 (1998); reversal of *endo/exo* selectivity with CuOTf or CuCl-Yb(OTf)$_3$ on addition of maleimides s. H. Suga et al., ibid. 3165-6.

**2,5-Bridged 4-oxazolidone ring from *in situ*-generated 4-hydroxyoxazolium betaines**
by 1,3-dipolar cycloaddition s. *43*, 740s*48*; *43*, 943s*49* (review); π-face diastereoselectivity s. J. Org. Chem. *62*, 6842-54 (1997); with asym. induction (based on (5R)- or (5S)-phenylmorpholine-2,3-dione as chiral auxiliary) s. R. Angell et al., Tetrahedron Lett. *38*, 3107-10 (1997); polymer-based cycloaddition with acetylene derivs. and conversion to furans, details and split-pool **combinatorial synthesis of a small furan library** s. D.L. Whitehouse, D.J. Austin et al., ibid. 7139-42.

*Rhodium(II) pivalate*      *Rh$_2$(OCOBu-t)$_4$*
**Cyclopropanation-Cope rearrangement** ←
s. *31*, 709s*49*; 6-carbalkoxy-6-azabicyclo[3.2.2]nona-2,8-dienes with Rh$_2$(OCOBu-*t*)$_4$ s. H.M.L. Davies et al., Tetrahedron Lett. *39*, 2707-10 (1998).

*Chiral dirhodium(II) tetracarboxylates* ←
**Asym. cyclopropanation-Cope rearrangement** ←
with asym. induction in the presence of Rh(II)-octanoate cf. *52*, 387; *31*, 709s49; chiral 1,4-cycloheptadienes with chiral rhodium(II) (N-dodecylbenzenesulfonyl)prolinate cf. J. Am. Chem. Soc. *120*, 3326-31 (1998).

*Palladous acetate*      *Pd(OAc)$_2$*
**Two-fold palladium-catalyzed reactions with bis(diazonium salts)** ←

366.

**Double Heck arylation.** A soln. of startg. bis(diazonium fluoroborate) and 4 eqs. ethyl acrylate in methanol treated with 2 mol% Pd(OAc)$_2$, and heated under reflux for 1 h → product. Y 70%. The procedure is mild, operationally simple, generally applicable, and a useful alternative to coupling with ar. dihalides or bistriflates which are often difficult to prepare. F.e., **also ar.**

**dicarboxylic acid esters by biscarbonylation,** double Suzuki coupling with PhB(OH)$_2$ or [PhBF$_3$]K, and 2-fold Gomberg-Bachmann reaction, s. S. Sengupta et al., J. Chem. Soc. Perkin Trans. 1 *1998*, 407-10.

*Via intermediates* v.i.
α-**Aminoketones from two N,N-disubst. carboxylic acid amide molecules** COCH(N<)
via 2-aminoenoxysilanes s. *55*, 346

## Halogen ↑ CC ↓↑ Hal

*Without additional reagents* w.a.r.
**Asym. aza-annelation via intramolecular Michael addition** ○
with β-amino-α,β-ethylenecarboxylic acid esters cf. *50*, 483; improved procedure, notably for creating quaternary C-centres, with carboxamide analogs s. J. Am. Chem. Soc. *120*, 2493-500 (1998).

*Irradiation s. under SmI$_2$ and Bu$_3$SnSnBu$_3$* ∭

*Electrolysis* ⚡
**2-Aminoenoxysilanes** C(OSi≤)=C(N<)
from two carboxylic acid amide molecules s. *55*, 346

*Electrolysis/dibromo(2,2′-bipyridyl)nickel(II)* ⚡/NiBr$_2$(bipy)
α-**Aryl- from α-chloro-carbonyl compds. and ar. halides** Cl → Ar
α-arylketones cf. *49*, 797; 2(3)-thienylacetic acid esters, also coupling with benzyl and vinyl halides, s. M. Durandetti et al., Tetrahedron Lett. *38*, 8683-6 (1997).

**Sym. diaryls from ar. halides** 2 ArHal → Ar-Ar
with Pd(PPh$_3$)$_4$ as catalyst cf. *35*, 549s*41*; with NiBr$_2$(bipy) in mixed alcoholic media s. V. Courtois, M. Troupel et al., Tetrahedron *53*, 11569-76 (1997).

*Sodium hydride* NaH
**2-Aminothiazoles from halides** ○
and N-thiocarbamylamidines cf. *37*, 776s*42*; 5-carbalkoxy derivs. from N-thiocarbamyl-iminoesters with NaH, also 4-amino-5-carbalkoxythiazoles from methyl thioglycolate with methanolic NaOMe, s. K. Dridi, H. Zantour et al., Synth. Commun. *28*, 167-74 (1998).

*Lithium hydroxide/N-(4-trifluoromethylbenzyl)cinchoninium bromide* ←
**Asym. Darzens-Claisen condensation** ▽$_\mathrm{O}$
glycidic acid esters with NaOH and chiral quaternary ammonium salts cf. *52*, 389; chiral α,β-epoxyketones with LiOH and N-(4-trifluoromethylbenzyl)cinchoninium bromide as phase transfer catalyst s. S. Arai, T. Shioiri, Tetrahedron Lett. *39*, 2145-8 (1998).

*Sodium hydroxide/benzyltriethylammonium chloride* NaOH/BnEt$_3$NCl
**1,1-Dihalogenocyclopropanes from ethylene derivs.** ▽
s. *27*, 833; 2,2-dihalogenocyclopropyl selenides and thioethers s. H.A. Stefani et al., Synth. Commun. *28*, 1667-77 (1998).

*Sodium hydroxide/hexadecyltrimethylammonium chloride* NaOH/C$_{16}$H$_{33}$Me$_3$NCl
**1,3-Nitroethylene derivs. from nitronates** ←
and acoxy-2-ethylenes under Pd-catalysis cf. *37*, 747; from β,γ-ethylenebromides with NaOH and hexadecyltrimethylammonium chloride as phase transfer catalyst, α-methylene-γ-nitro-carboxylic acid esters, s. R. Ballini, G. Bosica, Eur. J. Org. Chem. *1998*, 355-7.

*Lithium ethoxide*                                                             LiOEt
**2-Acyl-1-sulfonylaziridines**
**from β-acoxy-α,β-ethyleneiodonium salts and N-sulfonylaldimines**
**Stereospecific conversion via 2-ketoiodonium ylids**

367.

A soln. of (Z)-2-acetoxy-1-decenyl(phenyl)iodonium bromide and 1.5 eqs. benzaldehyde N-(phenylsulfonyl)imine in THF under argon treated at -78° with 1 eq. LiOEt, and the mixture allowed to go to completion at room temp. → product. Y 73% (69% *cis*-isomer). Electron-donating substituents on the benzenesulfonyl group increased the *cis*-selectivity, whereas the electron-withdrawing groups had the reverse effect. F.e., also *trans*-2-acyl-1-benzoylaziridines from N-benzoylaldimines, s. M. Ochiai, Y. Kitagawa, Tetrahedron Lett. *39*, 5569-70 (1998); from α-acylsulfonium ylids in low yield cf. U.K. Nadir, A. Arora, Synth. Commun. *26*, 2355-61 (1996).

*Potassium* tert-*butoxide*                                                  KOBu-t
**α-Acetonylation**                       H → $CH_2C(=CH_2)OCH_2OMe$ · $CH_2COCH_3$
with 1-chloro-2-(methoxymethoxy)-2-propene cf. *43*, 912; with the iodo analog and further O-derivs. s. S.Z. Janicki et al., J. Org. Chem. *63*, 3694-700 (1998).

**Darzens-Claisen condensation**
α,β-epoxysulfoximines cf. *34*, 767; *in situ*-generation of β-(*o*-hydroxyaryl)-α,β-epoxysulfones and conversion to 2-hydroxy-3-sulfonyl-2,3-dihydrobenzofurans in one pot s. M. Makosza et al., Tetrahedron *54*, 6811-6 (1998).

n-*Butyllithium*                                                          BuLi
**Nitriles from halides**                                              Hal → $CH_2CN$
Synthesis with addition of two C-atoms s. *55*, 330

**Asym. *o*-lithiation of functionalized tricarbonylchromium-complexed arenes**    ←
of complexed benzaldehyde cf. *51*, 400; of complexed carbohydrate-based 2-aryl-1,3-dioxanes s. J.W. Han et al., J. Org. Chem. *62*, 8264-7 (1997).

**Metalation of heterocyclics**                                                  ←
review s. *42*, 597s*46*; 5-metalation of 1-benzyloxymethyl-1*H*-tetrazole s. Y. Satoh, J. Moliterni, Synlett *1998*, 528-30; 2-metalation of 1-tritylimidazoles s. A.N. Rohrle, H. Schmidhammer, Helv. Chim. Acta *81*, 1070-6 (1998); 2-metalation of pyrroles with *n*-BuLi/N,N,N',N'-pentamethyldipropylenetriamine s. A. Thurner et al., Synth. Commun. *28*, 443-9 (1998); 5-metalation of 2-(methylthio)oxazole with *n*-BuLi/TMEDA s. C.F. Shafer, T.F. Molinski, J. Org. Chem. *63*, 551-5 (1998); 4-metalation of phenothiazines with *s*-BuLi/TMEDA s. S. Ebdrup et al., J. Chem. Soc. Perkin Trans. 1 *1998*, 351-4; 7-metalation of benzofurans s. A. Couture et al., Synth. Commun. *27*, 3669-76 (1997); 2-metalation of oxazole-borane complexes s. E. Vedejs, S.D. Monahan, ibid. *61*, 5192-3 (1996); 2-metalation of 4-chromones with cyclic acetals as directing group s. G.E. Daia et al., Tetrahedron Lett. *39*, 1215-8 (1998); regiospecific metalation of polymer-based heteroarenes s. Z. Li, A. Ganesan, Synlett *1998*, 405-6.

**1-α-(Organothio)benzotriazoles as acyl carbanion equivalents**                         ←
s. *47*, 954; α-hydroxyketones from oxo compds., α-diketones, α-ketocarboxamides, and ketones from two halide molecules s. J. Org. Chem. *63*, 2110-5 (1998); α-diketones from 1-α-alkoxybenzotriazoles s. German patent DE-19626120 (University of Heidelberg).

**Asym. syntheses with cyclic sulfoximines**

368.

1.1 eqs. 1.6 M n-BuLi in hexane added to a soln. of (S)-1-phenyl-4,5-dihydro-3H-isothiazole 1-oxide in THF at -50°, warmed to room temp. for 10 min, cooled to -78°, 1.1-1.5 eqs. benzyl bromide added, stirred for 3 h, and quenched with satd. aq. $NH_4Cl$ → (1S,5R)-5-benzyl-1-phenyl-4,5-dihydro-3H-isothiazole 1-oxide. Y 85% (d.e. ≥98%). F.e., also **asym. 1,4-addition** with chiral lithium organo(α-sulfoximinyl)cuprates (with preferential transfer of the organo residue) s. S. Bosshammer, H.-J. Gais, Synthesis *1998*, 919-27.

**Synthesis of N′-phosphorylamidines from cyanamides and phosphonic acid esters via C→N-phosphonyl group migration**

369.

with α-substitution. A stirred soln. of 1.1 eqs. diethyl methanephosphonate in dry THF treated with 1.1 eqs. 1.6 M n-BuLi in hexanes at -78° under $N_2$, after 1 h N,N-dimethylcyanamide added, the mixture warmed to -5° for 30 min, 1 eq. allyl bromide added dropwise, the mixture warmed to room temp., quenched after 1 h with satd. aq. $NH_4Cl$, and stirred for 10 min → product. Y 68%. The intermediate phosphorylamidine was isolable in 87% yield by warming the mixture to room temp. after addition of the cyanamide, then quenching with $NH_4Cl$ soln. as above after 30 min. The C→N migration (apparently the first reported example) is so fast that the reaction was complete within 5 min at -78°. However, a benzylphosphonate failed to rearrange. F.e. and electrophiles s. W.B. Jang, D.Y. Oh et al., Chem. Commun. *1998*, 609-10.

**2-Sulfonyl-2-azabicyclo[3.3.0]octa-4,6-dienes from 5-sulfonylamino-1,3-dienes and α,β-acetyleneiodonium salts via intramolecular cyclopropanation with α-(sulfonylamino)alkylidenecarbenes**

370.

Regio- and stereo-specific double ring closure. A soln. of startg. diene in THF deprotonated with n-BuLi, and 1.5 eqs. startg. iodonium salt in the same solvent added to the mixture at reflux over 4 h → product. Y 58% (80-90% conversion). Yields were higher where the intermediate radical was stabilized by the terminal alkene substituent (those with a terminal isopropylidene group being unreactive). Steric and electronic constraints in the intermediate orthogonal 1,2′-bisallylic diradical determine the regioselectivity (the isomeric 3-azabicyclo[3.3.0]octa-1,7-dienes not being formed). F.e.s. K.S. Feldman, D.A. Mareska, J. Am. Chem. Soc. *120*, 4027-8 (1998).

*n-Butyllithium/zinc bromide*  $BuLi/ZnBr_2$
**Synthesis of benzofurans from 1-(aryloxymethyl)benzotriazoles, aldehydes and halides**

371.

One-pot procedure via α-(aryloxy)ketones. 1.1 eqs. n-BuLi added under argon to a soln. of startg. 1-(aryloxymethyl)benzotriazole in dry THF at -78°, after 1 h n-hexyl bromide added, stirred at -78° for 3 h then at room temp. overnight, re-cooled to -78°, a further 1.1 eqs. n-BuLi added, followed after 2 min by 1.1 eqs. 4-chlorobenzaldehyde in THF, stirred for a further 3 h at -78° then at room temp. overnight, 1.4 eqs. $ZnBr_2$ in THF added, and the oily residue heated at 140° for 10 h → 2-hexyl-3-(4-chlorophenyl)-4,5,6-trimethylbenzofuran. Y 64%. The procedure is simple, efficient, and more general than existing methods. F.e. and with isolation of the intermediate ketone, **also benzo[*b*]thiophenes from 1-(arylthiomethyl)benzotriazoles,** s. A.R. Katritzky et al., J. Chem. Soc. Perkin Trans. 1 *1998*, 1059-64.

n-*Butyllithium/mercuric chloride*      $BuLi/HgCl_2$
**α-Alkylation of acetylene derivs.**      H → R
of terminal alkynes with n-BuLi cf. *35*, 554; of internal alkynes with n-BuLi/$HgCl_2$ (1.5 mol%), 1,4-diarylbut-1-ynes, s. S. Ma, L. Wang, J. Org. Chem. *63*, 3497-8 (1998).

n-*Butyllithium/hexamethylphosphoramide*      *BuLi/HMPA*
**Asym. C-α-alkylation of sulfonic acid amides**

372.

1.1 eqs. 1.6 N n-BuLi in hexane added to a soln. of startg. chiral sulfonamide in ether containing 1 eq. HMPA under argon at -70°, stirred for 1 h, treated with 1.5 eqs. benzyl bromide, and stirring continued for 2-8 h → intermediate (Y 67%; d.e. 83%; ≥98% after HPLC separation), suspended in concd. HCl, and refluxed for 3 days → product (Y 55%; e.e. ≥98%). F.e. and with 1 eq. $H_2SO_4$ (in chloroform) in the second step s. D. Enders et al., Helv. Chim. Acta *81*, 1329-36 (1998).

sec-*Butyllithium*      s-*BuLi*
**α-Lateral alkylation of 2-benzyl-Δ²-imidazolines with asym. induction**

373.

**N,C-Dianions as intermediates.** Startg. chiral [$C_2$-symmetric] imidazoline treated with 2.2 eqs. *s*-BuLi in THF at -25°, then with 1.1 eqs. methyl iodide at -78° for 4-6 h → product. Y 86% (d.e. >95%). The presence of electron-donating substituents on the aryl side chain resulted in a decrease in stereoselectivity. Use of the corresponding N-methylated imidazoline also resulted in lower diastereoselectivity (Y 86%, d.e. 72%), but interestingly the opposite diastereomer was obtained predominantly. This provides a route to either stereoisomeric **quaternary benzylic centre** independently of the stereochemistry of the inducing chiral auxiliary. F.e.s. P.I. Dalko, Y. Langlois, Chem. Commun. *1998*, 331-2.

**Asym. syntheses with bicyclic lactams**      ←
review s. *37*, 657s52; effect of remote substitution on π-facial α-alkylation via lithium enolates, stereo- and electronic effects, s. J. Am. Chem. Soc. *120*, 7429-38 (1998); asym. α-alkylation of monocyclic 2-piperidones s. T. Varea, J.-C. Quirion et al., Tetrahedron *52*, 7719-26 (1996); of tricyclic 2-pyrrolidones s. J.A. Ragan, M.C. Claffey, Heterocycles *41*, 57-70 (1995); of 1-amino-lactams (with LDA) s. D. Enders et al., Synthesis *1996*, 941-8; asym. synthesis of α-amino-carboxylic acid esters via asym. 3-alkylation of 2,5-piperazinediones with $LiN(SiMe_3)_2$ s. M. Orena et al., J. Chem. Res., Miniprint *1993*, 2125-52.

sec- or n-*Butyllithium/N,N,N',N'-tetramethylethylenediamine or*      ←
   *N,N,N',N',N'-pentamethyldipropylenetriamine*
**Regiospecific lithiation of heterocyclics** s. *42*, 597s55      ←

tert-*Butyllithium*     t-*BuLi*
(E)-α,β-Ethylenecarboxylic acids     C≡C-COOH
from α,α-dibromocarboxylic acid esters and oxo compds.
via lithium ynolates and β′-hydroxy-β-lactones

374.

A soln. of startg. α,α-dibromocarboxylic acid ester in THF at -78° treated with 4 eqs. *t*-BuLi, the mixture stirred at -78° for 3 h then at 0° for 30 min, warmed to room temp., 1.5 eqs. benzaldehyde added, stirring continued at room temp. for 30 min, then quenched with satd. aq. NH$_4$Cl → (E)-α-butylcinnamic acid. Y 73%. The method offers a simple alternative to the Horner synthesis. F.e. incl. tetrasubst. derivs. s. M. Shindo et al., Tetrahedron Lett. *39*, 4857-60 (1998).

**4-Subst. indans from 3-(*o*-fluoroaryl)iodides**
via intramolecular carbolithiation of benzynes

375.

A 0.1 M soln. of 3-(2-fluorophenyl)propyl iodide in 4:1 *n*-pentane/ether treated at -78° with 3.2 eqs. *t*-BuLi, the mixture stirred for 15 min, dry, deoxygenated THF (ca. 0.5 mL/mmol substrate: sufficient to render the residual equivalent of *t*-BuLi monomeric) added, the cooling bath removed, and the mixture allowed to warm for 30 min before the addition of an excess of ethyl chloroformate → product. Y 66%. This is a novel and convenient route to 4-substituted indans, which are difficult to prepare in isomerically pure form by classical techniques. It appears to be the first example of cyclization of a benzyne-tethered organolithium, a methodology which may prove useful for the preparation of other benzo-fused systems. F. electrophiles s. W.F. Bailey, S.C. Longstaff, J. Org. Chem. *63*, 432-3 (1998).

*Lithium diethylamide*     LiNEt$_2$
β,γ-Epoxycarboxylic acids from carboxylic acids and α-chloroketones
Dilithium ene-1,1-diolates as intermediates

376.

2.2 eqs. BuLi in hexane concentrated by a flush of argon, the residue dissolved in THF at -78°, warmed to 0° for 10 min, re-cooled to -78°, treated dropwise with Et$_2$NH, stirred at 0° for 15 min, re-cooled to -78°, phenylacetic acid in THF added dropwise, after stirring for 30 min at 0° the mixture re-cooled to -78°, 1 eq. startg. chloroketone in THF added slowly, stirring continued for a further 1 h, then quenched with water → product. Y 72% (91% conversion). The diastereoselectivity ranged from 7:3 to 100:0, the (R*,R*)-isomer being favoured. Although the yields are moderate (due to various transformations of the product during work-up), the method still offers a convenient and direct route from readily available startg. ms. The nature of the by-products (γ-hydroxy-β-lactones, β-hydroxy-γ-lactones, 2-ethylenealcohols or the expected 1,2-halohydrins) was dependent on the nature of the substrates and work-up conditions. F.e., and **β,γ-epoxy-β′,γ′-ethylene- from α,β-ethylene-carboxylic acids**, s. E.M. Brun, M. Parra et al., Tetrahedron Lett. *39*, 1055-8 (1998).

*Lithium diisopropylamide*          i-$Pr_2NLi$
**α-Alkylation of azomethines**          H → R
with Li/phenanthrene cf. *40*, 539, and with EtMgBr cf. *19*, 896; α-alkylation of *o*-hydroxyketimines with LDA as base s. C. Cimarelli, G. Palmieri, Tetrahedron *54*, 15711-20 (1998).

**α'-Alkylation of sym. α-diketones via 2,3-dihydropyrazines**

377.

A soln. of 2,2,5,6-tetramethyl-2,3-dihydropyrazine (prepared from butane-2,3-dione and 1,2-diamino-2-methylpropane) in THF treated at -78° with 1 eq. LDA, stirred for 5 min, 2 eqs. benzyl bromide added, the mixture allowed to warm to -50° over 1 h, 1 *N* HCl added, the cooling bath removed, and the mixture stirred for 1 h → product. Y 84%. The reaction is applicable to both activated and unactivated iodides and activated bromides, but chlorides and unactivated bromides failed to react. The selective deprotonation occurs on the *less hindered* methyl group of the dihydropyrazine. F.e.s. D. Gopal et al., Tetrahedron Lett. *39*, 1877-80 (1998).

**Asym. α-alkylation of 1-aminolactams** s. *37*, 657/s55

**Asym. C-acylation of N-acyl-N-heterocyclics**          H → Ac
of 3-acyl-2-oxazolidones cf. *39*, 749; of 1-acylpyrazoles s. C. Kashima et al., Tetrahedron *52*, 10335-46 (1996).

**3-Metalation of phthalimidines**          ←
with $KNH_2$ cf. *10*, 617s*31*; with LDA, and reduction to isoindolines (with $BH_3$-THF) s. A. Couture et al., Tetrahedron Lett. *39*, 2319-20 (1998).

*Chiral lithium amides/lithium chloride*          $LiNR_2$/LiCl
**Asym. 2-lithiation of phospholane 1-oxides**          ←

378.

1,2,5-Triphenylpholane oxide treated with Li-(R,R)-bis(α-methylbenzyl)amide in THF at -100° in the presence of LiCl, followed by the addition of ethyl iodide → product. Y 89% (e.e. 90%). The alkylation occurred *syn* to the P=O bond. F.e. and electrophiles, also asym. α'-lithiation of the product, and reduction to **chiral phospholanes** using $Cl_3SiH$, s. S.C. Hume, N.S. Simpkins, J. Org. Chem. *63*, 912-3 (1998).

*Lithium bis(trimethylsilyl)amide*          $LiN(SiMe_3)_2$
**Asym. C-α-alkylation of carboxylic acid amides**          H → R
s. *50*, 500; of chiral N-subst. N-(2-pyridyl)carboxylic acid amides with $LiN(SiMe_3)_2$ s. J.A. Parker, S.P Stanforth, J. Chem. Res., Synop *1998*, 302-3.

**Asym. synthesis of α-aminocarboxylic acid esters**
via asym. 3-alkylation of 2,5-piperazinediones s. *37*, 657s*55*

*Lithium bis(trimethylsilyl)amide/lithium chloride*          $LiN(SiMe_3)_2$/LiCl
**Asym. α-alkylation of 1-acyl-2-imidazolidones**
s. *44*, 776s*54*; of 1-[α-[N-bis(alkylthio)methyleneamino]acyl]-2-imidazolidones with $LiN(SiMe_3)_2$/LiCl, and conversion to chiral α-aminocarboxylic acids (cf. *31*, 804), s. G. Guillena, C. Nájera, Tetrahedron:Asym. *9*, 1125-9 (1998).

*Sodium bis(trimethylsilyl)amide s. under $CoBr_2$*          $NaN(SiMe_3)_2$
*Sodium cyanide s. under Palladium phosphine complexes*          NaCN

*Sodium iodide*                          *NaI*
**Diels-Alder reaction via heterocyclic *o*-quinodimethanes**
s. *16*, 870s*52*; via 4,5-dimethylene-$\Delta^2$-thiazolines and the 5-bromomethylene-analog s. M. Al Hariri et al., J. Org. Chem. *62*, 405-10 (1997).

*Triethylamine*                         *Et$_3$N*
**2-Azetidinones from azomethines with asym. induction**
s. *7*, 836s*51, 54*; chiral 2-azetidinones with *quaternary* stereogenic centres at C$_4$ s. C. Palomo et al., J. Org. Chem. *62*, 2070-9 (1997).

**Polymer-based synthesis of 2-azetidinones from azomethines**

379.

The first efficient 2-azetidinone synthesis on a *soluble* polymeric support is reported. **E:** A soln. of startg. polyethylene glycol monomethyl ether-supported imine in methylene chloride mixed with 20 eqs. each of phenoxyacetyl chloride and Et$_3$N at 23° for 15 h, the supported 2-azetidinone precipitated with ether in the usual way, filtered off, and treated with a little concd. H$_2$SO$_4$ in methanol at 60° for 4 h → product. Y 52% (85:15 mixture of stereoisomers). The support may also be cleaved under basic conditions (DBU in methylene chloride). F.e. and method s. V. Molteni et al., Tetrahedron Lett. *39*, 1257-60 (1998); with recoverable dendritic polyethylene glycols of high loading capacity s. M. Benaglia, F. Cozzi et al., J. Org. Chem. *63*, 8628-9 (1998).

*Triethylamine/magnesium chloride*            *Et$_3$N/MgCl$_2$*
**Cyclic β-ketomalonic acid esters
from halogenocarboxylic acid halides and malonic acid esters**

380.

Diethyl malonate (162 g) added over 15 min to a soln. of Et$_3$N (161 g) in acetonitrile (2.5 l), stirred for 30 min, treated with 95 g MgCl$_2$ (containing <1.5 wt% water), warmed to 15°, recooled to 0°, stirred for 1.5 h, 4-chlorobutyryl chloride (134 g) in the same solvent added dropwise over 40 min, and worked up by rotary evaporation → diethyl cyclopentanone-2,2-dicarboxylate (210 g). Alicyclic ketones with 3- to 10-carbon atoms in the ring can be obtained by this simple one-pot conversion. F.e. and bases s. German patent DE-19623063 (Bayer AG).

*1,8-Diazabicyclo[5.4.0]undec-7-ene*                  *DBU*
**Ring expansion of cyclopentanones with dihalides
via retro-Dieckmann reaction**

381.

**Cyclooctene ring.** 1 eq. 2,3-Bis(bromomethyl)-N-(phenylsulfonyl)indole in dry methanol added via syringe to a soln. of dimethyl cyclopentan-2-one-1,3-dicarboxylate and 2.5 eqs. DBU in the same solvent, and the mixture stirred at reflux under $N_2$ for 20 h → product. Y 81% (6:1 mixture of regioisomers). This fused indole substructure is found in caulerpin, and also constitutes the basic skeleton of antidepressant iprindole. The method is facile and generally applicable. Reactions are unoptimized but give reproducible results under the standard conditions. F.e. incl. 3,4-di(methylene)cyclooctane-1,1,6- and 3-alkylidenecycloheptane-1,1,5-tricarboxylic acid esters s. T. Lavoisier-Gallo, J. Rodriguez et al., J. Org. Chem. 63, 900-2 (1998).

*Pyridine* $C_5H_5N$
**Synthesis of 1,2-thiazetidine 1,1-dioxides** ←
review s. *38*, 266s*42*; polymer-based synthesis from azomethines and sulfonyl chlorides in the presence of pyridine s. M.F. Gordeev et al., J. Org. Chem. 62, 8177-81 (1997).

*Lithium organo(cyano)cuprates* $RCu(CN)Li$
**Selenolic acid esters from halides** Hal → COSeR
**Synthesis with addition of one C-atom**

382.

Phenyllithium in THF added dropwise to a slurry of 1 eq. CuCN in THF under argon at -78°, the mixture warmed until homogeneous, re-cooled to -78°, the soln. added via cannula to 1 eq. carbon oxide selenide (COSe) in THF at -78°, stirring continued for 5 min, 2 eqs. methyl iodide added, stirred for 30 min, then warmed to 20° → Se-methyl selenobenzoate. Y 86%. Unlike the reaction with COS, selenocarboxylation failed with Grignard compds. and organolithiums. However, the ready availability of COSe in THF is an advantage for a simple and general preparation of selenolic acid esters. F.e. and with Li-diorganocuprates s. S. Fujiwara, N. Sonoda et al., J. Org. Chem. 63, 1724-6 (1998).

*Silver carbonate s. under Pd(OAc)₂* $Ag_2CO_3$
*Cuprous cyanide s. under Mg and i-PrMgBr* $CuCN$
*Cuprous bromide s.a. under Mg and SmI₂* $CuBr$
*Cuprous iodide s.a. under Mg and Palladium(II) chloride complexes* $CuI$

*Cuprous bromide or iodide/potassium carbonate* $CuBr$ or $CuI/K_2CO_3$
**Stereospecific copper(I)-catalyzed Heck arylation** C=CH → C=CAr

383.

A soln. of iodobenzene, 2 eqs. methyl acrylate, 2 eqs. $K_2CO_3$, and *10 mol%* CuBr in N-methyl-2-pyrrolidone heated to 150° for 24 h → *trans*-product. Y 75%. Bromobenzene, chlorobenzene and aliphatic halides were unreactive. F.e. and with a stoichiometric amount of CuI, **also isocarbostyrils** by intramolecular Heck arylation, and Heck vinylation, s. S. Iyer et al., Tetrahedron Lett. *38*, 8113-6 (1997).

*Cupric chloride s. under Mn* $CuCl_2$
*Copper(I) salt s. under Mn* $Cu(I)$

*Magnesium* $Mg$
**Synthesis of α,β-ethylene-α-fluoraldehydes** RCH=C(F)CHO
from oxo compds. cf. *34*, 62; from Grignard reagents with 2,3,3-trifluoro-1-propenyl *p*-chlorobenzenesulfonate s. K. Funabiki et al., Tetrahedron Lett. *39*, 1913-6 (1998).

**C-β-(Hetaryl) glycosides from glycosyl fluorides** ←
and heteroarenes via hetarylalanes cf. *43*, 756; and hetarylmagnesium bromides s. M. Yokoyama et al., Synthesis *1998*, 409-12.

**Regio- and stereo-specific synthesis of 2-vinyltetrahydrofurans
from (E)-γ,δ-ethylene-ε-halogenooxo compds.**

384.

A soln. of startg. aldehyde treated with allylmagnesium bromide until reaction complete → product. Y 71% (>20:1 mixture of stereoisomers). α-Unsubst. (E)-substrates afforded a mixture of stereoisomers, while (Z)-substrates favoured *trans*-2,5-disubst. furans, the *trans*-stereoselectivity increasing with the bulk of the organometallic reagent. F.e. and details (in Supporting Material), also with organolithium and organocerium(III) compds., and reductive ring closure with DIBAL, s. P. Li, K. Zhao et al., J. Am. Chem. Soc. *120*, 7391-2 (1998).

*Magnesium/cuprous cyanide/lithium chloride*
**Synthesis of difluoromethylene compds.**   $C=CF_2$
s. *39*, 740; *32*, 867s*51* (review); regiospecific synthesis from 2-ethylene-1,1,1-bromodifluorides and Grignards with a little CuCN/LiCl cf. F. Tellier et al., Tetrahedron Lett. *38*, 5989-92 (1997).

*Magnesium/cuprous bromide/lithium bromide*
**Synthesis of allenes from β,γ-acetylenehalides**   $RC=C=C$
and Grignards cf. *19*, 892; with added CuBr/LiBr s. F. Taherirastgar, L. Brandsma, Synth. Commun. *27*, 4035-40 (1997).

*Magnesium/cuprous iodide*   Mg/CuI
**Regiospecific synthesis of allylarenes**   OThp → Ar
**from allyl tetrahydropyran-2-yl ethers and ar. bromides**

385.

6 eqs. Bromobenzene treated with Mg turnings in THF at reflux, the resulting Grignard soln. allowed to cool to ca. 40°, 1.5 eqs. CuI added in one portion followed by startg. tetrahydropyran-2-yl ether, and heated to ca. 50° until TLC indicated completion of reaction (2-4 h) → product. Y 81%. The proportion of rearranged ($S_N2'$) product was minimized, presumably for steric reasons. Tetrahydropyran-2-yl ethers of allyl alcohols are more stable and convenient to handle than the corresponding allyl halides. F.e.s. M.F. Mechelke, D.F. Wiemer, Tetrahedron Lett. *39*, 783-6 (1998).

**Sym. ketones from Grignard compds.**   $2\ RMgBr \to R_2CO$

386.   $2\ n\text{-}C_6H_{13}MgBr \xrightarrow{MeSCOSMe} n\text{-}C_6H_{13}COC_6H_{13}\text{-}n$

3.25 eqs. 1.1 *M* Hexylmagnesium bromide added slowly to a suspension of 1.67 eqs. CuI in THF at -50°, kept at the same temp. for 2 h, treated with dimethyl dithiolcarbonate in THF, reacted further for 30 min at -50°, gradually warmed to room temp. for 4 h, and quenched with satd. $NH_4Cl$ soln. → dihexyl ketone. Y 96%. The procedure is generally applicable to *prim-* and *sec-*alkylmagnesium bromides. Ethers and acetals were unaffected. F.e.s. C.-D. Chen, M. Leung et al., Tetrahedron *54*, 9067-78 (1998).

*Magnesium/manganese(II) chloride/lithium chloride/tetrasubst. ureas* ←
*Magnesium/dichlorobis(triphenylphosphine)palladium(II)/triethylamine* ←
**Cross-coupling with α,β-ethylenehalides**   C=C(Hal) → C=C(R)
s. *26*, 875s*46, 48*; (E)-1,3-enynes from (E)-1-chloro-1,3-enynes, also 1,5-dien-3-ynes, and 1,3,5-trienes from 1-chloro-1,3-dienes, s. P. Ramiandrasoa, M. Alami et al., Tetrahedron Lett. *38*, 2447-50 (1997); (E)-1,3-enynes and 1,3-dienes from Grignards and a little $MnCl_2$/LiCl/tetrasubst. ureas cf. Synlett *1998*, 325-7.

*Zinc*   Zn
**Friedel-Crafts acylation of electron-rich arenes**   H → Ac

387.

1 eq. Pivaloyl chloride in toluene stirred with 1 eq. activated zinc at room temp. for 15 min, anisole in toluene added, and the mixture heated at 70° for 6 h (monitored by TLC) → product. Y 90%. This is a simple, selective, economical and convenient method based on an inexpensive and reusable reagent. However, it is only applicable to activated arenes (benzene, chlorobenzene, and toluene being unreactive). F.e. incl. acylation of N-(2,6-dichlorophenyl)aniline, isobutylbenzene, and thiophene, s. H.M. Meshram, J.S. Yadav et al., Synth. Commun. *28*, 2203-6 (1998); **α-acylation of alkylidenephosphoranes** s. Tetrahedron Lett. *39*, 4107-10 (1998).

*Zinc/nickel(II) acetoacetonate/triphenylphosphine*   $Zn/Ni(acac)_2/Ph_3P$
*Zinc/tetrakis(triphenylphosphine)palladium(0)*   $Zn/Pd(PPh_3)_4$
**Diaryls from arylzinc chlorides and ar. halides**   Ar-Ar'
from ar. bromides with electro-generated arylzinc halides in the presence of $PdCl_2(PPh_3)_2$ cf. *48*, 812; *38*, 836s*48*; from arylzinc chlorides via arylmagnesium chlorides (effectively a diaryl synthesis **from two different ar. chloride molecules**) with $Ni(acac)_2/PPh_3$ as catalyst s. J.A. Miller, R.P. Farrell, Tetrahedron Lett. *39*, 6441-4 (1998); from arylzinc bromides **and aryl triflates** with added $Pd(PPh_3)_4$, 7-aryl-3-carbalkoxy-1,2-dihydronaphthalenes, s. E. Baston, R.W. Hartmann, Synth. Commun. *28*, 2725-9 (1998).

*Zinc/tris(dibenzylideneacetone)dipalladium/tris(p-methoxyphenyl)phosphine* ←
**Sym. β-diketones from carboxylic acid chlorides**   2 RCOCl → $(RCO)_2CH_2$
Synthesis with insertion of one C-atom s. *55*, 471

*Zinc/tetrakis(triphenylphosphine)palladium(0)*   $Zn/Pd(PPh_3)_4$
**Negishi cross-coupling with unsatd. organozinc halides**   ←
s. *38*, 836s*51-4*; synthesis of (2E,4E)-dienals s. N. Vicart, L. Duhamel, Synlett *1998*, 411-2; α-bromo-β,β-difluorostyrenes from ar. iodides s. B.V. Nguyen, D.J. Burton, J. Org. Chem. *63*, 1714-5 (1998); β,β-difluorostyrenes s. ibid. *62*, 7758-64 (1997); 2-aryloxazoles s. B.A. Anderson et al., ibid. 8634-9; functionalized (E,Z)- and (Z,E)-1,3-dienes s. J.S. Panek, T. Hu, ibid. 4912-3; 3-subst. 5-alkylidene-2(5*H*)-furanones s. R. Rossi et al., Tetrahedron Lett. *39*, 3017-20 (1998); 5-(indol-2-yl)-2-pyridones and -pyrones s. B. Danieli et al., Tetrahedron *54*, 14081-8 (1998); chiral 5-arylidene-1,3-dioxanes s. M. Amadji et al., Tetrahedron:Asym. *9*, 1657-60 (1998); 4-subst. 1-tritylimidazoles s. M.C. Jetter, A.B. Reitz, Synthesis *1998*, 829-31.

**Cross-coupling with functionalized alkylzinc halides**   ←
s. *41*, 795s*54*; stereospecific cross-coupling of cyclopropylzinc chlorides with unsatd. halides s. R.-J. de Lang, L. Brandsma, Synth. Commun. *28*, 225-32 (1998); syntheses with 2-alkoxy-6-iodo-3-oxabicyclo[3.1.0]hexanes with retention of configuration s. S.F. Martin, M.P. Dwyer, Tetrahedron Lett. *39*, 1521-4 (1998); N-protected 3-arylazetidines s. S. Billotte, Synlett *1998*, 379-80.

## Terminal acetylene derivs. from unsatd. iodides

I → C≡CH

388.

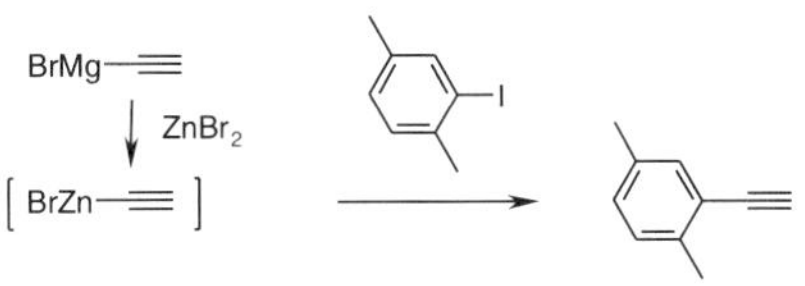

**Ethynylarenes.** 2-Iodo-$p$-xylene and 5 mol% Pd(PPh$_3$)$_4$ added sequentially to a soln. of 1.5 eqs. ethynylzinc bromide (prepared by treating a 0.5 $M$ soln. of 1.5 eqs. ethynylmagnesium bromide in THF with a soln. of 1.5 eqs. dry ZnBr$_2$ in THF) under argon, and the mixture stirred at 22° for 3 h → 2-ethynyl-$p$-xylene. Y 85%. Commercially available ethynylmagnesium bromide offers an inexpensive, *non*-toxic and operationally simple alternative to ethynyltri-*n*-butylstannane which reacts more slowly. Tolan by-products were formed in negligible amounts, if at all. F.e., also **terminal 1,3-enynes from α,β-ethyleneiodides,** and [in demanding cases] with ethynylmagnesium bromide itself, s. E. Negishi et al., J. Org. Chem. *62*, 8957-60 (1997).

## $o$-Bromophenylzinc iodide as $o$-phenylene dipole equivalent

←

389.

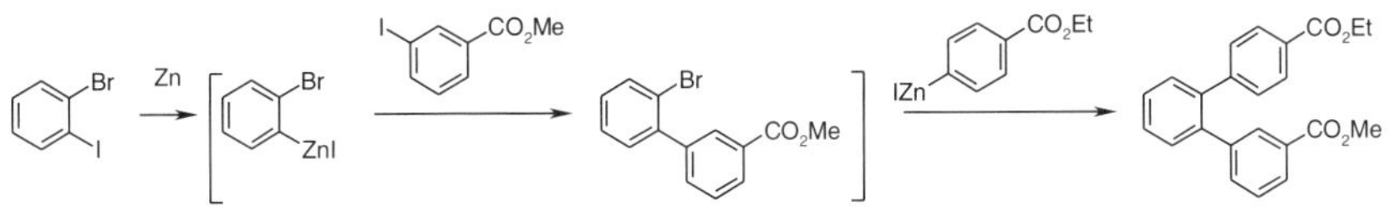

**$o$-Disubst. benzenes.** A mixture of $o$-bromoiodobenzene and ca. 1.5 eqs. Zn powder in THF heated at 70° for 24 h under N$_2$, 1 eq. methyl $m$-iodobenzoate and 2 mol% Pd(PPh$_3$)$_4$ added, stirred for 1 h at room temp. under N$_2$, treated with 2 eqs. 0.8 $M$ p-ethoxycarbonylphenylzinc iodide in tetramethylurea, and stirring continued at 70° for 18 h under N$_2$ → 4"-ethyl 3-methyl 1,1':2',1"-terphenyl-3,4"-dicarboxylate. Y 93%. The soln. of $o$-bromophenylzinc iodide is stable and can be stored for months. F.e. and electrophile/nucleophile pairs s. M. Okano et al., Tetrahedron Lett. *39*, 3001-4 (1998).

*Bromomagnesium* tert-*butoxide*  t-*BuOMgBr*
**γ-Aryl-β-diketones from ketones and aryl α-bromoketones**  CO-C-CO-C(Ar)
**via regiospecific aldol condensation-aryl migration**

390.

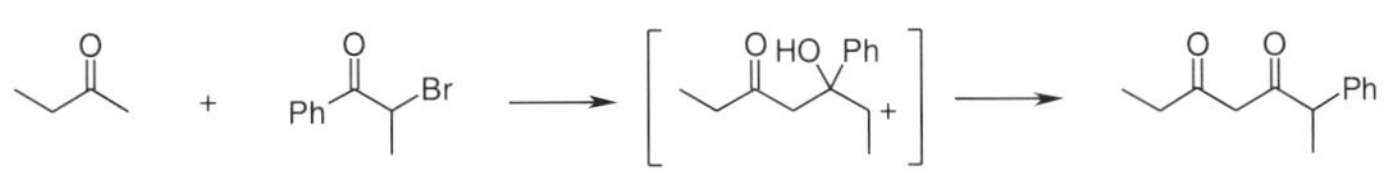

A soln. of 2.4 eqs. *tert*-butanol in benzene (toluene) added slowly to a soln. of 2.4 eqs. EtMgBr·Et$_2$O (prepared by dropwise addition of benzene (toluene) to a mixture of Mg and ethyl bromide in benzene (toluene) containing ether at 35-40°) at 0°, the cooling bath removed, 1.3 eqs. 2-butanone and startg. α-bromoketone added successively, and stirred under reflux for 2 h → product. Y 84%. The method is simple, efficient, and regiospecific, but the yield and reaction rate are reduced by steric hindrance. Dropwise addition of the ketone to the *in situ*-generated *t*-BuOMgBr is crucial to prevent self-condensation of the bromoketones. Esters and electron-deficient ethylene bonds were unaffected. F.e. incl. **γ-aryl-β-ketocarboxylic acid esters,** and method (with Et$_2$NMgBr) s. A.V. Kel'in, Y.Y. Kozyrkov, Synthesis *1998*, 729-34.

*Isopropylmagnesium bromide/cuprous cyanide/lithium chloride*
**Syntheses with polymer-based arylmagnesium halides under mild conditions**

391.

A mixture of startg. polymer-based iodide (based on the Wang resin) in THF treated at -35° under an inert atmosphere with 0.73 M *i*-PrMgBr in the same solvent, stirred for 15 min, 1 M CuCN·2LiCl added, followed after a further 15 min by 50 eqs. allyl bromide, stirring continued for 40 min, the mixture filtered, the resulting resin washed, and treated with 9:1:1 trifluoroacetic acid/methylene chloride/water for 20 min → product. Y 95%. The generated Grignard reagents may possess a variety of functions in the ring (Br, $CONR_2$, CN, COOR). F.e. and electrophiles, also generation of polymer-based hetarylmagnesium halides, and iodine-magnesium exchange with 1 eq. *i*-$Pr_2$Mg s. L. Boymond, P. Knochel et al., Angew. Chem. Int. Ed. Engl. 37, 1701-3 (1998).

*Diethylzinc/chiral 1,3,2-dioxaborolanes*
**Asym. Simmons-Smith cyclopropanation**
of 2-ethylenealcohols s. 47, 806s52; details and scope (incl. asym. cyclopropanation of 2,4-dienols and **of 3-ethylenealcohols**) s. J. Am. Chem. Soc. 120, 11943-52 (1998); $C_2$-symmetric polycyclopropanes s. W.S. McDonald et al., J. Org. Chem. 62, 1215-22 (1997).

*Magnesium chloride s. under $Et_3$N*     $MgCl_2$
*Zinc bromide s. under* n-*BuLi*     $ZnBr_2$
*Mercuric chloride s. under* n-*BuLi*     $HgCl_2$

*Indium*     In
**α-Methylene-γ-lactones from aldehydes**
with $CrCl_2$ and review cf. 40, 576; with In in aq. media (cf. 42, 826s51), also from ketones, s. P.K. Choudhury et al., Tetrahedron Lett. 39, 3581-4 (1998).

*Indium/lithium bromide/oxygen/hydrogen chloride*
**2-Homoallyl(vinyl)cyclopropanes from α,β-ethyleneketones**

392.

6.09 eqs. Allyl bromide added to 4 eqs. In powder (100 mesh) in THF at 25° (exothermic), treated after 70 min with startg. enone (as a solid), 4 eqs. LiBr added after 4 h (exothermic), air admitted after a further 12 h, ether and 1 M HCl introduced *in this order*, and the biphasic mixture shaken vigorously at 10 min intervals over 1 h → product. Y 83%. The order of addition of ether and aq. acid is critically important, its reversal favouring formation of the expected 1,5-dien-3-ols. Reaction is thought to involve an intermediate 'ate' complex, but the mechanistic details are not obvious. F.e.s. H.A. Höppe, G.C. Lloyd-Jones et al., Angew. Chem. Int. Ed. Engl. 37, 1545-7 (1998).

*Indium/hydrogen chloride*                                                                           *In/HCl*
**Stereospecific synthesis of γ-allyl-γ-lactones from γ-hydroxy-γ-lactones**    OH → C-C=C

393.

**in aq. media.** A soln. of startg. hydroxylactone and allyl bromide stirred vigorously overnight at room temp. with indium powder in dil. HCl (pH 3) containing 10% ethanol → product. Y 73% (6.5:1 mixture of β/α isomers). The high diastereoselectivity is a consequence of internal chelation of the formyl and carbonyl groups of the intermediate aldehydocarboxylic acid with an allyl-indium(III) species, which locks the system in a 6-membered transition state favouring preferential allylation on the *re* face of the aldehyde. F.e. and enhancement of diastereoselectivity with added Bu₄NBr s. P. Bernardelli, L.A. Paquette, J. Org. Chem. *62*, 8284-5 (1997).

*Aluminum chloride*                                                                                                 *AlCl₃*
**Friedel-Crafts reactions in the absence of solvent**                                             ←

394.

**Acylation.** 1.25 eqs. Toluene, benzoyl chloride, and 2 eqs. anhydrous AlCl₃ ground in an agate mortar and pestle for 45 min, the mixture kept at room temp. for 1 h, then mixed with crushed ice → 4-methylbenzophenone. Y 75%. The procedure is simple and affords yields comparable or higher than those reported for solvent-based procedures. However, allylation or benzylation did not proceed under these conditions. F.e. and with carboxylic acid anhydrides as acylating agent, **also alkylation**, s. M. Ghiaci, J. Asghari, Synth. Commun. *28*, 2213-20 (1998).

**4-Chloropyrimidine ring from nitriles**                                                           ○
and *o*-aminonitriles with HCl cf. *39*, 469; 2-aryl-4-chloropyrimidines from two nitrile molecules and benzotrichloride with AlCl₃ s. I. Somech, Y. Shvo, J. Heterocycl. Chem. *34*, 1639-41 (1997).

*Samarium diiodide/irradiation*                                                              *SmI₂/⚡*
**Bicyclic lactols from halogenoketones and α,β-ethylenecarboxylic acid esters**

395.

Equimolar amounts of startg. halogenoketone, enoate, and *tert*-butanol in THF added slowly dropwise over 20 min to 6 eqs. SmI₂ in the same solvent at -78°, stirred for 30 min, allowed to warm to room temp., the soln. (containing the intermediate lactone) irradiated with visible light (250 W krypton lamp) for 8 h while maintaining the temp. below 25°, and quenched with satd. aq. Rochelle's salt → product. Y 73%. Reaction involves ketyl-olefin coupling, followed by nucleophilic acyl substitution, and is suitable for generating 6-, 7- and 8-membered carbocyclics. Attempts to prepare 9- and 10-membered carbocyclics failed. Activation with visible light is particularly safe and efficient, while HMPA promotes chemoselective halide activation. F.e.s. G.A. Molander, M. Sono, Tetrahedron *54*, 9289-302 (1998).

*Samarium diiodide/hexamethylphosphoramide*
**Polymer-based ring closures via aryl radicals
with subsequent trapping of alkylsamarium(III) compds.**

*SmI$_2$/HMPA*

396.

A polymer-based variant of Curran's SmI$_2$-mediated radical ring closure-anion capture (*48*, 818) is reported. **E:** Startg. TentaGel S PHB-supported aryl iodide (dried at 3 mmHg at 65° overnight), 40 eqs. HMPA, and 20 eqs. diethyl ketone treated with 10 eqs. 0.1 *M* SmI$_2$ in THF, stirred for 2 h at room temp., the resin removed, washed and dried, and cleaved with 20% trifluoroacetic acid in methylene chloride → product. Y 33%. In certain instances, reaction (though substrate-specific) is cleaner than the corresponding solution-phase procedure. However, the timing of the electrophile quench is critical since the intermediate samarium(III) species is generated more slowly on the support. F.e.s. X. Du, R.W. Armstrong, Tetrahedron Lett. *39*, 2281-4 (1998).

*Samarium diiodide/hexamethylphosphoramide/cuprous bromide*
**Catalytic Grignard-type cross-coupling of alkylsamarium(III) compds.
with prim. iodides**

*SmI$_2$/HMPA/CuBr*
R-R'

397.

Cuprous halide-catalyzed cross-coupling of *prim-* or *sec-*alkylsamarium(III) compds. with prim. iodides is a useful alternative to the standard Grignard route (cf. *29*, 824; *30*, 597). **E:** 8.3 eqs. HMPA added under argon to a soln. of 2.5 eqs. 0.1 *M* SmI$_2$ in THF, stirred for 5 min, treated with 1-bromoheptane, stirred for a further 15 min, 0.17 eqs. CuBr added, followed after 5 min by 0.83 eq. 1-iodohexane, stirred for 15 min, and poured into brine and 10% HCl → product. Y 90%. Yields were lower with CuCl or CuI, but Li$_2$CuCl$_4$ (0.1 *M* in THF) gave higher yields and was easier to handle. The procedure is especially useful for small-scale cross-coupling, and is not complicated by homo-coupling. However, coupling with alkyl bromides was ineffective. F.e.s. W.F. Berkowitz, Y. Wu, Tetrahedron Lett. *38*, 3171-4 (1997).

*Imidazole*
***peri*-Fused 2,8-dioxa-1-azabicyclo[3.3.0]octanes by triple ring closure**

398.

A mixture of startg. aldehyde, 1 eq. imidazole and 1 eq. startg. nitro compd. in dichloromethane stirred at room temp. (ca. 25°) until reaction complete by TLC (1-6 h), an additional 2.4 eqs. imidazole and 1.2 eqs. dimethyl(vinyl)chlorosilane added, and stirring continued until reaction complete by TLC (3-12 h) → product. Y 90% (*cis/trans* ratio 0.56). The method is an outstanding example of efficiency and atom economy, where 5 new bonds and 4 new chiral centres are formed in one-step from inexpensive, readily available startg. ms. under mild conditions. It involves an initial Henry reaction, followed by intramolecular O-alkylation, O-silylation and intramolecular 1,3-dipolar cycloaddition. The products can lead to biologically important polyhydroxylated aminoacid derivs. F.e. and from α-bromoaldehydes s. E. Marotta et al., Tetrahedron Lett. 39, 1041-4 (1998).

*1,1,2,2-Tetraphenyldisilane/azodiisobutyronitrile*      $Ph_2Si(H)Si(H)Ph_2/RN{=}NR$
**Radical *o*-alkylation of cyclimmonium salts** s. *55*, 278      H → R

*Titanium tetrachloride/ethyldiisopropylamine*      $TiCl_4/i\text{-}Pr_2NEt_2$
**6-Amino-2,3-dihydro-4-pyrones from ketones and aldehydes**

399.

**Stereospecific ring closure.** A soln. of 3-pentanone in methylene chloride treated at -78° with 1.05 eqs. TiCl$_4$ in the same solvent, after 20 min the resulting yellow suspension treated with 1.1 eqs. ethyldiisopropylamine, stirred for 30 min at -78°, 1.2 eqs. isobutanal added to the red enolate soln., stirred for 30 min at 0°, re-cooled to -78°, treated with a further 2.1 eqs. ethyldiisopropylamine, stirred again for 30 min at 0°, 1.3 eqs. N-(dichloromethylene)dimethylammonium chloride added, stirring continued for 2 h at 0°, quenched with 50% satd. NH$_4$Cl, and stirred vigorously for 1 h → (5S*,6S*)-3,5-dimethyl-2-dimethylamino-6-(1-methylethyl)-5,6-dihydro-4*H*-pyran-4-one. Y 65%. F.e. and from two different ketone molecules, **also 2,3-dihydro-4-pyrones** in the presence of methyl orthoformate (in place of the iminium salt), s. J. Morris, R.B. Gammill et al., Tetrahedron *53*, 11211-22 (1997).

*Hexabutyldistannane/irradiation*      $(Bu_3Sn)_2/h\nu$
**Thiolic acid esters from iodides**      I → COSR
**Radical synthesis with addition of one C-atom**

400.

A 0.4 *M* soln. of cyclohexyl iodide, 2 eqs. S-phenyl chlorothioformate, and 1.2 eqs. hexabutyldistannane degassed in a quartz tube for 10 min, irradiated at 300 nm in a photochemical reactor for 9 h, concentrated under reduced pressure, ethyl acetate, water and KF added, and stirred at room temp. for 30 min → S-phenyl cyclohexanecarbothioate. Y 56%. F.e. incl. reaction with hindered alkyl iodides, also cycloalkylthiolacetic acid esters from ethyleneiodides via radical ring closure, s. S. Kim, S.Y. Jon, Chem. Commun. *1998*, 815-6.

*Lead(II) chloride* s. under Mn      $PbCl_2$

*Tri-n-butylphosphine/zinc*      $Bu_3P/Zn$
**(E)-α,β-Ethylenecarboxylic acid esters from aldehydes**      CH=CHCOOR
s. *44*, 805; chiral (E)-α,β-ethylene(polyhydroxy)carboxylic acid esters from unprotected aldoses s. V. Le Mignot, G. Demailly et al., Tetrahedron Lett. *39*, 983-4 (1998).

*2,8,9-Trimethyl-2,5,8,9-tetraaza-1-phosphabicyclo[3.3.3]undecane*      ←
**Mono-C-alkylation of active methylene groups**      H → R

401.      Ac$_2$CH$_2$ + MeI → Ac$_2$CHMe

A soln. of acetylacetone and 1 eq. non-ionic, superbasic proazaphosphatrane (cf. *53*, 494) in dry acetonitrile stirred for 10 min, 1.1 eqs. methyl iodide in the same solvent added under N$_2$, and stirring continued for 30 min → product. Y 96%. Yields and conversions were ca. 100%, and there was no dialkylation or O-alkylation. The basicity of the reagent is *seventeen* orders of magnitude greater than that of DBU, with which yields are moderate, reaction times are relatively longer, and with which dialkylation and O-alkylation are a complication. F.e.s. S. Arumugam et al., J. Org. Chem. *63*, 3677-9 (1998).

*Manganese/cupric chloride*                                                    $Mn/CuCl_2$
**Wurtz coupling of alkyl halides in aq. medium**                    2 RHal → R-R

402.                  2 n-$C_7H_{15}$I    ⟶    n-$C_7H_{15}$-$C_7H_{15}$-n

**Homo-coupling.** 3 eqs. Manganese added in one portion to a stirred mixture of heptyl iodide and 10 mol% $CuCl_2$ in water *under* $N_2$, stirring continued at room temp. for 16 h, then quenched with 1 $M$ HCl → tetradecane. Y 87%. Yields were low without a $N_2$ atmosphere, and reaction failed in the absence of $CuCl_2$. The method is free from previously encountered problems and limitations, such as the need for careful exclusion of moisture, handling and disposal of inflammable or toxic organic solvents, and poor yields [from sec. halides]. The method is also mild and general for prim. or sec. alkyl, cycloalkyl, and allyl bromides or iodides. Carboxyl groups remained intact under these conditions. F.e., **also cross-coupling** with benzyl or allyl bromides (using 2 eqs. Mn, 20 mol% $CuCl_2$ and 1:1 THF/water as solvent), s. J. Ma, T.-H. Chan, Tetrahedron Lett. *39*, 2499-502 (1998).

*Manganese/lead(II) chloride/sodium iodide*                                       ←
**Reductive generation of non-stabilized carbonyl ylids**                    ←
from 1,1'-dichloroethers with Sm cf. *51*, 443s52; with Mn/$PbCl_2$/NaI under mild conditions, and further 1,3-dipolar cycloadditions, e.g. 1,3-dioxolanes from oxo compds., s. M. Hojo, A. Hosomi et al., J. Org. Chem. *62*, 8610-1 (1997).

*Rieke manganese/copper(I) salt*                                                        $Mn/Cu(I)$
**Generation of arylmagnesium bromides from ar. bromides**                      ←
with Mn-$C_8$K cf. *52*, 413; with Rieke manganese (from $MnI_2$ and Li/$C_{10}H_8$), and subsequent conversion to diaryl ketones with a little Cu(I), s. S.-H. Kim, R.D. Rieke, Synth. Commun. *28*, 1065-72 (1998).

*Manganese(II) chloride s. under Mg*                                                   $MnCl_2$

*Chlorotetrakis(dimethylphenylphosphine)(dinitrogen)rhenium(I)*       $ReCl(N_2)(PMe_2Ph)_4$
**Furans from α-bromoketones and enolethers**                                  ○
**Rhenium-catalyzed radical ring closure**

403.

**2,5-Diarylfurans.** A soln. of *p*-(methoxy)bromoacetophenone and 3 eqs. α-methoxystyrene in DMF added to 2 mol% $ReCl(N_2)(PMe_2Ph)_4$, the mixture refluxed for 40 min, then quenched with pH 7 phosphate buffer → 2-*p*-methoxyphenyl-5-phenylfuran. Y 73%. A trace of unsym. γ-diketones was always detected as a result of reductive homocoupling of the bromoketone. The method is simple, efficient and general, leaving aromatic bromides and mesylates unaffected. However, yields were low with *p*-nitrobromoacetophenone. F.e. and 2,3,4,5-tetrasubst. furans, also from enoxysilanes, and application to the synthesis of the biologically active lignan, furoguaiacin, s. Y. Koga et al., Bull. Chem. Soc. Jpn. *71*, 475-82 (1998).

*Cobaltous bromide/sodium bis(trimethylsilyl)amide*  $CoBr_2/NaN(SiMe_3)_2$
**Ring closures with oxalimidoyl chlorides**

404.

Ar = p-MeC$_6$H$_4$

**5-(Carbalkoxyene)-3-amino-Δ$^3$-2-pyrrolones.** Startg. oxalimidoyl chloride treated with 2 eqs. ethyl cyanoacetate in the presence of 0.5 eq. CoBr$_2$ and excess of Na-bis(trimethylsilyl)amide in THF at 0° → product. Y 71%. This one-pot procedure - consisting of C-C-coupling, complexation (to fix the intermediate 3-amino-1-aza-diene configuration), Dieckmann condensation, rearrangement, decomplexation and Dimroth rearrangement - occurs with complete regioselectivity starting from simple readily available substrates. F.e. and from malonic acid esters, also with CoCl$_2$ s. J. Wuckelt, M. Döring et al., Tetrahedron Lett. *39*, 1135-8 (1998); pyrrolo[3,2-*b*]pyrrole-2,5-diones from two acetic acid ester molecules s. ibid. *38*, 5269-72 (1997); 2-alkylidene-3-aryliminoindolines from CH-active compds. s. Synlett *1998*, 396-8; 1-(aminoalkylidene)-2,3-diimino-2,3-dihydro-1*H*-pyrrolo[1,2-*a*]benzimidazoles from nitriles via N,C-dianions s. ibid. 399-401; 3-(1-aminoalkylidene)-4,5-di(imino)-2-pyrrolidones from carboxamides and nitriles s. Liebigs Ann. *1997*, 2553-61.

*Nickel(II) acetoacetonate s. under Zn*  $Ni(acac)_2$
*Dibromo(2,2'-bipyridyl)nickel(II) s. under ?*  $NiBr_2(bipy)$

*Dichlorobis(triphenylphosphine)nickel(II)*  $NiCl_2(PPh_3)_2$
**Intramolecular trapping of acylmetal complexes with enolates**
under copper catalysis cf. *45*, 473; also under nickel catalysis (with NiCl$_2$(PPh$_3$)$_2$), C- vs O-trapping, s. Tetrahedron *54*, 1095-106 (1998).

*Nickel(II) bromide/triphenylphosphine*  $NiBr_2/Ph_3P$
**2,5(Z),8-Triene-1,10-diones**  CO-C≡C-C-C≡C-C-C≡C-CO
from 1,3-dienes and two α,β-ethylene-β-iodoketone molecules s. *55*, 291

*Palladium-carbon/potassium carbonate*  $Pd-C/K_2CO_3$
**1-Aryl- from 1-bromo-adamantanes and arenes**  H → R
with FeCl$_3$ cf. *29*, 836s*36*; with Pd-C/K$_2$CO$_3$, also 1-vinyl derivs., s. S. Bräse et al., Synthesis *1998*, 148-52.

*Palladous acetate*  $Pd(OAc)_2$
**α,β-Ethylene-carboxylic acid esters from -iodonium fluoroborates**  C≡C-COOR
by carbonylation s. *55*, 324

*Palladous acetate/sodium carbonate/tetra-n-butylammonium chloride*  ←
**Regiospecific synthesis of N-protected benzo-condensed cyclic 2-ethyleneamines**  O
**from N-protected *o*-alkenylamines and α,β-ethylenehalides**

405.

**1-Tosyl-1,2-dihydroquinolines.** 3.5 eqs. Na$_2$CO$_3$, 1.2 eqs. Bu$_4$NCl, and 5 mol% Pd(OAc)$_2$ added to a soln. of 2-isopropenyl-N-tosylaniline and *2 eqs.* 1(E)-hexenyl iodide in DMF, and stirred under argon for 6 h at 100° → N-tosyl-1,2-dihydro-4-methyl-2-pentylquinoline. Y 75%. Reaction is thought to involve initial Heck vinylation of the alkenyl residue, followed by Pd-hydride shift prior to regiospecific ring closure of the developed N-anion on the intermediate palladium π-allyl species (cf. *54*, 416). **1-Tosyl-2(E)-vinylindolines** were obtained similarly from the corresponding N-protected *o*-allylamines. Yields were low from vinyl triflates, and reaction was slow with vinyl bromides. F.e. and limitations s. R.C. Larock et al., Tetrahedron Lett. *39*, 2515-8 (1998); 1-tosyl-2-vinyl-1,2,3,4-tetrahydroquinolines from *o*-allyltosylamines, and N-protected 2(E)-vinylindolines from *o*-aminostyrenes s. ibid. 1885-8.

*Palladous acetate/sodium hydrogen carbonate/tetra-*n-*butylammonium bromide*   ←
**β-Arylketones from 2-ethylenealcohols**   CH(OH)C=C → COCHC(Ar)
with Pd(OAc)$_2$/Et$_3$N cf. *31*, 847; α-benzyl-β-ketocarboxylic from β-hydroxy-α-methylenecarboxylic acid esters with Pd(OAc)$_2$/NaHCO$_3$/Bu$_4$NBr s. D. Basavaiah, K. Muthukumaran, Tetrahedron *54*, 4943-8 (1998).

*Palladous acetate/potassium carbonate*   *Pd(OAc)$_2$/K$_2$CO$_3$*
**Regiospecific benzannelation of *o*-subst. ar. iodides**
with 1,3-dienes s. *46*, 802s*52*; 2-(2-tosylvinyl)indolines from *o*-iodoamines and 1-tosyl-1,3-dienes with Pd(OAc)$_2$/K$_2$CO$_3$ s. T.G. Back, R.J. Bethell, Tetrahedron Lett. *39*, 5463-4 (1998).

*Palladous acetate/triethylenediamine*   *Pd(OAc)$_2$/dabco*
**Indoles from *o*-iodoamines**
and acetylene derivs. cf. *47*, 829; **from acylsilanes** with Pd(OAc)$_2$/dabco cf. World Intellectual Property Organization patent WO-9806725 (Merck & Co. Inc.); further polymer-based synthesis of indoles from *o*-halogen- or *o*-sulfonyloxy-amines (cf. *47*, 829s*54*) s. WO-9744319 (Pharmacia & Upjohn Spa.); with PdCl$_2$(PPh$_3$)$_2$/CuI/Et$_3$N cf. Tetrahedron Lett. *39*, 4449-52 (1998); from supported N-(tetrahydropyran-2-yl)-*o*-iodoamines with PdCl$_2$(PPh$_3$)$_2$/tetramethylguanidine cf. A.L. Smith et al., ibid. 8317-20; solution-phase synthesis of 5-azaindoles (cf. *47*, 829s*54*) s. L. Xu et al., ibid. 5159-62; polymer-based synthesis of benzofurans from *o*-iodophenols and acetylene derivs. with PdCl$_2$(PPh$_3$)$_2$/CuI/tetramethylguanidine (cf. *44*, 781) s. WO-9744338.

*Palladous acetate/water-soluble phosphinoguanidinium salts/cuprous iodide/triethylamine*   ←
**Arylacetylenes from halides in aq. media**   C≡CH → C≡CR
s. *46*, 798s*54*; f. details s. J. Org. Chem. *62*, 2362-9 (1997); coupling of water-soluble ar. iodides s. Tetrahedron Lett. *39*, 525-8 (1998).

*Palladous acetate/triphenylphosphine/potassium carbonate*   ←
**Palladium-catalyzed Heck-type arylation with diaryliodonium fluoroborates**   ←
of 2-ethylenealcohols cf. *52*, 415; 3-aryl-3-ethyleneepoxides or 4-α-styryl-1,3-dioxolan-2-ones from 2-allenealcohols with Pd(OAc)$_2$/Ph$_3$P/K$_2$CO$_3$, selectivity, s. Tetrahedron Lett. *39*, 2127-30 (1998).

*Palladous acetate/triphenylphosphine/cesium carbonate*   ←
**Palladium-catalyzed cross-coupling of alkylarenes with ar. bromides**   H → Ar

406.

4-Nitrotoluene, 2 eqs. 1-bromo-2-methoxynaphthalene, 5 mol% Pd(OAc)$_2$ and 0.2 eq. Ph$_3$P in DMF added to 2 eqs. Cs$_2$CO$_3$ (dried at 150° *in vacuo* for 2 h), and the mixture stirred under N$_2$ at 140° for 1 h → product. Y 79%. This is the first report of a direct Pd-catalyzed arylation of an alkyl chain. However, reaction appears limited to alkylnitrobenzenes. F.e. incl. triarylmethanes s. J.-I. Inoh, M. Miura et al., Tetrahedron Lett. *39*, 4673-6 (1998).

**Regio- and stereo-specific γ-arylation of α,β-ethyleneoxo compds.**

407.

2 eqs. (E)-2-Methyl-2-pentenal, bromobenzene, 5 mol% Pd(OAc)$_2$, 10 mol% Ph$_3$P, and DMF added to 2 eqs. Cs$_2$CO$_3$ (dried *in vacuo* at 150° for 2 h), and the mixture stirred at 120° for 1 h

under $N_2$ → (E)-2-methyl-4-phenyl-2-pentenal. Y 93%. This appears to be the first direct catalytic allylic arylation involving dienolates as principal intermediates. Yields were lower with $K_2CO_3$ or $Na_2CO_3$ and iodobenzene due to competing biphenyl formation. With aryl bromides bearing electron-donating groups, $Tol_3P$ afforded better results than $Ph_3P$ (due to undesirable cross-coupling with the latter). (E)-Isomers were obtained exclusively. F.e. incl. regiospecific γ-arylation of 3-subst. 2-cyclopentenones and -hexenones s. Y. Terao, M. Miura et al., Tetrahedron Lett. *39*, 6203-6 (1998).

*Palladous acetate/triphenylphosphine/silver carbonate*
**3-Component synthesis of 1-arylcyclohexenes
by Heck-Diels-Alder reaction with allenes**

408.

A stirred mixture of 2-iodothiophene, 5 eqs. 1,1-dimethylallene, 1.1 eqs. N-methylmaleimide, 2 eqs. $Ag_2CO_3$, 10 mol% $Pd(OAc)_2$ and 20 mol% $Ph_3P$ in toluene heated in a Schlenk tube at 120° (bath temp.) for 48 h → product. Y 84%. F.e. and regiospecific **intramolecular carbopalladation-allene insertion-Diels-Alder reaction**, s. R. Grigg et al., Tetrahedron Lett. *39*, 3247-50 (1998).

*Palladous acetate/triphenylphosphine/tetra-n-butylammonium chloride/sodium carbonate*
**Regio- and stereo-specific ring closures of allenes
with γ-functionalized α,β-ethylenehalides via palladium π-allyl complexes**

409.

**3-Alkylidene-3,6-dihydro-2H-pyrans.** A mixture of startg. allyl alcohol, 5 mol% $Pd(OAc)_2$, 5 mol% $Ph_3P$, 1 eq. n-$Bu_4NCl$ and 5 eqs. $Na_2CO_3$ in dry DMF stirred for 2 min, 5 eqs. startg. allene added, and the capped vial heated in an oil-bath at 80° for 48 h → product. Y 95% (single isomer). The regio- and stereo-selectivity is highly dependent on the nature of the nucleophile, the substitution pattern, the base and the solvent. F.e. incl. α-methylene-δ-lactols, 3-alkylidene-1,2,3,6-tetrahydropyridines, γ-alkylidene-δ-lactones or -lactams from α,β-ethylene-β-halogeno-carboxylic acid esters or amides, and 3-alkylidenecyclohexene-5,5-dicarboxylic acid esters via carboannelation, s. R.C. Larock et al., J. Org. Chem. *63*, 2154-60 (1998).

*Palladous acetate/1,3-bis(diphenylphosphino)propane/silver carbonate*
**Heck arylation of 4-sulfinyl-2,3-dihydrofurans with asym. induction**

410.

The chiral sulfinyl group serves as a novel auxiliary in asym. Heck arylation. **E:** A soln. of startg. chiral sulfinylfuran, 3 eqs. iodobenzene, 10 mol% $Pd(OAc)_2$, 10 mol% dppp, and 2 eqs. $Ag_2CO_3$ in DMF heated at 100° for 4 h → product. Y 77% ((2S,SR)/(2R,SR) 94:6). The highest enantioselectivity was recorded with chiral *o*-(dimethylamino)phenylsulfinyl groups, which presumably coordinate with palladium through the nitrogen atom, thereby directing the aryl substitution intramolecularly from the same side of the *o*-(dimethylamino)phenyl moiety; with non-coordinating phenylsulfinyl-subst. derivs., however, the sense of asym. induction was reversed. F.e. and stereospecific Heck arylation of racemic substrates, also **stereospecific sequential Heck arylation** with two different aryl iodide molecules, s. N.D. Buezo et al., J. Am. Chem. Soc. *120*, 7129-30 (1998).

*Palladous acetate/tetra-n-butylammonium bromide*             $Pd(OAc)_2/Bu_4NBr$
**Sym. diaryls from ar. halides**             2 ArHal → Ar-Ar
with Pd-C/Na-formate/cetyltrimethylammonium bromide cf. *34*, 825; from functionalized ar. bromides or iodides with 5 mol% Pd(OAc)$_2$ and Bu$_4$NBr s. V. Penalva et al., Tetrahedron Lett. *39*, 2559-60 (1998); with Pd(OAc)$_2$/Ph$_3$As/Bu$_3$N cf. German patent DE-3842622 (Bayer AG).

*Tris(dibenzylideneacetone)dipalladium s.a. under Zn*             $Pd_2(dba)_3$

*Tris(dibenzylideneacetone)dipalladium/(S)-2,2'-bis(diphenylphosphino)-1,1'-*    ←
*binaphthyl/sodium* tert-*butoxide*
**Asym. α-arylation of ketones**             H → Ar

411.

The first example of catalytic asym. arylation of ketone enolates is reported. **E:** 2 eqs. Startg. aryl bromide (and dodecane as internal standard) added to a soln. of 10-20 mol% Pd$_2$(dba)$_3$, 12-24 mol% (S)-BINAP, and 2 eqs. NaOBu-*t* in toluene under argon (preliminarily stirred for 1 min at room temp.), stirring continued for 1 min, 2-methyl-1-tetralone and further toluene added, heated with stirring at 100° until GC or TLC indicated completion of reaction, cooled to room temp., and quenched with satd. aq. NH$_4$Cl → product. Y 73% (e.e. 88%). 2-Alkylidenecyclopentanones reacted similarly (e.e. up to 98%), but low e.e. values were recorded from the corresponding cyclohexanone derivs. F.e.s. J. Åhman, S.L. Buchwald et al., J. Am. Chem. Soc. *120*, 1918-9 (1998).

*Palladium phosphine complexes/cuprous halide/tert. amine*    ←
**Acetylene derivs. from halides**             C≡CH → C≡CR
by Sonogashira coupling s. *27*, 851s*54*; coupling of 2-iodo-2-cycloalkenones s. M.W. Miller, C.R. Johnson, J. Org. Chem. *62*, 1582-3 (1997); 3-alkynyl- and 3,4-bis(alkynyl)-thiophenes s. X.-S. Ye, H.N.C. Wong, ibid. 1940-54; 3-aryl-2-acetylenealcohols with added LiBr s. G.T. Crisp, Y.-L. Jiang, Synth. Commun. *28*, 2571-6 (1998); 1-carbalkoxyamino-7-alkynylbenzotriazoles s. D.W. Knight, P.B. Little, Tetrahedron Lett. *39*, 5105-8 (1998); coupling of *o*-diiodoarenes with acetylene gas s. M. Iyoda et al., ibid. 4701-4; stereospecific synthesis of a *two million* compd. library of alkynyl-subst. tetracyclics compatible with miniaturized cell-based assays s. D.S. Tan et al., J. Am. Chem. Soc. *120*, 8565-6 (1998).

*Water-soluble palladium phosphine complex/sodium tetrahydridoborate/zinc chloride/*    ←
*sodium cyanide*
*Bromo(trans-17-diphenylphosphino-2,5,8,11,14-pentaoxabicyclo[13.4.0]-*    ←
*nonadeca-15,17,19-triene)(phenyl)palladium(II)/zinc/sodium cyanide*
**Ar. nitriles from ar. halides**             Hal → CN
with Pd$_2$(dba)$_3$/dppf cf. *29*, 845s*47*; from ar. bromides or iodides under solid-liq. phase transfer catalysis with a palladium(II) phosphinocrown complex in the presence of NaCN and a little Zn s. T. Okano et al., Synlett *1998*, 243-4; in an aq. organic 2-phase medium by inverse phase transfer catalysis with a water-soluble palladium phosphine complex in the presence of NaCN/NaBH$_4$/ZnCl$_2$ cf. Chem. Lett. *1998*, 425-6.

*Tetrakis(triphenylphosphine)palladium(0) s.a. under Zn*             $Pd(PPh_3)_4$

*Tetrakis(triphenylphosphine)palladium(0)/potassium carbonate*             $Pd(PPh_3)_4/K_2CO_3$
**Syntheses via intramolecular oxypalladation-cross coupling**
2-benzylfurans s. *48*, 831; 2,5-disubst. furans from alkyl 3-oxo-6-heptynoates s. S. Cacchi et al., J. Org. Chem. *62*, 5327-32 (1997).

*Cyclopallad(II)ated phosphine complexes/sodium carbonate* ←
**Heck arylation with highly active cyclopallad(II)ated phosphine complexes**  H →Ar

412.

Heck arylation with ar. iodides and bromides (incl. *unactivated* ar. bromides) can be performed with extremely high efficiency (TON up to 500,000) by using recyclable, thermally stable (up to 180°), moisture- and oxygen-resistant tridentate cyclopallad(II)ated phosphine complexes as catalyst. **E:** A slight excess (1.2 eqs.) of methyl acrylate added to a soln. of *p*-bromobenzaldehyde in freshly distilled N-methyl-2-pyrrolidone, treated with 1 eq. $Na_2CO_3$ followed by $7x10^{-4}$ mol% cyclopallad(II)ated phosphine complex, and stirred at 140° for 63 h → product. Y 79% (TON 113,300). Such catalysts are among the most active and stable reported thus far. However, ar. chlorides were unreactive. A classical Pd(0) cycle may not be involved. F.e. and catalysts s. M. Ohff, D. Milstein et al., J. Am. Chem. Soc. *119*, 11687-8 (1997).

peri-*Cyclopalladated tri(1-naphthyl)phosphines* ←
**Heck arylation with palladacyclics as catalyst**
s. *51*, 416; with *peri*-cyclopalladated tri(1-naphthyl)phosphines as catalyst, and an efficient product isolation based on cyanide ion treatment, s. B.L. Shaw et al., Chem. Commun. *1998*, 1361-2.

*Palladous chloride/triphenylphosphine*  $PdCl_2/Ph_3P$
**N-Unsubst. carboxylic acid amides from iodides or triflates**  I → $CONH_2$
**via carbonylation under mild conditions**

413.

**N-Unsubst. arylcarboxylic acid amides.** A mixture of 1-iodonaphthalene, 4 eqs. hexamethyldisilazane, 3 mol% $PdCl_2$, and 6 mol% $Ph_3P$ in dry DMF purged with CO for 5 min, stirred under a CO balloon for 1 h at 80°, cooled to room temp., methanol added, stirring continued for 10 min, and diluted with 2 $N$ $H_2SO_4$ → product. Y 94%. The corresponding carboxylic acid was obtained with $NH_4OAc$, but there was no reaction with $NH_3$. F.e. and from aryl triflates, **also N-unsubst. α,β-ethylenecarboxylic acid amides** from α,β-ethyleneiodides or enol triflates (in DMPU), s. E. Morera, G. Ortar, Tetrahedron Lett. *39*, 2835-8 (1998).

*Bis(acetonitrile)dichloropalladium(II)/tetraphenylphosphonium chloride/* ←
*N,N-dimethylglycine/sodium acetate*
**Heck arylation with normally unreactive ar. halides**  H → Ar

414.

A simple catalytic mixture comprising $PdCl_2$ (e.g. as $Pd(MeCN)_2Cl_2$) or $Pd(OAc)_2/Ph_4PCl/N,N$-dimethylglycine is currently the most active and selective system available for Heck reactions of normally unreactive ar. halides. **E:** 2 eqs. Anhydrous NaOAc, chlorobenzene, and 1.25 eqs. styrene added to 2 mol% $Pd(MeCN)_2Cl_2$ and 12 mol% $Ph_4PCl$ under argon, treated with 12 mol% N,N-dimethylglycine, the flask closed, and stirred for 30 min at 120° then for 12 h at 150° → *trans*-stilbene. Conversion 96% (96% purity). The catalyst is even more active than the recently introduced *trans*-di(μ-acetato)bis[*o*-(di-*o*-tolylphosphino)benzyl]dipalladium(II) (cf. *51*, 416). The proportion of 1,1-diphenylethylene in the product is much higher (15%) in the absence of N,N-dimethylglycine. TON values of 1300 can be achieved with as little as 0.05 mol% catalyst.

F.e. and with normally unreactive ar. bromides s. M.T. Reetz et al., Angew. Chem. Int. Ed. Engl. *37*, 81-3 (1998).

*Dichlorobis(triphenylphosphine)palladium(II)/triethylamine*          $PdCl_2(PPh_3)_2/Et_3N$
**5-Aryl-1,2,4-oxadiazoles from amidoximes and ar. iodides by carbonylation**

415.

Methyl 4-iodobenzoate, 3 eqs. acetamidoxime, 5 mol% $PdCl_2(PPh_3)_2$, and 2 eqs. $Et_3N$ in toluene heated under 1 atm of CO at 95° for 15 h → product. Y 70%. This mild procedure is applicable to both electron-rich and electron-deficient aryl iodides (aryl bromides being unreactive). F.e. and catalysts s. J.R. Young, R.J. DeVita, Tetrahedron Lett. *39*, 3931-4 (1998).

*Dichlorobis(triphenylphosphine)palladium(II)/tri-n-butylamine*          $PdCl_2(PPh_3)_2/Bu_3N$
**Carboxylic acid amides from halides**          Hal → CON≾
by carbonylation with $Pd(PPh_3)_4/Et_3N$ cf. *24*, 859(s*47*); indole-2-carboxylic acid amides with $PdCl_2(PPh_3)_2/Bu_3N$ s. J.M. Herbert, A.H. McNeill, Tetrahedron Lett. 39, 2421-4 (1998).

*Dichlorobis(triphenylphosphine)palladium(II)/cuprous iodide/triethylamine*      ←
**Polymer-based synthesis of arylacetylenes from ar. iodides**      C≡CH → C≡CAr

416.

**under mild conditions.** Dioxane, triethylamine, 0.2 eq. CuI, and 3,3-dimethyl-1-butyne added to startg. polymer-based ar. iodide, the suspension degassed for 20 min, 0.1 eq. $PdCl_2(PPh_3)_2$ added, shaken at 25° for 24 h, the resin removed, washed, and dried, suspended in dioxane, treated with 6 eqs. methanolic NaOMe, shaken for 24 h at room temp., and worked up → product. Y 77% (after purification). Propargylic hydroxyl groups were compatible with the reaction conditions, but amino groups required protection (as Boc derivs.). F.e. and ar. nitriles, also polymer-based Heck arylation of ethylene derivs. s. S. Berteina, A. De Mesmaeker et al., Synlett *1998*, 676-8.

*Dichlorobis(triphenylphosphine)palladium(II)/triethylamine or tetramethylguanidine/*      ←
*cuprous iodide*
**Polymer-based synthesis of indoles and benzofurans from acetylene derivs.**
s. *47*, 829s55 and *44*, 781s55

*Dichlorobis(triphenylphosphine)palladium(II)/triphenylphosphine/triethylamine*      ←
**Phthalimidines from *o*-iodocarboxylic acid derivs. and aldimines**
from *o*-iodocarboxylic acid esters with $PhLi/BF_3$ cf. *52*, 400; from *o*-iodocarboxylic acid chlorides with $PdCl_2(PPh_3)_2/Ph_3P/Et_3N$, 3-vinyl derivs., s. C.S. Cho, S.C. Shim et al., J. Heterocycl. Chem. *35*, 265-8 (1998).

**3-Functionalized phthalimidines from *o*-bromaldehydes and amines by carbonylation**
3-aminophthalimidines with $PdCl_2(PPh_3)_2/Ph_3P/Et_3N$ cf. *52*, 422s*53*; N-condensed 3-aminophthalimidines from diamines s. Synth. Commun. *28*, 849-57 (1998); 2,3,5,9b-tetrahydrooxazolo-[2,3-*a*]isoindol-5-ones from 2-aminoalcohols s. ibid. *27*, 4141-58 (1997).

*Dichlorobis[bis(1H,1H,2H,2H-perfluorooctyl)phenylphosphine]palladium(II)/
cuprous iodide/triethylamine*
**Palladium-catalyzed cross-coupling in supercritical carbon dioxide**

Ph—≡—H + IPh  $\xrightarrow{PdCl_2[P(Ph)(CH_2CH_2C_6F_{13})_2]_2}$  Ph—≡—Ph

The efficiency of Sonogashira, Suzuki, and Heck coupling in *benign* supercritical carbon dioxide is on a par with, or superior to, that reported in conventional solvents, and work-up is considerably easier. **E:** 5 Mol% dichlorobis[bis(1$H$,1$H$,2$H$,2$H$-perfluorooctyl)phenylphosphine]palladium(II), 5 mol% CuI, 1 eq. iodobenzene, 1 eq. phenylacetylene, and 1.1 eqs. Et$_3$N pressurized in a stainless steel cell to ca. 1000 psi CO$_2$, and stirred at 60° for 64 h → product. Y 62%. The crux of the method is the design of a soluble, 'fluorous' palladium complex. F.e.s. M.A. Carroll, A.B. Holmes, Chem. Commun. *1998*, 1395-6; Heck and Stille coupling with Pd$_2$(dba)$_3$/tris[3,5-bis(trifluoromethyl)phenyl]phosphine cf. D.K. Morita, W. Tumas et al., ibid. 1397-8.

*Dichloro[1,1'-bis(diphenylphosphino)ferrocene]palladium(II)/potassium phosphate/
9-borabicyclo[3.3.1]nonane*
**Hydroboration-cross-coupling**
(E)-eneselenides with Pd(PPh$_3$)$_4$/NaOMe/9-BBN cf. *52,* 419; *C*-β-benzyl glycosides from 1-methylenesugars and ar. bromides with PdCl$_2$(dppf)/K$_3$PO$_4$ s. C.R. Johnson, B.A. Johns, Synlett *1997,* 1406-8.

## Sulfur ↑                                          CC ↓↑ S

*Without additional reagents*                                                  *w.a.r.*
**Diels-Alder reaction with 2,5-dihydrothiophene 1,1-dioxides**
s. *35,* 393s*52*; via N-protected 3,4-di(methylene)-Δ$^2$-pyrazolines s. H.-H. Tso et al., Synth. Commun. *26,* 569-76 (1996); via carbazole-1,2-quinodimethanes s. A.C. Tomé et al., Synlett *1997,* 1444-6.

*Electrolysis*
**β-Ketocarboxylic acids from enol triflates**                C(OTf)=C→CO-C-COOH
**Cathodic carboxylation**

Startg. enol triflate in DMF containing 0.1 $M$ Bu$_4$NBF$_4$ electrolyzed at 5° under CO$_2$ at a constant current of 10 mA/cm$^2$ in a one-compartment cell equipped with a Pt-plate cathode and a Mg-rod anode until 3 F/mol passed, then treated with acid in the usual way → product. Y 75% (100% based on recovered enol triflate). It is essential that reduction of CO$_2$ followed by O-S cleavage of the enol triflate and the formation of magnesium ion by dissolution of the Mg-anode take place at the same time and in the same compartment. The O-S cleavage is believed to be induced by an anion radical of carbon dioxide (although magnesium ions may also play an important role). F.e. incl. cycloheptanone, cyclooctanone and tetralone derivs. s. H. Kamekawa et al., Tetrahedron Lett. *39,* 1591-4 (1998).

*Lithium/naphthalene*                                                        $LiC_{10}H_7$
**Syntheses with 1,1-aminothioethers via non-stabilized 1-aminocarbanions**
s. *46,* 811; generation of non-stabilized tert. (lithiomethyl)amines from *tert*-aminomethyl thioethers s. C. Strohmann, B.C. Abele, Angew. Chem. Int. Ed. Engl. *35,* 2378-890 (1996).

*Sodium hydride*                                                              *NaH*
**Aziridines from imines and sulfonium salts**
N-sulfinylaziridines cf. *23,* 871s*51*; 1-phosphinyl-2-(2-silylvinyl)aziridines from N-phosphinylaldimines, stereoselectivity, s. X.-L. Hou et al., Chem. Commun. *1998,* 747-8.

**Pyrroles from ethylene derivs.**
and tosylmethyl isocyanide s. *32,* 845; 3-sulfonylpyrroles s. R. Di Santo et al., Synth. Commun. *28,* 1801-5 (1998).

*Sodium/alcohol*                                                               *NaOR*
**α-Hydroxyacetals from ketones**                     CO → C(OH)CH(OR)$_2$
**Synthesis with addition of one C-atom**

419.

10 eqs. NaOMe in methanol added with stirring to a soln. of chloromethyl(dimethyl)sulfonium triflate and 5 eqs. startg. ketone in the same solvent, and stirring continued for 5 days → product. Y 56%. F.e.s. G. Kaczmarczyk, A. Jonczyk, Synlett *1997,* 921-2.

**4-Aminothiazole-5-carboxylic acid esters from N-thiocarbamyliminoesters** s. *37,* 776s55 ○

*Potassium bis(trimethylsilyl)amide*                               *KN(SiMe$_3$)$_2$*
**Ethylene derivs. from oxo compds.**                           CO → C=C
and 2-(alkylthio)benzothiazoles cf. *38,* 861; and 2-(alkanesulfonyl)benzothiazoles with LDA s. J.B. Baudin, S.A. Julia ct al., Tetrahedron Lett. *32,* 1175 8 (1991); from 5-(alkanesulfonyl)-tetrazoles with alkali metal bis(trimethylsilyl)amides cf. P.R. Blakemore, P.J. Kocienski et al., Synlett *1998,* 26-8.

*Potassium carbonate*                                                               *K$_2$CO$_3$*
**Imidazoles from 1-sulfonyl-1-isonitriles**
s. *28,* 841; N-unsubst. imidazoles from N-tosylaldimines and TosMIC s. R. ten Have, A.M. van Leusen et al., Tetrahedron *53,* 11355-68 (1997); from 1-arylthio-1-isonitriles and aldimines with 1,5,7-triazabicyclo[4.4.0]dec-5-ene cf. World Intellectual Property Organization patent WO-9621654 (Smithkline Beecham Corp.).

*1,5,7-Triazabicyclo[4.4.0]dec-5-ene*                                        ←
**Imidazoles from 1-(arylthio)-1-isonitriles** s. *28,* 841s55

*N-Methylmorpholine*                                                            ←
**Synthesis of 6-amino-2-pyridinethiones**
s. *27,* 680; *39,* 738; f. method from aldehydes and two cyanothioacetamide molecules (with N-methylmorpholine), 6-amino-3,5-dicyano-2-pyridinethiones, s. V.D. Dyachenko et al., Zh. Org. Khim. *33,* 1084-7 (1997) (Russ.).

*Iodozinc organo(cyano)cuprates*                                       *RCu(CN)ZnI*
**Synthesis of ethylene derivs. from thioenolethers**       C=C(SR) → C=C(R')
with RMgBr/CuI cf. *29,* 854; 1,1-nitroethylene derivs. from 2-nitrothioenolethers with iodozinc or bromomagnesium organo(cyano)cuprates s. P. Stanetty, M. Kremslehner, Synth. Commun. *28,* 2491-8 (1998).

*Magnesium (s.a. under Cp$_2$TiCl$_2$)*                                            *Mg*
**Carboxylic acid thioamides**                                   RMgBr → RC(S)N<
from 2,4-dinitrobenzenesulfonamides s. *55,* 163

*Zinc,copper*                                                                  *Zn,Cu*
**4-Aminoimidazoles from N-imidoylisothioureas**                       ○

420.

**4-Amino-1-arylimidazoles.** A small crystal of I$_2$ and 2.5 eqs. methylene iodide added to a well stirred soln. of 1 eq. Zn,Cu couple in dry ether under N$_2$, heated at reflux with stirring for 10 min, a soln. of 1 eq. startg. N-imidoylisothiourea in dry THF added slowly, and heated again at reflux with stirring for 3-4 h → product. Y 75%. This [4+1]-addition is facilitated by initial coordination of the Simmons-Smith reagent with the sulfur atom of the substrate. Reaction with N-imidoyl-amidines was less effective. F.e.s. S. Jayakumar et al., Tetrahedron Lett. *39*, 6557-60 (1998).

*Samarium diiodide* $SmI_2$
**Reductive coupling of sulfones with oxo compds.**
s. *50*, 531s*51*; 2-aminoalcohols from tosylmethylamines s. A.R. Katritzky et al., J. Org. Chem. *62*, 6222-5 (1997); C-α-disaccharides from glycosyl 2-pyridyl sulfones s. I.R. Vlahov et al., J. Am. Chem. Soc. *119*, 1480-1 (1997); C-α-mannosylation s. O. Jarreton et al., Tetrahedron Lett. *38*, 1767-70 (1997); C-α-glycosides from glycosyl phenyl sulfones s. Y. Du et al., ibid. *39*, 5007-10 (1998); C-α-(1-hydroxyalkyl) glycosides **from thioglycosides** cf. S. Ichikawa et al., ibid. 4525-8.

*Azodiisobutyronitrile* $RN=NR$
**Radical synthesis of ethylene derivs.** $C=C-C(SO_2CF_3) → C=C-C(R)$
**from trifluoromethyl β,γ-ethylenesulfones and hydrocarbon groups**
s. *52*, 425; regiospecific allylation of hydrocarbons s. Tetrahedron Lett. *39*, 4163-6 (1998).

*Tris(trimethylsilyl)silane/azodiisobutyronitrile* $(Me_3Si)_3SiH/RN=NR$
**Radical synthesis of ethylene derivs. from β,γ-ethylenesulfones and halides** Hal → C-C=C
with $(Bu_3Sn)_2$ under irradiation cf. *41*, 829s*52*; and from iodides with AIBN cf. *53*, 437; with tris-(trimethylsilyl)silane as mediator under high dilution, regioselectivity, s. C. Chatgilialoglu et al., Tetrahedron Lett. *37*, 6391-4 (1996); with cationic diiodocobalt(III) Schiff base complexes/Zn cf. B. Giese et al., Tetrahedron Lett. *33*, 4545-8 (1992).

*Titanocene dichloride/triethyl phosphite/magnesium* ←
**Syntheses with mercaptals via titanocene carbene complexes** ←
(E,E)-1,3-dienes cf. *51*, 423s*53*; alkylidenecyclobutanes from oxo compds., also 1-alkoxyene- and 1-(alkylthio)ene-derivs. from carboxylic and thiolic acid esters, respectively, s. Chem. Lett. *1998*, 741-2; 2-ethylenesilanes from α-silylmercaptals and oxo compds., also 3-functionalized derivs. from [thiol]esters, s. Tetrahedron Lett. *39*, 3753-6 (1998); enolethers and thioenolethers from oxo compds. and di- or tri-thioorthoformic acid esters, also ene-1,2-diol ethers and 2-(alkoxy)thioenolethers, s. ibid. 2153-6; (Z)-thioenolethers from thiolic acid esters s. Chem. Lett. *1998*, 115-6.

*Phosphazene base (EtP₂)* $EtP_2$
**Asym. synthesis of cyclopropanecarboxylic acid esters from sulfonium salts** ▽

421.

**Chiral *trans*-2-arylcyclopropanecarboxylic acid esters.** Phosphazene base $EtP_2$ ($EtN=P(NMe_2)_2-N=P(NMe_2)_3$) and 2 eqs. ethyl acrylate added sequentially at -30° to a stirred soln. (0.05 *M*) of startg. 1,3-oxathian-3-ium salt in anhydrous methylene chloride, and worked up after 15 min → (R,R)-product. Y 83% (*trans/cis* 95/5; e.e. of *trans*-isomer 96.7%). The use of $EtP_2$ as base ensures a high concentration of the intermediate ylid (unassociated with a metal cation); and the very high e.e. values (98-100%) could well be due to the participation of the salt base ($EtP_2H^+TfO^-$) in a coordinative and/or electrostatic interaction in the transition state. The sulfonium auxiliary is recoverable. F.e. **and asym. synthesis of epoxides from ketones** s. A. Solladié-Cavallo et al., Angew. Chem. Int. Ed. Engl. *37*, 1689-91 (1998).

*Cationic diiodocobalt(III) Schiff base complex/zinc* ←
**Radical synthesis of ethylene derivs.** Hal → C-C=C
from β,γ-ethylenesulfones and halides s. *41*, 829s*55*

## Remaining Elements ↑          CC ↓↑ Rem

*Without additional reagents*      *w.a.r.*
**Uncatalyzed aldol-type condensation with enoxy(hydrido)silanes**    CHO → CH(OH)C-CO

422.

Enoxysilanes possessing a silicon-hydrogen bond are more reactive nucleophiles than conventional trialkylsilyl derivs. to such an extent that aldol-type condensations do not require an activator. E: A soln. of 2 eqs. startg. enoxysilane and benzaldehyde *in DMF* heated at 50° for 48 h, and the crude adduct desilylated with 2 *M* aq. HCl in methanol at room temp. for 15 min → product. Y 79% (*syn:anti* 58:42). The increased reactivity is due to the enhanced Lewis acidity of the silicon centre. Reaction also takes place with unhindered aliphatic aldehydes (not pivalaldehyde), but ketones were unreactive. DMF plays a similar role to fluoride ion in the conventional condensation. Surprisingly, **β-hydroxycarboxylic acid esters** were obtained similarly **from α-(hydridosilyl)carboxylic acid esters** as ester enolate equivalents. F.e.s. K. Miura, A. Hosomi et al., Tetrahedron Lett. *39*, 2585-8 (1998).

**Uncatalyzed synthesis of 3-ethylenealcohols from oxo compds.**     C(OH)C-C=C
and 1,8-bis(allylstannyl)naphthalenes s. *49*, 909s*54*; in THF/2,2,2-trifluoroethanol cf. Synlett *1998*, 377-8.

**Synthesis of (E)-ethylene from 1,1-nitroethylene derivs.**     C=C(NO$_2$) → C=C(R)
and trialkylgalliums cf. *52*, 428; and trialkylboranes, (E)-styrenes, s. C.-F. Yao et al., J. Org. Chem. *63*, 719-22 (1998).

**Ring closures with ketenylidenetriphenylphosphorane**     ○
s. *41*, 624; *41*, 832s*52*; α,β-ethylenelactones from hydroxyketones s. P. Kumar, K. Saravanan, Tetrahedron *54*, 2161-8 (1998); Δ$^4$-2-oxazolones from α-hydroxycarboxylic acid amides with a little PhCOOH s. J. Löffler, R. Schobert, Liebigs Ann. *1997*, 217-20.

**Asym. synthesis of 3-methylene-2-pyrrolidones from aldimines**

423.

Startg. chiral allylboronate [derived from *endo*-2-phenyl-*exo*-2,3-bornanediol] and 1.5 eqs. startg. imine in toluene stirred under argon for 1 week, and treated with HCl → (R)-product. Y 92% (e.e. >95%). The chiral auxiliary is entirely recoverable. This is a simple and efficient route to chiral γ-lactams from achiral imines. Reaction of the allylboronate with ethyl N-cyclohexyliminoacetate gave a homoallylamine which could be cyclised under acidic conditions (*p*-TsOH) to give the γ-lactam. No reaction was observed between the allylboronate and ethyl N-*tert*-butyliminoacetate, probably due to steric hindrance. F.e. incl. tert. lactams s. I. Chataigner, J. Villiéras et al., Synlett *1998*, 275-6; reaction of the boronate with aldehydes s. idem., Tetrahedron Lett. *38*, 3719-22 (1997).

## Stereospecific synthesis of cyclopropyl ketones
## from 3,6-dihydro-1,2-dioxins and stabilized alkylidenephosphoranes

424.

Startg. *cis*-3,6-dihydro-1,2-dioxin and 1.1 eqs. benzyl triphenylphosphoranylideneacetate in methylene chloride allowed to react at room temp. → *trans*-product. Y 95% by NMR (≤2% *cis*-isomer and 3% γ-diketone). Typically, isolated yields were within 10% of the NMR yields whilst the diastereomers were easily separated by column chromatography. Reaction proceeds via P-ylid-promoted formation of the *trans*-α,β-ethylene-γ-hydroxyketone, followed by Michael addition of the ylid, cyclization, proton transfer, and extrusion of triphenylphosphine oxide. This method affords functionalized cyclopropanes with high diastereoselectivity and in excellent yield. F.e. incl. reaction of (α-acylalkylidene)phosphoranes, and regioselectivity s. T.D. Avery, D.K. Taylor et al., Chem. Commun. *1998*, 333-4.

*Irradiation (s.a. under 9,10-Dicyanoanthracene and $TiO_2$)*
**Radical C-alkylation with alkylcobaloximes**          H → R
s. *42*, 531s*53*; of maleic anhydrides, also 2-step procedure with added diphenyl disulfide via α-(arylthio)succinic anhydrides, s. R.M. Slade, B.P. Branchaud, J. Org. Chem. *63*, 3544-9 (1998).

*Sodium hydride*                                        NaH
**Horner synthesis of functionalized α,β-ethylenecarboxylic acid thioamides**   CO → C=C
s. *23*, 879s*51*; C-(α-thiocarbamyl) glycosides from aldoses (cf. *28*, 852s*49*) s. F. Sandrinelli, S. Masson et al., Tetrahedron Lett. *39*, 2755-8 (1998).

**Pyrazoles from aldehydes and β-(tosylhydrazono)phosphonic acid esters**

425.

A soln. of 1.4 eqs. diethoxyphosphonylacetaldehyde tosylhydrazone in THF added over 5 min to a suspension of 2.9 eqs. NaH (65% dispersion in mineral oil) in the same solvent at 0°, the mixture stirred for 30 min, a soln. of startg. aldehyde in THF added, stirring continued at room temp. for 1 h, then at reflux for a further 1 h → product. Y 85%. The method is operationally simple and applicable to a wide range of aldehydes (incl. aliphatic and hetaryl aldehydes). Functional groups such as alcohols, silyl ethers, esters, carboxylic acids and aromatic bromides and amines were all compatible with the reaction conditions. F.e.s. N. Almirante, M. Santagostino et al., Tetrahedron Lett. *39*, 3287-90 (1998).

**Ring closures of α-allenephosphonic acid esters
via regiospecific nucleophilic addition-intramolecular Horner synthesis
Activation by arenetricarbonylchromium(0) complexation**

426.

**Tricarbonylchromium(0)-complexed 3-aryl-2-alkylidene-Δ³-chromenes.** A soln. of salicyl-aldehyde in THF added under $N_2$ to a degassed suspension of 1.2 eqs. 97% NaH in the same solvent, stirred for 2 min at room temp., 1 eq. tricarbonyl{η$^6$-[1-(diethoxyphosphoryl)-3-methyl-buta-1,2-dien-1-yl]benzene}chromium(0) in THF added, and heated to reflux for 1-3 h → tricarbonyl[η$^6$-(2-isopropylidene-2H-chromen-3-yl)benzene]chromium(0). Y 87%. The electron-withdrawing Cr(CO)$_3$ group is necessary to accelerate the reaction at a reasonable rate. F.e. incl. aryl-subst. 3-alkylidenepyrrolizines and 2-alkylidene-2,5-dihydrofurans s. T.J.J. Müller, M. Ansorge, Tetrahedron *54*, 1457-70 (1998).

*Sodium hydroxide/tetra-*n-*butylammonium bromide*            NaOH/Bu$_4$NBr
**1,5-Diketones from α,β-ethyleneketones and enoxysilanes**       CO-C-C-C-CO
with Ti(IV)-alkoxides cf. *32*, 885; under *basic* conditions (NaOH) with Bu$_4$NBr as phase transfer catalyst s. V.M. Swamy, A. Sarkar, Tetrahedron Lett. *39*, 1261-4 (1998).

*Rubidium hydroxide/N-(4-*tert-*butylbenzyl)cinchoninium bromide*
**Asym. Horner synthesis** s. *55*, 464                            ←
                                                                       CO→C=C

*Potassium* tert-*butoxide*                                          KOBu-t
**Regiospecific synthesis of ketones from enoxysilanes** s. *31*, 890s55   C(OSi≤)=C→COC(R)
**Wittig synthesis of enolethers**                             CO→C=C(OR)
s. *37*, 841; 1-alkylidenesugars from glycosylphosphonium salts s. A. Lieberknecht et al., Tetrahedron *54*, 3159-68 (1998).

**Horner synthesis of α,β-ethylenenitriles**                 CO→C=CHCN
with Ba(OH)$_2$ cf. *41*, 868; *cis*-isomers with KOBu-*t*, effect of base on stereoselectivity, s. T.Y. Zhang et al., Tetrahedron Lett. *39*, 1461-4 (1998).

**β-Acoxy-α,β-ethyleneketones**                            COC=C(OCOR)
**from α-diketones and 2-ketobismuthonium salts**

427.

1 eq. KOBu-*t* added to a stirred suspension of startg. bismuthonium salt in THF, treated after 10 min with 1 eq. 4,4′-dimethylbenzil, and allowed to warm to room temp. gradually → product. Y 86% (based on recovered benzil deriv.; E/Z 42:58). Such C-C bond formation based on 1,2-carbonyl migration is unprecedented in ylid chemistry. F.e.s. M.M. Rahman et al., Chem. Commun. *1998*, 1359-60.

*Organolithium compds. (s.a. under VO(OEt)Cl$_2$)*                         RLi
**Synthesis of ketones from carboxylic acid selenoamides**      C(Se)N≤→C(O)R

428.

2 eqs. Methyllithium added to a soln. of startg. selenoamide in THF at 0°, the mixture stirred for 30 min, then poured into brine → product. Y 56%. The method is simple and generally applicable to reaction of alkyllithiums with α-disubst. selenoamides (notably those possessing siloxy groups, bromine or carbon-carbon double bonds). F.e. and with retention of α-chirality s. T. Murai, S. Kato et al., Tetrahedron Lett. *39*, 4329-32 (1998).

*Organolithium compds./2,3-dichloro-5,6-dicyanoquinone*              RLi/DDQ
**Monoalkylation of porphyrins**                                   H→R
mono-N-alkylation cf. *40*, 273; nucleophilic *meso*-alkylation with RLi/DDQ, also polyalkylation, s. W.W. Kalisch, M.O. Senge, Angew. Chem. Int. Ed. Engl. *37*, 1107-9 (1998)

n-*Butyllithium (s.a. under ZnCl₂)*  BuLi
**Wittig syntheses via P-ylid carbanions**  CO → C=CHCOOH
α,β-ethylene-carboxylic acid esters and -nitriles s. *44*, 837; (E)-α,β-ethylenecarboxylic acids from unstabilized P-ylid carbanions and oxo compds. via *in situ*-condensation with diethyl carbonate, also α,β-ethylenecarboxylic acid esters, s. H.J. Cristau, M. Taillefer, Tetrahedron *54*, 1507-22 (1998).

**Syntheses with unsatd. stannanes via tin-lithium exchange**  ←
with PhLi cf. *14*, 711; syntheses with chiral tricarbonylchromium-complexed *o*-phosphinostannanes (using *n*-BuLi) s. A. Ariffin, N.S. Simpkins et al., Synlett *1997*, 1453-5.

n-*Butyllithium/boron fluoride/iodine/triethylamine*  ←
**5-Membered heterocyclics**  ○
**from tungsten alkoxycarbene complexes and terminal acetylene derivs.**

429. [reaction scheme]

**Furan-3-carboxylic acid esters from aldehydes.** 2 eqs. 1.6 *M* n-BuLi in hexane added to a soln. of 2.33 eqs. startg. alkyne in THF at -78°, a soln. of startg. tungsten carbene complex in THF added dropwise, stirred for 30 min, treated successively with 2 eqs. BF₃-etherate and 2.67 eqs. benzaldehyde in THF, stirred for 1 h, Et₃N and 2 eqs. I₂ in THF added, treated slowly with methanol after 10 min, the mixture warmed to room temp., and quenched with aq. Na₂S₂O₃ → product. Y 84%. Reaction occurs via [3+2]-cycloaddition with concomitant migration of the metal to give a vinylic tungsten species, followed by oxidation of the latter with I₂. F.e., also 1-sulfonylpyrrole-3-carboxylic acid esters from N-sulfonylimines, 5-alkoxy-2(5*H*)-furanone-4-carboxylic acid esters with CO₂, and 5-alkoxy-1-sulfonyl-Δ³-2-pyrrolone-4-carboxylic acid esters with TsNCO, s. N. Iwasawa et al., J. Org. Chem. *63*, 3164-5 (1998).

*Lithium bis(trimethylsilyl)amide/n-butyllithium*  LiN(SiMe₃)₂/BuLi
**Reactions via Horner synthesis with ethyl dichloromethylphosphonate**  ←

430. [reaction scheme]   Ar = 2-ClC₆H₄

**Tolans from diaryl ketones via Fritsch-Buttenberg-Wiechell rearrangement.** A soln. of 1.2 eqs. hexamethyldisilazane in dry THF added slowly dropwise to a mixture of 1.1 eqs. 1.6 *M* n-BuLi in hexane and THF at -78° under dry N₂, the mixture allowed to warm slowly to 0°, recooled to -78°, 1.1 eqs. diethyl dichloromethylphosphonate and startg. diaryl ketone in THF added slowly maintaining the temp. at -78°, stirring continued for 10 min, allowed to warm to 0° over 30 min, recooled to -60°, treated with 2.3 eqs. *n*-BuLi, left to warm to 0° over 30 min, and water added with rapid stirring → product. Y 92%. Dichloromethylene compds. were recovered quantitatively with only 1 eq. *n*-BuLi in the second stage. A variety of substituents is tolerated. F.e. incl. sym. tolans, **also chloromethylene compds.** without rearrangement at -90° followed by quenching with ethanol, s. V. Mouriès et al., Synthesis *1998*, 271-4.

*Potassium bis(trimethylsilyl)amide*  KN(SiMe₃)₂
**Wittig synthesis with cyclic phosphonium salts**  CO → C=C
with tetrahydrophosphorinium salts using BuLi cf. *26*, 686; (E)-styrenes from phosphorinanium salts and ar. aldehydes, also (Z)-ethylene derivs. from acyclic phosphonium salts, s. N.J. Lawrence, H. Beynek, Synlett *1998*, 497-8.

*Cesium carbonate*  Cs₂CO₃
**Enamines from α-aminophosphonic acid esters and aldehydes**  CHO → CH=C(N<)
with KOH cf. *21*, 888; β-anilino-β-pyridylstyrenes (with Cs₂CO₃) and hydrolysis to benzyl pyridyl ketones s. M. Journet et al., Tetrahedron Lett. *39*, 1717-20 (1998).

*Ethanolamine*                                                             $H_2NCH_2CH_2OH$
**Allylboration**                                              $CO \rightarrow C(OH)C\text{-}C\!=\!\!=\!C$
s. *33, 865s51; 52, 54*; *anti*-3-ethylenealcohols from 2-ethyleneboranes prepared *in situ* **from allenes** cf. G. Narla, H.C. Brown, Tetrahedron Lett. *38*, 219-22 (1997).

*Trimethylamine N-oxide*                                       *Me₃NO*
**Pyridine ring from η¹-(1,3-diene)tungsten complexes and nitriles**

431.

Pyridine ring synthesis by [4+2]-cycloaddition with *unactivated* nitriles can be achieved by activating the diene component with a Cp(CO)₃W residue. **E: 2,3-Dihydrofuro[2,3-*b*]pyridines.** A mixture of startg. η¹-(1,3-diene)tungsten complex and nitrile treated with 5 eqs. trimethylamine N-oxide dihydrate at 23° for 8 h → product. Y 58%. Reaction is initiated by CO→nitrile ligand exchange at tungsten, and thought to proceed via a 7-membered, oxygen-stabilized nitrogen-tungsten carbenoid ring. The classical cobalt-catalyzed [4+2]-cycloaddition fails with unactivated nitriles. F.e. and intramolecular [4+2]-cycloaddition s. W.-T. Li, R.-S. Liu et al., J. Am. Chem. Soc. *120*, 4520-1 (1998).

*Pyridine N-oxide*                                                                        ←
**Stereospecific syntheses with 1-aza-2-zircona-4-cyclopentenes as homoenolate equivalents**
**γ-Lactols from ketones**

432.

1.05 eqs. Startg. ketone added under argon to a soln. of startg. azazirconacyclopentene (readily prepared from cinnamaldehyde) in toluene, heated to reflux, and worked up when the mixture had turned yellow → crude intermediate adduct, in THF treated with 1.2 eqs. pyridine N-oxide, water added with vigorous stirring, and stirred at room temp. for 8 h as [Cp₂Zr=O]ₙ precipitated → crude 2-aminotetrahydrofuran, in THF treated dropwise with 0.1 *N* HCl under vigorous stirring, and worked up after 6 h → product. Y 64% (d.e. >98%). F.e. and oxidation to **γ-lactones** s. D. Enders et al., Angew. Chem. Int. Ed. Engl. *37*, 1673-5 (1998).

*(S)-3,3'-Dimethyl-2,2'-biquinoline N,N'-dioxide/ethyldiisopropylamine*              ←
**Regiospecific asym. synthesis of 3-ethylenealcohols**         $CHO \rightarrow CH(OH)C\text{-}C\!=\!\!=\!C$
**from aldehydes and 2-ethylene(trichloro)silanes**

433.

ca. 1.2 eqs. Allyl(trichloro)silane added at -78° to a soln. of 10 mol% (S)-3,3'-dimethyl-2,2'-biquinoline N,N'-dioxide, 5 eqs. *i*-Pr₂NEt, and benzaldehyde in methylene chloride, stirred for 6 h, and subjected to aq. work-up → (R)-α-(2-propenyl)benzenemethanol. Y 85% (e.e. 88%). The reagent was recovered quantitatively with no loss of optical purity. The method is applicable to ar. aldehydes and α,β-ethylenealdehydes, but enantioselectivity was poor with aliphatic aldehydes.

The added base is crucial for acceleration of the catalytic cycle. A cyclic chair-like transition state is proposed in which the silyl group is hexacoordinated to both of the oxygen atoms of the reagent as well as the aldehyde. With subst. 2-ethylene(trichloro)silanes, reaction proceeds **with double bond shift**. F.e.s. M. Nakajima et al., J. Am. Chem. Soc. *120*, 6419-20 (1998).

*Lithium dialkylcuprates/ammonium chloride* $LiCuR_2/NH_4Cl$
**1,4-Addition-Horner synthesis** $C(R)CHC\!\!=\!\!C\text{-}COOR$
synthesis of α-allenecarboxylic acid esters cf. *28*, 851s*51*; α,β-ethylenecarboxylic acid esters from α,β-ethyleneoxo compds. via cuprate addition, followed by *in situ*-Horner synthesis with α-phosphonylcarboxylic acid esters, also via Michael addition, s. O. Piva, S. Comesse, Tetrahedron Lett. *38*, 7191-4 (1997).

*Cuprous chloride* $CuCl$
**Syntheses via copper(I)-catalyzed coupling of zirconacyclopentadienes with halides** ←
s. *54*, 444; polysubst. cyclopentadien-5-ylacetic acid esters from (Z)-α,β-ethylene-β-iodo-carboxylic acid esters via cross-coupling-intramolecular 1,4-addition s. M. Kotora et al., Tetrahedron Lett. *39*, 4321-4 (1998).

*Cuprous iodide s.a. under* $Pd_2(dba)_3$ $CuI$

*Cuprous iodide/sodium chloride* $CuI/NaCl$
**Copper(I)-catalyzed cross-coupling with stannanes** ←
s. *52*, 439s*53, 54*; polymer-based cross-coupling of unsatd. stannanes with supported aryl iodides with added NaCl s. S.-K. Kang et al., Tetrahedron Lett. *39*, 3011-2 (1998).

*Cupric fluoride/(S)-2,2'-bis(di-p-tolylphosphino)-1,1'-binaphthyl* ←
**Vinylogous asym. aldol-type condensation** ←
**via catalytic regeneration of chiral metal enolates**

434.

A novel catalytic procedure based on a chiral metal fluoride complex is reported for the generation and asym. aldol condensation of metal enolates from enoxysilanes *without* employing a Lewis acid. **E**: A soln. of startg. enoxysilane and benzaldehyde in THF treated with 2 mol% (S)-Tol-BINAP·CuF$_2$ (formed *in situ* from (S)-Tol-BINAP with Cu(OTf)$_2$ and Bu$_4$N$^+$Ph$_3$SiF$_2^-$) at -78°, and the mixture subjected to acidic work-up → product. Y 92% (e.e. 94%). Reaction is generally applicable to aliphatic, α,β-unsatd., ar., and heteroar. aldehydes. Mechanistically, it is quite distinct from Lewis acid-catalyzed conversions, reaction proceeding via a chiral metal enolate, followed by enantioselective aldol addition and silylation of the intermediate metal alkoxide *with the startg. enoxysilane*. The chiral metal enolate is thus regenerated recursively in a catalytic cycle. F.e.s. J. Krüger, E.M. Carreira, J. Am. Chem. Soc. *120*, 837-8 (1998).

*Magnesium/dichloro[1,3-bis(diphenylphosphino)propane]nickel(II)* $Mg/NiCl_2(dppp)$
**Cross-coupling of eneselenides with Grignard compds.** $C\!\!=\!\!C(SeR) \rightarrow C\!\!=\!\!C(R')$
s. *43*, 778s*52*; synthesis of 1,4-dienes from 2-organoseleno-1,4-dienes s. Y. Ma, X. Huang, J. Chem. Res., Synop *1998*, 312-3.

*Zinc chloride* $ZnCl_2$
**γ-Diketones from α-halogenoketones and enoxystannanes** CO-C-C-CO
with HMPA cf. *46*, 885s*50*; with ZnCl$_2$ or ZnBr$_2$ s. M. Yasuda, A. Baba et al., J. Org. Chem. *62*, 8282-3 (1997).

**β-Lactones from aldehydes and O-silylketene S,O-acetals**
s. *54*, 447; asym. induction with chiral aldehydes s. J. Org. Chem. *63*, 1344-7 (1998).

*Zinc chloride/n-butyllithium/tetrakis(triphenylphosphine)palladium(0)* ←
**2(E),4-Dienones from carboxylic acid chlorides**      COCl → COCH=CH-CH=CH$_2$
**Synthesis with addition of four C-atoms**

435.

1-(Butyltelluro)butadiene (E/Z mixture) treated with BuLi in THF at -78° for 30 min, ZnCl$_2$ in the same solvent added, allowed to warm to room temp., startg. acyl chloride and 5 mol% Pd(PPh$_3$)$_4$ added at -10°, and allowed to warm to 0° → product. Y 80% (100% E-isomer). The method is highly stereoselective regardless of the geometry of the parent diene. The reaction is believed to occur via Te→Li exchange and transmetalation to a dienylzinc chloride, followed by acylation. F.e., **also 2,4,6-trienones and 2,4-dien-6-ynones** s. Y.-Z. Huang, X.-S. Mo, Tetrahedron Lett. *39*, 1945-8 (1998).

*Trimethylaluminum/chiral 3,3'-bis(triphenylsilyl)-1,1'-bi-2-naphthol/*  ←
   *diethyl ether/triethylborane*
**Lewis acid-catalyzed asym. radical cross-coupling**      I → CH$_2$CH=CH$_2$
**of α-iodolactones with allyltri-n-butylstannane**

436.

The first construction of **chiral quaternary hydrocarbon groups** by asym. radical cross-coupling of a *monodentate* substrate in the presence of a chiral Lewis acid in *catalytic* amount is reported. E: **Chiral α-subst. α-allyllactones.** *0.2 eq.* Each of Me$_3$Al, chiral 3,3'-bis(triphenylsilyl)-1,1'-bi-2-naphthol, and *diethyl ether* mixed in toluene at room temp., the resulting chiral complex cooled to -78°, startg. α-iodolactone and a little Et$_3$B added, and worked up when reaction complete → product. Y 78% (e.e. 80%). A novel *pentacoordinate* intermediate (formed from the lactone, the chiral Al-complex, and diethyl ether) may play a decisive role in the reaction. Enantioselectivity was low in the absence of diethyl ether. F.e. and with the Lewis acid in stoichiometric amount s. M. Murakata, O. Hoshino et al., J. Am. Chem. Soc. *119*, 11713-4 (1997).

*Boron fluoride (s.a. under n-BuLi)*      *BF$_3$*
**Synthesis of cyclic ethers from lactol esters**      OAc → R
with RMgBr/CuBr cf. *45*, 449; stereospecific synthesis of 2-(silylethynyl)-O-heterocyclics from diethyl(trimethylsilylethynyl)aluminum with BF$_3$, and 2-allyl-O-heterocyclics from allyltrimethylsilane. s. S.D. Rychnovsky, V.H. Dahanukar, J. Org. Chem. *61*, 7648-9 (1996); 2-(alk-1-ynyl)-tetrahydropyrans from 2-formoxytetrahydropyrans and silylacetylenes with SnCl$_4$, and 2-allyl-derivs. with allyltrimethylsilane and Me$_3$SiOTf, s. E. Alvarez, J.D. Martín, Synlett *1996*, 1082-4.

**C-Glycosides from chalcogenoglycosides**      TeR → R'
C-vinyl glycosides from selenoglycosides s. *47*, 984; C-α-aryl glycosides from telluroglycosides with BF$_3$ or Et$_3$B (review s. *47*, 938s49) cf. W. He et al., Tetrahedron Lett. *38*, 5541-4 (1997).

**β-Hydroxyketones from enoxysilanes and aldehydes**      CO → C(OH)C-CO
with TiCl$_4$ cf. *30*, 621; with BF$_3$, 1,7- *vs.* 1,2-asym. induction with π-allyltricarbonyliron lactone and lactam derivs. s. S.V. Ley et al., J. Chem. Soc. Perkin Trans. I *1998*, 3349-54; *syn*-α-aryl-

seleno-β-hydroxyketones from 2-siloxyeneselenides s. S. Ponthieux et al., Tetrahedron Lett. *39*, 4017-20 (1998).

**β-Aminocarboxylic acid esters**                                                            CH(NHR)C-COOR
**from O-silyl O-alkyl keteneacetals and azomethines with asym. induction**
with TiI$_4$ cf. *52*, 457; from aldimines based on (R)-phenylglycinol with BF$_3$, also the opposite enantiomers **from oxazolidines** (derived from the *same* auxiliary) with Me$_3$SiOTf, s. K. Higashiyama et al., Synlett *1998*, 489-90.

**Parallel solution-phase synthesis of tetrahydro-4*H*-1,3-oxazin-4-ones**
**from 3-siloxy-2-aza-1,3-dienes and aldehydes**

437.

A soln. of startg. azadiene in dry methylene chloride distributed in ten vials under N$_2$, cooled to -78°, a different aldehyde (1.1 eqs.) in the same solvent added dropwise to each vial, followed immediately by 1 eq. BF$_3$-etherate in the same solvent, stirred for 3 h, slowly warmed to room temp., stirred overnight, and excess of the aldehyde removed by trapping with aminomethyl-polystyrene in the presence of methyl orthoformate → product. Y 80%. The products are of potential for the preparation of α-amino-β-hydroxycarboxylic acids. The diastereoselectivity was not determined. F.e. in varing degrees of purity s. M. Panunzio, P. Seneci et al., Tetrahedron Lett. *39*, 6585-8 (1998).

**1,3-Cyclopentanediones from 1,2-di(siloxy)cyclobutenes and ketones**
s. *48*, 886s50; from methyl-subst. 1,2-di(siloxy)cyclobutenes, also from acetals, s. J. Org. Chem. *62*, 8722-9 (1997).

*Indium(III) chloride*                                                                                *InCl$_3$*
**Lewis acid-catalyzed Michael-type addition under mild conditions**     C=C → CHC(R)

438.

**in the absence of solvent.** A mixture of 2-cyclohexenone and 20 mol% InCl$_3$ stirred at room temp. for 15 min, 1 eq. startg. enoxysilane added, stirring continued for 30 min, distilled water added, and the suspension stirred for a further 30 min at room temp. → product. Y 67%. The procedure is simple, applicable to acid-sensitive substrates, and does not require special precautions (e.g. strictly anhydrous or non-protic conditions). Furthermore, the Lewis acid can be readily recovered and reused. F.e. incl. 1,4-addition of enoxysilanes and O-silyl O-alkyl keteneacetals to acyclic enones and enoates s. T.-P. Loh, L.-L. Wei, Tetrahedron *54*, 7615-24 (1998).

*Indium(III) chloride/sodium dodecyl sulfate*                                *InCl$_3$/NaOSO$_2$OR*
**Indium(III)-catalyzed aldol-type condensation in aq. media**         CH(OH)C-CO
s. *52*, 447; in aq. micellar media with added sodium dodecyl sulfate s. S. Kobayashi et al., Tetrahedron Lett. *39*, 1579-82 (1998); β-hydroxy-α-siloxyketones from 1,2-di(siloxy)-1-ethylenes and formaldehyde with asym. induction, homologization of carbohydrates, s. T.-P. Loh et al., Chem. Commun. *1998*, 861-2.

*Cation exchanger-supported lanthanide(III)*                                            *Ln(III)*
*Lanthanide(III) triflates*                                                                                  *Ln(OTf)$_3$*
**Aldol-type condensation**                                                                   CO → C(OH)C-CO
s. *47*, 893s*48*, *50*; β-hydroxy-β-(3-sulfinylfuran-2-yl)carboxylic acid esters from chiral 3-sulfinyl-furfurals with asym. induction using Yb(OTf)$_3$, Nd(OTf)$_3$ or Sm(OTf)$_3$ s. Y. Arai et al., Synlett

*1997*, 1459-61; aldol-type condensations with cation exchanger-supported lanthanide(III), e.g. Yb(III)-Amberlyst 15, s. L. Yu et al., J. Org. Chem. *62*, 3575-81 (1997).

Scandium(III) triflate  Sc(OTf)$_3$
β-*prim*-Aminocarbonyl compds. from acylhydrazones  C(NHNHCOR)C-CO
and enoxysilanes via β-(acylhydrazino)carbonyl compds.

439.

A soln of 1.5 eqs. startg. ketene silyl acetal in acetonitrile added to a soln of 5 mol% Sc(OTf)$_3$ and startg. hydrazone in the same solvent at room temp., stirred at the same temp. for 4 h, and quenched with satd. aq. NaHCO$_3$ → methyl 2,2,5-trimethyl-3-[N'-(*p*-trifluoromethylbenzoyl)-hydrazino]hexanoate (Y 88%), in ethanol treated with a catalytic amount of Raney Ni (W-3) and stirred under 1 atm H$_2$ for 24 h → product (isolated in 71% yield as the NBoc deriv.). The method is simple and high yielding. F.e., incl. β-(acylhydrazino)-ketones and -thiolic acid esters, also conversion to 2-azetidinones, Δ$^2$-5-pyrazolones and 3-pyrazolidones, s. S. Kobayashi et al., Synlett *1998*, 1019-21.

Scandium(III) triflate  Sc(OTf)$_3$
Scandium(III) triflate/sodium dodecyl sulfate  Sc(OTf)$_3$/NaOSO$_2$OR
3-Ethyleneamines from aldehydes and amines  CHO → CH(N<)CH$_2$CH=CH$_2$
Synthesis with addition of three C-atoms in aq. medium
with lanthanide(III) triflates cf. *50*, 551s*51*; in water with 20 mol% Sc(OTf)$_3$ and sodium dodecyl sulfate as surfactant s. S. Kobayashi et al., Chem. Commun. *1998*, 19-20; with less toxic allyltriethyl-germane using Sc(OTf)$_3$ in nitromethane cf. T. Akiyama, J. Iwai, Synlett *1998*, 273-4.

Polymer-microencapsulated scandium(III) triflate  ←
Catalysis with Lewis acids microencapsulated by polymeric films  ←

440.

Lewis acids, *physically* entrapped in polymeric films by microencapsulation, are *more active* than the free reagents or covalently-bound polymeric equivalents, and can be simply recovered for re-use with no loss of activity over several experiments. They are effective (in batch mode or under continuous flow) in a variety of standard Lewis acid-catalyzed conversions (e.g. nucleophilic addition to aldehydes, Michael-type addition, Diels-Alder and Friedel-Crafts reactions), and are particularly useful for **reactions of basic aldimines** which are well known to trap and often decompose Lewis acids. **E**: A mixture of startg. aldimine and enoxysilane (0.5 mmol scale) in acetonitrile treated at room temp. with microencapsulated Sc(OTf)$_3$ (prepared by stirring the Lewis acid with polystyrene in cyclohexane at 0° for 1 h) in a flow system of circulating columns for 3 h → product. Y 90%. It is possible that the Lewis acid is stabilized by interaction of the arene π-electrons of the polystyrene with vacant orbitals of the central metal. F.e. and reactions s. S. Kobayashi, S. Nagayama, J. Am. Chem. Soc. *120*, 2985-6 (1998).

Ytterbium(III) triflate  Yb(OTf)$_3$
2,3-Dihydro-4-pyridones from 1-alkoxy-3-siloxy-1,3-dienes and azomethines
with ZnCl$_2$ cf. *38*, 887; solution-phase combinatorial synthesis of a dihydropyridine library with Yb(OTf)$_3$ (cf. *54*, 456) based on a parallel purification with a polymer-based tetraamine to scavenge unreacted imine and by-product, also conversion to a library of 4-acylaminopiperidines, s. M.W. Creswell et al., Tetrahedron *54*, 3983-98 (1998).

Azodiisobutyronitrile  RN=NR
δ,ε-Ethyleneketones  CO-CHC-C-C=C
from α,β-ethyleneketones and 2-ethylenestannanes
with TiCl$_4$ cf. *32*, 887s*42*; by radical Michael addition of electron-deficient 2-ethylenestannanes with AIBN as initiator, stereoselectivity, s. E.J. Enholm et al., Tetrahedron Lett. *39*, 971-4 (1998).

*Chiral formamides/hexamethylphosphoramide*
**Asym. synthesis of 3-ethylenealcohols
from 2-ethylene(trichloro)silanes and aldehydes**

$R_2NCHO/HMPA$
$CH(OH)C-C=C$

441.

1.5 eqs. Allyltrichlorosilane added dropwise to a soln. of cyclohexanecarboxaldehyde, 20 mol% (S,S)-N,N-bis(α-methylbenzyl)formamide and 1 eq. HMPA in propionitrile at -78° under argon, stirred at the same temp. for 2 weeks, poured into ice-cold 1:1 ether/satd. aq. $NaHCO_3$, and stirred for a further 15 min → (R)-1-cyclohexyl-3-buten-1-ol. Y 80% (e.e. 98%). This is the first report of allylation using a chiral formamide as Lewis base. The method is efficient with high diastereo- and enantio-selectivity for aliphatic aldehydes (low e.e. with ar. aldehyde). The chiral auxiliary is recoverable. F.e., also chiral *anti*-3-ethylenealcohols from (E)-crotyltrichlorosilane, s. K. Iseki et al., Tetrahedron Lett. *39*, 2767-70 (1998).

*9,10-Dicyanoanthracene/biphenyl/irradiation*
**Photo-induced electron transfer-catalyzed 1,4-addition**
Oxymethylsilanes as hydroxymethyl carbanion equivalents s. *55*, 442

←
$C=C → CHC(CH_2O-)$

*Benzoic acid*
**Δ⁴-2-Oxazolones from α-hydroxycarboxylic acid amides** s. *41*, 624s55

PhCOOH
○

*2,3-Dichloro-5,6-dicyanoquinone s. under RLi*

DDQ

*Dimethyl(phenyl)silyllithium*
**Synthesis of ketones from enoxysilanes via lithium enolates**
with $LiNH_2$ in liq. $NH_3$ cf. *31*, 890; rapidly with dimethyl(phenyl)silyllithium, also determination of the reagent, s. I. Fleming et al., J. Chem. Soc. Perkin Trans. I *1998*, 1209-14; regiospecific alkylation at the *more* hindered α-site with KOBu-*t* via potassium enolates s. Y. Quesnel, L. Duhamel et al., Synlett *1998*, 413-5.

$PhMe_2SiLi$
$C(OSi≤)=C → C(O)C(R)$

*Titanium dioxide/irradiation*
**Addition of benzyl radicals to maleic acid and its derivs.
via photo-induced electron transfer under mild conditions with a heterogeneous sensitizer**

$TiO_2/hν$
$C=C → CHC(R)$

442.

A 0.02 M soln. of *p*-methoxybenzyltrimethylsilane and 2 eqs. maleic acid in dry acetonitrile added to a little dry $TiO_2$ contained in a Pyrex tube, the latter sealed with a serum cap, sonicated under $N_2$ for 15 min, and irradiated under $N_2$ with four 15 W phosphor-coated lamps (350 nm centre of emission) for 30 h → product. Y 72% (combined yield from four batches undergoing simultaneous reaction; 100% conversion). Reactions were more rapid (on the 1 g scale) in an immersion well under irradiation with Pyrex-filtered light from a 150 W Hg arc. Work-up is simple by virtue of using a heterogeneous sensitizer. F.e. incl. addition to maleic anhydride and maleonitrile, also with arylacetic acids as benzyl radical source, s. L. Cermenati et al., Tetrahedron *54*, 2575-82 (1998); photo-induced electron transfer-catalyzed 1,4-addition of oxymethyl radicals (from alkoxy- or siloxy-methylsilanes) with 9,10-dihydroanthracene/biphenyl as electron transfer system s. G. Gutenberger et al., Angew. Chem. Int. Ed. Engl. *37*, 660-2 (1998).

*Titanium tetraisopropoxide/(S)-1,1'-bi-2-naphthol/trimethyl borate* ←
**Catalytic asym. synthesis of 3-ethylenealcohols**     CHO → CH(OH)CH$_2$CH=CH$_2$
**from aldehydes**
and allyltributylstannane s. *49*, 898; improved procedure with an added Lewis acid (trimethyl borate), also asym. synthesis of 3-acetylenealcohols from allenylstannanes, s. C.-M. Yu et al., Synlett *1997*, 889-90.

*Zirconium tetra-tert-butoxide/(R)-6,6'-dibromo-1,1'-bi-2-naphthol/* ←
*N-methylimidazole*
**2,3-Dihydro-4(1H)-pyridones from aldimines and 1-alkoxy-3-siloxy-1,3-dienes**    ○
**Catalytic asym. hetero-Diels-Alder reaction**

443.

22 Mol% (R)-6,6'-dibromo-1,1'-bi-2-naphthol in *toluene* and 0.3 eq. N-methylimidazole (NMI) in the same solvent added to 10 mol% Zr(OBu-*t*)$_4$ in the same solvent at room temp., stirred for 1 h, cooled to -45°, startg. aldimine and 1.5 eqs. Danishefsky's diene added, stirred for 35 h, quenched with satd. NaHCO$_3$, and the crude adduct treated with 20:1 THF/1 *N* HCl at 0° for 30 min → product. Y 83% (e.e. 82%). High enantioselectivity was also recorded with the corresponding Hf(IV) complex, but the Ti(IV) analog gave lower yields and enantioselectivity (e.e. 39-62%). Other bases were less effective. With a stoichiometric amount of chiral auxiliary cf. *50*, 543. F.e.s. S. Kobayashi et al., Angew. Chem. Int. Ed. Engl. *37*, 979-81 (1998).

*Zirconium tetra-tert-butoxide/(R)-6,6'-dibromo-1,1'-bi-2-naphthol/* ←
*1,2-dimethylimidazole*
**O-Protected β-amino-α-hydroxycarboxylic acid esters**     C(NHR)CH(O-)COOR
**from aldimines**
**Asym. synthesis with addition of two C-atoms**

444.

**Chiral *syn*-β-amino-α-siloxycarboxylic acid esters.** 22 Mol% (R)-6,6'-dibromo-1,1'-bi-2-naphthol and 20 mol% 1,2-dimethylimidazole (DMI) in toluene added to 10 mol% Zr(OBu-*t*)$_4$ in the same solvent, stirred for 1 h at room temp., cooled to -78°, a soln. of startg. azomethine and 1.25 eqs. startg. (E)-silyl acetal in toluene added successively, stirred for 20 h, quenched with satd. aq. NaHCO$_3$, the aq. layer extracted with methylene chloride, and the crude adduct treated with 10:1 THF/1 *N* HCl at 0° for 30 min → product. Y 100% (*syn/anti* 96/4; e.e. 95%). **Chiral *anti*-α-alkoxy-β-aminocarboxylic acid esters** were obtained in methylene chloride at 45° from the (Z)-silyl acetal with the same catalyst. The enantiomers are also obtainable with (S)-6,6'-dibromo-1,1'-bi-2-napthtol, so that all four diastereoisomers can be produced from the same aldimine. F.e.s. S. Kobayashi et al., J. Am. Chem. Soc. *120*, 431-2 (1998).

*Dichlorotitanium (4R,5R)-2,2-dimethyl-α,α,α',α'-tetraphenyl-1,3-dioxolane-* ←
*4,5-dimethoxide*
**β-Lactones from aldehydes by asym. [2+2]-cycloaddition**
with ketene in the presence of a chiral 1,3-disulfonyl-1,3,2-diazaaluminacyclopentane cf. *50*, 397; with more stable trimethylsilylketene in the presence of dichlorotitanium (4R,5R)-2,2-

dimethyl-α,α,α′,α′-tetraphenyl-1,3-dioxolane-4,5-dimethoxide s. H.W. Yang, D. Romo, Tetrahedron Lett. *39*, 2877-80 (1998).

*Titanium tetrachloride* $TiCl_4$
**Replacement of alkoxy groups by allyl** $OR \rightarrow CH_2CH{=}CH_2$
with allylsilanes cf. *37*, 893s*38*; 3-allyl-2,5-morpholinediones and -2,5-piperazinediones **with asym. induction**, also conversion to chiral α-amino-γ,δ-ethylenecarboxylic acids, s. G. Kardassis, E. Steckhan et al., Tetrahedron *54*, 3471-8, 3479-88 (1998).

*Tri-n-butyltin triflate* $Bu_3SnOSO_2CF_3$
**C-β-Allyl glycosides from 2-ethylenestannanes** ←
and thioglycosides cf. *39*, 882; and 1,2-anhydrosugars under mild conditions s. D.A. Evans et al., Tetrahedron Lett. *39*, 1709-12 (1998).

*Stannous chloride* $SnCl_2$
**β,γ-Ethyleneketones from α-halogenoketones** $C(Ar)COCH_2CH{=}CH_2$
**Synthesis with addition of three C-atoms**

445.

**via 1,2-aryl migration.** 1 eq. Allyltri-*n*-butylstannane added to a stirred suspension of 1 eq. $SnCl_2$ and 2-bromo-*p*-methoxyacetophenone in dry acetonitrile, and the mixture stirred at 25° for 1 h → product. Y 98%. Reaction proceeds via a homoallylic tin alkoxide in which the interaction between the tin(II) atom and the halogen directs the aryl rearrangement. The allylation is enhanced by an electron-withdrawing group on the aromatic ring, while rearrangement is disfavoured in the presence of chloro or nitro groups. In several runs, heating at 80° was required to effect rearrangement. In contrast, alkyl α-halogenoketones gave 5-allyl-2-oxazolines in low yields. F.e. incl. thienyl derivs., also isolation of the intermediate halogenhydrin, s. M. Yasuda et al., Chem. Commun. *1998*, 563-4.

*Stannic chloride* $SnCl_4$
**3-Ketothioethers from enoxysilanes** $C(OSi{\leqslant}){=}C \rightarrow CO\text{-}C\text{-}C(SR)$
and mercaptals cf. *37*, 891; and 1,1-acoxythioethers, 1-(2,2,2-trifluoroethyl)-3-ketothioethers, s. H.-P. Guan, C.-M. Hu et al., J. Chem. Soc. Perkin Trans. I *1998*, 279-81.

*Bis(pentafluorophenyl)tin dibromide* $Ar_2SnBr_2$
**Parallel differentiated recognition of ketones and acetals** ←

446.

The first examples of a parallel (or horizontal) strategy are reported, in which two functional groups of similar chemical reactivity undergo simultaneous but independent reaction with one or other component of a mixture of two reactive compds. **E: Aldol-type condensations**. A soln. of startg. O-silyl ketene acetal and 4 eqs. enoxysilane in methylene chloride added to a soln. of 0.4 eq. bis(pentafluorophenyl)tin dibromide and 1.1 eqs. startg. ketoacetal in the same solvent at -78°, and the mixture stirred at this temp. for 7 h before addition of water → intermediate (Y 82%), stirred in HF/acetonitrile soln. at room temp. for 7 h → ethyl 8-benzoyl-3-hydroxy-7-methoxy-3-phenyloctanoate (Y ca. 100%). The weak Lewis acidity of the organotin reagent is essential for detecting the subtle differences between ketone and acetal, the silyl ketene acetal reacting preferentially with the former and the silyl enolether with the latter. F.e. and with acetal/ketone mixtures s. J. Chen, J. Otera, Angew. Chem. Int. Ed. Engl. *37*, 91-3 (1998); parallel differentiated **recognition of aldehydes and ketones** s. Tetrahedron Lett. *39*, 1767-70 (1998).

Lead(II) chloride s. under Mn                                                           $PbCl_2$

Lead(II) iodide/hexamethylphosphoramide                                                 $PbI_2$/HMPA
**4-Ethyleneepoxides from α-bromooxo compds. and 2-ethylenestannanes**
with $Bu_2SnBr_2$/HMPA cf. 47, 904; with inexpensive $PbI_2$/HMPA, also *cis*-3-ethyleneepoxides from ar. aldehydes and γ-chloroallyltri-*n*-butylstannane, s. I. Shibata et al., Chem. Lett. *1998*, 533-4.

*Ethyl dichlorovanadate/organolithium compds.*                                          $VO(OEt)Cl_2$/RLi
**Oxidative cross-coupling of organoaluminum compds.
with unsatd. organolithium compds.**

447.

Formal reductive elimination *on aluminum* has been achieved for the first time via oxidation of organoaluminum ate complexes or aryldiethylalanes with an alkyl dichlorovanadate as reagent. **E: 1,3-Enynes.** 1.1 eqs. Startg. lithium acetylide added to startg. enalane in ether at -78°, the resulting soln. added to 3 eqs. $VO(OEt)Cl_2$ after 1 h, and worked up after a further 3 h → product. Y 80%. There was no homo-coupling of either the vinyl or isobutyl group of the intermediate ate complex. **Ethylarenes** were obtained similarly **from** [less reactive] **aryldiethylalanes** bearing electron-donating groups (e.g. MeO, MeS) on the aromatic ring. F.e., also **arylacetylenes** via aryldiisobutylalkynylaluminates, s. T. Ishikawa et al., J. Am. Chem. Soc. *120*, 5124-5 (1998).

*Trimethylsilyl triflate*                                                               $Me_3SiOSO_2CF_3$
**2-Alkoxy-4-cycloheptenone ring
from 1,3-dienes via [4+3]-cycloaddition with oxyallyl cations**
s. *39*, 883s*46*; colchicine synthesis s. J.C. Lee et al., J. Org. Chem. *63*, 2804-5 (1998); [4+3]-cycloaddition with asym. induction s. C.B.W. Stark et al., Angew. Chem. Int. Ed. Engl. *37*, 1266-8 (1998).

**β-Aminocarboxylic acid esters from O-silyl O-alkyl keteneacetals**                    C
and oxazolidines s. *52*, 457s*55*

*N-Trimethylsilyltriflimide*                                                            $Me_3SiN(SO_2CF_3)_2$
**δ,ε-Ethylene- from α,β-ethylene-ketones**                                             $COCHC-CH_2CH=CH_2$
**Catalytic 1,4-addition of three extra C-atoms under mild conditions**

448.

**with asym. induction.** A soln. of 0.1 eq. trifluoromethanesulfonimide in dry dichloromethane added to a soln. of startg. enone and 1.1 eqs. allyltrimethylsilane in the same solvent at -78° under $N_2$, the mixture allowed to warm to 20° over 1 h, then quenched with satd. aq. $NH_4Cl$ → product. Y 97% (d.e. >98%). The method avoids the use of toxic and/or air-sensitive organometallic or metal halide reagents, and the presence of moisture is not a problem. F.e. incl. 1,4-addition to α cyclic enones and enoates, also isolation of the silyl enol ethers (by avoiding aq. work-up), and sequential 1,4-addition-aldol-type condensation s. N. Kuhnert et al., Tetrahedron Lett. *39*, 3215-6 (1998).

*Chiral chromium(III) salen complex*
**2,3-Dihydro-4-pyrones from aldehydes via asym. hetero-Diels-Alder reaction**

449.

Benzaldehyde added at room temp. to a mixture of 2 mol% (R,R)-chromium(III) salen complex and oven-dried, powdered 4 Å molecular sieves in *tert*-butyl methyl ether in a flask sealed with a rubber septum under $N_2$, cooled to -30° followed by addition of 1 eq. 1-methoxy-3-trimethyl-siloxy-1,3-butadiene, stirred for 24 h at -30°, the flask removed from the cooling bath, the mixture diluted with methylene chloride, treated with 1 drop of trifluoroacetic acid, and stirred at room temp. for 10 min → (R)-2-phenyl-2,3-dihydro-4*H*-pyran-4-one. Y 85% (e.e. 87%). The method is applicable to a broad range of aldehydes, is simple, and the catalyst is readily accessible. Several of the products were obtained enantiomerically pure by recrystallization. A concerted [4+2] mechanism is invoked, there being no evidence for the intermediacy of a Mukaiyama aldol adduct. F.e.s. S.E. Schaus et al., J. Org. Chem. *63*, 403-5 (1998).

*Lithium perchlorate* $LiClO_4$
**Synthesis of 2,4-dialkoxythioethers**
with allyl bromide cf. *44*, 907s*52*; with Si-nucleophiles (allylsilanes, enoxysilanes, O-silyl O-alkyl keteneacetals), or allylstannanes in the presence of $LiClO_4$ or $TiCl_4$ s. Tetrahedron Lett. *39*, 1083-6 (1998).

*Cuprous perchlorate/(R)-2,2'-bis(di-o-tolylphosphino)-1,1'-binaphthyl*
**γ-Keto-α-tosylaminocarboxylic acid esters from enoxysilanes**     CH(NHTs)C-CO
**Asym. synthesis with addition of two C-atoms**

450.

A soln. of ethyl glyoxylate N-tosylimine in THF treated with 1.1 eqs. startg. enoxysilane at 0° in the presence of 5 mol% $CuClO_4$ and 5.2 mol% (R)-Tol-BINAP for 24 h → product. Y 91% (e.e. 98%; >99% after recrystallization). The high enantioselectivity (unusual for the reaction of an imine with a Si-nucleophile) is explained by the formation of a rigid 5-membered chelate complex involving the central metal (even at 2 mol%) and the nitrogen and carbonyl oxygen atoms of the iminoester. Enantioselectivity was slightly lower with $AgSbF_6$ or $Pd(ClO_4)_2$ in place of $CuClO_4$, and very low with $Ni(SbF_6)_2$. The products are highly crystalline, and the tosyl and ester groups can be readily cleaved with PhOH/HBr/AcOH to give the corresponding *unnatural* amino acids. F.e.s. D. Ferraris, T. Lectka et al., J. Am. Chem. Soc. *120*, 4548-9 (1998).

*Tetra-n-butylammonium fluoride* $Bu_4NF$
**3-Ethylenealcohols from 2-ethylenesilanes**     CHO → CH(OH)C-C≡C
s. *36*, 884s*39*; rate enhancement with chelating Si,Si'-diallyldi(silanes) s. N. Asao, K. Maruoka et al., Tetrahedron Lett. *39*, 3177-80 (1998).

**Trifluoromethyl ketones from carboxylic acid esters** s. *55*, 354     COOR → $COCF_3$

*Hydrogen chloride* HCl
**Trifluoromethyltrimethylsilane as trifluoromethyl carbanion equivalent**
2,2,2-trifluoroalcohols from ketones with $Bu_4NF$/HCl cf. *44*, 577; with HCl alone s. Japanese patent JP-08113580 (Sagami Chem. Res. Centre); 2-acylamino-1,1,1-trifluorides from ketones

by treatment of the intermediate silyl deriv. with $H_2SO_4$/AcOH in acetonitrile s. E.C. Tongco, G.A. Olah et al., Synlett *1997*, 1193-5.

*Manganese/lead(II) chloride*          $Mn/PbCl_2$
**Generation of non-stabilized carbonyl ylids from two 1,1-siloxyiodide molecules** ←
and subsequent 1,3-dipolar cycloaddition using $Sm/HgCl_2$ cf. *51*, 443; with Mn and a little $PbCl_2$, also from 1,1′-diiodoethers, s. K. Takai et al., J. Org. Chem. *62*, 8612-3 (1997); f. details s. Japanese patents JP-09227542, JP-09227541 (Sumitomo Chem. Co. Ltd.).

*Manganese dioxide*          $MnO_2$
**α,β-Ethylenecarboxylic acid esters**          $CH_2OH \rightarrow CH=C$
**from (carbalkoxymethylene)phosphoranes and alcohols**
**Stereospecific Wittig synthesis with *in situ*-generated aldehydes**

451.

20 eqs. $MnO_2$ added in 5 portions over 5 h to a stirred soln. of 2,3-dibromo-2-butene-1,4-diol and 6 eqs. (carbethoxymethylene)triphenylphosphorane in dichloromethane, and the mixture stirred at room temp. for 15 h → product. Y 84% (>98% E,E,E). The method is simple, and avoids the use of volatile, toxic or highly unstable aldehydes. It is general for allylic, propargylic and benzylic alcohols, and also allows double homologation with diols. F.e.s. X. Wei, R.J.K. Taylor, Tetrahedron Lett. *39*, 3815-8 (1998).

*Manganese(II) chloride*          $MnCl_2$
**Stille-type coupling with diaryliodonium salts**          Sn≤ → Ar
with a little CuI cf. *53*, 445; with a little $MnCl_2$, also coupling with α,β-ethyleneiodonium salts, and aryl and styryl ketones via carbonylative cross-coupling, s. Tetrahedron Lett. *39*, 2131-2 (1998); f. unsatd. ketones (benzophenones, enones, ynones) from unsatd. iodonium salts and stannanes by carbonylative cross-coupling in aq. media with $PdCl_2$ cf. Synthesis *1998*, 823-5.

*Chlorotetrakis(dimethylphenylphosphine)(dinitrogen)rhenium(I)*     $ReCl(N_2)(PMe_2Ph)_4$
**Furans from α-bromoketones and enoxysilanes** s. *55*, 403      ○

*Nickel(II) acetoacetonate/diisobutylaluminum hydride/lithium chloride*      ←
**1,4-Dien-6-ynes via nickel-ene reaction-Stille-type coupling**      ←
intermolecular process cf. *50*, 552; alicyclic and heterocyclic analogs by intramolecular process with added LiCl s. Tetrahedron *54*, 1063-72 (1998).

*Dichloro[1,3-bis(diphenylphosphino)propane]nickel(II) s. under Mg*      $NiCl_2(dppp)$

*Dichloro[1,1′-bis(diphenylphosphino)ferrocene]nickel(II)/n-butyllithium*    $NiCl_2(dppf)/BuLi$
**Diaryls from arylboronic acids and aryl mesylates or chlorides**    $ArB(OH)_2 \rightarrow Ar$-$Ar'$
s. *51*, 453; from aryl mesylates, f. details, s. M. Ueda, N. Miyaura et al., Tetrahedron *54*, 13079-86 (1998); from ar. chlorides, details, s. J. Org. Chem. *62*, 8024-30 (1997).

*Acetoacetonatobis(ethylene)rhodium(I)/(S)-2,2′-bis(diphenylphosphino)-*      ←
*1,1′-binaphthyl*
**Asym. 1,4-addition of α,β-unsatd. boronic acids to α,β-ethyleneketones**    C=C → CHC(R)

452.

**in aq. medium.** A mixture of 2-cyclohexenone, 1.4 eqs. phenylboronic acid, 3 mol% Rh(acac)-$(C_2H_4)_2$, and 3 mol% (S)-BINAP in 10:1 dioxane/water heated *at 100°* for 5 h → (S)-3-phenylcyclohexanone. Y 64% (e.e. 97%). The method is generally applicable to the asym. 1,4-addition of aryl- and α,β-ethylene-boronic acids to acyclic or cyclic enones with high enantioselectivity (91-9%). The aryl group of the arylboronic acid may be substituted by an electron-withdrawing or -donating group. Oxygen- and moisture-resistant organoboranes are more manageable than the customary organometallics used for this process; furthermore, reaction can take place in protic (incl. aq.) media, and there is no 1,2-addition. F.e.s. Y. Takaya et al., J. Am. Chem. Soc. *120*, 5579-80 (1998).

*Palladous acetate*     $Pd(OAc)_2$
**Double Suzuki coupling with bis(diazonium salts)** s. *55*, 366     $N_2^+ \to Ar$

*Palladous acetate/triethylamine*     $Pd(OAc)_2/Et_3N$
**Palladium-catalyzed reactions of chromium carbene complexes under mild conditions** ←

453.

Self-dimerization and insertion reactions of chromium carbene complexes, which usually require elevated temp., can now be achieved *at room temp.* under palladium catalysis. **E: Ene-1,2-diol ethers.** 10 mol% $Pd(OAc)_2$ and 1.1 eqs. $Et_3N$ added at room temp. to a soln. of startg. carbene complex in THF under argon, stirred for 1.5 h, worked up by distillation, and the resulting E/Z mixture of enediol ethers separated by flash chromatography → (E)-product (Y 37%) and (Z)-product (Y 16%). Complexes possessing an α-hydrogen undergo β**-elimination** to give the corresponding **enolethers,** while bis(chromium alkoxycarbene complexes) undergo ring closure via intramolecular insertion of one of the carbene residues into the acidic C-α-hydrogen of the other. Chromium aryl(amino)carbene complexes gave the corresponding β**-functionalized acylophenones** with electron-deficient ethylene derivs. Results are in accord with initial formation of a palladium carbene complex. F.e.s. M.A. Sierra et al., J. Am. Chem. Soc. *120*, 6812-3 (1998).

*Palladous acetate/triphenylphosphine/sodium carbonate/tetraethylammonium chloride* ←
**Regiospecific intramolecular carbopalladation-Suzuki coupling** ←

454.

2-Iodophenyl methallyl ether added to a suspension of 10 mol% $Pd(OAc)_2$ and 20 mol% $Ph_3P$ in dry toluene, stirred for 10 min at room temp., 1.5 eqs. phenylboronic acid added in the minimum amount of ethanol, 2 eqs. 2.6 M $Na_2CO_3$ soln. and 1 eq. $Et_4NCl$ added sequentially with stirring, and boiled under reflux for 2 h under $N_2$ → 3-benzyl-3-methyl-2,3-dihydrobenzofuran. Y 78%. F.e. incl. 3-benzyl- and 3-allyl-indolines and -oxindoles, also coupling with tert. boranes, α,β-ethyleneboronic acid esters, or $NaBPh_4$, and reaction with (*o*-iodoaryl)allenes, s. R. Grigg et al., Tetrahedron *53*, 11803-26 (1997).

*Bis(dibenzylideneacetone)palladium(0)/triphenylphosphine*     $Pd(dba)_2/Ph_3P$
**Regiospecific cross-coupling of benzoyloxy-2-ethylenes**     OBz → Ph
**with tetra-*n*-butylammonium triphenyldifluorosilicate under mild conditions**

455.

**with inversion of configuration.** A soln. of startg. benzoate and 2 eqs. tetra-*n*-butylammonium triphenyldifluorosilicate (TBAT) in THF treated with 5 mol% each of $Pd(dba)_2$ and triphenylphosphine at reflux for 12 h → product. Y 60%. Being air-stable, non-hygroscopic, and a non-toxic crystalline compound, TBAT is a useful alternative to toxic phenylstannanes which afford a mixture of regioisomers on coupling with allyl alcohol derivs. and show lower stereoselectivity. An electron-rich phosphine, e.g. $Ph_3P$ or dppe, is essential for reaction. F.e.s. M.-R. Brescia, P. DeShong, J. Org. Chem. *63*, 3156-7 (1998).

*Tris(dibenzylideneacetone)dipalladium/cesium fluoride/cesium bromide* ←
**Cross-coupling of boronic acids with triflates** $B(OH)_2 \rightarrow R$
s. *37*, 902s*46, 48, 51*; 2,3-bis(indol-3-yl)maleimides under phosphine-free conditions with $Pd_2(dba)_3$/CsF/CsBr s. D.A. Neel et al., Bioorg. Med. Chem. Lett. *8*, 47-50 (1998).

*Tris(dibenzylideneacetone)dipalladium/cuprous iodide/sodium methoxide* ←
**Cross-coupling of boronic acids with aryllead triacetates** $B(OH)_2 \rightarrow Ar$

456.   $Ph\diagup\!\!\!\diagdown B(OH)_2$ + $PhPb(OAc)_3$ ⟶ $Ph\diagup\!\!\!\diagdown Ph$

**Styrenes.** 5 mol% $Pd_2(dba)_3 \cdot CHCl_3$ and 10 mol% CuI added to a stirred soln. of phenyllead triacetate and 6 eqs. NaOMe in 1:1.3 acetonitrile/dimethoxyethane at room temp., followed by the addition of (E)-β-styrylboronic acid, and stirred at 60° for 2 h → product. Y 80%. This is the first cross-coupling of boron compds. with organolead compds. The base facilitates Pb→Pd exchange with the formation of a reactive mixed metal species, $RPdPb(OMe)_3$, prior to coupling. F.e. incl. **diaryls**, and coupling with boronic acid esters s. S.-K. Kang et al., Synlett *1998*, 771-3.

*Tris(dibenzylideneacetone)dipalladium/tris[3,5-bis(trifluoromethyl)phenyl]phosphine* ←
**Stille coupling in supercritical carbon dioxide** s. *55*, 417  $Sn\leqslant \rightarrow R$

*Tetrakis(triphenylphosphine)palladium(0) (s.a. under $ZnCl_2$)* $Pd(PPh_3)_4$
**Cross-coupling of trialkylboranes with halides** $R_3B + R'Hal \rightarrow R-R'$
s. *25*, 628s*47*; synthesis of simple trisubst. (Z)-ethylene derivs. from α,β-ethyleneiodides, total synthesis of (-)-epothilone B, s. S.J. Danishefsky et al., Angew. Chem. Int. Ed. Engl. *36*, 757-9 (1997).

**Polymer-based Stille coupling** $Sn\leqslant \rightarrow R$
with polymer-based ar. iodides s. *50*, 555; with benzoate-linked supported ar. bromides or iodides s. S. Chamoin, V. Snieckus et al., Tetrahedron Lett. *39*, 4175-8 (1998).

**4-Arylseleno-2(5H)-furanones from 2-acetylenealcohols and diaryl diselenides**  ○
**Carbonylation**

457.   $F_3C$-⟨⟩-Se-Se-⟨⟩-$CF_3$ + HO–≡  $\xrightarrow{CO}$  $F_3C$-⟨⟩-Se-[furanone]

Equimolar amounts of 2-propyn-1-ol and startg. diselenide in benzene containing 2 mol% $Pd(PPh_3)_4$ charged with 60 atm. CO in a stainless steel autoclave, and stirred with heating at 100° for 50 h → 3-[[(p-trifluoromethyl)phenyl]seleno]-2-buten-4-olide. Y 74%. F.e., also **4-arylthio-2(5H)-furanones** from diaryl disulfides, and two δ-lactone analogs, s. A. Ogawa et al., J. Org. Chem. *62*, 8361-5 (1997).

*Tetrakis(triphenylphosphine)palladium(0)/sodium carbonate* $Pd(PPh_3)_4/Na_2CO_3$
**Polymer-based Suzuki coupling** $B(OH)_2 \rightarrow R$
with an insoluble polymeric support cf. *50*, 556s*53*; with a *soluble* PEG-based support for preparation of diaryls from ar. iodides and arylboronic acids, with removal of the support by transesterification with $Et_3N$ in methanol, s. C.G. Blettner, T. Schotten et al., Synlett *1998*, 295-7; diaryl- and heterodiaryl-carboxaldehydes based on the Leznoff acetal linker s. S. Chamoin, V. Snieckus et al., Tetrahedron Lett. *39*, 4179-82 (1998).

*Tetrakis(triphenylphosphine)palladium(0)/sodium hydroxide or potassium carbonate  ←
or phosphate*
**Suzuki coupling of boronic acids with halides**                       $B(OH)_2 \to R$
s. *37*, 902s*51, 52*; (Z)-2,2-disubst. 1-(trifluoromethyl)enolethers with aq. NaOH as base s. L. Allain et al., Synthesis *1998*, 847-50; (E)-β-cyclopropyl-α,β-ethylenecarboxylic acid esters from cyclopropylboronic acids with $K_3PO_4$ as base s. S.-M. Zhou et al., Synlett *1998*, 198-200; 3- or 5-aryl-4-methoxy-2-pyrones with $K_2CO_3$ as base s. S. Cerezo et al., Tetrahedron *54*, 7813-8 (1998).

*Tetrakis(triphenylphosphine)palladium(0)/sodium carbonate or barium hydroxide*  ←
**Suzuki diaryl coupling**                                      $ArB(OH)_2 \to Ar\text{-}Ar'$
s. *37*, 902s*53, 54*; highly substituted diaryls and terphenyls s. M. Hird et al., J. Chem. Soc. Perkin Trans. I *1998*, 3479-84; N-Boc-protected 2-aryl-pyrroles and -indoles s. C.N. Johnson et al., Synlett *1998*, 1025-7; aryl- and diaryl-phenanthrolines with $Ba(OH)_2$ as base s. S. Toyota, J.S. Siegel et al., Tetrahedron Lett. *39*, 2697-700 (1998).

*Tetrakis(triphenylphosphine)palladium(0)/lithium chloride*        $Pd(PPh_3)_4/LiCl$
**Stille coupling of arylstannanes with enol triflates**         $ArSn{\Leftarrow} \to ArC{=}C$
2-aryl-1,4-naphthoquinones s. *44*, 884s*53*; with added LiCl s. K.W. Stagliano, H.C. Malinakova, Tetrahedron Lett. *38*, 6617-20 (1997).

*Tetrakis(triphenylphosphine)palladium(0)/cuprous iodide*          $Pd(PPh_3)_4/CuI$
**Stille coupling of enestannanes**                                  $Sn{\Leftarrow} \to R$
with halides s. *39*, 887s*54*; 2-organoseleno-1,4-dienes from 1-(organoseleno)enestannanes s. Y. Ma, X. Huang, J. Chem. Res., Synop *1998*, 312-3; (E)-enestannanes from 1,2-ene-1,1-distannanes with $Pd(OAc)_2/P(o\text{-tol})_3$, and conversion to trisubst. ethylene derivs., s. P. Quayle et al., Tetrahedron Lett. *39*, 485-8 (1998); coupling of hindered enestannanes using $Pd_2(dba)_3/CuI/Ph_3As$, Stille- vs. *cine*-substitution, s. A. Flohr, ibid. 5177-80; 3-ferrocenylquinolines s. C. Liu et al., Synth. Commun. *28*, 2731-5 (1998); chiral 2-sulfinyl-1,3-dienes with $Pd_2(dba)_3/Ph_3As$ s. R.S. Paley et al., J. Org. Chem. *62*, 6326-43 (1997); coupling of a chiral (E)-4-(2-stannylvinyl)oxazolidine *en route* to chiral (E)-2-amino-3-ethylenealcohols s. G. Reginato et al., ibid. 6187-92; coupling of enestannanes with N-protected cyclic 1-aminoenol triflates s. T. Luker et al., ibid. 8131-40.

**Stille coupling of hetarylstannanes with halides**
s. *34*, 862s*53*; 4-subst. pyridines s. J. Sauer, D.K. Heldmann, Tetrahedron Lett. *39*, 2549-52 (1998); coupling of N-protected 4-bromo-5-stannylimidazoles s. L. Revesz et al., ibid. 5171-4; of 2-hydroxymethyl-4-stannylthiazoles as part of an epothilone synthesis s. K.C. Nicolaou et al., Angew. Chem. Int. Ed. Engl. *37*, 81-4, 84-7 (1998); with 2-stannylpurine nucleosides s. K. Kato et al., J. Org. Chem. *62*, 6833-41 (1997).

*Tetrakis(triphenylphosphine)palladium(0)/thallous hydroxide*        $Pd(PPh_3)_4/TlOH$
**1,3-Dienes**                                            $C{=}CB(OH)_2 \to C{=}C\text{-}C{=}C$
**from α,β-ethyleneboronic acids and α,β-ethyleneiodides**
s. *37*, 902s*43*; pheromonal **polyenes** s. R. Alvarez, A.R. de Lera et al., Tetrahedron *54*, 6793-810 (1998).

*Di(μ-acetato)bis(tri-o-tolylphosphine)dipalladium*              $Pd_2(OAc)_2(Ar_3P)_2$
**Styrenes from diazonium fluoroborates and potassium ene(trifluoro)borates**  $N_2^+ \to C{=}C$

458.

A suspension of startg. diazonium fluoroborate, 1.2 eqs. K-vinyl(trifluoro)borate, and 5 mol% $Pd_2(\mu\text{-OAc})_2[P(o\text{-tolyl})_3]_2$ in degassed methanol stirred *at 20°* under argon in the dark → product. Y 81% (instantaneous reaction). Reaction is generally applicable to diazonium salts possessing either electron-withdrawing or -donating substituents, as well as to bulky *o*-subst. derivs. Unlike many vinylmetallics, the vinylborate is thermally stable, resistant to air and water, non-toxic, and can be stored at room temp. without decomposition. F.e. and **stilbenes** from K-β-styryl(trifluoro)borate, also with retention of ar. bromine and triflate groups, s. S. Darses et al., Tetrahedron Lett. *39*, 5045-8 (1998).

*Silica-supported palladium(0) phosphine complex/sodium salt*
**Cross-coupling with tetraarylborates**
diaryls with Pd(PPh$_3$)$_4$/Et$_3$N cf. *46*, 906s48; also benzophenones from arylcarboxylic acid halides with NaBPh$_4$ and a silica-supported palladium(0) phosphine complex s. M.-Z. Cai et al., Synth. Commun. *28*, 693-700 (1998).

*Chiral binuclear [2,2'-bis(diarylphosphino)-1,1'-binaphthyl]-*
*(µ-hydroxo)palladium(II) bis(fluoroborates)*
**Asym. synthesis of β-aminoketones from enoxysilanes and aldimines**     C(NHR)C-CO

459.

**via palladium(II) enolates.** The first example of palladium(II)-catalyzed asym. addition of enoxysilanes to imines is reported. E: **Chiral α-amino-γ-ketocarboxylic acid esters.** Startg. imine added in one portion to a soln. of 2 eqs. startg. enoxysilane and 5 mol% chiral binuclear palladium(II) µ-hydroxo complex at 28°, and worked up after 17-24 h → (S)- product. Y 95% (e.e. 90%). Enantioselectivity was lower with the diaquo complexes themselves since liberated HBF$_4$ catalyses the competitive and undesirable conversion to the racemic product. Reaction also takes place with simple imines and tosylimines with lower enantioselectivity. F.e.s. E. Hagiwara et al., J. Am. Chem. Soc. *120*, 2474-5 (1998).

*Palladous chloride*                                                                                    *PdCl$_2$*
**Unsatd. ketones from unsatd. iodonium salts and stannanes** s. *53*, 445s55     Sn≤ → COR

*Bis(η$^3$-allylpalladium chloride)/chiral phosphinoamidines*
**Asym. synthesis of γ,δ-ethylenecarboxylic acid esters**                               C=C-C-C-COOR
**from O-silyl O-alkyl keteneacetals and acoxy-2-ethylenes**

460.

(E)-1,3-Diphenylprop-2-enyl pivalate in methylene chloride added to a mixture of 5 mol% [Pd(η$^3$-C$_3$H$_5$)Cl]$_2$ and 20 mol% chiral phosphinoamidine ligand in the same solvent at room temp. under argon, 3 eqs. startg. O-silyl O-alkyl keteneacetal added, and allowed to react for 24 h → (S)-product. Y 81% (e.e. 90%; with 2.5 mol% Pd-catalyst: Y 78%, e.e. 90%). There was no reaction with the corresponding unsubst. keteneacetal, probably due to its lower nucleophilicity, but steric hindrance also affected the yield. F.e.s. A. Saitoh et al., Tetrahedron:Asym. *9*, 741-4 (1998).

*Bis(η$^3$-allylpalladium chloride)/tetra-n-butylammonium fluoride/iodine*
**Diaryls from aryl(fluoro)silanes and ar. halides**                                    ArSi(F)R$_2$ → Ar-Ar'
from ar. iodides with bis(η$^3$-allylpalladium chloride)/KF cf. *45*, 555; via cross-coupling of (η$^6$-chloroarene)tricarbonylchromium(0) complexes with aryl(fluoro)silanes in the presence of Bu$_4$NF s. S.-K. Kang, W.-Y. Kim, Synth. Commun. *28*, 3743-9 (1998).

*Chiral palladium π-allyl complex*
**3-Ethyleneamines from aldimines**  C(NHR)CH$_2$CH=CH$_2$
**Asym. synthesis with addition of three C-atoms under neutral conditions**

461.

5 Mol% chiral palladium π-allyl complex added to a soln. of startg. aldimine and 1 eq. allyltributylstannane in dry DMF at 0°, stirred for 90 h, quenched with water, the mixture extracted with ether and satd. aq. KF, and stirred again for 3 h → product. Y 62% (e.e. 81%). The key step in the catalytic cycle is the coordination of the imine to an intermediate *amphiphilic* chiral π-allyl-π-pinenylpalladium complex, followed by preferential transfer of the *nucleophilic* allyl residue to give a π-allylpalladium amide. This is a useful alternative to Lewis acid-catalyzed procedures, and applicable to substrates with base- or acid-labile functions. F.e.s. H. Nakamura et al., J. Am. Chem. Soc. *120*, 4242-3 (1998).

*Dichloropalladium(II) phosphine complexes/potassium carbonate or cesium fluoride*
**Suzuki diaryl coupling with arylboronic acid esters**  ArB(OR)$_2$ → Ar-Ar'
with Pd(PPh$_3$)$_4$ cf. *45*, 557; chiral biphenylylalanines and hetaryl analogs from aryl bromides, iodides or triflates with PdCl$_2$(dppf)/K$_2$CO$_3$ s. F. Firooznia et al., Tetrahedron Lett. *40*, 213-6 (1999); diaryls from ar. *chlorides* with PdCl$_2$(PCy$_3$)$_2$/CsF s. ibid. *39*, 3985-8 (1998); selective coupling [at the sp$^2$-site] of 1,2-ethylene-1,4-diboronic acid esters with ar. iodides s. G. Desurmont, M. Srebnik et al., J. Org. Chem. *62*, 8907-9 (1997).

*Dichlorobis(triphenylphosphine)palladium(II)*  PdCl$_2$(PPh$_3$)$_2$
**Synthesis of unsatd. hydroxamic acid esters**  Sn≤ → CON(OR)
**from stannanes via Stille-type coupling**

462.

**Arylhydroxamic acid esters from arylstannanes.** A mixture of tri-*n*-butyl(*p*-methoxyphenyl)-stannane, 1.1 eqs. N-methoxy-N-methylcarbamyl chloride, and 3 mol% PdCl$_2$(PPh$_3$)$_2$ in THF stirred at 60° for 6 h → methyl N-methyl-*p*-methoxyphenylhydroxamate. Y 80%. Esters, enolethers, enesilanes and phenolethers remained unaffected under these mild conditions. F.e., **also α,β-ethylenehydroxamic acid esters** from enestannanes (with retention of configuration), **and α,β-acetylenehydroxamic acid esters** from stannylacetylenes or directly from terminal acetylene derivs. via Sonogashira-type cross-coupling, s. M. Murakami, Y. Ito et al., Chem. Lett. *1998*, 163-4.

*Dichloro[1,1'-bis(diphenylphosphino)ferrocene]palladium(II)/potassium methoxide*
**Synthesis of allylarenes by Suzuki coupling**  ArCH$_2$CH=CH$_2$
**of B-allyl-9-borabicyclo[3.3.1]nonane**

463.

**with aryl triflates.** 1.2 eqs. KOMe added to a soln. of 1.2 eqs. B-allyl-9-borabicyclo[3.3.1]nonane in THF, stirred for 10 min until homogeneous, startg. triflate and 3 mol% PdCl$_2$(dppf) added, and the mixture refluxed under argon for 30 min → product. Y 86%. The method has distinct advantages over Stille coupling in terms of higher yields, shorter reaction times, easier work-up, and toxicity considerations. Functional groups such as phenolethers, lactones, cyclic mercaptals, and esters were all compatible, but aldehydes underwent 1,2-addition instead. F.e., also with ar. bromides or iodides, s. A. Fürstner, G. Seidel, Synlett *1998*, 161-2.

*Via intermediates* *v.i.*

**Enisocyclics from cyclic ketones and phosphonic acid esters** CO → C=C

**via β-hydroxyphosphonic acid esters - Asym. Horner synthesis**

464.

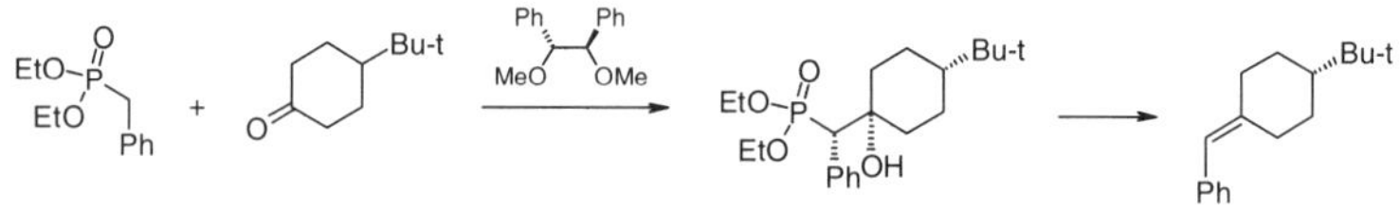


1.2 eqs. 1.48 *M* *n*-BuLi in hexane added to a soln. of 1.4 eqs. (1S,2S)-1,2-dimethoxy-1,2-diphenylethane in toluene at -78°, the mixture stirred for 30 min, a soln. of 1.2 eqs. startg. phosphonate in toluene added dropwise over 5 min, stirring continued at -78° for 30 min then at 0° for a further 30 min, re-cooled to -78°, a soln. of 4-*tert*-butylcyclohexanone in toluene added dropwise over 5 min, the mixture stirred at -78° for 30 min, then quenched with satd. aq. NaCl → intermediate hydroxyphosphonate, and 3.7 eqs. NaOAc in propionic acid stirred under reflux for 30 min → (S)-product (Y 85%; e.e. 84%). The chiral ligand was recovered in 90% yield. The method is efficient and highly enantioselective (e.e. 54-90%), and offers a simple alternative to procedures with chiral phosphonates which are tedious to prepare. F.e.s. M. Mizuno, K. Tomioka et al., Angew. Chem. Int. Ed. Engl. *37*, 515-7 (1998); carbethoxymethylene derivs. with triethyl phosphonoacetate in the presence of $RbOH{\cdot}H_2O$ and N-(4-*tert*-butylbenzyl)cinchoninium bromide cf. S. Arai et al., Tetrahedron Lett. *39*, 2997-3000 (1998).

## Carbon ↾ CC ⇃↾ C

*Without additional reagents* *w.a.r*

**1-Carbalkoxy-3-trifluoroacetyl-Δ²-pyrrolines** ←

**from 1-carbalkoxypyrrolidine-2-carboxylic acids**

**Anomalous Dakin-West reaction**

465.

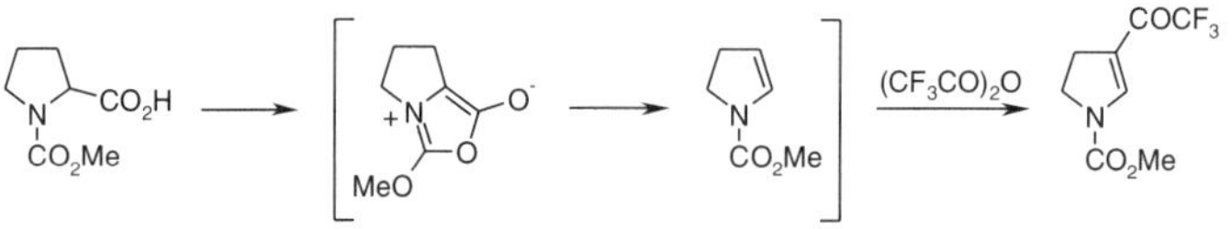


1-Methoxycarbonylproline treated with 3 eqs. trifluoroacetic anhydride in acetonitrile at 80° for 5 h → N-methoxycarbonyl-4-trifluoroacetyl-2,3-dihydropyrrole. Y 66%. Various solvents, such as acetonitrile, DMF, dichloroethane, benzene, nitromethane and acetone may be used, acetonitrile or DMF being the solvents of choice (Y 67% in DMF for the example above). In contrast, little or no reaction takes place in THF, DME or dioxane. Among the N-carbalkoxy groups examined, O-Me, -Et and -Bu esters gave good yields, while O-allyl, -fluoren-9-yl or -phenyl gave low yields, possibly due to the ease of cleavage of the alkoxy group in the intermediate mesoionic oxazolium-5-olates. Under the above reaction conditions, N-carbomethoxy-2-pyrroline gave the 3-trifluoroacetyl-deriv. in 65% yield, whereas N-carbomethoxy-2,3-dihydroindole-1-carboxylic acid gave N-carbomethoxyindole in 86% yield. F.e.s. M. Kawase et al., Chem. Commun. *1998*, 641-2.

**Decarboxylative 1,3-dipolar cycloaddition via azomethinium ylids** ○

s. *44*, 897; solution-phase synthesis of a 25,600 compd. library of spiro[pyrrolidine-2,3′-oxindoles] s. D. Fokas et al., Tetrahedron Lett. *39*, 2235-8 (1998).

**Pyrroles from 5-hydroxyoxazolium betaines** ←
and acetylene derivs. s. *19*, 911s*51*; and enephosphonium salts, enhanced regioselectivity, s. F. Clerici et al., Tetrahedron *54*, 5763-74 (1998).

**3-Nitropyrrolidines from oxazolidines and 1,1-nitroethylene derivs.** ←
**via regio- and stereo-specific 1,3-dipolar cycloaddition with azomethinium ylids**

466.

**1-Nitropyrrolizidines.** (E)-β-Nitrostyrene in ether added dropwise to a soln. of *tert*-butyl 1,3-diphenyltetrahydro-1*H*,3*H*-pyrrolo[1,2-*c*]oxazole-7a-carboxylate in the same solvent at room temp. under argon, and worked up after 144 h → (1R*,2S*,3R*,7aR*)-*tert*-butyl hexahydro-1-nitro-2,3-diphenyl-1*H*-pyrrolizine-7a-carboxylate. Y 88% (single regioisomer). F.e. and regioselectivity s. F. Felluga, E. Valentin et al., Helv. Chim. Acta *80*, 1457-72 (1997).

**Alder-Rickert synthesis** ←
s. *9*, 917; polyfunctionalized benzo[*b*]thiophenes from 6,7-dihydrobenzo[*b*]thiophenes and acetylene derivs., regioselectivity, s. S.S. Labadie, Synth. Commun. *28*, 2531-9 (1998).

*Microwaves s. under NH₄OAc* ←

*Lithium/naphthalene*                                         $LiC_{10}H_7$
**Synthesis of carbonyl compds. from α-cyanocarbonyl compds.**      CN → R
carboxylic acid esters cf. *54*, 473; α,α-disubst. ketones s. Tetrahedron Lett. *39*, 4183-6 (1998).

*Sodium hydride*                                                      NaH
**1-Naphthol ring from homophthalic anhydrides** ←
s. *22*, 877s*39*; 4-arylthio-1-naphthol ring from cyclic α,β-ethylenesulfoxides (incl. 2-sulfinyl-1,4-naphthoquinones), s. Y. Kita et al., Synlett *1998*, 292-4.

**1,4-Dihydropyridazines from N-carbamylenazo compds. and β-diketones** ○

467.

1 eq. NaH added to a stirred soln. of startg. β-dicarbonyl compd. in THF, stirred for 10 min at room temp., a soln. of startg. enazo compd. in the same solvent added dropwise, and the mixture stirred for a further 1 h at room temp. → product. Y 90%. The method is mild, simple and efficient. F.e., **also conversion to pyridazines** using phenyltrimethylammonium tribromide s. O.A. Attanasi, P. Filippone et al., Synlett *1997*, 1361-2.

*Lithium ethoxide*                                                *LiOEt*
**(E)-α,β-Epoxyketones from β-acoxy-α,β-ethyleneiodonium salts and aldehydes**

468.

1 eq. 0.43 *M* LiOEt in THF added at -30° under argon to a stirred soln. of (Z)-(2-acetoxy-1-decenyl)phenyliodonium bromide and 1.5 eqs. benzaldehyde in 12:1 THF/DMSO, the resulting

pale yellow soln. stirred for 2 h, and quenched with water → 1,2-epoxy-1-phenylundecan-3-one. Y 91% (95:5 E/Z). The intermediate iodonium ylid is stable up to -30°. F.e. and prepn. of the startg. m. from α,β-acetyleneiodonium salts, s. M. Ochiai et al., J. Am. Chem. Soc. *119*, 11598-604 (1997).

*Sodium/alcohol/sodium hydroxide*     NaOR/NaOH
**Synthesis of α-fluoroketones**     COOR → R
**via α-alkylation of α-fluoro-β-ketocarboxylic acid esters
and subsequent decarbalkoxylation**

469.

**One-pot procedure.** Ethyl 2-fluoro-3-oxobutanoate and 1 eq. NaOEt added under $N_2$ to dry ethanol, stirred at room temp. for 1 h, 1 eq. allyl bromide added, stirred overnight at room temp., 1.2 eqs. NaOH in water added, and heated at reflux for 3 h → 3-fluoro-5-hexen-2-one. Y 67%. F.e. and with isolation of the intermediates s. J. Hutchinson et al., Tetrahedron *54*, 2867-76 (1998).

*Potassium* tert-*butoxide*     KOBu-t
**(E)-α,β-Ethylenesulfonic acid amides from aldehydes**     CHO → CH=CHSO$_2$N<
**Synthesis with addition of one C-atom via β-(carbalkoxyoxy)sulfonic acid amides**

470.     Ar = p-ClC$_6$H$_4$

2 eqs. 1 *M* KOBu-*t* in THF added to a soln. of N-(*tert*-butoxycarbonyl)-N-(*p*-chlorobenzyl)methanesulfonamide in the same solvent at -78° under argon, the mixture stirred at -78° for 1 h, a soln. of 1 eq. 1-decanal in THF added via cannula, and allowed to warm to room temp. over 18 h with stirring → product. Y 67%. The method provides a one-pot alternative to the 2-step protocol via β-hydroxysulfonic acid amides (cf. *23*, 776). F.e.s. M.J. Tozer et al., Synlett *1998*, 186-8.

n-*Butyllithium*     BuLi
**Decarboxylative C-acylation**     COOH → Ac
aminoketones with Ac$_2$O cf. *17*, 898; α-fluoro-β-ketophosphonic acid esters from carboxylic acid halides with BuLi s. D.Y. Kim, Y.J. Choi, Synth. Commun. *28*, 1491-8 (1998).

*Lithium diisopropylamide*     i-$Pr_2NLi$
**β-Diketones from ketones and acylcyanides**     COCH → CO-C-CO
s. *35*, 642; γ,δ-diketocarboxylic acid esters with 3-(carbomethoxy)propionyl cyanide s. Q. Tang, S.E. Sen, Tetrahedron Lett. *39*, 2249-52 (1998).

*Magnesium s. under Cp$_2$TiCl$_2$*     Mg
*Zinc*     Zn
**Sym. β-diketones from acylcyanides**     2 RCOCN → RCOCH$_2$COR

471.

Benzoyl cyanide in THF added to 1 eq. bis(iodozincio)methane (0.55 *M*) in the same solvent, and the mixture stirred at room temp. for 2 h before quenching with 1 *M* HCl → dibenzoylmethane. Y 90%. Reaction of benzoyl cyanide with CH$_2$(ZnI)$_2$ in a ratio of 2:1 gave the product in 44% yield, while a reactant ratio of 1.5:2 gave the product in 59% yield. The optimum ratio of 1:1 is justified by the stabilisation of the product as the iodozinc enolate. F.e. **and from carboxylic acid chlorides** in THF/DMI in the presence of $Pd_2(dba)_3/P(C_6H_4OMe-p)_3$ s. S. Matsubara et al., Synlett *1998*, 267-8.

*Calcium hydroxide*          $Ca(OH)_2$
**β-Ketocarboxylic acid esters by C-acyl exchange**          $COCH_2COOR$
with $NH_4Cl/NaOH$ cf. *13*, 838; with $Ca(OH)_2$ and Sr or Ba reagents s. Japanese patent JP-10053561 (Takasago Perfumery Co. Ltd.).

*Zinc/ozone*          $Zn/O_3$
**3-Ethylenealcohols**          $CH(OH)C-C{=}C$
**from terminal ethylene derivs. and β,γ-ethylenebromides**
**One-pot procedure via ozonolysis**

472.

A soln. of styrene in dichloromethane at -78° purged with a stream of $O_2$ for 10 min, ozonolyzed until a blue colour persisted, purged again with $O_2$, concentrated under reduced pressure without heating, the residue dissolved in THF, diluted with satd. $NH_4Cl$ soln., cooled to 0°, 2.4 eqs. allyl bromide and 4.38 eqs. Zn dust added successively, and stirred for 15 min → product. Y 87%. The intermediate ozonides react with Zn powder to give the corresponding aldehydes *in situ*, which capture the generated allylzinc species (substituted allyl bromides reacting **with double shift**). F.e.s. J.D. Schloss, L.A. Paquette, Synth. Commun. *28*, 2887-92 (1998).

*Ammonium acetate/microwaves*          ←
**α,β-Ethylenecarboxylic acids from aldehydes and malonic acid**    $CHO \to CH{=}CHCOOH$
with piperidine or pyridine cf. *1*, 569/70; *2*, 657; *3*, 635/6; *7*, 779; *9*, 831; *trans*-cinnamic acids with $NH_4OAc$ under microwave irradiation without solvent s. H.M. Sampath Kumar et al., Synth. Commun. *28*, 3811-5 (1998); **(E)-β,γ-ethylenecarboxylic acids** with piperidinium acetate in DMSO or DMF, also ester analogs from malonic acid monoesters, cf. N. Ragoussis, V. Ragoussis, J. Chem. Soc. Perkin Trans. I *1998*, 3529-33.

*Piperidinium acetate*          ←
**(E)-β,γ-Ethylenecarboxylic acids and acid esters from aldehydes**    $CH{=}CHCH_2COO(H,R)$
s. *1*, 569s55

*Ethylenediammonium diacetate*          ←
**Knoevenagel condensation-hetero-Diels-Alder reaction**          CO
intramolecular process cf. *47*, 698; *54*, 357; δ-alkoxy-δ-lactones from aldehydes and enolethers via intermolecular cycloaddition s. L.F. Tietze et al., Liebigs Ann. *1997*, 881-6; polymer-based synthesis of 2-alkoxy-3,4-dihydro-2H-pyran-5-carboxylic acid esters s. Synlett *1996*, 1043-4.

*2-Ethoxy-N-ethoxycarbonyl-1,2-dihydroquinoline*          EDC
**Imidazoles from α-acylaminocarboxylic acids and N-sulfonylaldimines**          O
s. *47*, 927; polymer-based synthesis with EDC s. M.T. Bilodeau, A.M. Cunningham, J. Org. Chem. *63*, 2800-1 (1998).

*Titanocene dichloride/magnesium/triethyl phosphite*          $Cp_2TiCl_2/Mg/(EtO)_3P$
**(Z)-2-Ethylenesilanes from mercaptals**          $CH(SR)_2 \to CH{=}CHCH_2Si{\leqslant}$
**Synthesis with addition of two C-atoms**
**via titanocene-mediated metathesis with allylsilanes**

473.

6 eqs. Triethyl phosphite and 5 eqs. allyl(triisopropyl)silane added successively to a stirred mixture of finely powdered 4 Å molecular sieves, 6 eqs. Mg turnings, and 3 eqs. $Cp_2TiCl_2$ in THF, stirred for 2 h, startg. mercaptal in THF added, and the mixture refluxed for 6 h → *cis*-product. Y 64% (E/Z 12:88). *cis*-Isomers are obtained regardless of the substituents on the

thioacetal. The reaction is believed to proceed via initial formation of a disubst. titanacyclobutane which cleaves to form the γ-subst. *cis*-allylsilane and titanocene methylidene complex. F.e.s. T. Fujiwara et al., Chem. Commun. *1998*, 51-2.

*Stannous triflate*                                                            $Sn(OSO_2CF_3)_2$
**Regio- and stereo-specific synthesis of 3-ethylenealcohols**     CHO → CH(OH)C-C=C
**from aldehydes**
**Nucleophilic allylation with 3-ethylenealcohols via σ-bond metathesis**

474.

A soln. of 3-phenylpropionaldehyde and 1.5 eqs. startg. homoallyl alcohol in methylene chloride treated with 10 mol% Sn(OTf)$_2$ and 4 Å molecular sieve powder at -25° until reaction complete → product. Y 99% (100% E). The exclusive α-selectivity suggests that the Lewis acid is involved in the formation of an intermediate oxonium species, rather than in formation of a nucleophilic allyltin(II) species [from which γ-adducts would be anticipated]. The precise role of the molecular sieves is as yet undetermined. F.e.s. J. Nokami et al., J. Am. Chem. Soc. *120*, 6609-10 (1998).

*Ozone s. under Zn*                                                                               $O_3$

*Ruthenium carbene complex*                                                     ←
**Metathesis of ethylene derivs.**                                                ←
s. *49*, 932s52; solution-phase synthesis of unsatd. bis(iminodiacetic acid diamides) s. D.L. Boger, W. Chai, Tetrahedron *54*, 3955-70 (1998); libraries of compds. based on metathesis of internal olefins s. C. Brändli, T.R. Ward, Helv. Chim. Acta *81*, 1616 (1998).

*Tetrakis(triphenylphosphine)palladium(0)*                         $Pd(PPh_3)_4$
**Alkoxy-4-ethylenes**                                   C=C → C(OR)C-CH$_2$CH=CH$_2$
**from electron-deficient ethylene derivs. and alcohols**
**Regiospecific synthesis with addition of three C-atoms**

475.

5 Mol% Pd(PPh$_3$)$_4$ added at room temp. under argon to a soln. of startg. alkene, allyl ethyl carbonate, and 1 eq. benzyl alcohol in THF, and stirred until reaction complete → product. Y 78%. The formation of the corresponding ethoxy-4-ethylene was minimal (<1%), but increased with increase in the electronic charge on the oxygen atom of the alcohol (reaching ca. 50% with 1 eq. BuOH). However, increase in the proportion of the latter redressed the balance (ca. 10% ethoxy-4-ethylene being formed with 10 eqs. BuOH). Both electron-withdrawing and -donating groups on the phenyl ring are tolerated, and aliphatic alkylidenemalononitriles participated in the same way. Reaction did not take place with diethyl benzylidenemalonate, acrylonitrile, or ethyl propiolate, and isopropanol was unreactive for steric reasons. F.e. and synthesis of 4-ethylenealcohols via addition of allyl methoxymethyl carbonate s. H. Nakamura, Y. Yamamoto et al., J. Am. Chem. Soc. *120*, 6838-9 (1998).

*Palladous chloride/sodium bromide*                               $PdCl_2/NaBr$
**Styrenes from ethylene derivs. and arylcarboxylic acid anhydrides**    H → Ar
**Heck arylation without salt formation**

476.

A Schlenk tube charged with benzoic anhydride, 0.25 mol% PdCl$_2$ and 1 mol% NaBr repeatedly degassed under vacuum and purged with argon, 0.1 eq. *n*-hexyl ether (as internal standard), 1.2

eqs. dibutyl maleate and N-methyl-2-pyrrolidone (1 mL/mmol) injected successively, and the tube heated at 190° for 3 h (GC monitoring) → product. Y 73% (7:2 mixture of dibutyl phenyl-fumarate and -maleate). The aryl source is cheap and does not produce halide salts as by-products (as aryl halides would), the side products, CO and benzoic acid, being burnt to $CO_2$ or recycled as the anhydride, respectively. A number of Pd-catalysts may be used, such as $PdCl_2$, $Na_2PdCl_4$ and $Na_2PdCl_6$; however, all required a catalytic amount of chloride or bromide ion for optimal activity, suggesting that the active catalyst is a halide-ligated Pd(0)-species. No phosphine ligand is required. Olefins with electron-withdrawing groups generally gave high yields of β-arylated products, whereas reaction of those bearing electron-donating groups was less successful. F.e.s. M.S. Stephan, J.G. de Vries et al., Angew. Chem. Int. Ed. Engl. 37, 662-4 (1998).

## Elimination

## Hydrogen                                                                 CC ⇑ H

*Irradiation s. under $O_2$ and $I_2$*

*Potassium tert-butoxide/air*                                              $KOBu$-$t/O_2$
**Acetylene from ethylene derivs.**                                        CH=CH → C≡C
with supported $Pd(II)/HClO_4$ cf. 41, 924; with KOBu-t in DMF under air, arylacetylenes, s. S. Akiyama et al., Bull. Chem. Soc. Jpn. 68, 2043-51 (1995).

*Cupric chloride/aluminum chloride*                                        $CuCl_2/AlCl_3$
**Aromatization by cyclodehydrogenation**
Extended polyarenes s. 35, 655s55

*Thallic p-toluenesulfonate*                                               $Tl(OTs)_3$
**Dehydrogenation of benzo-condensed 4-ketoheterocyclics**                 CHCH → C=C
isoflavones with $Tl(ClO_4)_3$ cf. 29, 52s49; 2-aryl-4(1H)-quinolones with $Tl(OTs)_3$ s. O.V. Singh, R.S. Kapil, Synth. Commun. 23, 277-83 (1993).

*m-Chloroperoxybenzoic acid*                                               $m$-$ClC_6H_4COO_2H$
**Pyrroles from Δ³-pyrrolines**
with Raney nickel cf. 1, 397; 2H-pyrrolo[3,4-b]quinolin-9(4H)-ones with m-CPBA s. J.-F. Carniaux, H.-P. Husson et al., Tetrahedron Lett. 38, 2997-3000 (1997).

*2,3-Dichloro-5,6-dicyanoquinone*                                          DDQ
**Dehydrogenation of heterocyclics**
s. 10, 639s46; quinolines from 3,4-dihydroquinolines s. A.H. Moustafa, J.C. Jochims et al., Tetrahedron 53, 625-40 (1997).

*Oxygen/irradiation*                                                       $O_2$/⚡
**Aromatization by cyclodehydrogenation**
s. 28, 890; thieno-quinolines and -isoquinolines s. A.L. Marzinzik, P. Rademacher, Synthesis 1995, 1131-4.

*Iodine/irradiation*                                                       $I_2$/⚡
**Aromatization by cyclodehydrogenation**
s. 35, 655; 1,2,3,4-tetrahydronaphtho[2,1-f]isoquinolines s. E. Martínez et al., Tetrahedron Lett. 39, 1231-2 (1998); polycyclic aromatics from 2,2'-tethered bifluorenylidenes s. C.-H. Kuo et al., J. Org. Chem. 60, 7380-1 (1995); extended polyarenes with $CuCl_2/AlCl_3$ in $CS_2$ at room temp. s. M. Müller et al., Angew. Chem. Int. Ed. Engl. 34, 1583-6 (1995).

*Phenyltrimethylammonium tribromide*                                       $PhMe_3N^+Br_3^-$
**Pyridazines from 1,4-dihydropyridazines** s. 55, 467                     ←

*Manganese(III) acetate*                                                   $Mn(OAc)_3$
**Asym. intramolecular oxidative coupling of phenols**
chiral macrocyclic 1,1'-bi-2-naphthols with $Mn(acac)_3$ cf. 29, 910s52; with $Mn(OAc)_3$ s. B.H. Lipshutz, Y.-J. Shin, Tetrahedron Lett. 39, 7017-20 (1998).

*Palladium*                Pd
**Aromatization of dihydro-N-heterocyclics**    ←
with Pd-C cf. *13*, 844; isoquinolines with Pd-black s. V.I. Terenin et al., Khim. Geterotsikl. Soedin. *1997*, 376-9 (Russ.).

*Palladous trifluoroacetate/tri-p-tolylphosphine/oxygen*    ←
**Cyclic α,β-ethyleneketones from cyclic ketones**      CHCH → C≡C
with PdCl$_2$/HCl cf. *34*, 897; with Pd(OCOCF$_3$)$_2$/tri-*p*-tolylphosphine under O$_2$, and f. ligands, s. Y.W. Park, H.H. Oh, Bull. Korean Chem. Soc. *18*, 1123-4 (1997).

# Oxygen ↑                 CC ⇑ O

*Without additional reagents*            w.a.r.
**Benzofurans from α-aryloxyketones** s. *55*, 371    ○

*Irradiation*              ⇝
**Furans from β-alkoxy-α-methyleneketones**

477.

A 0.01 *M* soln. of startg. Baylis-Hillman ether in benzene irradiated for 6 h with a 100 W high-pressure Hg lamp (Riko UVL-100P) through Pyrex, and treated with 1 eq. each of trimethylsilyl triflate and Et$_3$N → product. Y 72%. Reaction is considered to proceed via β-C-H activation of the photo-excited carbonyl group. F.e.s. S. Matsumoto, K. Mikami, Synlett *1998*, 469-70.

*Potassium hydroxide or Potassium tert-butoxide*        KOH or KOBu-t
**Cyclopent-2-enones from γ-dioxo compds.**
with NaOH cf. *1*, 554; from γ-ketoaldehydes with KOH, spirocyclopent-2-enones, s. A. Srikrishna et al., Tetrahedron Lett. *37*, 1683-6 (1996); Synlett *1996*, 67-8; carbohydrate-fused cyclopent-2-enones with KOBu-*t* s. Chem. Commun. *1995*, 1567-8.

*Sodium/tert. alcohol*              NaOR
**Dieckmann cyclization**
with K,Na in toluene cf. *4*, 817; with Na/tert. alcohol in toluene, suppression of side reactions on formation of cyclopentanone-2-carboxylic acid esters, s. Japanese patent JP-09183755 (Kao Corp.).

*Lithium diisopropylamide*           i-Pr$_2$NLi
**Acetylene derivs. from enol triflates**      CH=C(OTf) → C≡C
with py cf. *29*, 920; silylacetylenes from acylsilanes via 1-silylenol triflates, one-pot conversion, also 2-acetylenesilanes from 3-silylenol triflates with LDA, chiral propargylsilanes, s. I. Fleming, J.M. Mwaniki, J. Chem. Soc. Perkin Trans. I *1998*, 1237-47.

*Lithium phenylselenide*            LiSePh
**Ethylene derivs. from glycol mesylates**      C(OMs)C(OMs) → C=C
2′,3′-ethylenenucleosides with Li$_2$Te cf. *49*, 938; with LiSePh s. D.L.J. Clive et al., J. Org. Chem. *62*, 3751-3 (1997).

*Amberlyst A 26 (hydroxide form)*        ←
**Dieckmann cyclization**           ○
4-hydroxy-Δ$^3$-2-pyrrolones cf. *54*, 481; 4-hydroxycarbostyrils from *o*-acylaminocarboxylic acid esters, e.g. 3-arylthio-, 3-aryl-derivs., s. Chem. Commun. *1998*, 785-6; polymer-based synthesis of 4-hydroxy-Δ$^3$-2-pyrrolones with LiN(SiMe$_3$)$_2$ or Bu$_4$NOH (the latter being scavenged after reaction by Amberlyst A-15) s. Tetrahedron Lett. *39*, 4369-72 (1998).

*Magnesium iodide*             MgI$_2$
**Ethylene derivs. from cyclic glycol sulfates**    C
with Li$_2$Te, retention of configuration, cf. *49*, 938s51; more efficiently with MgI$_2$ s. D.O. Jang, Y.H. Joo, Synth. Commun. *28*, 871-7 (1998).

*Zinc chloride/montmorillonite*
**Benzo[*b*]thiophenes from α-(arylthio)acetals in the gas phase** s. 44, 930s55

*Montmorillonite s. under ZnCl₂*

*Boron fluoride* $BF_3$
**Cyclodealcoholation**
Chiral 2-(arylseleno)tetralins s. 55, 230

**Benzo[*b*]thiophenes from α-(arylthio)oxo compds.**
from ketone derivs. with PPA cf. 44, 930; from aldehyde derivs. with BF₃ cf. World Intellectual Property Organization patent WO-9803501 (Teikoku Hormone Mfg. Co. Ltd.); **from α-(arylthio)acetals** in the gas phase over ZnCl₂ supported on montmorillonite K 10 s. P.D. Clark et al., J. Org. Chem. 60, 1936-8 (1995).

*Samarium diiodide/tetrakis(triphenylphosphine)palladium(0)* $SmI_2/Pd(PPh_3)_4$
**2-Vinylcyclopentanols from ε,ζ-ethylene-δ-lactolides**

478.

**Chiral polyoxy-2-vinylcyclopentanols.** A soln. of startg. pyranoside and ca. 5 mol% Pd(PPh₃)₄ in dry THF added under argon to 3 eqs. ca. 0.1 M SmI₂ in the same solvent, and refluxed for 2.5 h → product. Y 78% [(1S,5S)/(1R,5R)/(1S,5R)/(1R,5S) 3:66:10:21; *trans/cis* 69:31 for the relative configuration of the vinyl and hydroxyl group]. F.e.s. J.M. Aurrecoechea, B. López, Tetrahedron Lett. 39, 2857-60 (1998).

*Bis(cyclopentadienyl)phenyltitanium(III)* $Cp_2TiPh$
**Cyclic α-hydroxyketones from ketocarboxylic acid esters** s. 55, 482

*Titanium(II) porphyrin complexes*
**Ethylene derivs. from epoxides** s. 28, 950s55

*Titanium trichloride/sodium-alumina or zinc* $TiCl_3/Na-Al_2O_3$ or Zn
**Indoles from *o*-acylaminoketones**
with Ti-C₈ cf. 47, 940; indole alkaloids s. A. Fürstner et al., Tetrahedron 52, 7329-44 (1996); 2,2′-biindoles by double ring closure s. Angew. Chem. Int. Ed. Engl. 34, 678-81 (1995); with TiCl₃/Na-Al₂O₃, also cyclic ethylene derivs. (cf. 33, 930), s. Synthesis *1995*, 63-8.

*Stannic chloride* $SnCl_4$
**Stereospecific rearrangement of fused 3,4-epoxyalcohols with subsequent double ring closure**
**Condensed 8-oxabicyclo[3.2.1]oct-2-ene ring**

479.

**4,10-Oxido-1,2,3,3a,4,9,10,10a-octahydrobenz[*f*]azulenes.** A soln. of startg. epoxide in methylene chloride treated at -78° with 2 eqs. SnCl₄, stirred for 105 min, and poured onto ice → 1,2,3,3a,4,9,10,10a-octahydro-3a,10-dimethyl-4,10-epoxybenz[*f*]azulene. Y 80%. The initial Lewis acid-catalyzed ring contraction is stereoselective, proceeding with inversion of configuration at the new quaternary centre; a fused lactol is formed therefrom, followed by nucleophilic attack of the π-nucleophile (a benzene ring or an olefin) on a presumed oxonium species. F.e.s. C.M. Marson et al., Angew. Chem. Int. Ed. Engl. 37, 1122-4 (1998).

*Phosphorus pentoxide/sulfuric acid* $P_2O_5/H_2SO_4$
**4-Chromanones from β-aryloxycarboxylic acids**
with AlCl$_3$/PCl$_5$ cf. *28*, 909; with P$_2$O$_5$ in 97% H$_2$SO$_4$ s. Japanese patent JP-09268186 (Mitsui Toatsu Chem. Inc.).

*Polyphosphoric acid or Phosphorus oxide chloride* PPA or POCl$_3$
**Phenol ring from unsatd. β-diketones**
with NaOEt cf. *41*, 927; 6-hydroxybenzo[*b*]thiophenes from γ-(2-thienyl)-β-diketones with POCl$_3$, and 2-naphthols from γ-aryl-β-diketones using polyphosphoric acid, s. A.V. Kel'in, Y.Y. Kozyrkov, Synthesis *1998*, 729-34.

*p-Toluenesulfonic acid* *TsOH*
**Ethylene derivs. from alcohols** CHC(OH) → C═C
s. *7*, 891; medium-ring and large-ring α-(cycloalk-1-enyl)carboxylic acids s. B. Greve et al., Angew. Chem. Int. Ed. Engl. *35*, 1221-3 (1996).

**Cyclopentenes from cyclobutylcarbinols**
with AcOH/I$_2$ cf. *39*, 932; mono- and bi-cyclic cyclopentenes with anhydrous TsOH s. K. Mandelt, L. Fitjer, Synthesis *1998*, 1523-6.

*Sulfuric acid* $H_2SO_4$
**Ring closures via cyclic N-acylimmonium ions**
s. *27*, 947s*54*; 1,2,3,6,7,11b-hexahydro-4*H*-pyrazino[2,1-*a*]isoquinolin-4-ones by double ring closure s. J.H. Kim, C.S. Kim et al., Tetrahedron *54*, 7395-400 (1998).

**Carbostyrils from β-ketocarboxylic acid anilides**
with H$_2$SO$_4$ s. *18*, 954; and with PPA cf. *21*, 927; 5,8-dimethoxy derivs. with H$_2$SO$_4$ s. P. López-Alvarado et al., Synthesis *1998*, 186-94.

*Sulfuric acid/acetic acid* $H_2SO_4/AcOH$
**2-Pyridone from 1,3-oxazin-4(3*H*)-one ring**
4-hydroxy derivs. cf. *23*, 921; 5,6,7,8-tetrahydrocarbostyrils from spirocyclohexane-2′-1,3-oxazin-4′(3′*H*)-ones with H$_2$SO$_4$/AcOH s. J.F. Stambach et al., Synthesis *1998*, 265-6.

*Sulfuric acid-silica gel* $H_2SO_4\text{-}SiO_2$
**Ethylene derivs. from alcohols** CHC(OH) → C═C
with H$_2$SO$_4$ cf. *27*, 917; with H$_2$SO$_4$-silica gel in toluene s. F. Chávez et al., Synth. Commun. *24*, 2325-39 (1994).

*Palladous acetate/tri-n-butylphosphine/sodium hydrogen carbonate/molecular sieves* ←
**2-Cycloalkenones from di(epoxides)** ←
**via regiospecific double isomerization-intramolecular aldol condensation**

480.

**2-Aryl-2-cycloalkenones.** Startg. di(epoxide), 1 eq. NaHCO$_3$ and 3 Å molecular sieves added to a soln. of 10 mol% Pd(OAc)$_2$ and 30 mol% PBu$_3$ in *tert*-butanol under N$_2$, the mixture refluxed for 24 h, a further equivalent of NaHCO$_3$ added, and the mixture worked-up after a further 24 h → product. Y 72%. The remarkable regioselectivity observed for the isomerization is responsible for the exclusive formation of 2,3-disubst. 2-cyclopentenones. F.e. incl. 2-cyclohexenones in lower yields, **also from epoxyaldehydes**, s. J.-H. Kim, R.J. Kulawiec, Tetrahedron Lett. *39*, 3107-10 (1998).

*Tris(dibenzylideneacetone)dipalladium/triphenylphosphine/bis(trimethylsilyl)acetamide/* ←
*potassium acetate*
**Intramolecular C-α-allylation via palladium π-allyl complexes**
s. *44*, 938s*54*; 4-vinyl-2-pyrrolidones from 4-acoxy-2-ethyleneacylamines, stereoselectivity, with Pd$_2$(dba)$_3$/Ph$_3$P/bis(trimethylsilyl)acetamide/KOAc s. G. Giambastiani, G. Poli et al., J. Org.

Chem. *63*, 804-7 (1998); regio- and stereo-specific synthesis of 6,6-disulfonyl-$\Delta^3$-oxononenes with $Pd_2(dba)_3$/dppe or $(EtO)_3P$ s. J. Pohlmann et al., Angew. Chem. Int. Ed. Engl. *37*, 633-5 (1998).

*Tris(dibenzylideneacetone)dipalladium/tri-o-tolylphosphine/acetic acid* ←
**Intramolecular palladium-ene reaction with α,β-ethyleneacylals** ←

481.

E = $CO_2Et$

Oppolzer's intramolecular palladium-ene reaction (*43*, 721) has been applied successfully to α,β-ethyleneacylals. **E: Cyclic γ-methylenealdehydes.** A soln. of startg. acylal, 10 mol% $Pd_2(dba)_3\cdot CHCl_3$, and 40-60 mol% tri-*o*-tolylphosphine in acetic acid stirred at 80° *for 0.1 h* → intermediate enol acetate (Y 98%), in methanol treated with $Et_3N$ at room temp. for 10 min → product (Y 100%). The intermediate σ-alkylpalladium complex can also be trapped by *in situ*-**carbonylation.** F.e. incl. ring closures of enyne analogs and trapping of the intermediate vinylpalladium species by carbonylation, Stille coupling, and by chloride ion, s. C.W. Holzapfel, L. Marais, Tetrahedron Lett. *39*, 2179-82 (1998).

*Tetrakis(triphenylphosphine)palladium(0) s. under $SmI_2$* $Pd(PPh_3)_4$

# Nitrogen ↑ CC ⇑ N

*Irradiation s. under $SmI_2$* ///

*Lithium diisopropylamide* $i\text{-}Pr_2NLi$
**Cyclic ketones from N,N-disubst. carboxylic acid amides** ○
s. *34*, 929s*54*; 9(5*H*)-acridones s. S.L. MacNeil, V. Snieckus et al., Synlett *1998*, 419-21.

*Zinc bromide* $ZnBr_2$
**Intramolecular ar. alkylation with 1-subst. benzotriazoles**
1-(arylthio)tetralins with $ZnCl_2$ cf. *49*, 946; 1-subst. tetralins with $ZnBr_2$ s. J. Org. Chem. *63*, 3445-9 (1998).

*Boron fluoride* $BF_3$
**α,β-Ethyleneketones from α-diazoketones** $CHCN_2 \rightarrow C{=}CH$
with $Ag_2O$ cf. *13*, 879; 4-chromones from 3-diazo-4-chromanones with $BF_3$ or $Rh_2(OAc)_4$ s. P. Mandal, R.V. Venkateswaran, J. Chem. Res., Synop *1998*, 88-9.

*Samarium diiodide/*tert-*butanol/irradiation* $SmI_2/t\text{-}BuOH/$///
*Bis(cyclopentadienyl)phenyltitanium(III)* $Cp_2TiPh$
**Cyclic α-hydroxyketones from cyanoketones** ○
**Stereospecific radical ring closure under mild conditions**

482.

Cyano and ester groups serve as efficient ketyl radical acceptors in the $Cp_2TiPh$-promoted reductive (5- and 6-*exo*) radical cyclization of γ- and δ-cyanoketones and δ-ketoesters. **E: 3 eqs.** $Cp_2TiCl_2$ treated sequentially with dry, degassed ethereal solns. of 3.3 eqs. *i*-PrMgCl and 3.3 eqs. PhMgBr in dry, degassed toluene under argon at room temp., 0.1 *M* startg. ketone in toluene added dropwise to the soln. of $Cp_2TiPh$, stirred for 1 h, and hydrolyzed with acid → product. Y 77%. Coordination of the reagent to *both* keto and cyano (or ester) groups facilitates irreversible cyclization without formation of unstable iminyl or alkoxyl radicals. Such trapping of ketyl radicals is less facile with SmI$_2$ where dual coordination is not possible. Yields were lower from acyclic keto-nitriles and -esters. F.e. incl. perhydroindenones and tricyclic benzo-condensed analogs s. Y. Yamamoto et al., Chem. Commun. *1998*, 875-6; cyclization with SmI$_2$/t-BuOH promoted by visible light s. G.A. Molander, C.N. Wolfe, J. Org. Chem. 63, 9031-6 (1998); electrolytic method s. *46*, 169.

Ammonium sulfate $\quad\quad\quad\quad\quad\quad\quad\quad\quad\quad\quad\quad\quad\quad\quad\quad\quad\quad$ (NH$_4$)$_2$SO$_4$
**Glycals from 2′-deoxynucleosides** $\quad\quad\quad\quad\quad\quad\quad\quad\quad\quad\quad\quad\quad\quad\quad\quad$ ←
s. *50*, 591; gram-scale preparation of O-toluoyl or O-silyl derivs. s. M.A. Cameron et al., J. Org. Chem. *62*, 9065-9 (1997).

p-*Toluenesulfonic acid* $\quad\quad\quad\quad\quad\quad\quad\quad\quad\quad\quad\quad\quad\quad\quad\quad\quad\quad\quad\quad$ TsOH
**Phthalazones** $\quad\quad\quad\quad\quad\quad\quad\quad\quad\quad\quad\quad\quad\quad\quad\quad\quad\quad\quad\quad\quad\quad$ ○
from *o*-ketoacylhydrazones cf. *10*, 303; from N-aroylamidrazones with TsOH, 4-aryloxymethyl-1(2H)-phthalazones, s. A.M. Bernard, M.T. Cocco et al., Synthesis *1998*, 317-20.

Rhodium(II) acetate $\quad\quad\quad\quad\quad\quad\quad\quad\quad\quad\quad\quad\quad\quad\quad\quad\quad\quad\quad$ Rh$_2$(OAc)$_4$
**α-Acoxy-α,β-ethylenecarbonyl** $\quad\quad\quad\quad\quad\quad\quad\quad\quad\quad$ C(OAc)C(N$_2$) → C=C(OAc)
**from β-acoxy-α-diazocarbonyl compds.**

483.

via 1,2-acoxy group migration. A soln. of startg. α-diazoketone in chloroform treated with a little Rh$_2$(OAc)$_4$ at 25°, and stirred for 30 min with evolution of N$_2$ → product. Y 98%. F.e. incl. ester analogs s. F.S. García, F.J.L. Herrera et al., Tetrahedron *54*, 6867-96 (1998).

# Halogen ↑ $\quad\quad\quad\quad\quad\quad\quad\quad\quad\quad\quad\quad\quad\quad\quad\quad\quad\quad\quad\quad\quad\quad$ CC ⇑ Hal

*Irradiation s. under Et$_3$N and Bu$_3$SnH* $\quad\quad\quad\quad\quad\quad\quad\quad\quad\quad\quad\quad\quad\quad\quad\quad$ ⫽

*Sodium hydroxide/tetra*-n-*butylammonium chloride* $\quad\quad\quad\quad\quad\quad\quad\quad$ NaOH/Bu$_4$NCl
**Cyanocyclobutanes from δ-halogenonitriles** $\quad\quad\quad\quad\quad\quad\quad\quad\quad\quad\quad\quad$ □
with LiNEt$_2$ cf. *29*, 959; under solid-liq. phase transfer catalysis with NaOH/Bu$_4$NCl s. S. Cohen et al., Tetrahedron Lett. *39*, 3093-4 (1998).

n-*Butyllithium* $\quad\quad\quad\quad\quad\quad\quad\quad\quad\quad\quad\quad\quad\quad\quad\quad\quad\quad\quad\quad\quad$ BuLi
**Cyclic ketones from halogenocarboxylic acid esters** $\quad\quad\quad\quad\quad\quad\quad\quad\quad\quad$ ○
with *t*-BuLi cf. *41*, 947; chiral 1,6-dihydro-3(2H)-pyridone ring with *n*-BuLi s. H. Faltz et al., Synlett *1997*, 1071-2.

tert-*Butyllithium/cuprous cyanide/lithium bromide* $\quad\quad\quad\quad\quad\quad\quad\quad\quad\quad\quad$ ←
***o*-Allylphenols from *o*-allyloxyhalides** s. *55*, 305 $\quad\quad\quad\quad\quad\quad\quad\quad\quad\quad\quad$ ←

*Triethylamine/irradiation* $\quad\quad\quad\quad\quad\quad\quad\quad\quad\quad\quad\quad\quad\quad\quad\quad\quad\quad$ Et$_3$N/⫽
**Radical ring closures of unsatd. halides via photo-induced electron transfer** ○
via alkyl radicals cf. *50*, 577; ring closure of 2-iodo-2-en-6-ynones via vinyl radicals s. C.K. Sha et al., Chem. Commun. *1998*, 397-8.

*Cuprous bromide/potassium carbonate* $\quad\quad\quad\quad\quad\quad\quad\quad\quad\quad\quad\quad\quad$ CuBr/K$_2$CO$_3$
**Intramolecular copper(I)-catalyzed Heck arylation** s. *55*, 383

*Silver(I)-exchanged zeolite s. under Pd(OAc)$_2$* $\quad\quad\quad\quad\quad\quad\quad\quad\quad\quad\quad\quad$ ←

*Diethylzinc/nickel(II) acetoacetonate* $\quad\quad\quad\quad\quad\quad\quad\quad\quad\quad\quad\quad\quad$ Et$_2$Zn/Ni(acac)$_2$
**Cyclopentanols from δ-halogenoketones**
with EtZnBr/Ni(acac)$_2$ cf. *52*, 407; with Et$_2$Zn/Ni(acac)$_2$ or Et$_2$Zn/MnBr$_2$/CuCl, 2-carbalkoxy-cyclopentanols by regio- and stereo-specific ring closure s. T. Stüdemann, P. Knochel et al., Synlett *1998*, 143-4.

*Zeolites s.a. Silver(I)-exchanged zeolite* $\quad\quad\quad\quad\quad\quad\quad\quad\quad\quad\quad\quad\quad\quad\quad$ ←

*Aluminum chloride/1,3-dimethyl-2-imidazolidone*  ←
**3,4-Dihydrocarbostyrils from β-chlorocarboxylic acid anilides**  ○
with AlCl$_3$ cf. *20*, 680; with 1,3-dimethyl-2-imidazolidone as additive in liq. paraffin on the 100 g scale, with O-demethylation, s. Japanese patent JP-09124605 (Sumika Fine Chem. Co. Ltd.).

*Samarium diiodide/hexamethylphosphoramide*  SmI$_2$/HMPA
**3-Ethylenealcohols from γ-alkoxy-α,β-ethylenehalides**  ←
**Radical Wittig rearrangement via 1,5-hydrogen transfer**

484.

Startg. allyl ether (E:Z 46:54) in benzene added to a soln. of 2.5 eqs. SmI$_2$ in 9:1 benzene/HMPA at room temp. under N$_2$, and the mixture quenched with K$_2$CO$_3$ soln. after 10 min → product. Y 81%. Extension to unsym. diallyl ethers (affording 3-hydroxy-1,5-dienes) provides the first examples of regiospecific Wittig rearrangement under mild, *non-basic* conditions. F.e. incl. reaction with bromide analogs, and reaction conditions s. M. Kunishima, S. Tani et al., J. Org. Chem. *62*, 7542-3 (1997).

**Radical ring closures of ethylenehalides**  ○
s. *46*, 964s*54*; chiral polyoxyvinylcyclopentanes from D-ribonolactone-derived acyclic alkenyl iodides s. Z. Zhou, S.M. Bennett, Tetrahedron Lett. *38*, 1153-6 (1997); chiral polyoxycyclopentyl-acetic acid *tert*-butyl esters, stereoselectivity, s. ibid. *39*, 7075-8 (1998).

**Cyclic alcohols from halogenoketones**
from iodoketones with SmI$_2$/Fe(III) cf. *39*, 952; medium-ring cyclic 3-methylenealcohols from ω-chloro-(ω-1)-methylenealdehydes with SmI$_2$/HMPA s. F. Matsuda et al., Tetrahedron Lett. *39*, 863-4 (1998).

*Titanium(II) porphyrin complexes*  ←
**Ethylene derivs. from 1,2-dihalides**  C(Hal)C(Hal) → C=C
with Cp$_2$TiCl$_2$/Zn cf. *28*, 950s*40*; from 1,2-dichlorides with titanium(II) porphyrin complexes, also acetylene derivs. from 1,2-ethylene-1,2-dichlorides, and deoxygenation of epoxides or sulfoxides, s. X. Wang, L.K. Woo, J. Org. Chem. *63*, 356-60 (1998).

*Tri-n-butyltin hydride*  Bu$_3$SnH
**1,2-Condensed indoles by radical ring closure** s. *55*, 487  ○

*Tri-n-butyltin hydride/triphenylphosphine/irradiation*  ←
**Deoxygenative ring closure of iodoaldehydes via cyclic alkoxyl radicals**

485.

E = CO$_2$Bn

**Cyclopentanes.** A 0.05 *M* soln. of startg. iodide, 1.2 eqs. Bu$_3$SnH, and 2 eqs. triphenylphosphine in benzene degassed for 20 min, irradiated at 350 nm for 1 h, and worked up following treatment with aq. KF → product. Y 75%. There was no quenching of the intermediate cyclic alkoxyl radical by H-atom, or β-fragmentation, indicating that the phosphine-mediated deoxygenation is a far more rapid process. Ketone derivs., however, underwent predominant deiodination. F.e. incl. cyclohexanes, **also cyclic ethylene derivs.** from aldehydo(enebromides), and double ring closure of an iodoethylenealdehyde, s. S. Kim, D.H. Oh, Synlett *1998*, 525-7.

*Tri-n-butyltin hydride/dichloro[1,2-bis(diphenylphosphino)ethane]nickel(II)*  ←
**Ethylene derivs. from 1,2-dihalides**  C(Hal)C(Hal) → C=C
from 1,2-dibromides with EtMgBr/Ni(dppe)Cl$_2$ cf. *51*, 480; improved procedure from 1,2-dibromides or -dichlorides with Bu$_3$SnH or LiBHEt$_3$ as H-donor, also acetylene derivs. from 1,2-ethylene-1,2-dibromides, s. Tetrahedron *54*, 1021-8 (1998).

*Nickel(II) acetoacetonate s. under Et₂Zn*                                              $Ni(acac)_2$
*Dichloro[1,2-bis(diphenylphosphino)ethane]nickel(II) s. under Bu₃SnH*      $Ni(dppe)Cl_2$

*Palladous acetate/(R)-2,2'-bis(diphenylphosphino)-1,1'-binaphthyl/*          ←
  *silver(I)-exchanged zeolite/calcium carbonate/sodium formate*
**Regiospecific reductive asym. intramolecular Heck arylation**                     ○

486.

**Chiral 3-aryl-2,3-dihydrobenzofurans.** 1.1 eqs. Na-formate added to 2.2 eqs. 0.06 M CaCO₃ in acetonitrile, stirred at room temp. for 10 min, 10 mol% Pd(OAc)₂, Ag(I)-exchanged zeolite (containing ca. 6 eqs. Ag(I)), 20 mol% (R)-BINAP, and startg. iodide added, and stirred at 60° for 8 h → methyl (+)-3-methyl-3-(5,5,8,8-tetramethyl-5,6,7,8-tetrahydronaphthalen-1-yl)-2,3-dihydrobenzofuran-6-carboxylate. Y 42% (e.e. 81%). Addition of a potentially coordinating counter-ion for iodide, such as silver salts or silver-exchanged zeolite, induces formation of a cationic complex where palladium remains coordinated to the ligands in a 16-electron Pd⁺ intermediate. F.e. and racemic products with Ph₃P (cf. *47*, 974s*51*) s. P. Diaz et al., Tetrahedron *54*, 4579-90 (1998).

*Tris(dibenzylideneacetone)dipalladium/(S)-2,2'-bis(diphenylphosphino)-*          ←
  *1,1'-binaphthyl/1,2,2,6,6-pentamethylpiperidine*
**Asym. intramolecular Heck arylation**
s. *43*, 962s*50*; chiral 3-vinyloxindoles with 1,2,2,6,6-pentamethylpiperidine as base s. L.E. Overman et al., J. Am. Chem. Soc. *120*, 6500-3 (1998).

*Tetrakis(triphenylphosphine)palladium(0)/potassium carbonate*             $Pd(PPh_3)_4/K_2CO_3$
**Oxindoles from α-halogenocarboxylic acid anilides**
with AlCl₃ cf. *2*, 741; with Pd(PPh₃)₄/K₂CO₃ and other transition metal complexes (cf. *37*, 950s*41*) s. Japanese patent JP-09176117 (Kowa Co. Ltd.).

# Sulfur ↑                                                                       CC ↑ S

*1,8-Diazabicyclo[5.4.0]undec-7-ene*                                                 DBU
**Ramberg-Bäcklund rearrangement**                                                 ←
s. *20*, 685; dichloromethylene compds. from trichloromethyl sulfones with DBU or DABCO s. S. Braverman, Y. Zafrani, Tetrahedron *54*, 1901-12 (1998).

*Pyridine*                                                                                               $C_5H_5N$
**1,3-Dienes from 2,5-dihydrothiophene 1,1-dioxides**
s. *17*, 968s*48*; 5-siloxy-1,3,6-trienes s. T. Subramaniyan et al., Synth. Commun. *27*, 4067-72 (1997).

*Cupric acetate/sodium benzenesulfinate/formic acid*                               ←
**Radical syntheses with allyl sulfones**                                                 ←
s. *51*, 422; 1,2,3,4-tetrahydropyrid[1,2-*a*]indoles by radical ring closure with Cu(OAc)₂/Na-benzenesulfinate/formic acid s. S.-F. Wang, C.-P. Chuang, Tetrahedron Lett. *38*, 7597-8 (1997).

*Tri-*n-*butyltin hydride/azodiisobutyronitrile*                                        $Bu_3SnH/AIBN$
**Ethylene derivs. from tert. sulfones**                                      $CHC(SO_2R) \rightarrow C{=}C$
ionic elimination cf. *50*, 586; complementary radical elimination with Bu₃SnH/AIBN s. J. Org. Chem. *62*, 7142-7 (1997).

*Triphenyltin(4-*tert-*butylpyridine)cobaloxime*
**Radical ring closures of ar. halogenothioethers**

487.

**1,2-Condensed indoles.** A mixture of startg. bromothioether and 6 eqs. triphenyltin(4-*tert*-butylpyridine)cobaloxime in dry DMF heated at 130° for 24 h → product. Y 74%. It is possible to use higher substrate concentrations than those normally required for standard tin hydride-mediated ring closure (cf. *29*, 970s*46-53*). F.e. incl. condensed benzimidazoles and uracils s. T. Uetake et al., J. Chem. Soc. Perkin Trans. 1 *1997*, 3591-6; by Bu₃SnH-mediated ring closures of N-alkenyl-2-bromoindoles cf. A.P. Dobbs et al., Tetrahedron *54*, 2149-60 (1998).

# Remaining Elements ↑      CC ↑ Rem

*Sodium hydroxide*      NaOH
**Intramolecular Wittig synthesis**
review s. *31*, 973s*35*; 3a,5-dihydrofurano[2,3-*c*]quinoline-2,4-diones from α-(quinoline-2,4-dion-3-yloxycarbonyl)phosphonium salts with NaOH s. A. Klásek, S. Kafka, J. Heterocycl. Chem. *35*, 307-11 (1998).

*Sodium/alcohol*      NaOR
**Intramolecular Wittig synthesis**
review s. *31*, 973s*35*; 5,6-dihydro-2-pyridones s. A.S. Fisyuk et al., Khim. Geterotsikl. Soedin. *1998*, 281-2 (Russ.).

n-*Butyllithium*      BuLi
**Ring closures of unsatd. cyclic 1,1-aminostannanes**
via intramolecular carbolithiation s. *51*, 491; 3-vinylpyrrolidines from N-stannylmethyl-5-alkoxy-3-ethyleneamines, and 3-pyrrolidones from N-stannylmethyl-γ-aminocarboxylic acid amides, s. Tetrahedron Lett. *38*, 7621-4 (1997).

*Potassium carbonate/18-crown-6 polyether*      $K_2CO_3$/crown
**Macrocyclic α,β-ethylenelactones by intramolecular Horner synthesis**
with DBU/LiCl cf. *39*, 964s*48*; polymer-based synthesis, also combinatorial synthesis of a muscone library by the sort-pool method using Sort SMART Microreactors (in an IRORI Accutag-100 apparatus), s. K.C. Nicolaou et al., J. Am. Chem. Soc. *120*, 5132-3 (1998).

*Sodium acetate*      NaOAc
**Ethylene derivs. from β-hydroxyphosphonic acid esters**      C(OH)CPO(OR)₂ → C=C
Chiral enisocyclics s. *55*, 464

*Ammonium ceric nitrate*      $(NH_4)_2Ce(NO_3)_6$
**Regio- and stereo-specific ring closures of unsatd. cyclic 1,1-acylaminosilanes**
by photoinduced single electron transfer cf. *48*, 982; oxidative Pictet-Spengler-type ring closure with CAN under *non-acidic* conditions s. H.J. Kim, P.S. Mariano et al., J. Org. Chem. *63*, 860-3 (1998); with Si-nucleophiles as acylimmonium ion quenchers cf. ibid. 841-59.

*Ammonium ceric nitrate/di*-tert-*butylpyridine*
**γ-Diketones from two enoxysilane molecules**      RCO-C-C-COR
s. *45*, 533; from di(vinyloxy)silanes via stereospecific oxidative intramolecular enolate coupling with di-*tert*-butylpyridine as base s. M. Schmittel et al., J. Org. Chem. *63*, 396-400 (1998).

*Tri-n-butyltin hydride/triethylborane*            $Bu_3SnH/Et_3B$
**Radical ring closures of ethyleneselenides**
via alkoxyalkyl radicals s. *47*, 983s*48, 49*; of 2-allylamino-2-deoxyselenoglycosides, regio- and stereo-selectivity, s. S. Czernecki et al., Tetrahedron Lett. *37*, 9193-4 (1996); condensed oxepane ring, stereoselectivity, s. M. Sasaki, K. Tachibana et al., ibid. *39*, 2783-6 (1998); 2,3-condensed cyclopentanol ring s. I.-Y.C. Lee et al., ibid. *35*, 4173-4 (1994).

*Tri-n-butyltin hydride/azodiisobutyronitrile*            $Bu_3SnH/RN{=}NR$
**Cascade radical ring closures of polyeneselenolic acid esters**
s. *49*, 971; ketosteroids via cyclopropane ring expansion s. S. Handa et al., Chem. Commun. *1998*, 311-2; 17-keto-16-oxa-analogs s. G. Pattenden et al., J. Chem. Soc. Perkin Trans. I *1998*, 863-8.

*2,2,2-Trifluoroethyl dichlorovanadate*            $(CF_3CH_2O)VOCl_2$
**Oxidative radical cross-coupling with enoxysilanes**

488.

**3-Methylenecyclopentylcarbonyl compds.** A soln. of startg. enoxysilane in methylene chloride added via syringe over 30 min to a soln. of 2 eqs. 2,2,2-trifluoroethyl dichlorovanadate in the same solvent at -78°, stirred for a further 10 min, and quenched by addition to 1.5 *M* aq. HCl and ether → (2*H*)-hexahydro-5-methylene-1-pentalenone. Y 82%. The allylic silyl group facilitates the disfavoured 5-*endo-trig* cyclization. F.e., also **γ-diketones from two different enoxysilane molecules** (with $(CF_3CH_2O)VOCl_2$ or $(EtO)VOCl_2$), s. K. Ryter, T. Livinghouse, J. Am. Chem. Soc. *120*, 2658-9 (1998).

*Pentacarbonyl(tetrahydrofuran)tungsten*            $W(CO)_5 \cdot THF$
**Cyclic β,γ-ethyleneketones from 1-siloxy-1,ω-enynes**
**Regiospecific ring closure**

489.

**2,6-Bridged 3-cyclohexenones.** 0.1 eq. $W(CO)_5 \cdot THF$ (prepared by irradiating a suspension of $W(CO)_6$ in THF with a high-pressure Hg-lamp for 4 h) added to startg. enoxysilane, followed by 2 eqs. water (or methanol), and stirred at room temp. for 1 week → product. Y 90%. Contrasting with related ring closures, reaction is *endo*-specific and proceeds without isomerization of the double bond. However, the cyclization is limited to terminal alkynes, which are presumably activated by formation of an intermediate $\eta^2$-complex. The *endo*-selectivity is also favoured in less-donating solvents, e.g. methylene chloride. F.e. incl. isolated 3-cyclohexenones, and cyclopent-2-enyl ketones s. K. Maeyama, N. Iwasawa, J. Am. Chem. Soc. *120*, 1928-9 (1998).

*Sodium hypochlorite*            *NaOCl*
**Synthesis of internal acetylene derivs.**          $C{\equiv}CH \rightarrow C{\equiv}CR$
**from terminal acetylene derivs. and tellurides**
**via regio- and stereo-specific carbotelluration**

490.

***tert*-Butylacetylenes.** A mixture of phenylacetylene and *tert*-butyl methyl telluride irradiated with a tungsten lamp at 50° until reaction complete → intermediate enetelluride (Y 92%), in chloroform treated with 5-8 eqs. aq. NaOCl at 25°, the mixture stirred for 30 min, worked-up, and the crude telluroxide distilled gradually in a Kugelrohr apparatus at 250° → 1-*tert*-butyl-2-phenylethyne (Y 88%). The method is particularly useful since direct introduction of a *tert*-butyl group at the terminal carbon of a 1-alkyne is known to be difficult. Similar results were obtained with $H_2O_2$ or *t*-BuOOH as oxidants. F.e.s. J. Terao, N. Kambe et al., Tetrahedron Lett. *39*, 5511-2 (1998).

*Ferric nitrate/1,4-cyclohexadiene* ←
**Syntheses via oxidative radical siloxycyclopropane ring opening** ←
enones with $FeCl_3$/NaOAc cf. *46*, 989s*49*; bicyclo[3.3.0]octan-3-ones from 1-siloxybicyclo[5.1.0]-oct-2-enes with $Fe(NO_3)_3$/1,4-cyclohexadiene, stereoselectivity, s. K.I. Booker-Milburn, R.F. Dainty, Tetrahedron Lett. *39*, 5097-100 (1998).

*Tetrakis(triethylphosphine)nickel(0)/tris(pyrrolidino)phosphine* ←
**Diaryls from diaryl tellurides** ArTeAr → Ar-Ar

491.

Dianisyl telluride, 1.2 eqs. tris(pyrrolidino)phosphine, and 0.1 eq. $Ni(PEt_3)_4$ in acetonitrile heated at 80° under argon overnight (20 h) → 4,4′-bianisyl. Y 92%. With this phosphine, the amount of Ni-catalyst required could be reduced from 1 eq. to as low as 0.03 eq. The nature of the phosphine employed was important, with efficacy increasing in the order $PMePh_2 < PEt_3 = PBu_3 < P(NEt_2)_3 < P(piperidino)_3 < P(pyrrolidino)_3$. This agrees well with the reactivity of the phosphines towards Te to form phosphine tellurides. Methoxy and amino groups were unaffected. Diaryls were **also** formed **from** [more accessible] **diaryl ditellurides**, notably with retention of ar. chlorine. The reaction is believed to proceed via oxidative addition of the telluride to the Ni-complex, followed by disproportionation to form diarylnickel species, and reductive elimination. F.e.s. L.-B. Han, M. Tanaka, Chem. Commun. *1998*, 47-8.

# Carbon ↑ CC ⇑ C

*Without additional reagents* w.a.r.
**Retrodiene scission** C
s. *17*, 198s*51*; N-condensed 4(3*H*)-pyrimidinones s. F. Fülöp et al., Synth. Commun. *27*, 195-203 (1997).

*Irradiation* ⚡
**1,4-Naphthoquinone ring via photochemical cyclobutane ring fragmentation**

492.

**Benz[*a*]anthracene-7,12-diones.** A soln. of startg. cyclobutane deriv. in benzene exposed to fluorescent laboratory light → benz[*a*]anthracene-7,12-dione. Y 87%. Reaction involves an excited diradical whose strain energy is relieved by expulsion of isobutylene. This procedure is applicable in general to the synthesis of **angular polycyclic benzo-fused *p*-quinones** (incl. furoquinone analogs), and is part of a multistep synthesis from 2-(2-ethenylphenyl)-3-alkenyl-4,4-dimethoxycyclobutenones. F.e.s. M.J. Heileman et al., J. Am. Chem. Soc. *120*, 3801-2 (1998).

*Microwaves*
**Retro-Diels-Alder reaction under microwave irradiation in the absence of solvent**

493.

**(Z)-4-Amino-2-ethylene-*prim*-alcohols.** Startg. neat furan adduct in an open Pyrex flask irradiated in a focused microwave reactor (Synthewave S402 single mode, 2450 MHz; 300 W) at 140° *for 10 min* → product. Y >98% (Y 84% after 480 min at 140° under classical heating). F.e.s. M. Bortolussi et al., J. Chem. Res., Synop *1998*, 34-5.

*Lithium chloride*     LiCl
**Stereospecific decarbalkoxylative intramolecular Michael addition**
s. *49*, 981; 2-carbalkoxytetrahydropyran-3-acetic acid esters and tetrahydrofuran analogs s. R.A. Bunce et al., J. Org. Chem. *63*, 144-51 (1998).

*Sodium iodide*     NaI
**Cyclopropyl ketones from α-acyl-γ-lactones**
with NaBr in DMSO cf. *31*, 984; improved method with NaI or KI in PEG dimethyl ether 2000 s. European patent EP-820977 (Huels AG).

*Trimethylsilyl triflate/lithium perchlorate*     $Me_3SiOSO_2CF_3/LiClO_4$
**Stereospecific intramolecular cationic [5+2]-cycloaddition with *p*-quinone monoketals**

494.

1.05 eqs. Trimethylsilyl triflate added to a 0.2 M soln. of startg. *p*-quinone monoketal in 3 M $LiClO_4$ in ethyl acetate at -23°, stirred for 5 min, and quenched with satd. $NaHCO_3$ → 5-methoxy-8a-methyl-1,2,3,7,8,8a-hexahydro-3a,7-methanoazulene-4,9-dione. Y 86%. There was no reaction with alk-6-en-1-yl derivs. F.e.s. P.A. Grieco, J.K. Walker, Tetrahedron *53*, 8975-96 (1997).

*Vanadyl trichloride*     $VOCl_3$
**(Z)-α,β-Ethylene-α-fluorocarboxylic acids**     C═C(F)COOH
**from α-fluoro-β,β'-dihydroxycarboxylic acids**
**Deoxygenative elimination of aldehydes**

495.

Startg. α-fluorocarboxylic acid in chlorobenzene treated with 2 eqs. $VOCl_3$ at reflux (ca. 120°) for 1 h → product. Y 70%. The corresponding aldehydes were also obtained as the elimination product (aromatic aldehydes being eliminated in preference to aliphatic ones). The presence of at least one aryl group is imperative for the reaction to proceed. Phenolethers and aromatic chlorides and fluorides were unaffected. A radical mechanism is invoked. F.e., **also (Z)-α,β-ethylene-α-fluorocarboxylic acid esters**, s. T. Ishihara et al., Tetrahedron Lett. *39*, 4865-8 (1998).

*Ozone/dimethyl sulfide/*p-*toluenesulfonic acid/triethylamine*
**Cyclic α,β-ethylene-α-phosphonylketones
from ω-ethylene-β-ketophosphonic acid esters**
Ozonolysis-intramolecular aldol condensation

A stream of O₃ passed through a soln. of startg. ethyleneketone in dichloromethane at -78° until the blue colour persisted, excess of O₃ removed by introducing a stream of O₂ through the mixture for 10 min, allowed to warm to room temp., 2 eqs. Me₂S added, stirred at reflux for 1 h, treated with 0.1 eq. each of *p*-TsOH and Et₃N, and stirring continued at reflux for a further 3 h → product. Y 83%. A quaternary centre at the γ-carbon appears to be conducive to good yields. Substrates with a chain longer than 7 C-atoms gave a mixture of products. F.e. incl. cyclohexenone analogs s. J.M. Gil, D.Y. Oh, Tetrahedron Lett. *39*, 3205-8 (1998).

*Chiral molybdenum carbene complex*
**Ring closing metathesis with kinetic resolution**
s. *48*, 988s*51*; s.a. J.B. Alexander, A.H. Hoveyda, R.R. Schrock et al., J. Am. Chem. Soc. *120*, 4041-2 (1998).

*Tungsten carbyne complex*
**Macrocyclic acetylene derivs. from diynes by ring closing metathesis**

**Macrocyclic dilactones.** A *dilute* (≤ 0.02 M) soln. of startg. diyne and 6 mol% tungsten carbyne complex in chlorobenzene stirred under argon at 80° for 2 h → product. Y 73% (90% conversion). The alkyne by-product can be readily removed under reduced pressure. Partial hydrogenation of the product (e.g. with the Lindlar catalyst) affords the corresponding **macrocyclic (Z)-ethylene derivs.**, as yet not obtainable cleanly by ring closing metathesis of dienes (cf. *49*, 985). F.e. incl. macrocyclic lactones, dilactams and dialkoxysilanes, s. A. Fürstner, G. Seidel, Angew. Chem. Int. Ed. Engl. *37*, 1734-6 (1998).

*Lithium perchlorate s. under Me₃SiOSO₂CF₃*  *LiClO₄*

*Ruthenium carbene complex*
**Ring closing metathesis**
s. *49*, 985s*54*; macrocyclic N-(2-ethylene)urethans s. A.K. Ghosh, K.A. Hussain, Tetrahedron Lett. *39*, 1881-4 (1998); chiral medium-ring cyclic 2-ethyleneethers (satd. 7- and 8-membered O-heterocyclics) s. J.S. Clark et al., ibid. 8321-4; macrocyclic lactams and lactones, stereoselectivity, s. W.P.D. Golding, L. Weiler et al., ibid. 4955-8; (+)-aspicilin synthesis s. T. Nishioka, S. Hatakeyama et al., ibid. 5597-600; bicyclic peptidomimetic lactams s. L.M. Beal, K.D. Moeller, ibid. 4639-42; fused, bridged and spiro cyclics via sequential and cascade **ring closing metathesis-intramolecular Heck arylation** s. R. Grigg et al., ibid. 4139-42; α,β-ethylene-γ- or -δ-lactones s. A.K. Ghosh et al., ibid. 4651-4; ring closing metathesis of vinylglycine derivs. s. J.-M. Campagne, L. Ghosez, ibid. 6175-8; chiral 3,4-dihydro-2*H*-pyrans s. C.F. Sturino, J.C.Y. Wong, ibid. 9623-6; 3-chromenes s. S. Chang, R.H. Grubbs, J. Org. Chem. *63*, 864-6 (1998); medium-ring and large-ring benzo-fused O- and O,O-heterocyclics s. M. Stefinovic, V. Snieckus, ibid. 2808-9; bicyclo-

[m.n.1]alkenes s. A. Morehead, Jr., R.H. Grubbs, Chem. Commun. *1998*, 275-6; 10-membered bicyclic ketolactones s. A. Fürstner, T. Müller, Synlett *1997*, 1010-2; **epothilone partial synthesis** s. K. Gerlach et al., ibid. *1998* 1108-10; s.a. K.C. Nicolaou et al., Angew. Chem. Int. Ed. Engl. *37*, 84-7 (1998); f. method for [14]-, [15]-, [17]- and [18]-epothilones A s. ibid. 81-4; condensed carbohydrates s. D.J. Holt et al., ibid. 3298-300; 3-chromenes s.a. J.P.A. Harrity, A.H. Hoveyda, J. Am. Chem. Soc. *120*, 2343-51 (1998); chiral 3-chromenes with molybdenum carbene complex (cf. *48*, 988s*52*) cf. ibid. 8340-7.

**Polymer-based ring closing metathesis**
s. *49*, 985s*52*; *52*, 494; with simultaneous cleavage of a 'traceless' support s. A.D. Piscopio et al., Tetrahedron Lett. *38*, 7143-6 (1997); combinatorial synthesis of a 4200 compd. library of hexahydroisoindoles by polymer-based ring closing metathesis-Diels-Alder reaction s. D.A. Heerding et al., ibid. *39*, 6815-8 (1998); f. **combinatorial ring closing metathesis** s. T. Giger et al., Synlett *1998*, 688-91.

**Cyclic γ,δ-ethylenecarboxylic acid esters
via stereospecific Claisen rearrangement-ring closing metathesis**

498

**3,6-Dihydro-2H-pyran-2-carboxylic acid esters.** A soln. of startg. allyl ester in THF treated with LiN(SiMe₃)₂ and trimethylsilyl chloride at -95° to room temp. according to the standard Ireland ester enolate Claisen rearrangement, and the product esterified with benzyl alcohol in methylene chloride at room temp. in the presence of EDCI/DMAP → intermediate (Y 65%; 21:1 mixture of phenyl epimers), in methylene chloride treated with 2.5 mol% PhCH=RuCl₂(PCy₃)₂ at room temp. for 1-16 h according to the standard metathesis procedure (*49*, 985) → product (Y 90%). Thiopyran, Δ³-piperideine, and cyclohexene analogs were obtained similarly. F.e. and methods s. J.F. Miller, A.D. Piscopio et al., J. Org. Chem. *63*, 3158-9 (1998); s.a. S.D. Burke et al., ibid. 3160-1.

*Palladium-carbon/oxygen*      Pd-C/O₂
**Decarboxylative aromatization**      ←
of coumarins s. *33*, 990; 2-cyanobiphenyls s. Japanese patent JP-09087238 (Ube Ind. Ltd.).

# Formation of Electron Pair on Nitrogen

## Elimination ⇑

## Oxygen ↑      EIN ⇑ O

*Zinc/aluminum chloride*      Zn/AlCl₃
**Azomethines from nitrones**      C=N→O → C=N
with Zn/AcOH cf. *30*, 696s*37*; with Zn/AlCl₃, also N-deoxygenation of pyridine N-oxides (cf. *8*, 951), s. D.K. Dutta, D. Konwar, J. Chem. Res., Synop *1998*, 266-7.

## Carbon ↑      EIN ⇑ C

*Cupric acetate*      Cu(OAc)₂
**N-Dequaternization**      ≧N⁺R → ≧N
with PhSNa cf. *24*, 989s*34*; of N-condensed benzimidazolium salts with Cu(OAc)₂ s. J.G. Siro, J. Alvarez-Builla et al., Tetrahedron *54*, 1929-36 (1998).

# Formation of Electron Pair on Sulfur

## Elimination ⇑

### Oxygen ↑      EIS ⇑ O

*Titanium(II) porphyrin complexes*      ←
**Thioethers from sulfoxides**      $\geqslant$SO → $\geqslant$S
with TiCl$_4$/Sm cf. *41*, 995s*51*; with titanium(II) porphyrin complexes s. X. Wang, L.K. Woo, J. Org. Chem. *63*, 356-60 (1998).

*Nickel(II) chloride/sodium tetrahydridoborate*      $NiCl_2/NaBH_4$
**Thioethers from sulfoxides**
with FeCl$_3$/NaBH$_4$ cf. *43*, 995; with nickel boride generated *in situ* from NiCl$_2$/NaBH$_4$, also selenides from selenoxides, s. J.M. Khurana et al., Tetrahedron Lett. *39*, 3829-32 (1998).

# Formation of Electron Pair on Remaining Elements

## Elimination ⇑

### Oxygen ↑      ElRem ⇑ O

*Aluminum hydride*      $AlH_3$
**Phosphines from phosphine oxides**      $\geqslant$PO → $\geqslant$P
with trialkylboranes cf. *21*, 988; with AlH$_3$·THF s. S. Griffin et al., Tetrahedron Lett. *39*, 4405-6 (1998).

*Nickel(II) chloride/sodium tetrahydridoborate*      $NiCl_2/NaBH_4$
**Selenides from selenoxides** s. *43*, 995s55      $\geqslant$SeO → $\geqslant$Se

# Heteropolar Bond

## Uptake ⇓

### Addition to Nitrogen      Het ⇓ N

*Without additional reagents*      *w.a.r.*
**Amidinium salts from amidines**      [C(N$\leqslant$)=N$\leqslant$]$^+$
s. *6*, 902; cyclic amidinium salts with dimethyl carbonate as quaternizing agent s. Japanese patent JP-09278759 (Mitsubishi Chem. Corp.).

tert-*Butyl bromide*      *t-BuBr*
**Hydrobromides**      ←
with HBr/Ac$_2$O cf. *13*, 910; with *t*-BuBr as *neutral* HBr equivalent, 4-hydroxy- and -mercaptopyridinium and -pyrylium salts, s. E.A. Cioffe, W.F. Bailey, Tetrahedron Lett. *39*, 2679-80 (1998).

## Addition to Sulfur                                              Het ⇓ S

*Cupric acetate*                                                   $Cu(OAc)_2$
**Sulfonium salts from thioethers and iodonium salts**             ⩾S⁺
triarylsulfonium salts with Cu(OBz)₂ cf. *35*, 430; 1-phenylbenzo[*b*]thiophenium salts s. T. Kitamura et al., Bull. Chem. Soc. Jpn. *71*, 1215-9 (1998).

## Addition to Remaining Elements                                  Het ⇓ Rem

*Without additional reagents*                                      *w.a.r.*
**Phosphonium salts**                                              ⩾P⁺R
s. *6*, 911; 1*H*-phosphirenium salts from 1*H*-phosphirenes and alkyl triflates s. H. Heydt, M. Regitz et al., Synthesis *1998*, 175-80.

## Resolutions                                                     Res

(s.a. Subject Index under Resolution)

*Without additional reagents*                                      *w.a.r.*
**Kinetic resolution of amines by asym. N-acetylation** s. *55*, 149          ←

**Heterogeneous kinetic resolution of α-aminocarboxylic acid derivs.**        ←
by asym. aminolysis with combinatorially-designed 'selector' amines s. *45*, 210s55

**Optical resolution via host-guest complexation**                            ←
s. *5*, 666s*46, 48, 49, 54*; of 1-[2-(diarylphosphino)naphth-1-yl]isoquinolines via complexation with di-µ-chlorobis[(R)-dimethyl(1-phenyl)aminato-C²,N]dipalladium s. H. Doucet, J.M. Brown, Tetrahedron:Asym. *8*, 3775-84 (1997); resolution of 2,2'-dihydroxy-1,1'-biphenyl derivs. by inclusion complexation with chiral 1,2-diaminocyclohexane s. K. Tanaka, F. Toda et al., J. Org. Chem. *62*, 1192-3 (1997); enantiomeric enrichment of α-allenecarboxylic acid esters via complexation with tris[(R)-(1R*)-3-(2,2,3,3,4,4,4-heptafluoro-1-oxobutyl)-1,7,7-trimethyl-bicyclo[2.2.1]heptan-2-onato-O,O']europium s. Y. Naruse et al., ibid. 3862-6.

**Determination of absolute configuration**                                   ←
s. *5*, 666s*54*; of β-chiral prim. alcohols by ¹H NMR study of (R)- and (S)-9-anthrylmethoxyacetic acid esters s. S.K. Latypov, R. Riguera et al., J. Am. Chem. Soc. *120*, 4741-51 (1998); of sec. alcohols by the same procedure s. Tetrahedron *55*, 569-84 (1999); of β- or γ-methylated sec. alcohols by ¹H NMR study of chiral methoxy(2-naphthyl)acetic acid esters s. H. Takahashi, K. Iguchi et al., Tetrahedron Lett. *40*, 333-6 (1999); of linear sec. alcohols cf. H. Yamase, T. Kusumi et al., ibid. *39*, 8113-6 (1998); of tert. alcohols by NMR study of β-D- and β-L-fucofuranoside derivs. s. M. Kobayashi, Tetrahedron *54*, 10987-98 (1998); of α-hydroxycarboxylic acids by the CD exciton chirality method s. B.H. Rickman, N. Berova et al., ibid. 5041-64; of acyclic derivs. by the same approach s. K. Hör, H.-U. Humpf et al., J. Org. Chem. *63*, 322-5 (1998): of 3-methylcarboxylic acids by NMR study of 1-arylethylamide derivs. s. T.R. Hoye, D.O. Koltun, J. Am. Chem. Soc. *120*, 4638-43 (1998); of diamines, aminoalcohols, and amino acids by CD analysis of zinc porphyrin tweezer complexes s. X. Huang, K. Nakanishi et al., ibid. 6185-6; of cyclic ethylene derivs. by NMR study of cycloadducts with chiral 2'-methoxy-1,1'-binaphthalene-2-carbohydroximoyl chloride s. H. Fukui et al., Tetrahedron Lett. *40*, 325-8 (1999); of mycotoxic fumonisins (complex 9-amino-1,8-diols) s. M. Hartl, H.-U. Humpf, Tetrahedron:Asym. *9*, 1549-56 (1998).

**Determination of enantiomeric purity**                                      ←
s. *5*, 666s*54*; of chiral amines by NMR analysis of (5R)-methyl-1-chloromethyl-2-pyrrolidone derivs. s. P. Chen, M.B. Smith et al., Synth. Commun. *28*, 1641-8 (1998); e.e. determination (by NMR) of chiral amines, aminoalcohols, alcohols, carboxylic acids and amino acids bearing the 3,5-dinitrophenyl moiety with α-cyclodextrins as chiral solvating agent s. G. Uccello-Barretta et al., J. Org. Chem. *62*, 827-35 (1997).

*Microwaves s. under Lipase* ←
*Chromatography* ←
**Optical resolution on chiral stationary phases**
s. 5, 666s52; enantiomeric enrichment of chiral spirocyclics by dynamic HPLC s. K. Lorenz et al., Angew. Chem. Int. Ed. Engl. *37*, 1922-5 (1998); determination of enantiomeric impurities in common chiral reagents and auxiliaries by chromatographic analysis on chiral supports s. D.W. Armstrong et al., Tetrahedron:Asym. *9*, 2043-64 (1998).

*Potassium* tert-*butoxide* KOBu-t
**Deracemization of α-*prim*-aminocarboxylic acid esters** ←
**via asym. protonation of α-(alkylideneamino)carboxylic acid ester enolates**

499.

R = 2-naphthyl

2 eqs. KOBu-*t* added under argon to a soln. of startg. Schiff base (prepared from the racemic amino ester and 2-hydroxypinan-3-one) in dry THF at -78°, stirred for 30 min, and quenched with satd. $NH_4Cl$ soln. → intermediate (Y 96%; d.e. >98%), treated with 15% citric acid soln. or boric acid → product (Y 94%; e.e. >98%). This is a useful alternative to asym. protonation of enolates with a chiral base. F.e.s. M. Tabcheh, M.-L. Roumestant et al., Tetrahedron:Asym. *9*, 1493-5 (1998); **deracemization of α-*prim*-aminocarboxylic acids** via nickel(II) complexation with $Ni(NO_3)_2$ and chiral *o*-prolylaminoketones cf. B.B. De, N.R. Thomas, ibid. *8*, 2687-91 (1997).

sec-*Butyllithium/chiral 1-(o-aminoaryl)-1,2,3,4-tetrahydroisoquinolines* ←
**Asym. protonation of enolates** ←
with *n*-BuLi/chiral imides cf. *39*, 993s54; of amide enolates with *sec*-BuLi/chiral 1-(*o*-aminoaryl)-1,2,3,4-tetrahydroisoquinolines (0.1 eq.) and arylacetic acid esters as proton source, optimization of kinetic acidity, s. E. Vedejs, A.W. Kruger, J. Org. Chem. *63*, 2792-3 (1998); with chelating polymeric *o*-hydroxycarboxylic acid esters as proton source s. N. Krause, M. Mackenstedt, Tetrahedron Lett. *39*, 9649-50 (1998).

*Chiral amines* ←
**Optical resolution via salt formation** ←
s. 5, 666s51; partial resolution of carboxylic acids by supercritical fluid ($spCO_2$) extraction s. B. Simándi et al., J. Org. Chem. *62*, 4390-4 (1997).

*Chiral planar 4-dimethylaminopyridine-fused ferrocenes* ←
*Tetrapeptides* ←
**Kinetic resolution of sec. alcohols by catalytic asym. O-acylation** ←
s. 52, 497; enhanced enantioselectivity in *tert*-amyl alcohol at 0° with 1 mol% catalyst s. J. Org. Chem. *63*, 2794-5 (1998); kinetic resolution of 2-acylaminoalcohols with acylase-like tetrapeptides s. G.T. Copeland et al., ibid. 6784-5.

*Lipase* ←
**Kinetic resolution by asym. hydrolysis of carboxylic acid esters** ←
Chiral alcohols and carboxylic acids s. *28*, 13s55

**Aldehydes from acylals with kinetic resolution** s. 55, 6 ←
**Kinetic resolution of amines by asym. aminolysis of carboxylic acid esters** ←
s. 45, 210s52, 53; by lipase-catalyzed asym. methoxyacetylation s. F. Balkenhohl et al., J. Prakt. Chem. *339*, 381-4 (1997); *heterogeneous* kinetic resolution of cyclic α-aminocarboxylic acid derivs. using a 100-compd. combinatorial library (1 compd./bead) of chiral 'selector' amines s. M.D. Weingarten et al., J. Am. Chem. Soc. *120*, 9112-3 (1998).

*Lipase or Lipase/microwaves*
**Kinetic resolution by asym. O-acylation with enolesters** s. *44*, 214s*55*

*Immobilized lipase*
**Kinetic resolution by asym. esterification**
s. *41*, 175s*55*; of 2-tetralols with porcine pancreatin s. G.R. Martinez, Tetrahedron:Asym. *6*, 1491-4 (1995).

*Oxidase/oxygen*
**Kinetic resolution of sec. alcohols by asym. oxidation**
with yeast/oxygen cf. *49*, 995; chiral α-hydroxycarboxylic acids with glycolate oxidase from spinach s. W. Adam et al., J. Org. Chem. *62*, 7841-3 (1997).

*Cyclohexanone monooxygenase*
**Cyclic diol sulfates from sulfites with kinetic resolution** s. *55*, 51

*Tantalum pentachloride/(-)-2,3-O-isopropylidene-1,1,4,4-tetraphenyl-L-threitol*
**Kinetic resolution of sec. alcohols by asym. acylation** s. *55*, 84

*Chiral molybdenum carbene complex*
**Ring closing metathesis with kinetic resolution** s. *48*, 988s*55*

*Chiral manganese(III) salen complex/iodosobenzene/4-phenylpyridine N-oxide*
**Kinetic resolution of allenes by asym. epoxidation**

500.

20 Mol% 4-phenylpyridine N-oxide and 2 mol% chiral manganese(III) salen complex added to a soln. of 1,3-diphenyl-1,2-propadiene in methylene chloride, cooled to -40°, 1 eq. iodosobenzene added, and quenched with Bu₃P when 59.5% conversion had been achieved → unreacted (S)-1,3-diphenyl-1,2-propadiene (e.e. 96.3%). The (S)-enantiomer is epoxidized at ca. one-twentieth of the rate of the (R)-isomer. F.e.s. Y. Noguchi et al., Synlett *1998*, 543-4.

*Chiral cobalt(III) Schiff base complex*
**Kinetic resolution by hydrolysis of epoxides**
with yeast cf. *48*, 108s*53* and microsomal hydrolase cf. *48*, 108s*54*; isolation of chiral epoxides with a chiral cobalt(III) Schiff base complex (cf. *53*, 59) s. P.S. Savle et al., Tetrahedron:Asym. *9*, 1843-6 (1998).

*Nickel(II) nitrate/chiral o-(prolylamino)ketones*
**Deracemization of α-aminocarboxylic acids** s. *55*, 499

## Other Reactions      Oth

*Sodium hydridotriacetoxoborate*      $NaBH(OAc)_3$
*Tri-n-butyltin hydride*      $Bu_3SnH$
**Reductive decomplexation**
of (π-allyl)tricarbonyliron-lactone and acetylenedicobalt hexacarbonyl complexes s. *55*, 35

# Reviews

This is a collection of reviews in the field of synthetic organic chemistry published mainly from September 1998 to February 1999. The layout is to aid access via the Supplementary Reference Index, each entry being entered in the Subject Index, e.g.

**Calixarenes**
-, review 7, 281s55

4, 3   **Asym. synthesis with chiral lithium amides** as base, P. O'Brien, J. Chem. Soc. Perkin Trans. I *1998*, 1439-57.

5, 666  **Separation of enantiomers** via Selector/Selectand hydrogen bonding, B. Feibush, Chirality *10*, 382-95 (1998); **cyclodextrin chemistry**, eleven reviews, Chem. Rev. *98*, Issue No.5, (1998).

7, 281  **Calixarenes**, A. Casnatt, Gazz. Chim. Ital. *127*, 637-49 (1998); phosphorus-containing calixarenes, I.S. Antipin et al., Russ. Chem. Rev. *67*, 995-1012 (1998).

7, 541  **Ring opening of succinimides**, A.R. Katritzky et al., Heterocycles *48*, 2677-91 (1998).

10, 633 **Wittig synthesis of porphyrin derivs.**, A.K. Burrell, D.L. Officer, Synlett *1998*, 1297-307.

17, 117 **Halogen-substituted tin hydride systems** for chemo-, regio- and stereo-controlled reduction, I. Shibata, A. Baba, Rev. Heteroatom. Chem. *18*, 247-75 (1998).

17, 169 **Solid-phase synthesis of oligosaccharides and glycoconjugates** by the glycal method, a five year retrospective, P.H. Seeberger, S.J. Danishefsky, Acc. Chem. Res. *31*, 685-95 (1998); further review on solid-phase synthesis of oligosaccharides and glycopeptides, H.M.I. Osborn, T.H. Khan, Tetrahedron *55*, 1807-50 (1999); **synthetic cyclic oligosaccharides**, G. Gattuso et al., Chem. Rev. *98*, 1919-58 (1998).

17, 198 **Retro-Diels-Alder reaction**. Part II. Dienophiles with one or more heteroatom, B. Rickborn, Org. Reactions *53*, 223-629 (1998).

19, 33  **Cysteine-containing peptide synthesis**, peculiarities, K.E. Vital'evna et al., Russ. Chem. Rev. *67*, 611-30 (1998); **peptide nucleic acids**, synthesis and properties, E. Uhlmann et al., Angew. Chem. Int. Ed. Engl. *37*, 2796-823 (1998).

19, 265 **Glucuronide synthesis**, A.V. Stachulski, G.N. Jenkins, Nat. Prod. Reports *15*, 173-86 (1998).

19, 897 **Di-*tert*-butylation** of substituted arenes, S.A. Saleh, H.I. Tashtoush, Tetrahedron *54*, 14157-78 (1998).

22, 761 **Dehydroquadricyclanes**, G. Szeimies, J. Prakt. Chem. *340*, 11-9 (1998).

23, 381 **Aziridination** with 3-(acetoxyamino)-4(3*H*)-quinazolones and ring opening of the products, R.S. Atkinson, Tetrahedron *55*, 1519-60 (1999).

23, 819 **$\eta^3$-Vinylcarbene complexes**, chemistry, T. Mitsudo, Bull. Chem. Soc. Jpn. *71*, 1525-38 (1998).

24, 768 **Manganese-based organic and bioinorganic transformations**, G.G. Melikyan, Adrichimica Acta *31*, 50-64 (1998).

25, 167 **Carbonyl from thiocarbonyl groups**, A. Corsaro, V. Pistarà, Tetrahedron *54*, 15027-62 (1998).

25, 594 **Sultones** in organic synthesis, P. Metz, J. Prakt. Chem. *340*, 1-10 (1998).

26, 56  **Piperazic acids**, synthesis and chemistry, M.A. Ciufolini, N. Xi, Chem. Soc. Rev. *27*, 437-46 (1998).

27, 871 **Heck reactions**, mechanistic features and implications for synthesis, G.T. Crisp, Chem. Soc. Rev. *27*, 427-36 (1998).

27, 947 **Chiral 5-subst. $\Delta^3$-2-pyrrolones** from 5-isopropoxy-derivs., $Fe(CO)_4$-mediated synthesis via N-acyliminium precursors, H. de Koning, W.N. Speckamp et al., Eur. J. Org. Chem. *1998*, 1729-37.

28, 13 **Preparative biochemical reactions** (1997 literature), S.M. Roberts, J. Chem. Soc. Perkin Trans. I *1999*, 1-23; enzymatic synthesis of enantiopure 1,4-dihydropyridines, S. Marchalin, B. Decroix et al., Heterocycles *48*, 1943-58 (1998).

28, 854 **Medium-ring bridged ethylene derivs.** with hyperstable double bonds, W. Grimme et al., Synlett *1998*, 1175-81; **medium-ring synthesis**, diverse methods, G.A. Molander, Acc. Chem. Res. *31*, 603-9 (1998).

29, 697 **Thermal [3.3]-Claisen rearrangement** of 3-subst. phenyl allyl and propargyl ethers: synthesis of 4-halogenobenzofurans, V.G.S. Box, P.C. Meleties, Heterocycles *48*, 2173-203 (1998).

29, 970 **Radical ring closures** in alkaloid synthesis, M. Ikeda, T. Sato et al., Rev. Heteroatom Chem. *18*, 169-98 (1998).

31, 163 **α-Dicarbonyl and vicinal polycarbonyl compds.**, synthesis, oxidative, V.D. Filimonov et al., Russ. Chem. Rev. *67*, 803-26 (1998).

32, 11 **Glycopeptides and glycoproteins**: focus on the glycosidic linkage, C.M. Taylor, Tetrahedron *54*, 11317-62 (1998).

32, 44 **Hydrogenation** with heterogeneous catalysts, N.M. Dmitrievna, K.O. Valentinovich, Russ. Chem. Rev. *67*, 656-87 (1998).

32, 311 **1,2,4-Triazine N-oxides** and annelated derivs., D.N. Kozhevnikov et al., Russ. Chem. Rev. *67*, 633-48 (1998).

32, 593 **α,β-Epoxyphosphonic acid esters**, synthesis and properties, B. Iorga et al., Synthesis *1999*, 207-24.

32, 668 **2(5*H*)-Furanones**: photochemical transformations, A.I. Hashem et al., Org. Prep. Proc. Intern. *30*, 401-25 (1998).

32, 711 **Steroids**: reactions and partial synthesis, J.R. Hanson, Nat. Prod. Reports *15*, 261-73 (1998).

33, 403 **N-Methyladenines**, chemistry, T. Fujii, T. Itaya, Heterocycles *48*, 1673-724 (1998); N,N-dimethyladenines s. ibid. *51*, 393-454 (1999)

33, 730 **Pictet-Spengler reactions** of $N^b$-hydroxytryptamines and synthesis of eudistomins, T. Hino, M. Nakagawa, Heterocycles *49*, 499-530 (1998).

34, 46 **Catalytic transfer hydrogenation** of olefins, Z. Dobrovolna, L. Cerveny, Res. Chem. Intermed. *24*, 679-86 (1998).

34, 112 ***cis*-Glycols**: dioxygenase-catalyzed formation, D.R. Boyd, G.N. Sheldrake, Nat. Prod. Reports *15*, 309-24 (1998).

34, 238 **Isothiochromans**: recent progress in synthesis and reactions, Y.-C. Xu, Org. Prep. Proc. Intern. *30*, 243-89 (1998).

35, 152 **Synthesis of heterocyclics** from polyfunctionalized (fluoroalkyl)carbonyl compds., K.I. Pashkevich et al., Russ. Chem. Bull. *47*, 1239-47 (1998).

36, 117 **New asym. syntheses with tartaric acid esters**, K. Inomata, Y. Ukaji, Rev. Heteroatom Chem. *18*, 119-40 (1998).

37, 349 **Pyrazines**, chemistry, A. Ohta, Y. Aoyagi, Rev. Heteroatom Chem. *18*, 141-67 (1998).

37, 441 **N-Halides**, aqueous chemistry, X.L. Armesto et al., Chem. Soc. Rev. *27*, 453-60 (1998).

37, 669 **Ketene equivalents in [4+2]-cycloaddition**, V.K. Aggarwal et al., Tetrahedron *55*, 293-312 (1999).

*38*, 756 **Mesoporous supramolecular-templated materials** [silicates], synthesis and applications, J.Y. Ying et al., Angew. Chem. Int. Ed. Engl. *38*, 56-77 (1999).

*41*, 115 **Catalytic functionalization** of carbon-hydrogen and carbon-carbon bonds in protic media, A. Sen, Acc. Chem. Res. *31*, 550-7 (1998).

*41*, 139 **Bridged biscyclopentadienyl compds.**, P.V. Ivchenko, L.E. Nifant'ev, Russ. J. Org. Chem. *34*, 1-26 (1998).

*41*, 243 **Oxidation of alcohols** by modified oxochromium(VI)-amine reagents, F.A. Luzzio, Org. Reactions *53*, 1-221 (1998).

*41*, 280 **Benzeneselenenyl compds.** in organic synthesis, L.A. Wassjohann, U. Sinks, J. Prakt. Chem. *340*, 189-203 (1998).

*41*, 336 **Pyrazoles,** synthesis, K. Makino et al., J. Heterocycl. Chem. *35*, 489-97 (1998).

*41*, 463 **Ring closures via fluoroalkyl radicals** involving chiral sulfur-stabilized compds., P. Bravo et al., Gazz. Chim. Ital. *127*, 629-35 (1997).

*41*, 622 **Sulfonyl-1,3-dienes in synthesis,** J.-E. Bäckvall et al., Chem. Rev. *98*, 2291-312 (1998).

*41*, 913 **Carbaporphyrin chemistry**, highlights, H.J. Nilsen, A. Ghosh, Acta Chem. Scand. *52*, 827-30 (1998).

*42*, 54 **Zinc bis(tetrahydridoborate)**, S. Narasimhan, R. Balakumar, Aldrichimica Acta *31*, 3-15 (1998).

*42*, 308 **Aminosugar and aminocyclitol synthesis** via intramolecular delivery of tethered nitrogen functions, S. Knapp, Chem. Soc. Rev. *28*, 61-72 (1999).

*42*, 557 **Phosphorylated aldehydes**, preparation and synthetic uses, B. Iorga et al., Tetrahedron *54*, 14637-78 (1998).

*42*, 616 **Ligand design** with the right bite, P.C.J. Kamer et al., CHEMTECH *28*, 27-33 (1998); planar chiral arenechromium(0) complexes: potential ligands for asym. catalysis, C. Bolm, K. Muñiz, Chem. Soc. Rev. *28*, 51-60 (1999); cis-1-aminoindan-2-ol in asym. synthesis, C.H. Senanayake, Aldrichimica Acta *31*, 3-15 (1998).

*42*, 761 **Silicon-mediated synthesis of organosulfur compds.,** A. Degl'Innocenti, A. Capperucci, Sulfur Reports *20*, 279-395 (1998).

*42*, 970 **Di(hetaryl)ethenes**, photochromic, synthesis, M. Irie, K. Uchida, Bull. Chem. Soc. Jpn. *71*, 985-96 (1998).

*42*, 997 **Chiral 3-coordinated selenium and tellurium compds.**, isolation and stereochemistry, T. Shimizu, N. Kamigata, Rev. Heteroatom Chem. *18*, 11-35 (1998).

*43*, 45 **Asym. reduction of ketones** with borane using chiral 1,3,2-oxazaborolidines as catalyst, E.J. Corey, C.J. Helal, Angew. Chem. Int. Ed. Engl. *37*, 1986-2012 (1998).

*43*, 270 **Azolium N-imides**, triazolidinium and pyrazolidinium ylids, L.L. Rodina et al., Heterocycles *49*, 587-618 (1998).

*43*, 299 **Unnatural α-aminocarboxylic acids**, synthesis with transaminases, P.P. Taylor et al., Trends Biotechnol *16*, 412-8 (1998).

*43*, 587 **β,β-Difunctionalized keteneaminals**, synthesis and properties, V.A. Makarov, V.G. Granik, Russ. Chem. Rev. *67*, 1013-31 (1998).

*43*, 715 **Alkynylcarbenium and related unsatd. cations**, S.M. Luk'yanov et al., Russ. Chem. Rev. *67*, 899-939 (1998).

*43*, 722 **Phosphorylated allenes**, reaction with electrophiles, I.V. Alabugin, V.K. Brel, Russ. Chem. Rev. *66*, 205-24 (1997).

*43*, 877 **Aldehyde synthesis from thiazoles**, A. Dondoni, Synthesis *1998*, 1681-706.

*43*, 962 **Intramolecular Heck reactions**, J.T. Link, L.E. Overmann, CHEMTECH *28*, 19-26 (1998).

*43*, 981 **Functionalized bicyclo[3.2.1]octanes**, synthesis and use, M.-H. Filippini, J. Rodriguez, Chem. Rev. *99*, 27-76 (1999).

*44*, 7 **Heterocyclic N-hydroxyamides**, synthesis and reactivity, J. Ohkanda, A. Katoh, Rev. Heteroatom Chem. *18*, 87-118 (1998).

*44*, 229 **Chiral organofluorine compds.**, catalytic asym. synthesis, K. Iseki, Tetrahedron *54*, 13887-914 (1998).

*44*, 410 **Trimethylsilyl halide-oxidant** combinations in organic synthesis, P.S. Vankar et al., Org. Prep. Proc. Intern. *30*, 373-400 (1998).

*44*, 651 **Microwave techniques** in synthesis and **modification of zeolite catalysts**, C.S. Cundy, Coll. Czech. Chem. Commun. *63*, 1699-723 (1998).

*46*, 3 **Protective groups** (literature review of 1997), K. Jarowicki, P. Kocienski, J. Chem. Soc. Perkin Trans. I *1998*, 4005-37.

*46*, 47 **Asym. reduction of endocyclic carbon-nitrogen double bonds**, biomolecules, M.A. Yurovskaya, A.V. Karchava, Tetrahedron:Asym. *9*, 3331-52 (1998).

*46*, 214 **Glycosidation of silylated alcohols**, T. Ziegler, J. Prakt. Chem. *340*, 204-13 (1998).

*46*, 317 **Reductions with sodium tetrahydridoborate in carboxylic acid media**, G.W. Gribble, Chem. Soc. Rev. *27*, 395-404 (1998).

*46*, 572 **Electrochemistry of phosphorus and sulfur compds.**, and synthetic applications, H. Maeda, H. Ohmori, Acc. Chem. Res. *32*, 72-80 (1999); **organometallic electrochemistry**, recent advances, F. Battaglini et al., J. Organometal Chem. *547*, 1-21 (1997).

*46*, 736 **Water-soluble functionalized phosphines**, design and development, K.V. Katti et al., Acc. Chem. Res. *32*, 9-17 (1999).

*46*, 766 **Five- and six-membered silicon-carbon heterocycles**. Part 2. Synthetic modification and applications, J. Hermanns, B. Schmidt, J. Chem. Soc. Perkin Trans. I *1999*, 81-102.

*46*, 767 **Acyclic quaternary α-aminocarboxylic acids**, stereoselective synthesis, Part 1, C. Cativiela et al., Tetrahedron:Asym. *9*, 3517-99 (1998); **χ-constrained aromatic α-aminocarboxylic acids**, synthesis, conformational analysis and use, S.E. Gibson et al., Tetrahedron *55*, 585-615 (1999).

*47*, 113 **Heterogeneous catalysts** for liquid-phase oxidation, R.A. Sheldon et al., Acc. Chem. Res. *31*, 485-93 (1998).

*47*, 287 **Novel amine chemistry** based on DMAP-catalyzed acylation, U. Ragnarsson, L. Grehn. Acc. Chem. Res. *31*, 494-501 (1998).

*47*, 427 **Electrophilic cyclization of unsaturated amides**, S. Robin, G. Rousseau, Tetrahedron *54*, 13681-736 (1998).

*47*, 549 **Tricarbonyliron complexes**: an approach to acyclic stereocontrol, L.R. Cox, S.V. Ley, Chem. Soc. Rev. *27*, 301-14 (1998).

*47*, 552 **Selenothiocarboxylic and diselenocarboxylic acid esters**, synthesis, T. Murai, S. Kato, Sulfur Reports *20*, 397-418 (1998).

*47*, 646 **Non-linear effects in asym. synthesis** and stereoselective reactions: a ten year investigation, C. Girard, H.B. Kagan, Angew. Chem. Int. Ed. Engl. *37*, 2922-59 (1998); catalytic asym. synthesis (literature review from April-December 1996), M. Wills, J. Chem. Soc. Perkin Trans. I *1998*, 3101-20.

*47*, 955 **Asym. intramolecular insertion of metal carbenes** in carbon-hydrogen bonds, G.A. Sulikowski et al., Tetrahedron:Asym. *9*, 3145-69 (1998).

*48*, 356 **Intermolecular radical reactions** of phosphorus-containing carbon-centred radicals with alkenes, P. Balczewski, M. Mikolajczyk, Rev. Heteroatom Chem. *18*, 37-59 (1998).

*48*, 640 **Bucky-balls and bucky-bowls**, synthesis, G. Mehta, H.S.P. Rao, Tetrahedron *54*, 13325-70 (1998); **fulleropyrrolidines**, M. Prato, M. Maggini, Acc. Chem. Res. *31*, 519-26 (1998).

*48*, 691   **Transition metal catalysis** in organic synthesis, review of 1997 literature, L. Tonks, J.M.J. Williams, J. Chem. Soc. Perkin Trans. I *1998*, 3637-52; **transition metals** in organic synthesis, 1997 highlights, L.S. Hegedus, Coord. Chem. Rev. *175*, 159-270 (1998).

*49*, 211   **Hypervalent iodine reagents** in carbohydrate chemistry, A. Kirschning, Eur. J. Org. Chem. *1998*, 2267-74.

*49*, 230   **Ring expansion of squaric acid derivs.** for synthesis of polyfunctionalized carbo- and hetero-cyclics, M. Ohno, S. Eguchi et al., Synlett *1998*, 1167-74.

*49*, 515   **Chiral organoselenium compds.**, T. Wirth, Tetrahedron *55*, 1-28 (1999).

*49*, 638   **α,β-Unsatd. nitriles**, ring closures with carbonyl compds., Y.A. Sharanin et al., Russ. Chem. Rev. *67*, 393-422 (1998).

*49*, 703   **Asym. Claisen rearrangement**, H. Ito, T. Taguchi, Chem. Soc. Rev. *28*, 43-50 (1999).

*49*, 985   **Epothilones**, total syntheses and biological properties, K.C. Nicolaou et al., Angew. Chem. Int. Ed. Engl. *37*, 2014-45 (1998); chemistry and biology of epothilones, R. Finlay, Chem. Ind. *24*, 991-6 (1997).

*50*, 53    **Homogeneous oxidation of alkanes** by electrophilic late transition metals, S.S. Stahl et al., Angew. Chem. Int. Ed. Engl. *37*, 2180-92 (1998).

*50*, 341   **Polarity-reversal catalysis** of hydrogen-atom abstraction: concepts and applications, B.P. Roberts, Chem. Soc. Rev. *28*, 25-36 (1999).

*50*, 498   **Asym. Michael addition**, J. Leonard, S. Merino et al., Eur. J. Org. Chem. *1998*, 2051-61.

*50*, 555   **Solid-phase organic reactions**. Part 3: A review of the literature November 1996-December 1997, S. Booth et al., Tetrahedron *54*, 15385-444 (1998); review of literature covering October 1996 to October 1997, R.C.D. Brown, J. Chem. Soc. Perkin Trans. I *1998*, 3293-320; **monitoring solid-phase organic reactions** directly on the resin support, B. Yan, Acc. Chem. Res. *31*, 621-30 (1998); **solid-supported reagent strategies** for rapid purification of combinatorial synthesis products, R.J. Booth, J.C. Hodges, Acc. Chem. Res. *32*, 18-26 (1999); **synthesis of compound libraries**, new methodologies, S. Kobayashi, Chem. Soc. Rev. *28*, 1-16 (1999); combinatorial synthesis: seven papers, Chem. Ind. (London) *1998*, Issue No.19.

*51*, 24    **Chiral Δ$^2$-oxazolines** in asym. synthesis, A.I. Meyers, J. Heterocycl. Chem. *35*, 991-1002 (1998).

*51*, 30    **Modular approach in supramolecular chemistry**, I. Higler, D.N. Reinhoudt et al., Eur. J. Org. Chem. *1998*, 2689-702.

*51*, 38    **Tin-free radical sources**, P.A. Baguley, J.C. Walton, Angew. Chem. Int. Ed. Engl. *37*, 3072-82 (1998).

*51*, 91    **Organic halides** (annual review), S.D.R. Christie, J. Chem. Soc. Perkin Trans. I *1998*, 1577-88.

*51*, 138   **Chemistry of 1,2-diamines**, D. Lucet, T. Le Gall et al., Angew. Chem. Int. Ed. Engl. *37*, 2562-79 (1998).

*51*, 162   **Amines and amides** (literature review of 1997), M. North, J. Chem. Soc. Perkin Trans. I *1998*, 2959-72.

*51*, 171   **Aromatic and heteroaromatic substitution** with heteroatom nucleophiles, recent advances, C.G. Frost, P. Mendonça, J. Chem. Soc. Perkin Trans. I *1998*, 2615; **2,3-arylamines and aryl ethers** from aryl halides and triflates under transition metal catalysis, J.F. Hartwig, Angew. Chem. Int. Ed. Engl. *37*, 2046-67 (1998).

*51*, 227   **Aldehydes and ketones** (annual review), N.J. Lawrence, J. Chem. Soc. Perkin Trans. I *1998*, 1739-49.

*51*, 312   *trans*-**Hydrindan ring synthesis** and their origins in steroidal chemistry. Vitamin D total synthesis, P. Jankowski et al., Tetrahedron *54*, 12071-150 (1998).

*51*, 376 **Saturated N-heterocyclics** (literature review of 1997), A. Nadin, J. Chem. Soc. Perkin Trans. I *1998*, 3493-513.

*51*, 399 **Asym. synthesis with chiral 1,3-dithiane 1-oxides**, S.M. Allin, P.C. Bulman Page, Org. Prep. Proc. Intern. *30*, 145-76 (1998).

*51*, 435 **Use of Lewis acids in radical reactions**, P. Renaud, M. Gerster, Angew. Chem. Int. Ed. Engl. *37*, 2562-79 (1998).

*52*, 9 **Carboxylic acids and esters**, literature review from August 1996 to 31st July 1997, A.S. Franklin, J. Chem. Soc. Perkin Trans. I *1998*, 2451-65.

*52*, 267 **Catalysts from an encoded polymer-bound library**, thermographic selection, S.J. Taylor, J.P. Morken, Science *280*, 267-70 (1998).

*52*, 274 **Reactions of carbenes and nitrenes** in noble gas matrices at cryogenic temp., H. Tomioka, Bull. Chem. Soc. Jpn. *71*, 1501-24 (1998).

*52*, 284 **Cycloaddition**, literature review from July 1996 to December 1997, C.P. Dell, J. Chem. Soc. Perkin Trans. I *1998*, 3873-905.

*52*, 317 **Bimetallic catalysis** by late transition metal complexes, E.K. van den Beuken, B.L. Feringa, Tetrahedron *54*, 12985-3012 (1998).

*52*, 319 **Chelation-assisted hydroacylation**, C.-H. Jun et al., Synlett *1999*, 1-12.

*52*, 407 **Saturated O-heterocyclics** (3-membered to medium-ring compds.), literature review from 1st October 1996 to 31st March 1998, M.C. Elliott, J. Chem. Soc. Perkin Trans. I *1998*, 4175-200.

*52*, 435 **Silylketenes**, A. Pommier et al., J. Chem. Soc. Perkin Trans. I *1998*, 2105-18.

*52*, 497 **Chiral ferrocenes**, synthesis and applications in asym. synthesis, C.J. Richards, A.J. Locke, Tetrahedron:Asym. *9*, 2377-408 (1998).

*53*, 16 **Synthesis of S-functions and Se-functions** (thiols, sulfides, sulfoxides, sulfones and Se analogs), C.P. Baird, C.M. Rayner, J. Chem. Soc. Perkin Trans. I *1998*, 1973.

*53*, 31 **Supercritical fluids**, eleven reviews (incl. homogeneous and heterogeneous catalysis in supercritical fluids and organic reactions in supercritical water), Chem. Rev. *99*, Issue No.2, (1999).

*53*, 57 **Fluorous phase separation techniques** in catalysis, E. de Wolf et al., Chem. Soc. Rev. *28*, 37-42 (1999); **fluorous biphase chemistry**, I.T. Horvath, Acc. Chem. Res. *31*, 641-50 (1998); **separations** with potential, K. Bartle, P. Myers, Chem. Brit. *34*, 42-4 (1998).

*53*, 266 **Asym. catalysis** with synthetic chiral polymers, L. Pu, Tetrahedron:Asym. *9*, 1457-77 (1998).

*53*, 280 **Chromium(II)- and chromium(III)-mediated syntheses**, L.A. Wessjohann, G. Scheid, Synthesis *1999*, 1-36.

*53*, 321 **Ring opening metathesis**, G.D. Cuny, J.R. Hauske, CHEMTECH *28*, 25-31 (1998).

*53*, 322 **Saturated and unsaturated lactones**, synthesis, literature review from November 1996-October 1997, I. Collins, J. Chem. Soc. Perkin Trans. I *1998*, 1869-88.

*53*, 386 **Michael addition of benzotriazole-stabilized carbanions**, A.R. Katritzky, M.M. Qi, Coll. Czech. Chem. Commun. *63*, 599-613 (1998); **benzotriazole-based intermediates,** use in synthesis, A.R. Katritzky, S.A. Belyakov, Aldrichimica Acta *31*, 35-45 (1998).

*53*, 395 **Acylsilanes** in organic synthesis, B.F. Bonini et al., Gazz. Chim. Ital. *127*, 619-28 (1997).

*53*, 407 **Main group organometallics** in synthesis, I. Coldham, J. Chem. Soc. Perkin Trans. I *1998*, 1343-64.

*54*, 51 **N-O Compds.** (nitro compds., nitrones, hydroxylamines, N-oxides, nitrates): recent developments in organic synthesis, S.-C. Tsay, J.R. Hwu et al., Synlett *1998*, 939-49.

*54*, 52 **Steroidal isoxazoles, isoxazolines and isoxazolidines**, C. Camoutsis, S. Nikolaropoulos, J. Heterocyc. Chem. *35*, 731-59 (1998).

*54*, 133 **1,1-Nitrosoethylene derivs.**, L.I. Mikhailovich, I.S. Leibovich, Russ. Chem. Rev. *67*, 523-41 (1998).

*54*, 160 **Seven-membered oxacycles**, synthesis, J.O. Hoberg, Tetrahedron *54*, 12631-70 (1998).

*54*, 240 **Syntheses with α,β-acetyleneiodonium salts**, V.V. Zhdankin, P.J. Stang, Tetrahedron *54*, 10927-66 (1998).

*54*, 306 **Ethylene derivs.**, new syntheses, Y. Shen, Acc. Chem. Res. *31*, 584-92 (1998).

*54*, 316 **Asym. Pauson-Khand reaction**, S.T. Ingate, J. Marco-Contelles, Org. Prep. Proc. Intern. *30*, 121-43 (1998).

*54*, 349 **Reduced quinolines**, chemistry, V. Kouznetsov et al., J. Heterocycl. Chem. *35*, 761-93 (1998).

*54*, 365 **Zirconocene olefin and alkyne complexes**, preparation and use, E. Negishi, T. Takahashi, Bull. Chem. Soc. Jpn. *71*, 755-69 (1998).

*55*, 79 **Solvent-free syntheses** using focused microwaves, A. Loupy et al., Synthesis *1998*, 1213-34.

*55*, 220 **Asym. synthesis of chiral phosphines** as ligands for asym. catalysis from organophosphorus(III)-borane complexes, M. Ohff, A. Börner et al., Synthesis *1998*, 1391-415; chemistry of phosphine- and amine-borane complexes, B. Carboni, L. Monnier, Tetrahedron *55*, 1197-248 (1999).

## Index to Volume 55

As in previous volumes, reactions are indexed from both the starting material and product aspects, e.g. '**Azides** startg. m.f. amines' and '**Amines** from azides'. Nomenclature for complex functions can be located under the 'special s.' sub-entry, e.g. '**Carboxylic acids** special s. aminocarboxylic acids' or by consulting the Formula Index of Complex Functional Groups (Volume *48*, p. 471).

Hydrogenated and functionalized ring systems are indexed by the conventional reversal, e.g. '**Pyridines, aryl-**', the only important exception to the rule being alkylideneisocyclics which are indexed as such, e.g. '**Alkylidenecyclopentanes**'.

As from Volume *51*, '**Epoxides**' has been used in place of 'Oxido compds.'; '**Thiiranes**' in place of 'Sulfido compds.'; '**Diels-Alder reaction**' in place of 'Diene synthesis'; and '**Benzo[*b*]thiophenes**' in place of 'Thianaphthenes'.

References to abstracts in this volume are in the format **55**, 234. An entry such as '**Oxazoles, 2-aryl-, 38,** 836s**55**' refers to the indexing of a supplementary reference, which must be followed up via the Supplementary References Index (p. 296).

**Absolute configuration** s. Configuration, abs.
**Acetalation 28**, 148s55
**Acetals** (s.a. Ketals, Transacetalation)
–, aldol-type condensation with parallel differentiated recognition **55**, 446
–, cleavage under neutral conditions **55**, 9
– special s.
  ethyleneacetals
  hydroxyacetals
  stannylacetals
– startg. m. f.
  *anti*-glycol monoethers **55**, 352
  mercaptals, cyclic **55**, 202, 204
*p*-**Acetamidophenyl glycosides**
– as intermediates **55**, 11
**Acetate aldol condensation, asym.**
–, equivalent **55**, 233
**Acetic anhydride**
– as reactant **55**, 79
**Acetonitrile**
– as reactant **55**, 330
**Acetox...** s. Acoxy...
**Acetyl...** s.a. Acyl...
**2-Acetylamino-2′-diacetylamino-1,1′-binaphthyl, chiral**
– as reagent **55**, 149
**Acetylation**
– under microwave irradiation, solventless **55**, 79
**N-Acetylation, asym.**
–, resolution, kinetic of amines via – **55**, 149
**O-Acetylation 55**, 80
**O-Acetylation, asym.**
–, resolution, kinetic of alcohols, sec. via – **55**, 84
–, **heterogeneous 55**, 84
–, **partial, heterogeneous 55**, 98
–, **selective, solid-state 32**, 161s55
**Acetyl chloride**
– as reactant **55**, 98
**Acetylene**
– as reactant **55**, 328
–, Sonogashira coupling with – **27**, 851s55
**2-Acetylenealcohol O-derivs.**
– startg. m. f.
  acetylene derivs., synthesis, asym. **55**, 347
**2-Acetylenealcohols**
– special s.
  aryl-2-acetylenealcohols
– startg. m. f.
  1,4-dioxanes, 2,5-dialkoxy- (from 2 molecules) **55**, 63
  2(5*H*)-furanones, 4-arylseleno-, carbonylation **55**, 457
  –, 4-arylthio-, – **55**, 457
**2-Acetylenealcohols, chiral 55**, 347
**3-Acetylenealcohols**
– from
  allenylstannanes, synthesis, asym. **49**, 898s55
**Acetylenealdehydes**
– startg. m. f.
  2(5*H*)-furanones, 4,5-fused **55**, 292
α,β-**Acetylenealdehydes**
– from
  acetylene derivs., terminal **55**, 361
**2-Acetylene-2′-aminoalcohols, chiral 24**, 663s55
α,β-**Acetylenecarbonyl compds.**

–, Michael addition to – **47**, 631s55
*o*-**Acetylenecarboxylic acid halides**
–, ring closures **55**, 223
α,β-**Acetylenecarboxylic acids**
– startg. m. f.
  coumarins **55**, 336
**Acetylene derivs.**
–, addition, gold(I)-catalyzed of alcohols to – **55**, 63
–, allylmercuration, intramolecular, regiospecific **55**, 274
–, 1,2-allylsilylation, –, – **55**, 315
– from
  2-acetylenealcohol O-derivs., synthesis, asym. **55**, 347
  acetylene derivs., terminal, synthesis **55**, 490
  enetellurides **55**, 490
  1,2-ethylene-1,2-dihalides **28**, 950s55; **51**, 480s55
– special s.
  acoxyacetylenes
  diynes
  enynes
  sulfinyloxyacetylenes
  tolans
– startg. m. f.
  (E,E)-1-aryltelluro-1,3-dienes, synthesis, regiospecific **55**, 272
  benzene ring (from 3 molecules) **55**, 289
  2-cyclopentenones **55**, 281
  enestannanes, conversion, regiostereospecific **55**, 216
  enetellurides, synthesis **55**, 272
  (E)-1,3-enynes, via hydroboration **55**, 271
  (E)-α,β-ethylene-α′-hydroxyketones **55**, 244
  (E)-α,β-ethylene-β-nitroiodides **55**, 179
  α,β-ethylenephosphine oxides, reversal of regioselectivity **55**, 217
  (Z)-α,β-ethylene-β-silylaldimines **55**, 294
  *p*-quinone methids, 6-acyl- **55**, 259
  1-stannyl-1,3-enynes, synthesis **55**, 300
  vinylcyclopropanes **55**, 282
**Acetylene derivs., macrocyclic**
– from
  diynes, metathesis **55**, 497
**Acetylene derivs., terminal** (s.a. Lithium acetylides)
–, C-alkylation with ethylene derivs. **55**, 271
– special s.
  ethynylarenes
– startg. m. f.
  α,β-acetylenealdehydes **55**, 361
  acetylene derivs., synthesis **55**, 490
  (Z)-β-arylseleno-α,β-ethyleneketones **55**, 267
  enetellurides, synthesis **55**, 490
  enol phosphinates **55**, 71
  (E)-1,3-enynes **55**, 271
  heterocyclics, 5-membered **55**, 429
  ketals **55**, 63
  methyl ketones **55**, 63
  (E)-styrenes **55**, 280
**Acetylenedicobalt hexacarbonyl complexes**
–, decomplexation, reductive **55**, 35

– startg. m. f.
  ethylene derivs. **55**, 35
**3-Acetyleneepoxides, chiral 51**, 65s55
β,γ-**Acetylenehalides, chiral 55**, 347
α,β-**Acetylenehydroxamic acid esters**
– from
  acetylenestannanes **55**, 462
α,β-**Acetyleneiodonium salts**
– startg. m. f.
  2-azabicyclo[3.3.0]octa-4,6-dienes, 2-sulfonyl- **55**, 370
–, syntheses with –, review **54**, 240s55
**1-Acetylenesilanes** s. Silylacetylenes
**2-Acetylenesilanes**
– from
  3-silylenol triflates **29**, 920s55
**Acetylenestannanes**
– special s.
  tri-*n*-butyl(ethynyl)stannane
– startg. m. f.
  α,β-acetylenehydroxamic acid esters **55**, 462
  1-stannyl-1,3-enynes, synthesis **55**, 300
**Acetylides**
– special s.
  lithium acetylides
**Acetyl nitrite**
– as reagent **55**, 8
**Acids, solid** s. Solid acids
**Acoxy-2-acetylenes**
– from
  acetylene derivs. **51**, 72s55
α-**Acoxycarboxylic acid esters**
– from
  α-acoxy-α,β-ethylenecarboxylic acid esters, reduction, asym. **55**, 38
–, hydrolysis, asym. **28**, 13s55
**Acoxy compds.** (s.a. Carboxylic acid esters)
– from
  *tert*-butyldimethylsilyl ethers **55**, 110
  ethers **55**, 105
  pyran-2-yl ethers, tetrahydro- **55**, 110
β-**Acoxy-α-diazocarbonyl compds.**
– startg. m. f.
  α-acoxy-α,β-ethylenecarbonyl compds. **55**, 483
**Acoxyepoxides**
– from
  ethylenealcohols **55**, 68
α-**Acoxy-α,β-ethylenecarbonyl compds.**
– from
  β-acoxy-α-diazocarbonyl compds. **55**, 483
α-**Acoxy-α,β-ethylenecarboxylic acid esters**
– startg. m. f.
  α-acoxycarboxylic acid esters, reduction, asym. **55**, 3
**4-Acoxy-2-ethyleneethers**
– from
  1,3-dienes, regiostereospecific conversion **55**, 72
β-**Acoxy-α,β-ethyleneiodonium salts**
– startg. m. f.
  aziridines, 2-acyl-, N-protected **55**, 367
  (E)-α,β-epoxyketones **55**, 468
β-**Acoxy-α,β-ethyleneketones**
– from
  α-diketones **55**, 427
  2-ketobismuthonium salts **55**, 427

Acoxy-2-ethylenes (s.a. Carboxylic acid allyl esters)
-, C-α-allylation, regiostereospecific with – 55, 358
- from
allenes 55, 73
- special s.
allyl acetate
- startg. m. f.
γ,δ-ethylenecarboxylic acid esters, synthesis, asym. 55, 460
ethylene derivs., synthesis, regiostereospecific 55, 455
1,2-Acoxy group migration 55, 483
ω-Acoxyhalides
- from
ethers, cyclic 55, 105
1,2-Acoxyhalides
- from
ethylene derivs. 53, 186s55
trans-1,2-Acoxyhalides
- from
ethylene derivs. 55, 180
α-Acoxyketones
-, hydrolysis, asym. 28, 13s55
1,2-Acoxysulfonates
- from
2-furyl ketones 55, 111
glycols 55, 111
9(5H)-Acridones 34, 929s55
Acylals
- special s.
ethyleneacylals
- startg. m. f.
aldehydes, with kinetic resolution 55, 6
Acylamines (s.a. Carboxylic acid amides)
- special s.
di(acylamines)
- startg. m. f.
β-acylaminoaldehydes 55, 350
2-Acylaminoalcohols
-, resolution, kinetic 52, 497s55
β-Acylaminoaldehydes
- from
acylamines 55, 350
aldehydes (2 molecules) 55, 350
α-Acylaminocarboxylic acid esters
- from
α-acylamino-α,β-ethylenecarboxylic acid esters, hydrogenation, asym. 55, 36
Δ²-5-oxazolones, resolution, kinetic, dynamic 55, 57
– – –, α,α-disubst., chiral 20, 116s55
α-Acylamino-α,β-ethylenecarboxylic acid esters
- startg. m. f.
α-acylaminocarboxylic acid esters, hydrogenation, asym. 55, 36
α-Acylamino-β-ketocarboxylic acid esters
-, reduction with dynamic kinetic resolution 55, 26
o-Acylaminoketones
- special s.
o-(prolylamino)ketones
α-Acylamino-γ-lactones, chiral 35, 474s55
α-Acylaminonitriles
- special s.
α-(trifluoroacetylamino)nitriles
2-Acylamino-1,1,1-trifluorides 44, 577s55

Acylation
- special s.
acetylation
C-Acylation (s.a. Friedel-Crafts acylation)
- of alkylidenephosphoranes 55, 387
C-Acylation, asym.
- of pyrazoles, 1-acyl- 39, 749s55
C-Acylation, polymer-based
- of methylene groups, active 55, 349
N-Acylation
- special s.
N-acetylation
N-formylation
- using a polymer-based base 55, 340
- using 4-dimethylaminopyridine (as catalyst), review 47, 287s55
N-Acylation, selective
- under microwave irradiation 22, 365s55
O-Acylation
- of alcohols, prim. 55, 110
- special s.
O-acetylation
O-formylation
per-O-acetylation
- with N-acylpyridinium salts 38, 158s55
-, Lewis-acid catalyzed 55, 81
Acyl carbanion equivalents
-, acylzirconocene chlorides as – 55, 244
-, 1,4-addition with – 55, 302
N-Acylcarboxylic acid amides
- from
carboxylic acid pentafluorophenyl esters 55, 165
N-silylcarboxylic acid amides 55, 165
Acylcyanides
- startg. m. f.
β-diketones, sym. 55, 471
Acyl glycosides
- special s.
acyl 2-iodo-2-deoxyglycosides
β-Acyl glycosides
- from
glycosides, polymer-based 55, 104
N→C-Acyl group migration
- in N-acylurethans 55, 313
Acyl halides s. Carboxylic acid halides
β-(Acylhydrazino)carbonyl compds.
- from
acylhydrazones 55, 439
enoxysilanes 55, 439
Acylhydrazones
- startg. m. f.
β-(acylhydrazino)carbonyl compds. 55, 439
thiochromans 55, 362
Acyl hydroxamates
- from
nitro compds. 55, 137
N-Acylimmonium salts, cyclic
-, syntheses, polymer-based via – 38, 982s55
-, synthesis, asym. of Δ³-2-pyrrolones, 5-subst. via –, review 27, 947s55
Acyl 2-iodo-2-deoxyglycosides 55, 180
O-Acylisoureas
- as intermediates 47, 54s55
Acylmanganation 55, 301
Acylnitroso compds.
-, ene reaction with – 55, 128
Acylophenones, β-functionalized 55, 453

Acylphosphonic acid esters
- special s.
ethyleneacylphosphonic acid esters
Acylsilanes
- in synthesis, review 53, 395s55
N-Acylsuccinimides
- special s.
N-(ethyleneacyl)succinimides
N-Acylsulfonic acid amides
- startg. m. f.
nitriles 55, 144
N-Acylurethans
- startg. m. f.
α-(carbalkoxyamino)ketones 55, 313
Acylzirconocene chlorides
- as acyl carbanion equivalents 55, 244
Adamantanes, 1-vinyl- 29, 836s55
Adenines, N-methyl- and N,N-dimethyl-
-, chemistry, review 33, 403s55
1,4-Addition (s.a. CC⇓CC, Michael addition)
- special s.
radical 1,4-addition
- to α,β-ethylenecarboxylic acids 55, 260
with
acyl carbanion equivalents 55, 302
2-ethylenesilanes 55, 448
lithium compds., organo- 55, 260
1,4-Addition, asym.
- of boronic acids, α,β-unsatd. to α,β-ethyleneketones 55, 452
- to
N-(α,β-ethyleneacyl)-N-heterocyclics 37, 658s55
α,β-ethylenesulfoxides 55, 270
1,1-nitroethylene derivs. 52, 297s55
- with lithium organo(α-sulfoximinyl)-cuprates, chiral 55, 368
-, asym., nickel-catalyzed
- to α,β-ethyleneacetals 55, 268
1,6-Addition-α-alkylation, stereo-specific
- of Δ²-oxazolines, 2-(1-naphthyl)- 55, 331
Alcohols
-, addition, gold(I)-catalyzed to acetylene derivs. 55, 63
-, determination of abs. configuration 5, 666s55
- from
N-alkoxyphthalimides 55, 1
carboxylic acids, radical degradation with loss of 1 C-atom 55, 108
α,β-ethyleneoxo compds., reduction 55, 25
oxo compds., reduction 55, 21, 23, 24, 25
– –, –, heterogeneous 55, 22
– –, (sec. alcohols), hydrogenation, homogeneous, asym. 55, 29
– –, (– –), Noyori hydrogenation, asym. 55, 26
– –, (– –), reduction, asym. 55, 26, 28, 29
– –, (– –) –, –, cathodic, enzyme-catalyzed 42, 22s55
– –, (– –) –, –, 1,3,2-oxazaborolidine-catalyzed, review 43, 45s55
– –, synthesis 55, 231, 238
– –, (sec. alcohols), synthesis 55, 242
– –, (– –), synthesis, asym. 55, 237

trialkylboranes, synthesis **55**, 231
–, oxidation with oxochromium(VI)-
  amine reagents, review **41**, 243s**55**
– special s.
  acetylenealcohols
  allenealcohols
  aminoalcohols
  benzylalcohols
  deuterioalcohols
  diols
  epoxyalcohols
  ethylenealcohols
  halogenhydrins
– startg. m. f.
  alkoxysilanes, polymer-based **55**, 24
  amines, prim., via azides with inversion **55**, 142
  oxo compds. (ketones) **55**, 113
  sulfenic acid esters **55**, 54
  trihalogenomethyl sulfones **55**, 209
  urethans **55**, 133
  –, (from tert. alcohols) **55**, 60
**Alcohols, prim.**
–, O-acylation **55**, 110
– from
  carboxylic acid esters **55**, 43
  – acids **15**, 71s**55**; **55**, 41
  Δ⁴-thiazoline-2-thiones, 3-acoxy-, oxidative decarboxylation **55**, 108
– startg. m. f.
  carboxylic acids **55**, 77
  α,β-ethylenecarboxylic acid esters, via in situ-Wittig synthesis with 2 extra C-atoms **55**, 451
**Alcohols, sec.**
–, racemization, catalyzed **53**, 500s**55**
–, resolution, kinetic by O-acetylation, asym. **55**, 84
**Alcohols, tert.**
– from
  ketones, synthesis, asym. **55**, 239
– resolution **44**, 214s**55**
– startg. m. f.
  isonitriles, tert. **55**, 140
**Aldehydes** (s.a. Carbonyl compds., Hydroacylation, Hydroformylation, Oxo compds., Tischchenko reaction)
–, aldol-type condensation with parallel differentiated recognition **55**, 446
– from
  acylals, with kinetic resolution **55**, 6
  alcohols s. OC↑H and under Oxo compds.
  carboxylic acids **55**, 47
  thiazoles, review **43**, 877s**55**
–, reduction s. under Oxo compds.
–, review (annual) **51**, 227s**55**
– special s.
  acetylenealdehydes
  acylaminoaldehydes
  aminoaldehydes
  epoxyaldehydes
  ethylenealdehydes
  halogenaldehydes
  hydroxyaldehydes
  phosphorylaldehydes
  siloxyaldehydes
– startg. m. f.
  β-acylaminoaldehydes (from 2 molecules) **55**, 350
  alcohols s. HC↓OC and under Oxo compds.

amines, prim., 3-component synthesis **55**, 332
2-aminoalcohols, synthesis **55**, 236
α-*prim*-amino-β-hydroxycarboxylic acids, synthesis, asym. **55**, 325
α-aminonitriles **55**, 341
β-arylseleno-β-carbalkoxy-γ-lactones, synthesis, stereospecific **55**, 329
benzofurans **55**, 371
benzo[*b*]thiophenes **55**, 371
α-(carbalkoxyamino)carboxylic acid amides **55**, 319
carboxylic acid esters **55**, 107
– – –, (with halides) **55**, 94
cyanohydrins **55**, 245
4,8-dioxa-1-azabicyclo[4.3.0]nonan-5-ones (from 2 molecules), synthesis, asym. **55**, 325
(E)-α,β-epoxyketones **55**, 468
3-ethylenealcohols, synthesis **55**, 286
–, –, asym. **55**, 441
–, –, –, regiospecific **55**, 433
–, –, regiostereospecific **55**, 474
4-ethylenealcohols, –, –, **55**, 290
α,β-ethyleneketones **55**, 355
–, polymer-based synthesis **55**, 327
(E)-α,β-ethylenesulfonic acid amides, with 1 extra C-atom **55**, 470
furan-3-carboxylic acid esters **55**, 429
*anti*-glycol monoethers **55**, 352
β-hydroxycarboxylic acids, synthesis, asym. with 2 extra C-atoms **55**, 233
α-hydroxyketones, synthesis **55**, 244
imidazoles, 5-amino-, N-condensed, polymer-based synthesis **55**, 340
mercaptals, unsym. **55**, 203
nitriles **55**, 146
4*H*-1,3-oxazin-4-ones, tetrahydro-, parallel synthesis **55**, 437
Δ²-oxazoline-4-carboxylic acid esters, asym. conversion **55**, 241
2*H*-pyrans, 3,6-dihydro-, 4-siloxy- **55**, 274
pyrazoles **55**, 425
4-pyrones, 2,3-dihydro-, via asym. cycloaddition **55**, 449
–, –, 6-amino- **55**, 399
β-siloxyaldehydes, synthesis, asym. with 2 extra C-atoms **55**, 233
γ′-siloxy-γ,δ-ethyleneboronic acid esters, synthesis **55**, 251
β-siloxyketones, synthesis, asym. **55**, 233
α-siloxynitriles, conversion, asym. **55**, 246
1,3,5-trioxanes, cyclotrimerization, catalytic **55**, 59
–, Wittig synthesis with *in situ*-generated – **55**, 451
**Aldehydes, ar.**
– from
  benzyl ethers **55**, 118
  – halides **55**, 99
δ-**Aldehydocarboxylic acid esters, chiral** **55**, 266
**Aldimines** (s.a. Azomethines)
– from
  α-iminocarboxylic acids **55**, 48
– startg. m. f.
  β-aminoketones **55**, 440
  α-di(azomethines), sym. **55**, 321

3-ethyleneamines, synthesis, asym. with 3 extra C-atoms **55**, 461
α-(trifluoroacetylamino)nitriles, –, – **55**, 253
**Aldol condensation** (s.a. Michael addition-aldol condensation, Olefin aldol reaction, Ozonolysis-Aldol condensation)
**Aldol condensation, asym.**
–, α-cyano-β-hydroxycarboxylic acid esters by – **55**, 250
– special s.
  acetate aldol condensation, asym.
– –, **heterogeneous**
  – with hydrotalcite as base **55**, 335
– –, **Lewis acid-catalyzed, regiostereo-specific**
  – with ketones **55**, 248
– –, **regiospecific**
  – with aryl migration **55**, 390
– –, **ruthenium(III)-catalyzed 55**, 355
– –, **vinylogous 55**, 234
**Aldol-type condensation**
–, parallel reactions with discrimination between ketones and acetals (or aldehydes) **55**, 446
– –, asym., vinylogous **55**, 434
– –, **chelation-controlled, double-asym.**
  – with α-amino-β-hydroxyaldehydes, protected **55**, 240
– –, **uncatalyzed**
  – with enoxy(hydrido)silanes **55**, 422
**Aldonohydrazonolactones**
– from
  aldose hydrazones **55**, 112
**Aldose hydrazones**
– startg. m. f.
  aldonohydrazonolactones **55**, 112
**Aldoximes**
– startg. m. f.
  benzimidazoles **55**, 151
**Alkaloids**
– by radical ring closure, review **29**, 970s**55**
**Alkanes** s. Hydrocarbons
**Alkenes** s. Ethylene derivs.
**Alkoximes**
– special s.
  ethylenealkoximes
– startg. m. f.
  pyrrolidine-3-carboxylic acid esters, 1-alkoxy- **55**, 257
*anti*-α-**Alkoxy-β-aminocarboxylic acid esters, chiral** **55**, 444
**N-Alkoxycarbamyl halides**
– startg. m. f.
  hydroxamic acid esters, synthesis **55**, 462
**N-Alkoxydicarboxylic acid imides**
– special s.
  N-alkoxyphthalimides
γ-**Alkoxy-α,β-ethylenehalides**
– startg. m. f.
  3-ethylenealcohols, rearrangement, reductive **55**, 484
α-**Alkoxy-α,β-ethyleneketones**
– special s.
  α-allyloxy-α,β-ethyleneketones
β′-**Alkoxy-α,β-ethyleneketones**
– special s.
  β-alkoxy-α-methyleneketones

Alkoxy-2-ethylenes (s.a. 2-Ethyleneethers)
– special s.
  allyl ethers
– startg. m. f.
  α,β-ethyleneoxo compds. 55, 118
Alkoxy-4-ethylenes
– from
  ethylene derivs., electron-deficient, with 3 extra C-atoms 55, 475
o-Alkoxyhalides
– special s.
  o-allyloxyhalides
α-Alkoxylactones 34, 46s55
δ-Alkoxy-δ-lactones 47, 698s55
Alkoxyamines
– special s.
  O-benzylhydroxylamine
  benzyloxylamino...
β-Alkoxylaminosulfoxides, chiral 48, 38s55
Alkoxyl radicals
– from
  N-alkoxyphthalimides 55, 1
Alkoxyl radicals, cyclic
– as intermediates 55, 485
β-Alkoxy-α-methyleneketones
– startg. m. f.
  furans 55, 477
N-Alkoxyphthalimides
– startg. m. f.
  alcohols 55, 1
  alkoxyl radicals 55, 1
Alkoxysilanes (s.a. Siloxy..., O-Silylation, Silyl ethers)
– special s.
  disiloxy compds.
  trialkoxy(aryl)silanes
Alkoxysilanes, polymer-based
– from
  alcohols 55, 24
1-Alkoxy-3-siloxy-1,3-dienes
– special s.
  1-methoxy-3-trimethylsiloxy-1,3-butadiene
– startg. m. f.
  4(1H)-pyridones, 2,3-dihydro-, asym. conversion 55, 443
Alkylarenes
– special s.
  allylarenes
  diarylalkanes
  ethylarenes
– startg. m. f.
  2-arylamines 55, 339
  aryloxo compds. 55, 78
  1,1-diarylalkanes 55, 406
C-Alkylation
– of
  acetylene derivs., terminal with ethylene derivs. 55, 271
  α-diketones, sym. (α'-alkylation) 55, 377
– special s.
  C-allylation
  C-monoalkylation
C-Alkylation, ar. (s.a. Friedel-Crafts alkylation)
– in supercritical media 55, 351
– of arenes, deactivated 55, 322
– special s.
  tert-butylation, ar.

– with hydrocarbons 55, 322
–, –, intramolecular
– with benzotriazoles, 1-subst. 49, 946s55
–, asym.
– of sulfonic acid amides 55, 372
–, asym., α-lateral
– of Δ²-imidazolines, 2-benzyl- 55, 373
–, decarbalkoxylative
–, α-fluoroketones via – 55, 469
N-Alkylation
– of o-(tetrahydropyran-2-yloxymethyl)-carboxamides 55, 154
– special s.
  Mitsunobu N-alkylation
N-Alkylation, reductive
  (s.a. Hydroformylation-reductive N-alkylation)
– of 2-aminoalcohols with nitriles 55, 152
O-Alkylation
– of phenols with dialkyl sulfates 55, 100
– special s.
  O-benzylation
  O-tritylation
o-Alkylation s. Radical o-alkylation
α-Alkylidenation
– of methylene groups, active with aldimines 55, 364
α-(Alkylideneamino)carboxylic acid esters
–, deracemization of α-amino esters via – 55, 499
–, N-formylation of α-amino esters via – 55, 170
Alkylidenecarbenes
– special s.
  (sulfonylamino)alkylidenecarbenes
Alkylidenecyclobutanes 51, 423s55
3-Alkylidenecyclopentenes
– from
  cyclopropanes, allenyl- 55, 317
Alkylidenecyclopropane ring
– special s.
  (cyclopropylalkylidene)cyclopropane ring
Alkylidenecyclopropanone ketals s.
  Cyclopropanone ketals, alkylidene-
γ-Alkylidene-δ-lactams
– from
  α,β-ethylene-β-halogenocarboxylic acid amides 55, 409
γ-Alkylidene-δ-lactones
– from
  α,β-ethylene-β-halogenocarboxylic acid esters 55, 409
(E)-Alkylidenemalonic acids 3, 632s55
Alkylidenemalononitriles
– special s.
  arylidenemalononitriles
Alkylidenephosphoranes
–, C-α-acylation 55, 387
– special s.
  (carbalkoxymethylene)phosphoranes
– startg. m. f.
  cyclopropyl ketones 55, 424
1-Alkylidenesugars 37, 841s55
Alkylsamarium(III) compds.
–, cross-coupling, catalyzed with iodides, prim. 55, 397
1-Alkyltelluro-1,3-dienes
– special s.
  (Z)-1-(butyltelluro)-1,3-butadiene
Alkynes s. Acetylene derivs.

N-(o-Alk-1-ynylaryl)ketenimines
–, ring closures via 1,4-diradicals 55, 311
1,4-Alkylthio group migration 55, 214
2-Allenealcohols
– startg. m. f.
  3-aryl-3-ethyleneepoxides 52, 415s55
α-Allene-α-arylphosphonic acid esters, tricarbonylchromium(0)-complexed
–, ring closure with – 55, 426
γ-Allenecarboxylic acids
– startg. m. f.
  δ,ε-ethylene-δ-halogeno-γ-lactones 55, 186
α-Allenephosphonic acid esters
– special s.
  α-allene-α-arylphosphonic acid esters
Allenes
–, resolution, kinetic by asym. epoxidation 55, 500
–, ring closure with γ-functionalized α,β-ethylenehalides 55, 409
– special s.
  cyclopropanes, allenyl-
  enyne-allenes
– startg. m. f.
  acoxy-2-ethylenes 55, 73
  cyclohexenes, 1-aryl- 55, 408
  1,3-dienes, isomerization 55, 73
  anti-3-ethylenealcohols 33, 865s55
  α,β-ethylenecarboxylic acid derivs., carbonylation, regiostereospecific 55, 298
  ethylene derivs., synthesis, asym. 55, 297
–, vinylpalladation-ring closure 55, 409
Allenes, phosphorylated
–, reactions with electrophiles, review 43, 722s55
α-Allenesulfones
– from
  sulfinyloxy-2-acetylenes, terminal, asym. induction 55, 201
Allenyltitanium(IV) complexes, chiral
– as intermediates 55, 347
Allyl acetate
– as reagent 55, 120
Allyl alcohols s. 2-Ethylenealcohols
Allylarenes
– from
  acoxy-2-ethylenes, synthesis, regiostereospecific 55, 455
  allyl tetrahydropyran-2-yl ethers, –, – 55, 385
  aryl triflates 55, 463
  halides, ar. 55, 463
–, –, synthesis, regiospecific 55, 385
C-α-Allylation, asym.
– in aq. media 48, 772s55
–, ligand update 48, 772s55
–, –, molybdenum-catalyzed, regiospecific 55, 353
–, regiospecific, rhodium-catalyzed 55, 357
–, regiostereospecific
– with acoxy-2-ethylenes 55, 358
O-Allylation, preferential
– with 3-ethylenealcohols, allyl rearrangement 55, 85
in situ-Allylboration 33, 865s55
Allyl bromide
– as reactant 55, 212, 254, 392, 393
– as reagent 55, 176

β-Allyl elimination
– from
3-ethylene-*tert*-alcohols 55, 120
Allyl ethers (s.a. Alkoxy-2-ethylenes, O-Allylation, Diol monoallyl ethers, 2-Ethyleneethers)
–, cleavage, Ni-catalyzed 55, 10
Allyl ethyl carbonate
– as reactant 55, 475
C-β-Allyl glycosides
– from
1,2-anhydrosugars 39, 882s55
2-Allyl-O-heterocyclics 45, 449s55
α-Allyllactones
– from
α-halogenolactones, synthesis, asym. 55, 436
γ-Allyl-γ-lactones
– from
γ-hydroxy-γ-lactones, synthesis, stereospecific 55, 393
Allylmanganese(II) compds.
–, syntheses with – 52, 273s55
Allylmercuration, intramolecular, regiostereospecific
– of acetylene derivs. with 2-ethylenesilanes 55, 279
α-Allyloxy-α,β-ethyleneketones
– startg. m. f.
γ,δ-ethylene-α-hydroxyketones 55, 309
*o*-Allyloxyhalides
–, carbopalladation, intramolecular, regiospecific-Suzuki coupling 55, 454
– startg. m. f.
*o*-allylphenols, rearrangement 55, 305
*o*-Allylphenols
– from
*o*-allyloxyhalides, rearrangement 55, 305
– startg. m. f.
3-chromenes 55, 114
Allylsilanes (s.a. 2-Ethylenesilanes)
– startg. m. f.
(Z)-2-ethylenesilanes, metathesis 55, 473
1,2-Allylsilylation, intramolecular, regiospecific
– of acetylene derivs. 55, 315
Allylstannanes s. 2-Ethylenestannanes
2-Allylsuccinic acid monoesters, chiral 28, 683s55
Allyl tetrahydropyran-2-yl ethers
– startg. m. f.
allylarenes, synthesis, regiospecific 55, 385
Allyl thioethers
– from
thiosulfuric acid S-monoesters 55, 212
N-Allyl-N-tosylsulfenamides
– from
2-ethylenethioethers, asym. conversion 55, 124
Allyltri-*n*-butylstannane
– as reactant 55, 445
– startg. m. f.
3-ethyleneamines, synthesis, asym. 55, 461
(π-Allyl)tricarbonyliron-lactone complexes
–, decomplexation, reductive 55, 35
Allyltriethylgermane
– as reactant 50, 551s55

Aluminacyclopent-2-enes
–, syntheses, zirconium-catalyzed via – 55, 282
Aluminum alkoxides
– isopropoxide 55, 307
Aluminum aroxides
– tris(2,6-diphenylphenoxide) 55, 234
– –, organo-
2,7-dimethyl-1,8-biphenylenedioxy-bis(dialkylaluminums) (as reactant) 55, 242
– –, –, chiral
trimethylaluminum/(R)-1,1'-bi-2-naphthol 55, 241
–/1,1'-bi-2-naphthol, 3,3'-bis(triphenyl-silyl)-, chiral 55, 436
– bromide (s.a. Carbon tetrabromide/aluminum bromide)
– chloride 55, 320, 394
– –/alumina 55, 17
– compds., organo- (s.a. Hydro-alumination)
trialkylalanes, prepn. 55, 241
triethylaluminum 55, 282
trimethylaluminum (s.a. under Aluminum aroxides) 55, 242 (as reactant)
–, cross-coupling, oxidative with lithium compds., organo-, unsatd. 55, 447
– special s.
aryldiethylalanes
– halides, organo-
dimethylaluminum chloride 55, 274
– hydrides, organo-
diisobutylaluminum hydride 55, 47
– oxide (s.a. Aluminum chloride/alumina, Potassium peroxymonosulfate/–) 55, 151
– salen complexes, chiral
– as reagent 55, 253
Amberlite IRA-400 55, 364
Amberlyst 15 55, 107, 116
–, scavenging and purification of amines with – 55, 18
Amidines
– from
amines, polymer-based synthesis 55, 164
carboxylic acid thioamides, – – 55, 164
– special s.
cyanamidines
phosphinoamidines
phosphorylamidines
Amidinium salts (s.a. Halogeno-formamidinium salts)
Amidinoureas
– via N-(N'-carbo-*tert*-butoxyamidino)-ureas 16, 262s55
Amidoximes
– startg. m. f.
1,2,4-oxadiazoles, 5-aryl- 55, 415
Aminals (s.a. 1,1-Diamines)
Amine-borane complexes s. Borane-amine complexes
Amines
–, resolution, kinetic via asym. N-acetylation 55, 149
–, review (annual) 51, 162s55
–, scavenging and purification with Amberlyst 15 55, 18
– special s.
2-arylamin...

benzylamines
deuterioamines
diamines
enamines
epoxyamines
ethyleneamines
– startg. m. f.
amidines, polymer-based synthesis 55, 164
ureas 55, 133
–, sym., (N,N'-diaryl-derivs.) 55, 131
urethans 55, 155
Amines, ar.
– from
halides, ar. 55, 160
Amines, ar., prim.
– from
aryl triflates 55, 162
halides, ar. 55, 162
–, –, or aryl triflates, transition metal catalysis, review 51, 171s55
nitro compds., ar. 55, 13
nitrogen, molecular 55, 162
– special s.
polyamines, ar.
– startg. m. f.
iodides, ar. 55, 188
Amines, ar., prim., *o*-functionalized
– startg. m. f.
benzazoles 55, 151
Amines, ar., sec.
– from
triarylbismuthines 40, 286s55
Amines, prim.
– from
alcohols via azides with inversion 55, 142
aldehydes, 3-component synthesis 55, 332
nitriles 55, 40
nitro compds. 55, 40
siloximes 55, 12
– special s.
isobutylamine
– startg. m. f.
guanidines, cyclic 55, 156
ketimines 55, 138
phthalimides 55, 143
Amines, sec.
– from
amines, tert. 55, 19
azomethines, reduction 55, 25
–, –, asym. 55, 31
halides 55, 154
phthalimides 55, 154
thionocarbamic acid esters, N,N-disubst. 55, 19
– startg. m. f.
hydroxylamines, N,N-disubst. 55, 49
Amines, sec., cyclic
– from
azomethines, cyclic, reduction, asym., review 46, 47s55
Amines, sec., sym.
– from
azides 55, 153
ethylene derivs. (2 molecules) 55, 356
Amines, tert.
– by hydroformylation-reductive N-alkylation 55, 356
– from
amines, sec., parallel solution-phase synthesis 21, 499s55

(Amines, tert.
− from)
 carboxylic acid amides, N,N-disubst.
  **55**, 42
− − −, −, synthesis **55**, 346
− special s.
 trialkylamines
− startg. m. f.
 amines, sec. **55**, 19
**Amines, tert., cyclic**
− from
 ethyleneketones **55**, 356
**Amines, tert., sym.**
− from
 ethylene derivs. (2 molecules) **55**, 356
**Aminoalcohols**
−, determination of abs. configuration **5**,
 666s55
**2-Aminoalcohols**
−, N-alkylation, reductive with nitriles **55**,
 152
− from
 aldehydes, synthesis **55**, 236
 α-alkoximinoketones, reduction, asym.
  **25**, 15s55
 α-aminocarboxylic acids (with
  simultaneous purification) **55**, 18
 tosylmethylamines **50**, 531s55
− special s.
 acetylene-2-aminoalcohols
 α-amino-β-hydroxy...
− startg. m. f.
 aziridines, 1-phosphinyl-, (chiral
  compds.) **55**, 125
*cis*-**2-Aminoalcohols, cyclic, chiral 55,**
 **176**
− special s.
 1-aminoindan-2-ol, chiral
**3-Aminoalcohols**
− special s.
 vinyl-3-aminoalcohols
**α-Aminoaldehydes, N-protected 45,**
 **510s55**
**α-Amino-α-arylcarboxylic acids,**
 **constrained**
−, synthesis and use, review **46**, 767s55
**α-Amino-β-(arylseleno)succinic acid**
 **esters 6,** 364s55
**β-*prim*-Aminocarbonyl compds.**
− from
 enoxysilanes **55**, 439
**β-Aminocarboxylic acid amides, chiral**
 **42,** 290s55
**α-Aminocarboxylic acid complexes**
− special s.
 copper(II) α-aminocarboxylic acid
  complexes
**α-Aminocarboxylic acid derivs., cyclic**
−, resolution, kinetic, heterogeneous **45**,
 210s55
**α-Aminocarboxylic acid esters**
−, N-allylation, asym. **50**, 195s55
−, deracemization **55**, 499
−, N-formylation **55**, 170
− from
 α-aminocarboxylic acids (with
  simultaneous purification) **55**, 18
 oxazolidines, asym. induction **52**,
  457s55
−, synthesis, asym. **37**, 657s55
− − −, N-protected, chiral **37**, 58s55
**β-Aminocarboxylic acid esters**

− special s.
 alkoxy-β-aminocarboxylic acid esters
− − −, **chiral 41,** 63s55
**α-Aminocarboxylic acids**
−, deracemization by Ni(II) complexation
 **55**, 499
−, determination of abs. configuration **5**,
 666s55
− special s.
 α-amino-α-arylcarboxylic acids
 α-arylglycines
 deuterio-α-aminocarboxylic acids
− −, **chiral 44,** 776s55
− −, **isocyclic, chiral 41,** 671s55
− −, **quaternary, acyclic**
−, synthesis, stereoselective, review **46**,
 767s55
− −, **unnatural**
−, synthesis with transaminases, review
 **43**, 299s55
**β-Aminocarboxylic acids, N-protected,**
 **chiral 22,** 813s55
**α-Aminocarboxylic acid thioamides**
− by Ugi condensation **55**, 319
**2-Amino-1,3-dienes**
− special s.
 2,3-diamino-1,3-dienes
**2-*tert*-Aminoenoxysilanes**
− as intermediates **55**, 346
**2-Amino-4-en-6-ynecarboxylic acid**
 **esters, N-protected 49,** 703s55
**(E)-2-Amino-3-ethylenealcohols, chiral**
 **39,** 887s55
**4-Amino-2-ethylenealcohols, N-**
 **protected**
− startg. m. f.
 aziridines, 2-vinyl-, N-protected **55**,
  173
**(Z)-4-Amino-2-ethylene-*prim*-alcohols**
− by retro-Diels-Alder reaction **55**, 493
**α-Amino-γ,δ-ethylenecarboxylic acids,**
 **chiral 37,** 893s55
**γ-Amino-γ,δ-ethylene-β-ketocarboxylic**
 **acid esters, N-protected**
− startg. m. f.
 γ-amino-β-hydroxycarboxylic acid
  esters, N-protected, hydrogenation,
  asym. **55**, 37
**(Z)-β-Amino-α,β-ethylenenitriles**
− from
 nitriles (2 different molecules) **55**, 256
**β-Amino-α,β-ethylenenitriles, cyclic**
 **55,** 256
**Amino(halogeno)phosphines**
− startg. m. f.
 phosphines, tert., mixed, synthesis **55**,
  224
 phosphinous acid amides, synthesis **55**,
  224
**Amino-N-heterocyclics**
− from
 hydroxy-N-heterocyclics **55**, 135
 triflyloxy-N-heterocyclics **55**, 135
*o*-**Amino-N-heterocyclics**
− startg. m. f.
 imidazoles, 5-amino-, N-condensed,
  polymer-based synthesis **55**, 340
**β-Aminohydroxamic acid esters, N-**
 **protected 55,** 150
**α-Amino-β-hydroxyaldehydes,**
 **protected**

−, aldol-type condensation, chelation-
 controlled, double-asym. with − **55**,
 240
**α-Amino-β-hydroxycarboxylic acid**
 **esters 55,** 145
**β-Amino-α-hydroxycarboxylic acid**
 **esters, N-protected, chiral 55,** 130
− − −, **O-protected**
− from
 azomethines, synthesis, asym. with 2
  extra C-atoms **55**, 444
**α-Amino-β-hydroxycarboxylic − −, N-**
 **protected, chiral 55,** 130
**γ-Amino-β-hydroxycarboxylic − −, −, −**
 **55**, 37
**α-Amino-β-hydroxycarboxylic acids,**
 **chiral 9,** 741s55; **20,** 239s55
− −, **β,β-disubst. 25,** 484s55
**α-*prim*-Amino-β-hydroxycarboxylic**
 **acids**
− from
 aldehydes, synthesis, asym. **55**, 325
 4,8-dioxa-1-azabicyclo[4.3.0]nonan-5-
  ones, (chiral compds.) **55**, 325
*cis*-**1-Aminoindan-2-ol, chiral**
− in asym. synthesis, review **12,** 616s55
**α-Amino-δ-ketocarboxylic acid esters,**
 **chiral 55,** 459
**α-Amino-γ-ketocarboxylic acids, chiral**
 **55**, 450
**α-*tert*-Aminoketones**
− from
 carboxylic acid amides, N,N-disubst. (2
  molecules) **55**, 346
**β-Aminoketones**
− from
 aldimines **55**, 440
 enoxysilanes **55**, 440
−, synthesis, asym. **55**, 459
 imines, synthesis, asym. **55**, 459
−, via Michael addition, polymer-based
 **55**, 349
**β-Amino-γ-lactones 52,** 278s55
**α-Aminomalonic acid esters**
−, desymmetrization **28,** 13s55
*o*-**Aminomercaptans**
− startg. m. f.
 benzothiazoles **55**, 151
**α-Aminonitriles**
− from
 aldehydes **55**, 341
*o*-**Aminophenols**
− startg. m. f.
 benzoxazoles **55**, 151
**β-Aminophosphonic acids 20,** 334s55
**Aminophosphonium salts**
− special s.
 triaminophosphonium salts
**2-Amino-4-picoline**
− as reagent **55**, 323
**Aminoselenation, intramolecular, asym.**
 **51,** 258s55
**Aminosilanes**
− startg. m. f.
 carbodiimides **55**, 167
*syn*-**β-Amino-α-siloxycarboxylic acid**
 **esters, chiral 55,** 444
*o*-**Aminostyrenes, N-protected**
−, ring closures, regiospecific with α,β-
 ethylenehalides **55**, 405
**Aminosugars**

- by intramolecular amination, review
42, 308s55
**2-Aminothioethers**
- from
  mercaptans, with retention of chirality
  55, 213
  2-oxazolidones, – – – – 55, 213
**Ammonia 55,** 18
**Ammonium acetate 55,** 326
**Ammonium cerium(IV) nitrate 55,** 11
– **chloride** (s.a. under Zinc) **55,** 69
– **iron(II) sulfate 55,** 170
– **nitrate, clay-supported 55,** 17, 89
– **thiocyanate 55,** 205
**Anilines** s. Amines, ar.
**Anisole**
– as reagent **55,** 15
**Ansa macrolides**
–, protection, steric of functional groups
  within – **55,** 74
**Anthraquinones**
- special s.
  1,4-bis(9-O-dihydroquinidine)anthra-
  quinone
**Arenes** (s.a. Benzene ring)
- special s.
  alkylarenes
  allylarenes
  ethylenearenes
  ethynylarenes
- startg. m. f.
  dithiocarbamic acid benzyl esters,
  (N,N-disubst. derivs.) **55,** 359
**Arenes, deactivated**
–, C-alkylation with hydrocarbons **55,** 322
**Arenes, o-disubst.**
- from
  o-dihalides **55,** 389
**Arenes, electron-rich**
–, Friedel-Crafts acylation **55,** 387
**Arenesulfonic acid amides**
- special s.
  2,4-dinitrobenzenesulfonamide(s)
**Arenesulfonic acid halides**
- startg. m. f.
  β-(arylthio)carboxylic acid esters **55,**
  198
**Arenetricarbonylchromium(0)
complexes**
- as ligands for asym. catalysis, review
  42, 616s55
- special s.
  α-allene-α-arylphosphonic acid esters,
  tricarbonylchromium-complexed
  (potassioarene)tricarbonylchromium
  complexes
**Arylacetic acids**
- from
  mandelic acids **13,** 733s55
**3-Aryl-2-acetylenealcohols 27,** 851s55
**Arylacetylenes**
- from
  halides, ar., polymer-based synthesis
  **55,** 416
  lithium acetylides **55,** 447
- special s.
  alkynylaryl...
  o-(hydroxymethyl)arylacetylenes
  tolans
–, **terminal** s. Ethynylarenes
**2-Arylamines**
- from

alkylarenes **55,** 339
carboxylic acid amides, hindered **55,**
  339
styrenes **6,** 367s55
**C-Arylation** (s.a. Heck arylation)
**C-Arylation, intramolecular** (s.a. Ring
  closing metathesis-intramolecular
  arylation)
**C-α-Arylation, asym.**
– of ketones **55,** 411
**C-γ-Arylation, regiostereospecific**
– of α,β-ethyleneoxo compds. **55,** 407
**N-Arylation**
–, acceleration **55,** 160
– with arylboronic acids **55,** 166
**N-Arylation, preferential 55,** 161
**O-Arylation**
– with arylboronic acids **55,** 166
**Aryl benzyl sulfones 55,** 210
**Arylboronic acids**
–, arylation with – **55,** 166
- startg. m. f.
  diaryls **55,** 456
  halides, ar. **55,** 191
**α-Arylcarboxylic...** (s.a. Arylacetic...)
**Arylcarboxylic acid amides** (s.a. Friedel-
  Crafts carbamylation)
– – –, **N-unsubst. 55,** 413
**Arylcarboxylic acid esters**
- from
  arylcarboxylic acids **55,** 101
  dialkyl sulfates **55,** 101
  diaryliodonium salts, carbonylation **55,**
  324
**α-Arylcarboxylic acid esters**
- from
  acylophenones **48,** 439s55
**Arylcarboxylic acids**
- from
  methylarenes **51,** 76s55
- startg. m. f.
  arylcarboxylic acid esters **55,** 101
**S-Aryl O,O-dialkyl dithiophosphates 43,**
  498s55
**Aryldiethylalanes**
- startg. m. f.
  ethylarenes **55,** 447
**γ-Aryl-β-diketones**
- from
  aryl α-halogenoketones **55,** 390
  ketones **55,** 390
**2-Aryl-1,3-diols**
- from
  oxo compds. (2 molecules) **55,** 360
**3-Aryl-2-ethyleneamines, chiral 52,**
  249s55
**3-Aryl-3-ethyleneepoxides 52,** 415s55
**α-Arylglycines, N-protected, chiral 55,**
  130
**C-α-Aryl glycosides**
- from
  telluroglycosides
**3-Arylhalides**
- special s.
  3-(o-fluoroaryl)halides
**Aryl α-halogenoketones**
- startg. m. f.
  γ-aryl-β-diketones **55,** 390
**Arylhydroxamic acid esters**
- from
  arylstannanes **55,** 462
**Arylidenemalononitriles 55,** 364

**γ-Aryl-β-ketocarboxylic acid esters 55,**
  390
**Aryl ketones**
- from
  alkylarenes **42,** 233s55
  benzylalcohols, prim., via hydroacylation *in situ* **55,** 323
  ethylene derivs., terminal, – – – – **55,**
  323
- special s.
  diaryl ketones
- startg. m. f.
  benzylalcohols, transfer-hydrogenation, asym. **55,** 27
**β-Arylketones**
- from
  α,β-ethyleneketones, synthesis, asym.
  **55,** 452
**β-Aryl-γ-lactones, chiral 26,** 827s55
**Aryllead triacetates**
–, cross-coupling with boronic acids **55,**
  456
- startg. m. f.
  styrenes **55,** 456
**Arylmagnesium halides, polymer-based**
–, syntheses with – **55,** 391
**Arylmanganese(II) bromides**
–, syntheses via – **52,** 413s55
**Aryloxo compds.**
- from
  alkylarenes **55,** 78
**α-Aryloxyketones**
- startg. m. f.
  benzofurans **55,** 371
**Arylphosphine oxides**
–, o-metalation **55,** 182
**Aryl radicals**
–, radical ring closure, polymer-based via
  – **55,** 396
**β-Arylseleno-β-carbalkoxy-γ-lactones**
- from
  aldehydes, synthesis, stereospecific **55,**
  329
**β-(Arylseleno)carboxylic acid esters**
- special s.
  α-(arylselenomethyl)-β-hydroxy-
  carboxylic acid esters
**β-Arylseleno-α,β-ethylenecarboxylic
acid esters**
- special s.
  2-(arylseleno)fumaric acid esters
**(Z)-β-Arylseleno-α,β-ethyleneketones**
- from
  acetylene derivs., terminal **55,** 267
  selenolic acid aryl esters **55,** 267
**2-(Arylseleno)fumaric acid esters**
- special s.
  dimethyl 2-(phenylseleno)fumarate
*syn*-**α-Arylseleno-β-hydroxyketones 30,**
  621s55
**β-Arylseleno-γ-lactones**
- special s.
  β-arylseleno-β-carbalkoxy-γ-lactones
**α-(Arylselenomethyl)-β-hydroxy-
carboxylic acid esters 55,** 261
**Arylsilanes**
- from
  halides, ar. **55,** 227
  silicon hydrides, organo- **55,** 227
**Arylstannanes**
- startg. m. f.
  arylhydroxamic acid esters **55,** 462

α-Arylsulfones
– special s.
  aryl benzyl sulfones
(E,E)-1-Aryltelluro-1,3-dienes
– from
  acetylene derivs., synthesis, regiospecific 55, 272
β-(Arylthio)carboxylic acid esters
– from
  arenesulfonic acid halides 55, 198
  α,β-ethylenecarboxylic acid esters 55, 198
– special s.
  α-(arylthiomethyl)-β-hydroxycarboxylic acid esters
2-(Arylthio)eneselenides 47, 568s55
2-Arylthio-2-ethylenealcohols, chiral 43, 45s55
α-(Arylthiomethyl)-β-hydroxycarboxylic acid esters
– via Michael addition-aldol condensation, stereospecific 55, 261
Aryl triflates
– startg. m. f.
  allylarenes 55, 463
  amines, ar., prim. 55, 162
Arynes
– special s.
  benzyn...
Asymmetrization s. Desymmetrization
Asym. synthesis s. Synthesis, asym.
6-Azabicyclo[3.1.0]hex-3-en-2-ols
– from
  pyridinium salts 55, 62
2-Azabicyclo[3.3.0]octa-4,6-dienes, 2-sulfonyl-
– from
  α,β-acetyleneiodonium salts 55, 370
  5-sulfonylamino-1,3-dienes 55, 370
Azadioxa... s. Dioxaaza...
Azaenolates
– special s.
  zinc azaenolates
1-Aza-2-zircona-4-cyclopentenes
–, syntheses with – 55, 432
Azetidines, 3-aryl-, N-protected 41, 795s55
2-Azetidinones
– from
  azomethines, polymer-based 55, 379
Azides
– as intermediates 55, 142
– startg. m. f.
  amines, sec., sym. 55, 153
Azidoformic acid esters
– special s.
  tert-butyl azidoformate
α-Azidophosphonic acid esters 30, 232s55
Aziridination
– with 4(H)-quinazolones, 3-(acetoxyamino)-, review 23, 381s55
Aziridines
– startg. m. f.
  pyrrolidines, 2-imino-, retention of configuration 55, 255
Aziridines, 2-acyl-, N-protected
– from
  β-acoxy-α,β-ethyleneiodonium salts 55, 367
  imines, N-protected 55, 367
–, 1-carbalkoxy-2-(siloxymethyl)-

– startg. m. f.
  2-carbalkoxyamino-3-siloxyhalides 55, 177
–, 2-deuterio- 41, 77s55
–, 1-phosphinyl-
– from
  2-aminoalcohols, (chiral compds.) 55, 125
–, 1-sulfonyl-
– from
  ethylene derivs. 55, 159
  N-halogeno-N-sodiosulfonic acid amides 55, 159
– startg. m. f.
  2-(sulfonylamino)silanes 55, 14
–, 2-vinyl-, N-protected
– from
  4-amino-2-ethylenealcohols, N-protected 55, 173
Azo compds.
– special s.
  enazo compds.
Azolium N-imides
–, review 43, 270s55
Azomethines (s.a. Imines)
–, α-alkylidenation of methylene groups, active with – 55, 364
– special s.
  aldimines (alkylideneamino)...
  di(azomethines)
  enazomethines
  ketimines
  silylazomethines
– startg. m. f.
  amines, sec., reduction 55, 25
  –, –, –, asym. 55, 31
  β-amino-α-hydroxycarboxylic acid esters, O-protected, synthesis, asym. with 2 extra C-atoms 55, 444
  2-azetidinones, polymer-based synthesis 55, 379
  4(1H)-pyridones, 2,3-dihydro-, asym. conversion 55, 443
Azomethines, cyclic
– startg. m. f.
  amines, sec., cyclic, reduction, asym., review 46, 47s55
Azomethinium ylids
–, cycloaddition, 1,3-dipolar, regiostereospecific with – 55, 466
– from
  oxazolidines 55, 466


Baeyer-Villiger oxidation, asym.
– of ketals, cyclic 55, 65
Barbier-type reaction, double 55, 232
Bases (s.a. Superbases)
Bases, solid
– special s.
  hydrotalcite, basified
Baylis-Hillman-type reaction, polymer-based 55, 334
Beckmann rearrangement, solid-state 11, 217s55
Benz[a]anthracene-7,12-diones 55, 492

Benzazoles
– from
  amines, ar., prim., o-functionalized 55, 151
Benz[f]azulenes, 1,2,3,3a,4,9,10,10a-octahydro-, 4,10-oxido- 55, 479
o-Benzenedisulfonimides
– special s.
  N-(p-methoxybenzyl)-o-benzenedisulfonimide
Benzene ring (s.a. Arenes)
– from
  acetylene derivs. (3 molecules) 55, 289
Benzeneselenenyl compds.
– in synthesis, review 41, 280s55
Benzils
– from
  benzoins 53, 108s55
Benzimidazoles
– from
  aldehydes, polymer-based synthesis 46, 321s55
  aldoximes 55, 151
  o-diamines 55, 151
1,2-Benziodoxol-3(1H)-one, 1-tosyloxy-
– as reagent 55, 183
5H-Benzo[b]carbazoles 55, 311
1H-1,4-Benzodiazepines, 2,3,4,5-tetrahydro-, tricyclic 49, 713s55
1,5-Benzodioxepin-2-ones, 3,4-dihydro- 45, 70s55
Benzofurans
– from
  aldehydes 55, 371
  benzotriazoles, 1-aryloxymethyl-, synthesis 55, 371
–, 7-metalation 42, 597s55
–, synthesis, polymer-based 44, 781s55
Benzofurans, 2,3-dihydro- (s. Coumarins in Vol.1-40)
– from
  o-allylphenols 23, 182s55
–, –, 3-aryl-, chiral 55, 486
–, –, 2-hydroxy-3-sulfonyl- 34, 767s55
–, 4-halogeno-
– by o-Claisen rearrangement, review 29, 697s55
Benzoic acid
– as reagent 55, 57
Benzolactams 55, 78
Benzolactones 55, 78
Benzophenone
– as sensitizer 55, 276, 304
Benzophenones (s.a. Diaryl ketones)
– from
  arylcarboxylic acid halides 46, 906s55
Benzopyran... s. Chrom[a,e]n..., Coumarin...
Benzoquinone
– as reagent 55, 186
Benzo[c]selenophen-1-ones s. Selenophthalides
Benzo[c]tellurophen-1-ones s. Tellurophthalides
2H-1,2,4-Benzothiadiazine-3(4H)-thione 1,1-dioxides 21, 393s55
Benzothiazoles
– from
  o-aminomercaptans 55, 151
Benzo[b]thiophenes (s. under Thianaphthenes in Vol.1-50)
– from

aldehydes 55, 371
α-(arylthio)acetals 44, 930s55
benzotriazoles, 1-arylthiomethyl-,
  synthesis 55, 371
–, 6-hydroxy- 41, 927s55
–, polyfunctionalized 9, 917s55
**Benzotriazole derivs.**
– special s.
  carbanions, benzotriazole-stabilized
–, syntheses via –, review 53, 386s55
**Benzotriazoles**
– special s.
  N-hydroxybenzotriazole
**Benzotriazoles, 1-acoxy-**
– as intermediates 55, 41
–, 7-alkynyl- 27, 851s55
–, 1-amino-7-γ-hydroxy-
– startg. m. f.
  chromans, 8-iodo- 55, 187
–, 1-aryloxymethyl-
– startg. m. f.
  benzofurans, synthesis 55, 371
–, 1-arylthiomethyl-
– startg. m. f.
  benzo[*b*]thiophenes, synthesis 55, 371
**Benzotriazol-1-yl carbonates, polymer-based**
–, N-carbalkoxylation with – 55, 134
**(Benzotriazol-1-yloxy)tris(dimethylamino)phosphonium hexafluorophosphate**
– as reagent 55, 41
**(Benzotriazol-1-yloxy)tris(pyrrolidino)phosphonium –**
– as reagent 55, 143
**1,3-Benzoxazine-2,4-diones**
– from
  *o*-hydroxycarboxylic acid esters 55, 136
  isocyanates 55, 136
**4*H*-3,1-Benzoxazin-4-ones, 2-amino-**
–, synthesis, solution-phase, parallel, automated 21, 378s55
**Benzoxazoles**
– from
  aldehydes 55, 151
  *o*-aminophenols 12, 432s55; 55, 151
**Benzylalcohols**
– from
  aryl ketones, transfer-hydrogenation, asym. 55, 27
– special s.
  *o*-(hydroxymethyl)...
**Benzylalcohols, prim.**
– startg. m. f.
  aryl ketones, via hydroacylation *in situ* 55, 323
–, tert.
– from
  ketones, synthesis, asym. 55, 239
**Benzylamines**
– special s.
  nitrobenzylamines
**Benzylamines, sec.**
–, synthesis, poymer-based 28, 753s55
–, α-subst., chiral 42, 621s55
**Benzylamines, tert.**
– startg. m. f.
  carbamyl halides 55, 171
**O-Benzylation**
– special s.
  O-*p*-methoxybenzylation

–, polymer-based 37, 152s55
**Benzyl dicarbanion equivalents**
–, bis(benzotriazol-1-yl)methylarenes
  as – 55, 360
**Benzyl ethers**
– startg. m. f.
  aldehydes, ar. 55, 118
**Benzyl fluorides 30**, 365s55
**C-β-Benzyl glycosides 52**, 419s55
**Benzyl halides**
– special s.
  benzyl fluorides
– startg. m. f.
  aldehydes, ar. 55, 99
**O-Benzylhydroxylamine**
– as reactant 55, 129
–, prepn. 55, 129
**α-Benzyl-β-ketocarboxylic acid esters 31**, 847s55
**β-(Benzyloxylamino)carboxylic acid amides**
– from
  α,β-ethylenecarboxylic acid amides, asym. conversion 55, 129
**Benzylpotassium compds.**
–, prepn. 10, 511s55
**Benzyl radicals**
–, addition to maleic acid and derivs. 55, 442
**Benzylsodium compds.**
– from
  alkylarenes 10, 511s55
**Benzylsulfonium salts**
– startg. m. f.
  5-methylene-1,3-cyclohexadienes, 6-α-alkylthio- 55, 314
**Benzyl trityl ether**
–, O-tritylation with – 55, 106
**Benzynes**
–, carbolithiation, intramolecular 55, 375
–, iodoetherification, – 55, 187
**Biaryls** s. Biphenyls, Diaryls
**Bicyclo[n.m.0]alkane-1,3-diols**
– from
  diene-α,β-epoxyketones 55, 275
**Bicyclo[n.1.0]alkanes, 1-vinyl- 55**, 282
**Bicyclo[3.3.0]octan-3-ones 46**, 989s55
**Bicyclo[5.3.1]undec-10-ene ring 55**, 316
**Biferrocenylphosphine complexes, chiral**
– special s.
  (R,R)-2,2″-bis[(S)-1-(diphenyl-phosphino)ethyl]-1,1″-biferrocene
**Biginelli synthesis, catalytic 55**, 337
**Biguanides**
– from
  carbodiimides 6, 357s55
–, polymer-based 6, 357s55
**2,2′-Biindoles 47**, 940s55
**BINAP** s. 2,2′-Bis(diphenylphosphino)-1,1′-binaphthyl
**(S)-1,1′-Bi-2-naphthol**
– as reagent 55, 297
**1,1′-Bi-2-naphthols, chiral**
– special s.
  (R)-3,3′-bis[2,5-di(hexyloxy)phenyl]-1,1′-bi-2-naphthol
  3,3′-bis(triphenylsilyl)-1,1′-binaphthol
  (R)-6,6′-dibromo-1,1′-bi-2-naphthol
**1,1′-Bi-2-naphthoxides, mixed-metal, chiral** s. Lithium aluminum bis((R,R)-

1,1′-bi-2-naphthoxide)
**1,1′-Binaphthyls, chiral**
– special s.
  2-acetylamino-2′-diacetylamino-1,1′-binaphthyl, chiral
  2,2′-bis(diphenylphosphino)-1,1′-binaphthyl
  (S)-2,2′-bis(di-*p*-tolylphosphino)-1,1′-binaphthyl
**Biochemical reactions, preparative** (s.a. Enzymes)
–, review (annual) 28, 13s55
**1,1′-Bi-2-phenols**
–, resolution 5, 666s55
**Biphenyls** (s.a. Diaryls)
– special s.
  2,2′-di(phosphino)biphenyls
**2,2′-Bipyridinium salts**
– special s.
  N,N′-difluoro-2,2′-bipyridinium...
**2,2′-Bipyridyl** (s.a. under Electrolysis)
**2,2′-Biquinoline N,N′-dioxide, (S)-3,3′-dimethyl-**
– as reagent 55, 433
**Bis(benzotriazol-1-yl)methylarenes**
– as benzyl dicarbanion equivalents 55, 360
**Biscarbonylation**
– of bis(diazonium salts) 55, 366
**Biscyclopentadienyl compds., bridged**
–, review 41, 139s55
**Bis(diazonium salts)**
–, reactions, palladium-catalyzed, 2-fold 55, 366
**1,1′-Bis(di-*tert*-butylphosphino)ferrocene**
– as reagent 55, 160
**(R)-3,3′-Bis[2,5-di(hexyloxy)phenyl]-1,1′-bi-2-naphthol**
– as reagent 55, 237
**1,4-Bis(9-O-dihydroquinidine)-anthraquinone**
– as reagent 55, 130
**2,2′-Bis(diphenylphosphino)-1,1′-binaphthyl**
– as reagent 55, 161
**(R)-2,2′-Bis(diphenylphosphino)-1,1′-binaphthyl**
– as reagent 55, 343, 486
**(S)-2,2′-Bis(diphenylphosphino)-1,1′-binaphthyl**
– as reagent 55, 411, 452
**1,4-Bis(diphenylphosphino)butane**
– as reagent 55, 115
**(S,S)-2,3-Bis(diphenylphosphino)butane**
– as reagent 55, 268
**(R,R)-2,2″-Bis[(S)-1-(diphenylphosphino)ethyl]-1,1″-biferrocene**
– as reagent 55, 250
**1,1′-Bis(diphenylphosphino)ferrocene**
– as reagent 55, 73, 211
**1,6-Bis(diphenylphosphino)hexane**
– as reagent 55, 201
**1,3-Bis(diphenylphosphino)propane**
– as reagent 55, 410
**(R)-2,2′-Bis(di-*o*-tolylphosphino)-1,1′-binaphthyl**
– as reagent 55, 450
**(S)-2,2′-Bis(di-*p*-tolylphosphino)-1,1′-binaphthyl** s. under Copper(II) halides
**Bis(epoxides)**
– startg. m. f.
  2-cycloalkenones 55, 480

1,1'-Bis(2-furyl)alkanes, sym. 55, 351
Bis(halogenosilanes)
– startg. m. f.
  (poly-Si)-heterocyclics 55, 221
ω,ω-Bis(hydroxymethyl)-ω-
nitrocarboxylic acids
– from
  α-nitroketones, cyclic 55, 262
2,3-Bis(indol-3-yl)maleimides 37, 902s55
Bis(iodozincio)methane
– as reactant 55, 471
1,2-Bis(ketenes)
– startg. m. f.
  2(3H)-furanones, 5-alkoxy- 55, 264
Bismuth(III) nitrate 55, 172
Bismuthonium salts
– special s.
  2-ketobismuthonium salts
Bismuth tribromide 55, 168
Bis(Δ²-oxazolines), chiral
– as reagent 55, 124, 129
– special s.
  bis(4(R)-phenyl-Δ²-oxazolin-2-
  ylmethyl)amine
Bis(pentafluorophenyl)tin dibromide
– as reagent 55, 446
Bis(4(R)-phenyl-Δ²-oxazolin-2-
  ylmethyl)amine
– as reagent 55, 27
Bis(phosphine oxides), chiral
– special s.
  (R)-2,2'-bis(diphenylphosphinyl)-1,1'-
  binaphthyl
Bis(phosphorodiamidates), chiral
– as reagent 55, 246
(R,R)-1,2-Bis(picolinoylamino)-
cyclohexane
– as reagent 55, 353
Bis(tetraethylammonium) tribromotricarbonylrhenate
– as reagent 55, 91
Bis(trichloromethyl) carbonate
– startg. m. f.
  carbamyl chlorides 55, 171
–, Vilsmeier-type formylation with – 55, 365
Bis(trimethylsilyl) peroxide
– as reagent 55, 50
Bis(trimethylsilyl)thioketene
– as reactant 55, 252
9-Borabicyclo[3.3.1]nonane
– as reagent 55, 272
9-Borabicyclo[3.3.1]nonane, B-allyl-
–, Suzuki coupling with – 55, 463
Borane/tetrahydrofuran 55, 12
Borane-amine complexes
–, review 55, 220s55
Borane-phosphine complexes s.
  Phosphine-borane complexes
Boranes, sec.
– special s.
  dicyclohexylborane
Boranes, tert.
– special s.
  trialkylboranes
  triethylborane
  tris(pentafluorophenyl)borane
Borates, organo-
– special s.
  potassium ene(trifluoro)borates
Boron fluoride 55, 63, 104, 107, 235, 244, 274, 337, 338, 429, 437

Boronic acid esters (s.a. Silaboration)
– special s.
  ethyleneboronic acid esters
  B-silylboronic – –
Boronic acids (s.a. Suzuki coupling)
–, cross-coupling with aryllead triacetates 55, 456
– special s.
  arylboronic acids
  ethyleneboronic acids
Boronic acids, α,β-unsatd.
–, 1,4-addition, asym. to α,β-ethylene-
  ketones 55, 452
Boronylenynes
– special s.
  diboronylenynes
α-Borylalkyl radicals
–, radical 1,4-addition, Cr(II)-mediated
  with – 55, 287
Bridgehead carbon-carbon double bonds
  s.a. Ethylene derivs., bridged
Brij 25 55, 70
Bromamine-T
– as reagent 55, 159
Bromination (s.a. Halogenation)
Bromination, ar. 55, 183
Bromine
– as reagent 55, 230
Bromine-amine complexes
– special s.
  hexamethylenetetramine-bromine
  complex
o-Bromophenylzinc iodide
– as o-phenylene dipole equivalent 55, 389
N-Bromosuccinimide
– as reagent 55, 191
Bucky-balls and -bowls
–, synthesis, review 48, 640s55
Burgess' reagent s. Methyl(carboxysulfamyl)triethylammonium hydroxide
  inner salt
tert-Butanol
– as reagent 55, 343
tert-Butylation, ar. s. Di-tert-butylation, ar.
tert-Butyl azidoformate
– as reactant 55, 123
tert-Butyldimethylsilyl ethers
– startg. m. f.
  acoxy compds. 55, 110
tert-Butyl hydroperoxide
– as reagent 55, 64, 67
tert-Butyl hypochlorite
– as reagent 55, 130
tert-Butyl phenolethers 45, 96s55
n-Butylstannonic acid
– as reagent 55, 109
(Z)-1-(Butyltelluro)-1,3-butadiene
– as reactant 55, 435


Calcium hydride 55, 239
Calcium hypochlorite 55, 151
Calixarenes
–, review 7, 281s55
–, phosphorus-containing

–, review 7, 281s55
α-(Carbalkoxyamino)carboxylic acid
amides
– by Ugi 5-component synthesis 55, 319
α-Carbalkoxyamino-γ,δ-ethylene-
carboxylic acid esters 26, 827s55
α-(Carbalkoxyamino)ketones
– from
  N-acylurethans 55, 313
2-Carbalkoxyamino-3-siloxyhalides
– from
  aziridines, 1-carbalkoxy-2-
  (siloxymethyl)- 55, 177
β-Carbalkoxy-γ-lactones 55, 329
– special s.
  arylseleno-β-carbalkoxy-γ-lactones
N-Carbalkoxylation, polymer-based 55, 134
(Carbalkoxymethylene)phosphoranes
– as reactant 55, 451
β-(Carbalkoxyoxy)sulfonic acid amides
– as intermediates 55, 470
N-Carbalkoxysulfilimines
– special s.
  N-carbo-tert-butoxysulfilimines
N-Carbalkoxysulfoximines
– special s.
  N-carbo-tert-butoxysulfoximines
Carbamic acid esters s. Urethans
C-Carbamylation s. Friedel-Crafts
  carbamylation
O-Carbamylation, preferential 55, 81
N-Carbamyldicarboxylic acid imides
– special s.
  N-carbamylmaleimides
N-Carbamylenazo compds.
– startg. m. f.
  pyridazines, 1,4-dihydro- 55, 467
Carbamyl halides
– from
  benzylamines, tert. 55, 171
– special s.
  N-alkoxycarbamyl halides
N-Carbamylmaleimides
–, N-decarbamylation 55, 16
Carbanion equivalents
– special s.
  dicarbanion equivalents
Carbanions, benzotriazole-stabilized
–, Michael addition, review 53, 386s55
Carbaporphyrins
–, chemistry, review 41, 913s55
Carbasugars 28, 13s55
Carbazic acid esters
–, transesterification 55, 103
Carbenes
– special s.
  alkylidenecarbenes
  metal carbenes
  vinylcarbenes
–, reactions, cryogenic in noble gas
  matrixes, review 52, 274s55
2-(Carbethoxy)benzoic acid
– as reactant 55, 143
Carbo-tert-butoxyamines
– from
  carbo-9-fluorenylmethoxyamines,
  polymer-based 48, 381s55
N-(Carbo-tert-butoxy)methane-
sulfonamides
– as reactant 55, 470
Carbo-tert-butoxynitrene

– as reactant **55**, 123
**N-Carbo-*tert*-butoxysulfilimines**
– from
  thioethers **55**, 123
**N-Carbo-*tert*-butoxysulfoximines**
– from
  sulfoxides **55**, 123
**Carbocyclics** s. Cyclo..., Isocyclics
**Carbodiimides**
– from
  aminosilanes **55**, 167
  isocyanates **55**, 167
– special s.
  diisopropylcarbodiimide
  1-ethyl-3-(3-dimethylaminopropyl)-
    carbodiimide
  silylcarbodiimides
**N-Carbo-9-fluorenylmethoxylation**
– with N-(9-fluorenylmethoxycarbonyl-
  oxy)succinimide **11**, 283s**55**
**Carbohydrates** (s.a. Carbasugars)
– special s.
  aldose...
  alkylidenesugars
  aminosugars
  deoxysugars
  glyc...
  oligosaccharides
  thiouronic acids
  trisaccharides
**Carbolithiation, intramolecular**
– of
  benzynes **55**, 375
  vinyllithium compds. **55**, 222
**Carbometalation**
– special s.
  carbolithiation
  carbopalladation
**Carbon dioxide**
– as reactant **55**, 319
– startg. m. f.
  2-cyclopentenone ring **55**, 282
– –, liq., dense **55**, 67
– –, supercritical
–, cross-coupling, palladium-catalyzed
  in – **55**, 417
**Carbon disulfide**
– as reactant **55**, 319, 359
– startg. m. f.
  carboxylic acid thioamides, N-subst.
    **55**, 163
**Carbonic acid esters**
– from
  oxalic acid esters **55**, 117
– special s.
  benzotriazol-1-yl carbonates
  bis(trichloromethyl) carbonate
  carbalkoxyoxy...
  ethylenecarbonic acid esters
**Carbonium ions**
– special s.
  propargyl cations
**Carbon monoxide** (s.a. Carbonylation)
– as π-acid **55**, 120
**Carbon oxide selenide**
– as reactant **55**, 382
**Carbon tetrabromide** (s.a. Triphenyl-
  phosphine/carbon tetrabromide)
– –/aluminum bromide
– as superacid **55**, 322
**Carbon tetrachloride**
– as reagent **55**, 54

**Carbonylation** (s.a. Biscarbonylation,
  Cyclocarbonylation, Hydroformylation,
  Silylformylation)
–, arylcarboxylic acid esters from iodine
  compds., ar., hypervalent **55**, 324
–, carboxylic acid amides, N-unsubst.
  by – **55**, 413
–, α,β-ethylenecarboxylic acid derivs.
  from allenes **55**, 298
**Carbonyl compds.** (s.a. Aldehydes,
  Carboxylic acid..., Ketones, Oxo
  compds.)
– from
  thiocarbonyl compds., review **25**,
    165s**55**
– special s.
  aminocarbonyl compds.
  dicarbonyl –
  diazocarbonyl –
  ethylenecarbonyl –
  (fluoroalkyl)carbonyl –
  halogenocarbonyl –
  hydroxycarbonyl –
  (organoseleno)carbonyl –
  polycarbonyl –
**Carbonyl ylids, non-stabilized**
– from
  1,1'-diiodoethers **51**, 443s**55**
**Carbopalladation, intramolecular,
regiospecific-Suzuki coupling 55,** 454
–, intramolecular-allene insertion-Diels-
  Alder reaction **55**, 408
**Carbopalladation-carbanion capture,
asym.**
– via palladium π-allyl complexes **55**, 297
**Carboselenation, intramolecular, asym.
55,** 230
**Carbostyrils, 4-benzyl-** **51**, 337s**55**
–, 3,4-dihydro-
– from
  β-halogenocarboxylic acid anilides **20**,
    680s**55**
–, 4-hydroxy- **54**, 481s**55**
–, 5,6,7,8-tetrahydro- **23**, 921s**55**
**Carboxylation, cathodic**
– of enol triflates **55**, 418
**Carboxylic acid allyl esters** (s.a. Acoxy-
  2-ethylenes)
–, cleavage **55**, 5
**Carboxylic acid amides** (s.a.
  Acylamines)
– from
  carboxylic acid anhydrides **55**, 139
  – – halides **55**, 157
  – acids (with amines) **55**, 139
  nitriles, without solvent **55**, 61
–, review (annual) **51**, 162s**55**
– special s.
  N-acylcarboxylic acid amides
  arylcarboxylic – –
  (benzyloxyamino)carboxylic – –
  (carbalkoxyamino)carboxylic – –
  ethylenecarboxylic – –
  formamides
  halogenocarboxylic acid amides
  N-silylcarboxylic – –
– startg. m. f.
  carboxylic acid esters **55**, 90
**Carboxylic acid amides, N,N-disubst.**
– startg. m. f.
  amines, tert., **55**, 42
– –, –, synthesis **55**, 346

α-*tert*-aminoketones (from 2
  molecules) **55**, 346
– – –, hindered
– startg. m. f.
  2-arylamines **55**, 339
– – –, N-subst.
– from
  2,4-dinitrobenzenesulfonamides **55**,
    163
  thiolic acids **55**, 163
– – –, N-unsubst.
– from
  halides or triflates, carbonylation **55**,
    413
**Carboxylic acid anhydrides**
– special s.
  arylcarboxylic acid anhydrides
– startg. m. f.
  carboxylic acid amides **55**, 139
**Carboxylic acid anilides**
–, monoiodination, ar. **50**, 272s**55**
– – –, atropisomeric, chiral **41**, 63s**55**
**Carboxylic acid azides**
– from
  carboxylic acid chlorides **40**, 176s**55**
**Carboxylic acid derivs.**
– special s.
  ethylenecarboxylic acid derivs.
**Carboxylic acid diphenylmethyl esters
29,** 547s**55**
**Carboxylic acid esters** (s.a. Acoxy...,
  O-Acylation, Carbalkoxy...)
– from
  aldehydes **55**, 107
  – (with halides) **55**, 94
  carboxylic acid amides **55**, 90
  – – halides **55**, 96
  – acids (with halides) **55**, 95
  2-oxazolidones, 3-acyl- **55**, 88
–, hydrolysis, asym., enzymatic **28**, 13s**55**
  (update)
–, review (annual) **52**, 9s**55**
– special s.
  acoxycarboxylic acid esters
  acylaminocarboxylic – –
  aldehydocarboxylic – –
  (alkylideneamino)carboxylic – –
  aminocarboxylic – –
  arylcarboxylic – –
  (arylseleno)carboxylic – –
  (arylthio)carboxylic – –
  carboxylic acid allyl esters
  – – diphenylmethyl –
  – – – pentafluorophenyl –
  – – – phenyl –
  ethylenecarboxylic acid esters
  furan-2-carboxylic – –
  halogenocarboxylic – –
  hydroxycarboxylic – –
  (hydridosilyl)carboxylic – –
  ketocarboxylic – –
  mercaptocarboxylic – –
  nitrocarboxylic – –
  siloxycarboxylic – –
  sulfonylaminocarboxylic – –
  sulfonyloxycarboxylic – –
  tricarboxylic – –
– startg. m. f.
  alcohols, prim. **55**, 43
  carboxylic acids **55**, 7
  trifluoromethyl ketones **55**, 354
–, transesterification **55**, 109

**Carboxylic acid halides**
- special s.
  acetylenecarboxylic acid halides
  halogenocarboxylic – –
- startg. m. f.
  carboxylic acid amides **55**, 157
  – – esters **55**, 96
  (E)-2,4-dienones, with 4 extra C-atoms
    **55**, 435
  β-diketones, sym. **55**, 471
  nitriles **55**, 144

**Carboxylic acid hydrazides**
- from
  carboxylic acids **31**, 336s55

**Carboxylic acid pentafluorophenyl esters**
- startg. m. f.
  N-acylcarboxylic acid amides **55**, 165

**Carboxylic acid phenyl esters**
- from
  carboxylic acids **55**, 82

**Carboxylic acids**
–, determination of abs. configuration **5**, 666s55
- from
  alcohols, prim. **55**, 77
  carboxylic acid esters **55**, 7
–, review (annual) **52**, 9s55
- special s.
  acetylenecarboxylic acids
  allenecarboxylic –
  aminocarboxylic –
  arylcarboxylic –
  epoxycarboxylic –
  ethylenecarboxylic –
  halogenocarboxylic –
  hydroxycarboxylic –
  iminocarboxylic –
  ketocarboxylic –
  nitrocarboxylic –
  nucleoside-5′-carboxylic –
  sulfonylaminocarboxylic –
  stannylcarboxylic –
- startg. m. f.
  alcohols, prim. **55**, 41
  alcohols, radical degradation with loss of 1 C-atom **55**, 108
  aldehydes **55**, 47
  carboxylic acid amides (with amines) **55**, 139
  – – esters (with halides) **55**, 95
  – – phenyl esters **55**, 82
  β,γ-epoxycarboxylic acids **55**, 376
  nitriles **55**, 144

**Carboxylic acid selenoamides**
- startg. m. f.
  ketones **55**, 428

**Carboxylic acid silyl esters**
- as intermediates **55**, 47

**Carboxylic acid thioamides**
- from
  Grignard compds. **55**, 163
- special s.
  aminocarboxylic acid thioamides
  ethylenecarboxylic – –
- startg. m. f.
  amidines, polymer-based synthesis **55**, 164
– – –, N-subst.
- from
  2,4-dinitrobenzenesulfonamides **55**, 163

**Carboxylic acid vinyl esters** s. Enolesters
**Carbozincation, (η²-olefin)titanium(II)-catalyzed**
- of enynes **55**, 269
**Catalysis** (s.a. Transition metal catalysis)
- in supercritical fluids, review **53**, 31s55
**Catalysis, asym.**
–, review (annual) **47**, 646s55
– with arenetricarbonylchromium(0) complexes, review **42**, 616s55
**Catalyst ligands** s. Ligands
**Catalyst screening, combinatorial**
- of amines, chiral **45**, 210s55
–, thermographic selection, review **52**, 267s55
– –, high-throughput **48**, 772s55
**Catalysts, heterogeneous**
- for oxidation, liquid-phase, review **47**, 113s55
**Celite** (s.a. Cesium fluoride/Celite)
**Cephalosporin 1,1-dioxides, 2α-bromo-36**, 211s55
Δ³-**Cephems, 3-organothio- 39**, 545s55
**Cerium(IV) ammonium nitrate** s.
  Ammonium cerium(IV) nitrate
–**(III) chloride 55**, 81
– **dioxide** (s.a. Ruthenium/cerium dioxide)
**Cesium carbonate 55**, 163, 406, 407
**Cesium fluoride 55**, 141, 333
– –/**Celite 55**, 95
**Chloramine-T**
- as reactant **55**, 159, 169
**Chlorination, ar. 55**, 183
**Chlorine**
- as reactant **55**, 185
- as reagent **55**, 54
**Chlorins 28**, 39s55
**Chloroacetyl chloride**
- as reagent **55**, 82
**Chlorodimethylsilane**
- as reagent **55**, 345
**Chloromethyl(dimethyl)sulfonium triflate**
- as reactant **55**, 419
*m*-**Chloroperoxybenzoic acid**
- as reagent **55**, 65, 107, 170
**N-Chlorosuccinimide/sodium iodide**
- as reagent **55**, 191
**Chromans, 8-iodo-**
- from
  benzotriazoles, 1-amino-7-γ-hydroxy- **55**, 187
**Chromate, chloro-** s. Pyridinium chlorochromate
**3-Chromenes**
- from
  *o*-allylphenols **55**, 114
–, 2-alkylidene-, 3-aryl-, tricarbonyl-chromium(0)-complexed **55**, 426
–, chiral
– by ring closing metathesis **49**, 985s55
–, 8-iodo- **55**, 187
**Chromium carbene complexes**
–, syntheses, palladium-catalyzed with – **55**, 453
– **carbonyl complexes, organo-**
- special s.
  arenetricarbonylchromium complexes
**Chromium(II) chloride 55**, 286, 352
–(II) –/1,2-diamines **55**, 287
**Chromium-(II)- and -(III)-mediated syntheses**

–, review **53**, 280s55
**Chromium(VI)-oxo-amine reagents**
–, oxidation of alcohols with -, review **41**, 243s55
–(III) **salen complex, chiral**
– as reagent **55**, 449
**4-Chromones 13**, 879s55
–, 2-metalation **42**, 597s55
**Cinchonidine**
– as reagent **55**, 30
*trans*-**Cinnamic acids 1,** 569s55
**Claisen rearrangement, abnormal, regiostereospecific**
–, *o*-allylphenols via – **55**, 305
– –, asym.
–, review **49**, 703s55
– –, radical-mediated **55**, 309
– **rearrangement-ring closing metathesis**
–, γ,δ-ethylenecarboxylic acid esters, cyclic via – **55**, 498
–, 2*H*-pyran-2-ylcarboxylic – –, 3,6-dihydro- by – **55**, 498
*o*-**Claisen rearrangement**
–, benzofurans, 4-halogeno- via –, review **29**, 697s55
**Clay**
– special s.
  kaolinitic clay
**Cobaltation** s. Hydrocobaltation
**Cobalt(II) bromide 55**, 404
**Cobalt carbonyl complexes, organo-**
– special s.
  acetylenedicobalt hexacarbonyl complexes
**Cobalt complexes**
  chlorotris(triphenylphosphine)cobalt(I) **55**, 99
  (η⁴-cycloocta-1,5-diene)(η⁵-4-hydroxybutyrylcyclopentadienyl)cobalt(I) **55**, 289
  tetrakis(triphenylphosphine)cobalt(0) **55**, 249
  tetramethylammonium [*o*-phenylenebis(N′-methyloxamidate)]-cobalt(III)ate **55**, 119
  triphenyltin(4-*tert*-butylpyridine)-cobaloxime **55**, 487
**Collidine**
– as reagent **55**, 230
**Combinatorial synthesis** (s.a. Compound libraries, Polymer-based...,)
– by ring closing metathesis **49**, 985s55
– of
  2,6-dideoxytrisaccharides **45**, 285s55
  furans **43**, 740s55
  isoindoles, hexahydro- **49**, 985s55
  muscones **39**, 964s55
  taxoid side chains **28**, 144s55
–, review **50**, 555s55
– –, **solution-phase** (s.a. Solution-phase synthesis, parallel, automated)
– of
  2-aminoalcohols from epoxides **46**, 267s55
  piperazines, N-(nitroaryl)- **8**, 563s55
  4-pyridones, 2,3-dihydro- **38**, 887s55
  spiro[pyrrolidine-2,3′-oxindoles] **44**, 897s55
**3-Component synthesis**
– by ring closure, triple **55**, 398

- of
  amines, prim. **55**, 332
  –, tert. **55**, 356
  cyclohexenes, 1-aryl- **55**, 408
  2,9-dioxa-1-azabicyclo[4.3.0]nonanes, 3-alkoxy-, asym. induction **55**, 258
  tricarbonyl(acoxy-$\eta^5$-cyclopentadienyl)rhenium complexes **55**, 91
- –, regiostereospecific
- of 3-ethylenealcohols **55**, 286
**4-Component synthesis**
- of (Z)-$\alpha,\beta$-ethylene-$\beta$-silylaldimines **55**, 294
**5-Component synthesis**
- special s.
  Ugi 5-component synthesis
**Compound libraries**
- by olefin metathesis **49**, 932s55
- of
  pyridines **47**, 727s55
  quinolines, 1,2,3,4-tetrahydro- **55**, 342
  –, –, polysubst. **52**, 363s55
–, synthesis, review **50**, 555s55
– –, 2-million-fold **27**, 851s55
**Configuration, absolute**
–, determination, update **5**, 666s55
**Cope rearrangement** (s.a. Cyclopropanation-Cope rearrangement)
**Copper(I) acetate 55**, 271
**Copper(II)** – **55**, 166
–(II) acetoacetonate **55**, 271
–(I) acetylides
- as intermediates **55**, 271
- startg. m. f.
  (Z)-$\beta$-arylseleno-$\alpha,\beta$-ethyleneketones **55**, 267
–(II) $\pi$-allyl complexes
- as intermediates **55**, 305
–(II) $\alpha$-aminocarboxylic acid complexes, chiral
- as reagent **55**, 265
–(II) bis($\Delta^2$-oxazolines), chiral
- as reagent **55**, 266
–(I) cyanide **55**, 391
–(I) –/lithium bromide **55**, 305
–(I) halides
- bromide **55**, 383, 397
- chloride **55**, 159, 337
- iodide **55**, 385, 386, 416, 417, 456
–(II) halides
- chloride **55**, 159, 402
- fluoride/(S)-2,2′-bis(di-$p$-tolylphosphino)-1,1′-binaphthyl **55**, 434
–(II) nitrate **55**, 80
–(II) –/dinitrogen tetroxide **4**, 274s55
–(I) perchlorate **55**, 450
–(II) Schiff base complex **55**, 264
–(II) sulfate/ammonia **55**, 112
–(I) trifluoromethanesulfonate **55**, 124
**Coumarins**
- from
  $\alpha,\beta$-acetylenecarboxylic acids **54**, 367s55; **55**, 336
–, 4-carbalkoxy- **54**, 367s55
–, 3,4-dihydro-
- from
  $\alpha,\beta$-ethylenecarboxylic acids **55**, 336
  phenols **55**, 336
**Cross-coupling**
- of alkylarenes with halides, ar. **55**, 406
- special s.
  radical cross-coupling

–, ar., sequential
- with $o$-phenylene dipole equivalents **55**, 389
–, catalyzed
- of alkylsamarium(III) compds. with iodides, prim. **55**, 397
–, electroreductive **49**, 797s55
–, palladium-catalyzed
- in carbon dioxide, supercritical **55**, 417
**Crown dilactams, macrocyclic**
- as reagent **55**, 175
**18-Crown-6 polyether**
- as reagent **55**, 189
**Cuprates**
- special s.
  lithium organo(cyano)cuprates
**Cuprates, higher-order**
- special s.
  dilithium dimethyl(cyano)cuprate
**Cyanamides**
- startg. m. f.
  $N'$-phosphorylamidines, synthesis **55**, 369
$\alpha$-**Cyanamidines 55**, 164
**Cyanides** (s.a. Nitriles)
- special s.
  acylcyanides
$\alpha$-**Cyano-$\alpha,\beta$-ethylenecarboxylic acid esters**
- startg. m. f.
  cyclohexene-1,3-dicarboxylic acid esters, 2-amino-3-cyano-5-nitro- (from 2 molecules) **55**, 263
**Cyanohydrins**
- from
  aldehydes **55**, 245
$\alpha$-**Cyano-$\beta$-hydroxycarboxylic acid esters**
- by aldol condensation, asym. **55**, 250
**Cyanoketones**
- startg. m. f.
  $\alpha$-hydroxyketones, cyclic **55**, 482
$\alpha$-**Cyanoketones**
–, synthesis, polymer-based **55**, 349
**Cyanosilanes**
- special s.
  trimethylsilyl cyanide
**Cyanostannanes**
- special s.
  tri-$n$-butyltin cyanide
**Cyclimmonium salts**
–, radical $o$-alkylation **55**, 278
**Cycloaddition**
–, review (annual) **52**, 284s55
**Cycloaddition, 1,3-dipolar, asym.** (s.a. Hetero-Diels-Alder reaction-1,3-dipolar cycloaddition, asym.)
- with oxazolium betaines, 4-hydroxy- **43**, 740s55
–, –, polymer-based
- with
  nitrile oxides **16**, 888s55
  oxazolium betaines, 4-hydroxy- **43**, 740s55
–, –, regiostereospecific
- with azomethinium ylids **55**, 466
**[3+2]-Cycloaddition**
- with trimethylenemethane equivalents **55**, 257
**[4+2]-Cycloaddition** s. Diels-Alder reaction, Hetero-Diels-Alder –
**[5+2]-Cycloaddition, cationic,**

intramolecular, stereospecific
- with $p$-quinone monoketals **55**, 494
–, intramolecular, stereospecific
- to ethylene derivs. **55**, 318
- with vinylcyclopropanes **55**, 318
**Cycloalkenes** (s.a. under specific rings and Ethylene derivs., cyclic)
- special s.
  vinylcycloalkenes
**2-Cycloalkenones** (s.a. $\alpha,\beta$-Ethyleneketones, cyclic)
- from
  bis(epoxides) **55**, 480
  epoxyaldehydes **55**, 480
–, 2-alkynyl- **27**, 851s55
–, 2-phosphonyl- **55**, 496
**Cyclobutane ring fragmentation, photochemical**
–, 1,4-naphthoquinone ring via – **55**, 492
**Cyclobutanes**
- special s.
  alkylidenecyclobutanes
  di(methylene)cyclobutanes
–, cyano- **29**, 959s55
**Cyclobutenes**
- startg. m. f.
  1,5-cyclooctadienes, sym. **55**, 276
**Cyclobut-2-en-4-olones** (s.a. Squaric acid derivs.)
**Cyclocarbonylation**
–, 2(5$H$)-furanones, 4-aryl-seleno- or -thio- via – **55**, 457
–, 3-isochromanones via – **55**, 293
–, 1,2,4-oxadiazoles, 5-aryl- via – **55**, 415
**Cyclodextrins**
–, chemistry, review **5**, 666s55
**1,4-Cycloheptadienes, chiral 52**, 387s55
**1,3-Cyclohexadienes**
- special s.
  methylene-1,3-cyclohexadienes
**Cyclohexene-1,3-dicarboxylic acid esters, 2-amino-3-cyano-5-nitro- 55**, 263
**Cyclohexenes, 1-aryl-**
- from
  allenes **55**, 408
  ethylene derivs., electron-deficient **55**, 408
  halides, ar. **55**, 408
**3-Cyclohexenones, 2,6-bridged 55**, 489
**1,5-Cyclooctadienes, sym.**
- from
  cyclobutenes **55**, 276
**Cyclooctene ring 55**, 381
**Cyclopallad(II)ated phosphine complexes** s. under Palladium complexes
**Cyclopentadienes**
- special s.
  biscyclopentadien…
–, 5-hydroxy-, 2,3-condensed
- from
  diynes **55**, 301
**Cyclopentadien-5-ylacetic acid esters 54**, 444s55
**Cyclopentane-1,2-diols, polyoxy-, chiral 53**, 22s55
**Cyclopentanes**
- special s.
  vinylcyclopentanes
**Cyclopentanols**
- special s.
  vinylcyclopentanols

**Cyclopentanones**
–, ring expansion with dihalides, unsatd. **55**, 381
–, α,α-disubst., chiral **28**, 13s55
**Cyclopentenes**
– special s.
  alkylidenecyclopentanes
–, 1-amino-5-cyano-
– from
  α,β-ethylenenitriles (2 molecules) **55**, 284
–, 4-amino-3,5-dihydroxy- **55**, 62
**2-Cyclopentenone ring** (s.a. Pauson-Khand)
– from
  enynes **55**, 282
**2-Cyclopentenones**
– from
  acetylene derivs. **55**, 281
– special s.
  spirocyclopent-2-enones
**Cyclopentylacetic acid esters, polyoxy-, chiral 46**, 964s55
**Cyclopentylcarbonyl compds., 3-methylene- 55**, 458
**(Cyclopentylmethyl)silanes 55**, 299
**Cyclopropanation, asym.**
– of 3-ethylenealcohols **47**, 806s55
–, –, Ru-catalyzed **23**, 819s55
**Cyclopropanation-Cope rearrangement, asym. 52**, 387s55
–, intramolecular
– with α-(sulfonylamino)alkylidenecarbenes **55**, 370
**Cyclopropanecarboxylic acid esters**
– from
  ethylene derivs., synthesis, asym. **55**, 421
  sulfonium salts, –, – **55**, 421
– – –, *trans*-2-aryl-, chiral **55**, 421
**Cyclopropane ring**
– special s.
  alkylidenecyclopropane ring
**Cyclopropanes**
– special s.
  3-oxabicyclo[3.1.0]hexan-2-ones
  polycyclopropanes
  vinylcyclopropanes
–, allenyl-
– startg. m. f.
  3-alkylidenecyclopentenes **55**, 317
–, 1,2-disulfonyl- **16**, 644s55
**Cyclopropanone ketals, 2-alkylidene-**
– startg. m. f.
  pyrrolidine-3-carboxylic acid esters, 1-alkoxy- **55**, 257
– –, 2-α-hydroxy-
– from
  oxo compds. **55**, 348
**(Cyclopropylalkylidene)cyclopropane ring**
–, ring expansion, double, regiospecific **55**, 316
**Cyclopropylamines, 1-aryl- 55**, 339
**(E)-β-Cyclopropyl-α,β-ethylenecarboxylic acid esters 37**, 902s55
**Cyclopropyl ketones**
– from
  alkylidenephosphoranes **55**, 424
  1,2-dioxins, 3,6-dihydro- **55**, 424
**Cyclopropyltrimethylenemethane 1,3-diradicals**

– as intermediates **55**, 316
**Cyclopropylzinc chlorides**
–, cross-coupling **41**, 795s55
**Cysteine peptides** s. Peptides, cysteine-containing

**Dakin-West reaction, anomalous 55**, 465
**DBU** s. 1,8-Diazabicyclo[5.4.0]undec-7-ene
**N-Deacylation** s. HN↕C
**O-Deacylation** s. HO↕C
**S-Deacylation 55**, 20
**N-Dealkylation** (s.a. HN↕C)
– special s.
  N-deallylation
**O-Dealkylation** (s.a. HO↕C)
– special s.
  O-deallylation
  O-debenzylation
**N-Deallylation, nickel(0)-catalyzed 55**, 10
**O-Deallylation, heterogeneous**
– of allyl carboxylates **33**, 9s55
–, nickel(0)-catalyzed **55**, 10
–, selective
– via addition of perfluoroalkyl iodides **55**, 5
**O-Debenzylation** (s.a. under *p*-Methoxybenzyl ethers)
–, selective **43**, 17s55
**Decarbalkoxylation** (s.a. C-Alkylation, decarbalkoxylative)
**N-Decarbalkoxylation** (s.a. HN↕C)
– special s.
  N-decarbo-*tert*-butoxylation
**N-Decarbamylation**
– of N-carbamylmaleimides **55**, 16
**N-Decarbo-*tert*-butoxylation**
– under microwave irradiation **55**, 17
– with O-desilylation **27**, 110s55
– with simultaneous purification **55**, 18
**Decarbonylation**
– of α-ketocarboxylic acid esters **55**, 117
**Decarboxylation** s.a. HC↕C
–, aerobic, catalytic
–, ketones via – **55**, 119
**Decomplexation, reductive**
– of
  acetylene dicobalt hexacarbonyl complexes **55**, 35
  (π-allyl)tricarbonyliron-lactone – **55**, 34
**O-De-*p*-methoxybenzylation 16**, 201s55
**N-Deoxygenation 30**, 696s55
**2-Deoxyglycosides**
– special s.
  2-iodo-2-deoxyglycosides
**2-Deoxysugars**
– special s.
  2-fluoro-2-deoxysugars
**Deracemization**
– of
  α-aminocarboxylic acid esters **55**, 499
  – acids by Ni(II) complexation **55**, 499
**O-Desilylation** (s.a. HO↕Rem)
–, polymer-based **29**, 415s55
**N-Desulfonylation, cathodic, polymer-**

based **27**, 18s55
–, preferential **55**, 14
**Desymmetrization**
– of
  diols by asym. O-acylation **44**, 214s55
  epoxides **55**, 176
  – (on aminolysis) **48**, 269s55
**1-Deuterioalcohols 55**, 25
**α-Deuterioamines 55**, 25
**α-Deuterio-α-aminocarboxylic acids**
– special s.
  α,β-dideuterio-α-aminocarboxylic acids
**Deuterium compds.** (s.a. Dideuterio...)
**1,1-Diacoxy compds.** s. Acylals
**Diacylamines, mixed** s. N-Acylcarboxylic acid amides
**1,2-Di(acylamines), cyclic, chiral**
– special s.
  (R,R)-1,2-bis(picolinoylamino)cyclohexane
**γ,γ-Dialkoxyallylzirconium complexes**
– as intermediates **55**, 348
**(E,E)-1,4-Dialkoxy-1,3-butadienes, sym., chiral 34**, 648s55
**α,α'-Di(alkylidene)ketones, cyclic 55**, 355
**Dialkyl sulfates**
–, O-alkylation of phenols with – **55**, 100
– startg. m. f.
  arylcarboxylic acid esters **55**, 101
**Si,Si'-Diallyldi(silanes)**
– as reactant **36**, 884s55
**Diamines**
–, determination of abs. configuration **5**, 666s55
**1,1-Diamines**
– special s.
  diaminomethanes
**1,2-Diamines**
–, chemistry, review **51**, 138s55
– special s.
  ene-1,2-diamines
**1,3-Diamines, hindered 19**, 382s55
**2,3-Diamino-1,3-dienes**
–, α-diketones, sym. via – **55**, 346
**Diaminomethanes**
– startg. m. f.
  dithiocarbamic acid benzyl esters, N,N-disubst. **55**, 359
**N,C-Dianions**
– as intermediates **55**, 362, 373
**1,2-Diarylacetylenes** s. Tolans
**1,1-Diarylalkanes**
– from
  alkylarenes **55**, 406
  halides, ar. **55**, 406
**Diaryl ditellurides**
– startg. m. f.
  diaryls **55**, 491
**Diaryl ethers 55**, 166
**Diaryliodonium salts**
– startg. m. f.
  arylcarboxylic acid esters, carbonylation **55**, 324
  2-ethyleneselenides, ar. **55**, 225
  (E)-styrenes **55**, 280
**Diaryl ketones 52**, 413s55
– startg. m. f.
  tolans, synthesis with rearrangement **55**, 430
**Diaryls** (s.a. Biaryl..., Biphenyls)

- by Suzuki coupling, polymer-based **50,** 556s**55**
- from
  arylboronic acids **55,** 456
  aryllead triacetates **55,** 456
  aryl triflates **48,** 812s**55**
  chlorides, ar. **45,** 557s**55**
  –, – (2 different molecules) **48,** 812s**55**
  (η⁶-chloroarene)tricarbonyl-chromium(0) complexes **45,** 555s**55**
  diaryl ditellurides **55,** 491
  diaryl tellurides **55,** 491
**–, 2-cyano-** 33, 990s**55**
**Diaryl tellurides**
- startg. m. f.
  diaryls **55,** 491
**1,8-Diazabicyclo[5.4.0]undec-7-ene**
- as reagent **55,** 4, 107, 193, 381
**α-Diazocarbonyl compds.**
- special s.
  acoxy-α-diazocarbonyl compds.
**α-Diazoketones**
- startg. m. f.
  hydroxamic acid esters, rearrangement **55,** 150
**α-Di(azomethines), sym.**
- from
  aldimines **55,** 321
**Diazonium fluoroborates**
- startg. m. f.
  styrenes **55,** 458
**Diazonium salts**
- special s.
  bis(diazonium salts)
**Diazotization**
- in neutral non-aq. media **55,** 188
- with nitrogen dioxide, liq. **55,** 188
**α,ω-Di(boronyl)enynes**
–, ring closure **42,** 679s**55**
**(R)-6,6′-Dibromo-1,1′-bi-2-naphthol**
 (s.a. under Zirconium aroxides, chiral)
**Di-*tert*-butylation, ar.**
–, review **19,** 897s**55**
**Di-*tert*-butyl hyponitrite**
- as reagent **55,** 218, 277
**Di-*n*-butyltin oxide**
- as reagent **55,** 83
**Dicarbanion equivalents**
- special s.
  benzyl dicarbanion equivalents
**α-Dicarbonyl compds.** (s.a. α-Diketones, Malonic...)
–, synthesis, oxidative, review **31,** 163s**55**
**α-Dicarboxylic...** s. Malonic...
**β-Dicarboxylic...** s. Succinic...
**Dicarboxylic acid amide esters**
- special s.
  phthalamic acid esters
**Dicarboxylic acid imides**
- special s.
  N-alkoxydicarboxylic acid imides
  N-carbamyldicarboxylic acid imides
  succinimides
***o*-Dicarboxylic acid monoesters**
- special s.
  2-(carbethoxy)benzoic acid
**2,3-Dichloro-5,6-dicyanoquinone**
- as reagent **55,** 106
**N-(Dichloromethylene)dimethyl-ammonium chloride**
- as reactant **55,** 399
**Dicyclohexylborane**

- as reagent **55,** 271
**Dicyclohexylcarbodiimide**
- as reagent **55,** 139
**α,β-Dideuterio-α-*prim*-aminocarboxylic acids**
- from
  2,5-piperazinediones, 3-alkylidene-, asym. conversion **55,** 39
**Dieckmann cyclization** (s.a. Retro-Dieckmann reaction)
**Diels-Alder reaction** (s.a. CC⇓CC and under Diene synthesis in Vol.**1-50**; s.a. Carbopalladation, intramolecular-allene insertion-Diels-Alder reaction, Heck-Diels-Alder –, Retro-Diels-Alder –)
- with ketene equivalents, review **37,** 669s**55**
**Diels-Alder reaction, asym.**
- with 1,1-nitroethylene derivs. **49,** 622s**55**
– –, – –, Lewis acid-catalyzed
- in water **55,** 265
– –, polymer-based **36,** 667s**55**
– –, regiostereospecific
- with
  α,β-etheneselenolic acid esters **55,** 283
  α,β-ethylenethiolic – – **55,** 283
  (η²-styrene)osmium complexes **55,** 285
**Diels-Alder-Sakurai-Hosomi reaction 22,** 721s**55**
**(2E,4E)-Dienals 38,** 836s**55**
**Diene-α,β-epoxyketones**
- startg. m. f.
  bicyclo[n.m.0]alkane-1,3-diols **55,** 275
**1,3-Dienes**
- from
  allenes, isomerization **55,** 73
- special s.
  alkyltelluro-1,3-dienes
  2-amino-1,3-dienes
  aryltelluro-1,3-dienes
  siloxy-1,3-dienes
  silyl-1,3-dienes
  sulfinyl-1,3-dienes
  sulfonylamino-1,3-dienes
  sulfonyl-1,3-dienes
- startg. m. f.
  4-acoxy-2-ethyleneethers, regiostereo-specific conversion **55,** 72
  3-ethylenealcohols, synthesis **55,** 286
  4-ethylenealcohols, –, regiostereo-specific **55,** 290
  γ-siloxy-γ,δ-ethyleneboronic acid esters, – **55,** 251
  siloxy-3-ethylenes, –, regiostereo-specific **55,** 290
  2,5(Z),8-triene-1,10-diones **55,** 291
–, synthesis **26,** 875s**55**
**1,3-Dienes, 2-α-functionalized 42,** 354s**55**
**1,4-Dienes 36,** 43s**55**
- from
  2-organoseleno-1,4-dienes **43,** 778s**55**
- special s.
  organoseleno-1,4-dienes
  silyl-1,4-dienes
**1,6-Dienes**
–, ring closure, regiostereospecific via silylpalladation **55,** 299
- special s.

siloxy-1,6-dienes
**η¹-(1,3-Diene)tungsten complexes**
- startg. m. f.
  pyridine ring **55,** 431
**(E)-2,4-Dienones**
- from
  carboxylic acid halides, with 4 extra C-atoms **55,** 435
**1,5-Dien-3-ynes**
–, synthesis **26,** 875s**55**
**2,4-Dien-6-ynones 55,** 435
**Diethyl dichloromethanephosphonate**
- as reactant **55,** 430
**Diethyl phosphorocyanidate**
- as reactant **55,** 349
**1,1-Difluorides**
- from
  ethylene derivs., cyclic with ring contraction **55,** 181
**1,2-Difluorides**
- from
  ethylene derivs. **55,** 181
**N,N′-Difluoro-2,2′-bipyridinium bis(fluoroborate)**
–, fluorination with – **55,** 184
**Difluoromethylene compds.**
–, synthesis **39,** 740s**55**
**β,β-Difluorostyrenes 38,** 836s**55**
**Dihalides**
- special s.
  ethylenedihalides
**1,1-Dihalides**
- special s.
  1,1-difluorides
**1,2-Dihalides**
- from
  ethylene derivs. (1,2-dibromides) **55,** 178
- special s.
  1,2-difluorides
***o*-Dihalides**
- startg. m. f.
  arenes, *o*-disubst. **55,** 389
**α,α-Dihalogenocarboxylic acid esters**
- startg. m. f.
  (E)-α,β-ethylenecarboxylic acids **55,** 374
**Dihalogenomethyleneammonium salts**
- special s.
  N-(dichloromethylene)dimethyl-ammonium chloride
**Dihalogenomethylene compds.**
- from
  trihalogenomethyl sulfones **20,** 685s**55**
**α,α-Dihalogenophosphonic acid esters**
- special s.
  diethyl dichloromethanephosphonate
**Dihalogenostannanes**
- special s.
  bis(pentafluorophenyl)tin dibromide
**Di(hetaryl)ethenes, photochromic**
–, synthesis, review **42,** 970s**55**
**β,β′-Dihydroxycarboxylic acids**
- special s.
  halogeno-β,β′-dihydroxycarboxylic acids
**Dihydroxylation** (s.a. under Glycols)
**Dihydroxylation, asym.**
- of N-(α,β-ethyleneacyl)sultams **21,** 858s**55**
**2,4-Dihydroxymercaptans**
- startg. m. f.
  1,2-oxathianes, 4-hydroxy- **55,** 55

**2,4-Dihydroxythioethers**
- startg. m. f.
  4-ethylene-3-hydroxythioethers, rearrangement **55**, 214
  thiophenes, tetrahydro-, 3-hydroxy- **55**, 214

**Diisopropylcarbodiimide**
- as reagent **55**, 158

**γ,δ-Diketocarboxylic acid esters 35,** 642s55

**Diketones**
- special s.
  trienediones

**α-Diketones 47,** 954s55
- special s.
  benzils
- startg. m. f.
  β-acoxy-α,β-ethyleneketones **55**, 427

**α-Diketones, sym.**
-, C-α'-alkylation via pyrazines, 2,3-dihydro- **55**, 377
- via 2,3-diamino-1,3-dienes **55**, 346

**β-Diketones**
- special s.
  aryl-β-diketones
- startg. m. f.
  pyridazines, 1,4-dihydro- **55**, 467

**β-Diketones, sym.**
- from
  acylcyanides **55**, 471
  carboxylic acid halides **55**, 471

**γ-Diketones**
- from
  enoxysilanes (2 different molecules) **55**, 488
  α,β-ethylene-β'-hydroxyketones **55**, 302

**1,6-Diketones, sym. 47,** 656s55

**Dilactams, macrocyclic**
- special s.
  crown dilactams

**Dilactones, macrocyclic 55,** 497

**Dilithium dimethyl(cyano)cuprate**
- as catalyst **55**, 215

**Dilithium ene-1,1-diolates**
- as intermediates **55**, 376

**(1S,2S)-1,2-Dimethoxy-1,2-diphenylethane**
- as reagent **55**, 464

**(−)-3-exo-(Dimethylamino)isoborneol**
- as reagent **55**, 239

**4-Dimethylaminopyridine**
- as catalyst for N-acylation, review **47**, 287s55
- as reagent **55**, 136

**4-Dimethylaminopyridines, ferrocenyl-fused, chiral**
- as reagent **55**, 57

**Dimethyldioxirane**
-, prepn. of concentrated soln. **44**, 117s55

**1,2-Di(methylene)cyclobutanes 24,** 694s55

**Dimethylformamide**
- as reactant **55**, 361

**N,N-Dimethylglycine**
- as reagent **55**, 414

**Dimethyl 2-(phenylseleno)fumarate**
- as reactant **55**, 329

**Dimethylphenylsilyllithium**
- as reagent **31**, 890s55; **55**, 346

**N,N'-Dimethyl-N,N'-propyleneurea**
- as reagent **55**, 313

**Dimethyl sulfate**
- as reagent **55**, 19

**Dimethyl sulfide**
- as reactant **55**, 199
- as reagent **55**, 496

**Dimethyl sulfoxide**
- as reactant **55**, 199

**Dinitriles**
- startg. m. f.
  β-amino-α,β-ethylenenitriles, cyclic **55**, 256

**2,4-Dinitrobenzenesulfonamide**
- as reagent **55**, 144

**2,4-Dinitrobenzenesulfonamides**
- startg. m. f.
  amines, N-functionalized **55**, 163

**Dinucleosides, acetylene-linked 17,** 169s55
**−, formal-linked 17,** 169s55
**−, sulfamide-linked 17,** 169s55

**Diol monoallyl ethers**
- by preferential O-allylation **55**, 85

**Diols**
-, desymmetrization by asym. O-acylation **44**, 214s55
- special s.
  enediols

**Diols, sym.**
-, O-acetylation, partial **55**, 98

**1,2-Diols** s. Glycols

**1,3-Diols**
- from
  2,3-epoxyalcohols, with stereospecific isocyclic ring expansion **55**, 307
- special s.
  aryl-1,3-diols
  ene-1,3-diols
  nitro-1,3-diols

**1,3-Diols, bicyclic**
- special s.
  bicyclo[n.m.0]alkane-1,3-diols

**−, cyclic**
- from
  ethylene-α,β-epoxyketones **55**, 275
**−, spirocyclic 55,** 307

**1,5-Diols**
- special s.
  methylene-1,5-diols

**Diol sulfates, cyclic**
- from
  diol sulfites, cyclic, kinetic resolution **55**, 51
- special s.
  glycol sulfates, cyclic

**Diol sulfites, cyclic**
- startg. m. f.
  diol sulfates, cyclic, kinetic resolution **55**, 51

**2,9-Dioxa-1-azabicyclo[4.3.0]nonanes, 3-alkoxy-**
-, 3-component synthesis with asym. induction **55**, 258

**4,8-Dioxa-1-azabicyclo[4.3.0]nonan-5-ones**
- from
  aldehydes (2 molecules), synthesis, asym. **55**, 325
- startg. m. f.
  α-prim-amino-β-hydroxycarboxylic acids, (chiral compds.) **55**, 325

**2,8-Dioxa-1-azabicyclo[3.3.0]octanes, peri-fused 55,** 398

**2,8-Dioxabicyclo[3.3.0]octanes 47,** 576s55

**1,4-Dioxane-2,5-diones, sym.**
- from
  α-hydroxycarboxylic acid esters **55**, 83

**1,3-Dioxanes, 5-arylidene-, chiral 38,** 836s55

**1,4-Dioxanes, 2,5-dialkoxy-**
- from
  2-acetylenealcohols (2 molecules) **55**, 63

**1,2-Dioxins, 3,6-dihydro-**
- startg. m. f.
  cyclopropyl ketones **55**, 424

**1,3-Dioxolanes, 4-sulfonylmethyl-**
- startg. m. f.
  oxo compds. **55**, 4

**Dioxygen**
-, oxidation, catalytic, heterogeneous with − **55**, 113

**Dipeptide esters**
- startg. m. f.
  tetrapeptides, cyclic, sym. **55**, 148

**Diphenylphosphine oxide**
- as reactant **55**, 217

**Diphenylphosphinic acid**
- as reagent **55**, 217

**N-[2-(Diphenylphosphino)benzylidene]-2-phenylethylamine**
- as reagent **55**, 300

**Diphenylphosphinyl chloride**
- as reactant **55**, 125

**Diphenyl phosphorazidate**
- as reagent **55**, 142

**Diphenylsilane**
- as reagent **55**, 42

**Di(phosphines)**
- special s.
  1,1'-bis(di-tert-butylphosphino)-ferrocene
  bis(diphenylphosphino)...

**Di(phosphines), chiral 55,** 220

**o-Di(phosphines)**
- special s.
  p,p'-1,2-phenylenebis(...

**2,2'-Di(phosphino)biphenyls, chiral 55,** 26

**Dipole equivalents**
- special s.
  o-phenylene dipole equivalents

**1,3-Diradicals**
- special s.
  trimethylenemethane 1,3-diradicals

**1,4-Diradicals**
-, ring closures via − **55**, 311

**C-α-Disaccharides 50,** 531s55

**Diselenocarboxylic acid esters**
-, synthesis, review **47**, 552s55

**Disilanes**
- special s.
  1,1,2,2-tetraphenyldisilane

**Disilazanes**
- special s.
  hexamethyldisilazane

**Disiloxanes**
- special s.
  1,1,3,3-tetraisopropyl-3-[2-(triphenylmethoxy)ethoxy]disiloxan-1-yl ethers

**1,2-Disiloxy compds., sym.**
- from
  oxo compds. **55**, 243

**N,N-Disiloxyenamines**
– from
 nitro compds., aliphatic **55**, 56
**Distannanes**
– special s.
 hexabutyldistannane
**Disulfides**
– startg. m. f.
 thioethers **55**, 207
**Disulfides, cyclic 16**, 172s**55**
**Disulfimides**
– special s.
 *o*-benzenedisulfonimides
**1,2-Di(sulfonium salts)**
– from
 ethylene derivs., stereospecific
 conversion **55**, 199
**1,4-Di(sulfonium salts)**
– special s.
 ene-1,4-di(sulfonium salts)
**Ditellurides**
– special s.
 diaryl ditellurides
**1,3-Dithiane 1-oxides, chiral**
–, synthesis, asym. with –, review **51**,
 399s**55**
**1,2-Dithiins, 3,6-dihydro-**
– from
 thiiranes, 2-vinyl- **55**, 200
**Dithiocarbamic acid benzyl esters**
– special s.
 *p*-hydroxybenzyl dithiocarbamates
– – –, **N,N-disubst.**
– from
 arenes **55**, 359
 diaminomethanes **55**, 359
**1,4-Di(thioethers)**
– special s.
 ene-1,4-di(thioethers)
**Dithiols**
– startg. m. f.
 mercaptals, cyclic **55**, 202
**Dithiophosphoric acid esters**
– special s.
 S-aryl O,O-dialkyl dithiophosphates
**Dithiourethans** s. Dithiocarbamic acid
 esters
**Diynes**
–, ring closing metathesis **55**, 497
– startg. m. f.
 acetylene derivs., macrocyclic,
  metathesis **55**, 497
 cyclopentadienes, 5-hydroxy-, 2,3-
  condensed **55**, 301
***tert*-Dodecanethiol**
– as reagent **55**, 108, 218


**Electrochemistry**
– of phosphorus and sulfur compds.,
 review **46**, 572s**55**
–, **organometallic**
–, review **46**, 572s**55**
**Electrolysis** (s.a. Reduction, cathodic,
 enzyme-catalyzed) **55**, 21, 231, 346,
 418
– under continuous flow **55**, 121

–/**dehydrogenase 42**, 22s**55**
–/**nickel(II) chloride/2,2′-bipyridyl 55**,
 219
**Electron-transfer, photo-induced**
– with a heterogeneous sensitizer **55**, 442
**Enamines**
– special s.
 disiloxyenamines
 enediamines
 tosylenamines
– startg. m. f.
 3-ketothioethers **55**, 363
 mercaptals, cyclic **55**, 202
**δ-Enaminolactams**
– from
 nitrogen, atmospheric **55**, 141
**Enantiomeric excess**
–, determination, update **5**, 666s**55**
**Enantiomeric separation** s. under
 Resolutions and **Res** section
**Enazo compds.**
– special s.
 carbamylenazo compds.
**Enazomethines**
– special s.
 3-siloxy-2-aza-1,3-dienes
**(Z)-Ene-1,2-di-*tert*-amines**
– as intermediates **55**, 346
**Ene-1,1-diolates**
– special s.
 lithium ene-1,1-diolates
**Ene-1,2-diol ethers, sym.**
– from
 chromium alkoxycarbene complexes
 **55**, 453
**(Z)-2-Ene-1,n-diol monocarbonates**
– startg. m. f.
 2-vinyl-O-heterocyclics **55**, 115
***anti*-3-Ene-1,2-diol 2-monoethers 55**,
 352
**1,2-Ene-3,n-diols**
– from
 vinyloxyketones, O→C-vinyl migration,
  stereospecific **55**, 308
**(Z)-Ene-1,2-di(selenides) 23**, 703s**55**
**2-Ene-1,4-di(sulfonium salts) 55**, 199
**Ene-1,3-di(thioethers)**
– startg. m. f.
 2-ethylenegermanes **55**, 228
 2-ethylenestannanes **55**, 228
**2,3-Ene-1,4-di(thioethers) 47**, 568s**55**
**Ene reaction** (s.a. CC⇓OC, CC⇓CC)
– special s.
 palladium ene reaction
– with acylnitroso compds. **55**, 128
– –, asym., Lewis acid-catalyzed
– with azodicarboxylates **49**, 256s**55**
**Eneselenides**
– special s.
 β-arylseleno-α,β-ethylen...
 2-(arylseleno)fumaric acid esters
 (arylthio)eneselenides
 enedi(selenides) **23**, 703s**55**
**Enesilanes**
–, hydrosilylation, regiospecific **55**, 35
– special s.
 siloxyenesilanes
**Enestannanes**
– from
 acetylene derivs., conversion,
  regiostereospecific **55**, 216
– special s.

silylenestannanes
stannylenynes
– startg. m. f.
 α,β-ethylenehydroxamic acid esters
 **55**, 462
**(E)-Enestannanes**
– by Stille coupling **39**, 887s**55**
**Enetellurides**
– from
 acetylene derivs., synthesis **55**, 272
– – –, terminal, synthesis **55**, 490
– special s.
 1-alkyltelluro-1,3-dienes
 aryltelluro-1,3-dienes
 iodoenetellurides
 (organoseleno)enetellurides
– startg. m. f.
 acetylene derivs. **55**, 490
**Eneurethans**
–, hydrogenation, asym. **42**, 45s**55**
**Ene-yne metathesis 54**, 319, 320
– – –, polymer-based **54**, 320s**55**
**Ene-ynes** s. Enynes
**Enisocyclics** (s.a. Alkylidenecyclo...)
– from
 β-hydroxyphosphonic acid esters,
  cyclic, conversion, asym. **55**, 464
 ketones, cyclic, synthesis, asym. **55**,
  464
 phosphonic acid esters, –, – **55**, 464
**Enolates** (s.a. Azaenolates,
 Homoenolates)
– special s.
 enediolates
 potassium enolates
**Enolesters**
– from
 α,β-ethyleneboronic acids or esters,
  with inversion **55**, 102
–, hydrogenation, asym. **55**, 38
– special s.
 α-acoxy-α,β-ethylen...
**Enolethers**
– from
 carboxylic acid esters **51**, 423s**55**
 chromium alkoxycarbene complexes
 **55**, 453
 dithioorthoformic acid esters **51**,
 423s**55**
– special s.
 α-alkoxy-α,β-ethylen...
 (trifluoromethyl)enolethers
 vinyloxy...
– startg. m. f.
 furans **55**, 403
 2*H*-pyran-6-phosphonic acid esters,
 3,4-dihydro-, 2-alkoxy-, asym.
 cycloaddition **55**, 266
 2*H*-pyrans, 3,4-dihydro-, 2-alkoxy- **55**,
 288
**Enolethers, exocyclic**
– special s.
 1-alkylidenesugars
**Enol phosphinates**
– from
 acetylene derivs., terminal **55**, 71
**Enol triflates**
– startg. m. f.
 α,β-ethylenecarboxylic acid amides,
  N-unsubst., carbonylation **55**, 413
 β-ketocarboxylic acids, carboxylation,
  cathodic **55**, 418

**Enones** s. α,β-Ethyleneketones
**Enoxy(hydrido)silanes**
–, aldol-type condensation, uncatalyzed with – **55**, 422
**Enoxysilanes**
–, radical cross-coupling, oxidative with – **55**, 488
– special s.
  aminoenoxysilanes
  enoxy(hydrido)silanes
  1-siloxy-1,ω-enynes
– startg. m. f.
  β-(acylhydrazino)carbonyl compds. **55**, 439
  β-*prim*-aminocarbonyl compds. **55**, 439
  β-aminoketones **55**, 440
  –, synthesis, asym. **55**, 459
  γ-diketones (from 2 different molecules) **55**, 488
  furans **55**, 403
  γ-keto-α-(tosylamino)carboxylic acid esters, asym. synthesis with 2 extra C-atoms **55**, 450
  α-(sulfonyloxy)ketones, asym. conversion **55**, 169
**Enyne-allenes**
–, generation **51**, 312s55
–, radical ring closures, double **51**, 312s55
**Enynes**
–, carbozincation, (η²-olefin)titanium(II)-catalyzed **55**, 269
– special s.
  boronylenynes
  siloxyenynes
– startg. m. f.
  2-cyclopentenone ring **55**, 282
  vinylcyclopropanes, fused **55**, 269
**1,3-Enynes**
– special s.
  stannyl-1,3-enynes
**1,3-Enynes, terminal**
– from
  α,β-ethylenehalides, with 2 extra C-atoms **55**, 388
**(E)-1,3-Enynes**
– from
  acetylene derivs., via hydroboration **55**, 271
  – –, terminal **55**, 271
  copper(I) acetylides **55**, 271
  lithium acetylides **55**, 447
–, synthesis **26**, 875s55
**Enzymes** (s.a. Reduction, cathodic, enzyme-catalyzed)
– as electrocatalyst **42**, 22s55
  cyclohexanone monooxygenase **55**, 51
  lipase **55**, 6
  Novozym **55**, 68
  nucleoside oxidase **55**, 77
  transaminases, reactions with –, review **43**, 299s55
**Epothilones**
–, synthesis, review **49**, 985s55
**Epothilone synthesis, partial 49**, 985s55
**Epoxidation**
– in carbon dioxide, dense liq. phase **55**, 67
*syn*-**Epoxidation**
– of (E)-ethylene derivs., 1,2-disubst. **55**, 74
**Epoxidation, asym.** (s.a. Sharpless epoxidation)

– of
  1,3-dienes **51**, 65s55
  1,3-enynes **51**, 65s55
  ethylenealcohols **51**, 65s55
  *trans*-α,β-ethyleneketones **18**, 193s55
–, resolution, kinetic of allenes by – **55**, 500
–, catalytic
– in aq. micellar media **55**, 70
–, intramolecular, stereospecific **55**, 75
**Epoxidation-transesterification, enzymatic 55**, 68
**Epoxides** (s. under Oxido compds. in Vol.1-50)
–, desymmetrization on aminolysis **48**, 269s55
– from
  glycols, retention of configuration **55**, 190
  glycol sulfates, cyclic, – – – **55**, 190
  ketones, synthesis, asym. **55**, 421
  sulfonium salts, –, – **55**, 421
– special s.
  acetyleneepoxides
  acoxyepoxides
  bis(epoxides)
  sulfonyloxyepoxides
– startg. m. f.
  1,2-halogenhydrins, regiostereospecific ring opening **55**, 175
  2-siloxyhalides, desymmetrization **55**, 176
  2-siloxymercaptans **55**, 193
  thiiranes, inversion of configuration **55**, 205
**Epoxyalcohols**
– from
  ethylenealcohols **55**, 67
**2,3-Epoxyalcohols**
– special s.
  siloxy-2,3-epoxyalcohols
– startg. m. f.
  1,3-diols, with stereospecific isocyclic ring expansion **55**, 307
**2,3-Epoxy-*tert*-alcohols, chiral 9**, 741s55
**3,4-Epoxyalcohols, unsatd.**
– startg. m. f.
  8-oxabicyclo[3.2.1]oct-2-ene ring, condensed **55**, 479
**Epoxyaldehydes**
– from
  oxaziridines, 3-alkenyl- **55**, 75
– startg. m. f.
  2-cycloalkenones **55**, 480
**2,3-Epoxyamines, N-protected, functionalized 20**, 112s55
**α,β-Epoxycarboxylic...** s. Glycidic...
**β,γ-Epoxycarboxylic acids**
– from
  carboxylic acids **55**, 376
  α-halogenoketones **55**, 376
**α,β-Epoxyketones**
– special s.
  ethylene-α,β-epoxyketones
–, **chiral 52**, 389s55
**(E)-α,β-Epoxyketones**
– from
  β-acoxy-α,β-ethyleneiodonium salts **55**, 468
  aldehydes **55**, 468
**α,β-Epoxyphosphonic acid esters**
–, chemistry, review **32**, 593s55

**N-(2,3-Epoxy)urethans, polymer-based**
– as intermediates **55**, 147
**Ethers**
–, cleavage s. HO↿C
– special s.
  allyl ethers
  benzyl ethers
  benzyl trityl ether
– startg. m. f.
  acoxy compds. **55**, 105
**Ethers, cyclic** (s.a. O-Heterocyclics)
– from
  N-(alkenyloxy)phthalimides **55**, 1
  ethylenealcohols, with 1,2-silyl group migration **55**, 76
– startg. m. f.
  ω-acoxyhalides **55**, 105
**Ethyl acetate**
– as reactant **55**, 110
**Ethyl acetoacetate**
– as reactant **55**, 131
**Ethylarenes**
– from
  aryldiethylalanes **55**, 447
**Ethyl α-(boronylmethyl)acrylates, chiral**
– as reactant **55**, 423
**Ethyl dichlorovanadate**
– as reagent **55**, 447
**Ethyldiisopropylamine**
– as reagent **55**, 41, 126, 143, 211, 227, 399, 433
**1-Ethyl-3-(3-dimethylaminopropyl)-carbodiimide hydrochloride**
– as reagent **55**, 164
**α,β-Ethyleneacetals**
–, 1,4-addition, asym., nickel-catalyzed to – **55**, 268
**α,β-Ethyleneacylals**
–, palladium-ene reaction, intramolecular with – **55**, 481
**α,β-Ethyleneacylphosphonic acid esters**
– startg. m. f.
  2H-pyran-6-phosphonic acid esters, 3,4-dihydro-, 2-alkoxy-, asym. cycloaddition **55**, 266
**N-(α,β-Ethyleneacyl)succinimides**
–, cycloaddition, 1,3-dipolar, asym. to – **51**, 317s55
**N-(α,β-Ethyleneacyl)sultams**
–, dihydroxylation, asym. **21**, 858s55
**Ethylenealcohols**
–, 3-component synthesis, regiostereospecific **55**, 286
– startg. m. f.
  acoxyepoxides **55**, 68
  epoxyalcohols **55**, 67
  ethers, cyclic, with 1,2-silyl group migration **55**, 76
  3-hydroxy-O-heterocyclics **55**, 66
**2-Ethylenealcohols**
– special s.
  amino-2-ethylenealcohols
  arylthio-2-ethylenealcohols
  α,β-ethylene-β'-hydroxy...
  4-ethylene-3-hydroxy...
–, **4-functionalized 47**, 576s55
**3-Ethylenealcohols** (s.a. Allylboration, Barbier...)
–, O-allylation, preferential with – with allyl rearrangement **55**, 85
– by metathesis, regiospecific **55**, 474

–, cyclopropanation, asym. **47,** 806s**55**
– from
  aldehydes, synthesis **55,** 286
  –, –, asym. **55,** 441
  –, –, asym., regiospecific **55,** 433
  –, –, regiostereospecific **55,** 474
  γ-alkoxy-α,β-ethylenehalides,
    rearrangement, reductive **55,** 484
  1,3-dienes, synthesis **55,** 286
  ethylene derivs., via ozonolysis **55,** 472
  β,γ-ethylenehalides **55,** 472
  2-ethylene(trihalogeno)silanes,
    synthesis, asym. **55,** 441
  –, –, –, regiospecific **55,** 433
*anti*-3-Ethylenealcohols
– from
  allenes **33,** 865s**55**
**3-Ethylenealcohols, cyclic**
– special s.
  3-methylenealcohols, cyclic
**3-Ethylene-*tert*-alcohols**
– startg. m. f.
  ketones, C-cleavage **55,** 120
**4-Ethylenealcohols**
– from
  aldehydes, synthesis, regiostereo-
    specific **55,** 290
  1,3-dienes, –, – **55,** 290
**α,β-Ethylenealdehydes** (s.a.
  Ethyleneoxo compds.)
– startg. m. f.
  2*H*-pyrans, 3,4-dihydro-, 2-alkoxy- **55,**
    288
**γ,δ-Ethylenealdehydes**
– special s.
  γ-methylenealdehydes
**Ethylenealkoximes**
–, radical ring closure **54,** 299s**55**
**2-Ethyleneamines** (s.a. N-Allylation)
– special s.
  4-amino-2-ethylenealcohols
  aryl-2-ethyleneamines
–, cyclic, benzo-condensed, N-protected
  **55,** 405
**3-Ethyleneamines**
– from
  aldimines, synthesis, asym. with 3 extra
    C-atoms **55,** 461
*o*-Ethyleneamines
– special s.
  *o*-aminostyrenes
**Ethylenearenes**
–, ring closure, asym., selenylative **55,**
  230
**α,β-Ethyleneboronic acid esters**
– startg. m. f.
  enolesters, with inversion **55,** 102
**β,γ-Ethyleneboronic acid esters**
– special s.
  ethyl α-(boronylmethyl)acrylates
**γ,δ-Ethyleneboronic acid esters**
– special s.
  siloxy-γ,δ-ethyleneboronic acid esters
**α,β-Ethyleneboronic acids**
– startg. m. f.
  enolesters, with inversion **55,** 102
  styrenes **55,** 456
**2-Ethylenecarbonic acid esters**
–, C-α-allylation with – **55,** 357
– special s.
  allyl ethyl carbonate
  2-ene-1,n-diol monocarbonates

**α,β-Ethylenecarbonyl compds.**
– special s.
  acoxy-α,β-ethylenecarbonyl compds.
**Ethylenecarboxylic acid amides**
–, ring closures, electrophilic, review **47,**
  427s**55**
**α,β-Ethylenecarboxylic acid amides**
– startg. m. f.
  β-(benzyloxylamino)carboxylic acid
    amides, asym. conversion **55,** 129
– – –, **N-unsubst.**
– from
  enol triflates, carbonylation **55,** 413
**β,γ-Ethylenecarboxylic – –**
– from
  isocyanates, with 3 extra C-atoms **55,**
    254
**α,β-Ethylenecarboxylic acid derivs.**
– from
  allenes, carbonylation, regiostereo-
    specific **55,** 298
**α,β-Ethylenecarboxylic acid esters**
– by 1,4-addition-Horner synthesis **28,**
  851s**55**
– from
  alcohols, prim., via *in situ*-Wittig
    synthesis with 2 extra C-atoms **55,**
    451
  α,β-ethyleneiodonium salts **55,** 324
– special s.
  acoxy-α,β-ethylenecarboxylic acid
    esters
  acylamino-α,β-ethylenecarboxylic – –
  arylseleno-α,β-ethylenecarboxylic – –
  cyano-α,β-ethylenecarboxylic – –
– startg. m. f.
  β-(arylthio)carboxylic acid esters **55,**
    198
  lactols, bicyclic **55,** 395
  γ-lactones, synthesis, asym. **55,** 343
**β,γ-Ethylenecarboxylic acid esters**
– from
  oxo compds. **55,** 348
**γ,δ-Ethylenecarboxylic acid esters**
– from
  acoxy-2-ethylenes, synthesis, asym. **55,**
    460
  O-silyl O-alkyl keteneacetals, –, – **55,**
    460
**γ,δ-Ethylenecarboxylic – –, cyclic**
– via Claisen rearrangement-ring closing
  metathesis **55,** 498
**α,β-Ethylenecarboxylic acids**
–, 1,4-addition to – **55,** 260
– special s.
  α,β-ethylene(sulfonylamino)carboxylic
    acids
– startg. m. f.
  coumarins, 3,4-dihydro- **55,** 336
  β′,γ′-ethylene-β,γ-epoxycarboxylic
    acids **55,** 376
**(E)-α,β-Ethylenecarboxylic acids**
  **44,** 837s**55**
– from
  α,α-dihalogenocarboxylic acid esters
    **55,** 374
  oxo compds. **55,** 374
**β,γ-Ethylenecarboxylic acids**
– special s.
  β,γ-ethylene(epoxy)carboxylic acids
**(E)-β,γ-Ethylenecarboxylic acids**
– from

  aldehydes **1,** 569s**55**
**β,γ-Ethylenecarboxylic acid thioamides**
– from
  isothiocyanates, with 3 extra C-atoms
    **55,** 254
**Ethylene derivs.** (s.a. Alkylidenation, C-
  Allylation)
–, C-alkylation of acetylene derivs.,
    terminal with – **55,** 271
–, [5+2]-cycloaddition, intramolecular,
    stereospecific to – **55,** 318
– from
  acetylenedicobalt hexacarbonyl
    complexes **55,** 35
  acoxy-2-ethylenes, synthesis,
    regiostereospecific **55,** 455
  allenes, synthesis, asym. **55,** 297
  benzothiazoles, 2-(alkanesulfonyl)- **38,**
    861s**55**
  enoxysilanes, reduction **47,** 981s**55**
  tetrazoles, 5-(alkanesulfonyl)- **38,**
    861s**55**
–, hydrogenation, heterogeneous **55,** 40
–, reactions with radicals, phosphorus-
    subst., review **48,** 356s**55**
– special s.
  acoxyethylenes
  alkoxyethylenes
  dienes
  di(hetaryl)ethenes
  nitroethylene derivs.
  nitrosoethylene –
  siloxyethylenes
  styrenes
– startg. m. f.
  *trans*-1,2-acoxyhalides **55,** 180
  amines, sym. (from 2 molecules) **55,**
    356
  aziridines, 1-sulfonyl- **55,** 159
  cyclopropanecarboxylic acid esters,
    synthesis, asym. **55,** 421
  1,2-difluorides **55,** 181
  1,2-dihalides (1,2-dibromides) **55,** 178
  1,2-di(sulfonium salts), stereospecific
    conversion **55,** 199
  3-ethylenealcohols, via ozonolysis **55,**
    472
  2-ethylenehydroxamic acids **55,** 128
  thiiranes **55,** 197
–, synthesis, recent, review **54,** 306s**55**
–, transfer-hydrogenation, catalytic,
    review **34,** 46s**55**
**(E)-Ethylene derivs., 1,2-disubst.**
–, *syn*-dihydroxylation and -epoxidation
  **55,** 74
**(Z)-Ethylene derivs., trisubst.**
– from
  α,β-ethyleneiodides, synthesis **25,**
    628s**55**
**Ethylene derivs., bridged, medium-ring**
– with hyperstable double bonds, review
  **28,** 854s**55**
**Ethylene derivs., cyclic**
– by radical ring closure, deoxygenative
  **55,** 485
–, determination of abs. configuration **5,**
    666s**55**
– special s.
  cycloalkenes
  enisocyclics
– startg. m. f.
  1,1-difluorides with ring contraction **55,**
    181

**Ethylene derivs., electron-deficient**
- startg. m. f.
   alkoxy-4-ethylenes, with 3 extra C-atoms **55**, 475
- – –, **electron-deficient, terminal**
- –, radical 1,4-addition, Cr(II)-mediated to – **55**, 287
- – –, **electron-rich**
- –, radical addition, polarity reversed to – **55**, 277
- – –, **terminal** (s.a. Methylene compds.)
- startg. m. f.
   aryl ketones, via hydroacylation *in situ* **55**, 323

**(Z)-Ethylene derivs., macrocyclic 55**, 497

**Ethylenedihalides**
- –, ring expansion of cyclopentanones with – **55**, 381

**3-Ethyleneepoxides**
- special s.
   aryl-3-ethyleneepoxides

*cis*-**Ethyleneepoxides 47**, 904s55

**β′,γ′-Ethylene-β,γ-epoxycarboxylic acids**
- from
   α,β-ethylenecarboxylic acids **55**, 376

**Ethylene-α,β-epoxyketones**
- special s.
   diene-α,β-epoxyketones
- startg. m. f.
   1,3-diols, cyclic **55**, 275

**Ethyleneethers** (s.a. Alkoxyethylenes)

**2-Ethyleneethers**
- special s.
   acoxy-2-ethyleneethers
   allyl ethers
   allyloxy...
   diol monoallyl ethers

**2-Ethyleneethers, cyclic**
- special s.
   2-vinyl-O-heterocyclics
- –, –, **medium-ring, chiral 49**, 985s55

**α,β-Ethylene-α-fluorocarboxylic acid esters 55**, 495

**(Z)-α,β-Ethylene-α-fluorocarboxylic acids**
- from
   α-fluoro-β,β′-dihydroxycarboxylic acids, C-cleavage **55**, 495

**γ,δ-Ethylene-α-fluorocarboxylic acids 27**, 738s55

**2-Ethylenegermanes**
- from
   ene-1,3-di(thioethers) **55**, 228
   α,β-ethylenemercaptals **55**, 228
- special s.
   allyltriethylgermane

**α,β-Ethylenehalides**
- from
   ketones, with 1 extra C-atom **55**, 430
- –, ring closures, regiospecific of *o*-aminostyrenes, N-protected with – **55**, 405
- special s.
   alkoxy-α,β-ethylenehalides
   δ,ε-ethylene-δ-halogen...
   α,β-ethylene-β-nitroiodides
- startg. m. f.
   1,3-enynes, terminal, with 2 extra C-atoms **55**, 388
- –, **γ-functionalized**

- –, ring closures with allenes **55**, 409

**β,γ-Ethylenehalides**
- special s.
   allyl bromide
- startg. m. f.
   3-ethylenealcohols **55**, 472
   2-ethyleneselenides, ar. **55**, 225

**α,β-Ethylene-β-halogenocarboxylic acid amides**
- startg. m. f.
   γ-alkylidene-δ-lactams **55**, 409
- **acid esters**
- startg. m. f.
   γ-alkylidene-δ-lactones **55**, 409

**α,β-Ethylene-α-halogenocarboxylic acids**
- special s.
   α,β-ethylene-α-fluorocarboxylic acids

**α,β-Ethylene-α-halogenoketones**
- startg. m. f.
   1,2-halogenhydrins, reduction, asym. **55**, 34

**α,β-Ethylene-β-halogenoketones**
- startg. m. f.
   2,5(Z),8-triene-1,10-diones (from 2 molecules) **55**, 291

**δ,ε-Ethylene-δ-halogeno-γ-lactones**
- from
   γ-allenecarboxylic acids **55**, 186

**(E)-γ,δ-Ethylene-ε-halogenooxo compds.**
- startg. m. f.
   furans, tetrahydro-, 2-vinyl-, synthesis, regiostereospecific **55**, 384

**Ethylenehydrazones**
- –, olefin aldol reaction, intramolecular **55**, 303
- –, radical ring closure **54**, 299s55

**α,β-Ethylenehydroxamic acid esters**
- from
   enestannanes **55**, 462

**2-Ethylenehydroxamic acids**
- from
   ethylene derivs. **55**, 128
   hydroximinohalides **55**, 128

**(E)-α,β-Ethylene-α′-hydroxyketones**
- from
   acetylene derivs. **55**, 244

**α,β-Ethylene-β′-hydroxyketones**
- startg. m. f.
   γ-diketones **55**, 302

**α,β-Ethylene-γ-hydroxyketones, cyclic 32**, 26s55

**γ,δ-Ethylene-α-hydroxyketones**
- from
   α-allyloxy-α,β-ethyleneketones **55**, 309
- startg. m. f.
   α,β-ethylenecarboxylic acid esters **55**, 324

**4-Ethylene-3-hydroxythioethers**
- from
   2,4-dihydroxythioethers, rearrangement **55**, 214

**α,β-Ethyleneiodonium salts**
- special s.
   acoxy-α,β-ethyleneiodonium salts

**γ,δ-Ethylene-β-ketocarboxylic acid esters**
- special s.
   amino-γ,δ-ethylene-β-ketocarboxylic acid esters

**α,β-Ethyleneketones** (s.a. α,β-Ethyleneoxo compds.)
- –, 1,4-addition, asym. of boronic acids, α,β-unsatd. to – **55**, 452
- from
   aldehydes **55**, 355
   ketones, via aldol condensation **55**, 355
- –, Michael addition, asym. of phosphonic acid esters to – **55**, 273
- –, – –, –, catalytic of mercaptans to – **55**, 195
- special s.
   acoxy-α,β-ethyleneketones
   alkoxy-α,β-ethyleneketones
   arylseleno-α,β-ethyleneketones
   2,4-dienones
   α-methyleneketones
   2,5,8-triene-1,10-diones
- startg. m. f.
   δ,ε-ethyleneketones, 1,4-addition **55**, 448
   vinylcyclopropanes, 2-homoallyl- **55**, 392
- –, synthesis, polymer-based and ring closures **55**, 327

**α,β-Ethyleneketones, cyclic** (s.a. 2-Cycloalkenones)
- from
   1-siloxy-1,ω-enynes **55**, 489
- special s.
   α,α′-di(alkylidene)ketones, cyclic
- –, **polymer-based**
- startg. m. f.
   N-heterocyclics **55**, 327

**β,γ-Ethyleneketones**
- from
   α-halogenoketones, with 3 extra C-atoms, 1,2-aryl migration **55**, 445

**δ,ε-Ethyleneketones**
- from
   α,β-ethyleneketones, 1,4-addition **55**, 448
   2-ethylenesilanes, – **55**, 448

**ω-Ethylene-β-ketophosphonic acid esters**
- startg. m. f.
   2-cycloalkenones, 2-phosphonyl- **55**, 496

**Ethylenelactams** (s.a. Alkylidenelactams, Enaminolactams)

**α,β-Ethylenelactams**
- by ring closing metathesis **49**, 985s55
- from
   hydroxyketones **41**, 624s55

**γ,δ-Ethylene-δ-lactolides** (s.a. 2H-Pyrans, 3,4-dihydro-, 2-alkoxy-)

**ε,ξ-Ethylene-δ-lactolides**
- startg. m. f.
   2-vinylcyclopentanols **55**, 478

**Ethylenelactones**
- special s.
   allyllactones

**ε,ξ-Ethylene-γ-lactones**
- special s.
   γ-allyl-γ-lactones

**α,β-Ethylenemercaptals**
- startg. m. f.
   2-ethylenegermanes **55**, 228
   2-ethylenesilanes **55**, 228

**α,β-Ethylenenitriles**
- –, ring closures with carbonyl compds., review **49**, 638s55

- special s.
  amino-α,β-ethylenenitriles
- startg. m. f.
  cyclopentenes, 1-amino-5-cyano-
    (from 2 molecules) 55, 284
  pyridines, 2-amino- 55, 326
(E)-α,β-Ethylene-β-nitroiodides
- from
  acetylene derivs. 55, 179
α,β-Ethyleneorthocarboxylic acid
  esters
- special s.
  triethyl orthoacrylate
α,β-Ethyleneoxo compds.
-, aldol condensation, vinylogous with
    aldehydes 55, 234
-, γ-arylation, regiostereospecific 55, 407
- from
  alkoxy-2-ethylenes 55, 118
- startg. m. f.
  alcohols, reduction 55, 25
α,β-Ethylenephosphine oxides
- from
  acetylene derivs., reversal of
    regioselectivity 55, 217
- special s.
  α-methylenephosphine oxides
α,β-Ethylenephosphonic acid esters
-, oxyamination, asym. 51, 132s55
α,β-Ethylene-α-phosphonylketones,
  cyclic
- special s.
  2-cycloalkenones, 2-phosphonyl-
Ethyleneselenides
-, radical ring closures 47, 983s55
2-Ethyleneselenides, ar.
- from
  diaryliodonium salts 55, 225
  β,γ-ethylenehalides 55, 225
α,β-Ethyleneselenolic acid esters
-, Diels-Alder reaction, regiostereo-
    specific with – 55, 283
2-Ethylenesilanes
-, 1,4-addition, catalytic with – 55, 448
-, allylmercuraion, intramolecular with –
    55, 279
- from
  α,β-ethylenemercaptals 55, 228
  α-silylmercaptals 51, 423s55
- special s.
  allylsilanes
  Si, Si'-diallyldi(silanes)
  2-ethylene(trihalogeno)silanes
(Z)-2-Ethylenesilanes
- from
  mercaptals, with 2 extra C-atoms 55,
    473
α,β-Ethylene-β-siloxy-α-(silyl)thio-
  lactams
- from
  lactams, ring expansion 55, 252
- startg. m. f.
  β-ketothiolactams 55, 252
(Z)-α,β-Ethylene-β-silylazomethines
- by 4-component synthesis 55, 294
2-Ethylenestannanes
- from
  ene-1,3-di(thioethers) 55, 228
-, radical cross-coupling, asym., Lewis
    acid-catalyzed with – 55, 436
- special s.
  allyltributylstannane

α,β-Ethylene-β-stannylcarboxylic acid
  esters 47, 77s55
(E)-α,β-Ethylene-β-stannylcarboxylic
  acids 46, 533s55
α,β-Ethylenesulfones
- via α-sulfonylphosphonates 43, 547s55
β,γ-Ethylenesulfones
-, radical cross-coupling with – 41,
    829s55
(E)-α,β-Ethylenesulfonic acid amides
- from
  aldehydes, with 1 extra C-atom 55, 470
  1,2-thiazetidine 1,1-dioxides 55, 312
α,β-Ethylene-β'-sulfonylamino-
  carboxylic acids
- special s.
  α-methylene-β-sulfonylamino-
    carboxylic acids
α,β-Ethylenesulfoxides
-, 1,4-addition, asym. to – 55, 270
-, chiral 26, 827s55
2-Ethylenethioethers
- special s.
  allyl thioethers
α,β-Ethylenethiolic acid esters
-, Diels-Alder reaction, regiostereo-
    specific with – 55, 283
-, Michael addition, asym., catalytic of
    mercaptans to – 55, 196
3-Ethylene-1,1,1-tricarboxylic acid
  esters 26, 827s55
2-Ethylene(trihalogeno)silanes
- startg. m. f.
  3-ethylenealcohols, synthesis, asym.,
    regiospecific 55, 433, 441
Ethyl glyoxylate N-tosylimine
- as reactant 55, 450
Ethyl thioglycolate
- as reactant 55, 213
Ethynylarenes
- from
  halides, ar., with 2 extra C-atoms 55,
    388
Ethynylmagnesium bromide
- as reactant 55, 388
Ethynylzinc bromide
- as reactant 55, 388



Ferrocenes
- special s.
  biferrocen...
Ferrocenes, chiral
-, synthesis and use, review 52, 497s55
Ferrocenylmetal complexes s. under
  Palladium complexes
Flash vacuum pyrolysis 55, 316
Fluorides (s.a. under Replacement)
Fluorides, ar. (s.a. Fluoroaryl...)
- by diazotization, aprotic 22, 580s55
Fluorides, chiral
-, synthesis, asym., catalytic, review 44,
    229s55
Fluorination
- with N,N'-difluoro-2,2'-bipyridinium
    bis(fluoroborate) 55, 184
α-Fluorination 55, 184

(Fluoroalkyl)carbonyl compds.,
  polyfunctionalized
- startg. m. f.
  heterocyclics, review 35, 152s55
Fluoroalkyl radicals
-, ring closures, sulfur-mediated via –,
    review 41, 463s55
3-(o-Fluoroaryl)halides
- startg. m. f.
  indans, with 4-substitution 55, 375
2-Fluoro-2-deoxysugars 49, 407s55
α-Fluoro-β,β'-dihydroxycarboxylic
  acids
- startg. m. f.
  (Z)-α,β-ethylene-α-fluorocarboxylic
    acids, C-cleavage 55, 495
α-Fluoro-β-ketocarboxylic acid esters
- startg. m. f.
  α-fluoroketones, synthesis 55, 469
α-Fluoroketones
- from
  α-fluoro-β-ketocarboxylic acid esters,
    synthesis 55, 469
α-Fluoro-β-ketophosphonic acid esters
  17, 898s55
α-Fluoromalonic acid esters 52, 40s55
N-Fluoropyridinium salts
- special s.
  N,N'-difluoro-2,2'-bipyridinium
    bis(fluoroborate)
Fluorosulfonimide, N-trimethylsilyl- s.
  N-(Trimethylsilyl)fluorosulfonimide
N-Fluorosultams, chiral
- as reagent 47, 435s55
Fluorous medium
-, S-oxidation in – 55, 53
Fluorous 2-phase medium
-, epoxidation, asym., aerobic 48, 134s55
-, reactions in –, review 53, 57s55
Fluorous reagents
- special s.
  manganese(III) salen complex,
    fluorous
  palladium complexes, –
Formaldehyde
- as reactant 55, 262
Formamides
- from
  oxaziridines 55, 170
- startg. m. f.
  isonitriles 55, 174
  ureas 55, 133
  urethans 55, 133
Formamides, chiral
- as reagent 55, 441
C-Formylation s. Vilsmeier...
N-Formylation
- of α-aminocarboxylic acid esters 55,
    170
O-Formylation 55, 80, 110
Friedel-Crafts acylation
- in the absence of solvent 55, 394
- of arenes, electron-rich 55, 387
Friedel-Crafts alkylation
- in the absence of solvent 55, 394
- -, reductive
- with oxo compds. 55, 345
- carbamylation 55, 320
Fritsch-Buttenberg-Wiechell
  rearrangement 55, 430
Fullerenes (s.a. Bucky...)
Fulleropyrrolidines
-, review 48, 640s55

**Fulvenes, 6-aryl-6-hydroxy-**
– from
7-oxabicyclo[2.2.1]hepta-2,5-dienes, 4-aryl- **55**, 306
**Fumaric acid esters**
– special s.
(arylseleno)fumaric acid esters
**Furan**
– as leaving group **55**, 111
**Furan-3-carboxylic acid esters**
– from
aldehydes **55**, 429
**2(5H)-Furanone-4-carboxylic acid esters, 5-alkoxy- 55**, 429
**2(3H)-Furanones, 5-alkoxy-**
– from
1,2-bis(ketenes) **55**, 264
**2(5H)-Furanones**
–, reactions, photochemical, review **32**, 668s55
–, 5-alkylidene- **38**, 836s55
–, 4-arylseleno-
– from
2-acetylenealcohols, carbonylation **55**, 457
–, 4-arylthio-
– from
2-acetylenealcohols, carbonylation **55**, 457
–, 4-carbalkoxy- **55**, 329
–, 4,5-fused
– from
acetylenealdehydes **55**, 292
**Furano[2,3-c]quinoline-2,4-diones, 3a,5-dihydro- 31**, 973s55
**Furans**
– from
β-alkoxy-α-methyleneketones **55**, 477
enolethers **55**, 403
enoxysilanes **55**, 403
α-halogenoketones **55**, 403
– special s.
bis(furyl)...
**Furans, 2,3-dihydro-, 4-sulfinyl-**
–, Heck arylation, asym. **55**, 410
–, 2,5-dihydro-, 2-alkylidene- **55**, 426
–, tetrahydro-, *trans*-3-silyl-, 2-subst. **55**, 76
–, tetrahydro-, 2-vinyl-
– from
(E)-γ,δ-ethylene-ε-halogenooxo compds, synthesis, regiostereo- specific **55**, 384
**Furo[2,3-b]pyridines, 2,3-dihydro- 55**, 431
**2-Furyl ketones**
– startg. m. f.
1,2-acoxysulfonates **55**, 111

**Germanes**
– from
germanium hydrides, organo- **55**, 228
mercaptals **55**, 228
– special s.
ethylenegermanes
**Germanium diiodide/potassium 55**, 247

**Germanium hydrides, organo-**
– startg. m. f.
germanes **55**, 228
**Glycidic acid esters, chiral 55**, 190
**Glucuronosides**
–, synthesis, review **19**, 265s55
**Glycidyl sulfonates**
– startg. m. f.
3-oxabicyclo[3.1.0]hexan-2-ones, 1-carbalkoxy-, asym. induction **55**, 333
**Glycoconjugates**
–, synthesis, solid-phase (from glycals), review **17**, 169s55
**Glycol ethers**
– special s.
1,2-dimethoxy-1,2-diphenylethane
**Glycol monoethers**
– special s.
ene-1,2-diol monoethers
*anti*-**Glycol monoethers**
– from
acetals **55**, 352
aldehydes **55**, 352
**Glycols** (s.a. Dihydroxylation)
– from
α-acoxycarboxylic acid esters (chiral compds.) **55**, 38
– startg. m. f.
1,2-acoxysulfonates **55**, 111
epoxides, retention of configuration **55**, 190
**Glycols, O-silylated** s. 1,2-Disiloxy compds.
*cis*-**Glycols**
– from
(E)-ethylene derivs., (1,2-disubst. derivs.) **55**, 74
–, synthesis, dioxygenase-catalyzed, review **34**, 112s55
**Glycol sulfates, cyclic**
– startg. m. f.
epoxides, retention of configuration **55**, 190
1,2-halogenhydrins, regiospecific conversion **55**, 190
**Glycopeptides**
–, synthesis, solid-phase **17**, 169s55
(review); **19**, 33s55; **28**, 144s55
**Glyco-peptides and -proteins**
–, focus on glycosidic linkage, review **32**, 11s55
**Glycosidation, polymer-based**
–, solvent effect **44**, 211s55
**Glycosides**
– from
alkoxysilanes, review **46**, 214s55
– special s.
*p*-acetamidophenyl glycosides
acyl –
deoxyglycosides
imidoyl glycosides
4-iodobutyl –
*p*-nitrophenyl –
– startg. m. f.
cyclopentanols, polyoxy- **55**, 478
**Glycosides, polymer-based**
– startg. m. f.
β-acyl glycosides **55**, 104
**β-Glycosides**
– from
β-glycosyl fluorides **55**, 97
**C-Glycosides**

– special s.
C-allyl glycosides
C-aryl –
C-benzyl –
C-disaccharides
C-thiocarbamyl glycosides
C-vinyl –
**C-α-Glycosides**
– from
glycosyl sulfones **50**, 531s55
thioglycosides **50**, 531s55
**N-Glycosylcarbodiimides 34**, 420s55
**β-Glycosyl fluorides**
– startg. m. f.
β-glycosides **55**, 97
**Glycosyl halides**
– special s.
glycosyl fluorides
**Glycosyl hydrogen phosphates 22**, 106s55
**Glycuronosides**
– special s.
glucuronosides
**Gold complexes**
methyl(triphenylphosphine)gold(I) **55**, 63
tris(*p*-fluorophenyl)phosphinegold(I) nitrate **55**, 63
**Graphite 55**, 105
–, expansive **39**, 214s55
**Grignard compds.** (s.a. Magnesium halides, organo-)
– startg. m. f.
carboxylic acid thioamides, N-subst. **55**, 163
ketones, sym. **55**, 386
tosylsulfilimines, synthesis, asym. **55**, 206
**Grignard syntheses, polymer-based 55**, 391
**Guanidines**
–, synthesis, polymer-based **5**, 346s55
**Guanidines, cyclic**
– from
amines, prim. **55**, 156
halogenoformamidinium salts **55**, 156
**Guanylureas** s. Amidinoureas


**Hafnium tetrachloride 55**, 315
**Halides**
–, reduction, regiostereospecific, tin hydride-mediated, review **17**, 117s55
–, review (annual) **51**, 91s55
– special s.
acetylenehalides
acoxyhalides
alkoxyhalides
allyloxyhalides
3-arylhalides
benzyl halides
dihalides
ethylenehalides
fluorides
iodides
nitrohalides
siloxyhalides

trihalides
- startg. m. f.
  amines, sec. **55**, 154
  carboxylic acid amides, N-unsubst.,
    carbonylation **55**, 413
  – – esters **55**, 95
  nitriles, with 2 extra C-atoms **55**, 330
  phosphine oxides, sym. **55**, 219
  selenides **55**, 229
  sulfones **55**, 210
  thioethers **55**, 207
  thiolic acid esters, with 1 extra C-atom
    **55**, 400
  urethans **55**, 155
-, Wurtz coupling in aq. medium **55**, 402
**Halides, ar.**
- from
  arylboronic acids **55**, 191
- special s.
  iodides, ar.
- startg. m. f.
  allylarenes **55**, 463
  –, synthesis, regiospecific **55**, 385
  amines, ar. **55**, 160
  –, –, prim. **55**, 162
  –, –, transition-metal catalysis, review
    **51**, 171s**55**
  arylacetylenes, polymer-based
    synthesis **55**, 416
  arylsilanes **55**, 227
  cyclohexenes, 1-aryl- **55**, 408
  1,1-diarylalkanes **55**, 406
  ethynylarenes, with 2 extra C-atoms **55**,
    388
  1,2,4-oxadiazoles, 5-aryl- **55**, 415
  phenolethers, transition-metal catalysis,
    review **51**, 171s**55**
  thioethers, ar., polymer-based synthesis
    **55**, 211
**Halides, ar., normally unreactive**
-, Heck arylation with – **55**, 414
**N-Halides**
-, chemistry, aqueous, review **37**, 441s**55**
**Halogenalcohols** s. Halogenhydrins
**Halogenaldehydes**
- special s.
  iodoaldehydes
**N-Halogenamines** (s.a. N-Halides)
**Halogenation**
- special s.
  bromination
  chlorination
  fluorination
  iodination
**Halogenethers, cyclic** s.
  Iodoetherification, intramolecular
**Halogen exchange** s. under Replacement
**1,2-Halogenhydrins**
- from
  epoxides, regiostereospecific ring
    conversion **55**, 175
  α,β-ethylene-α-halogenoketones,
    reduction, asym. **55**, 34
  glycol sulfates, cyclic, regiospecific
    conversion **55**, 190
- startg. m. f.
  epoxides **55**, 190
**1,2-Halogenhydrins, chiral 43, 45s55**
**α-Halogenocarbonyl compds.**
- startg. m. f.
  α-(organoseleno)carbonyl compds. **55**,
    225

**β-Halogenocarboxylic acid amides**
- special s.
  ethylene-β-halogenocarboxylic acid
    amides
**Halogenocarboxylic acid esters**
- special s.
  iodocarboxylic acid esters
**α-Halogenocarboxylic acid esters**
- from
  α-halogeno-β-ketocarboxylic acid
    esters **55**, 46
- special s.
  α,α-dihalogenocarboxylic acid esters
**β-Halogenocarboxylic acid esters**
- special s.
  ethylene-β-halogenocarboxylic acid
    esters
**Halogenocarboxylic acid halides**
- startg. m. f.
  β-ketomalonic acid esters, cyclic **55**,
    380
**α-Halogenocarboxylic acid halides**
- special s.
  chloroacetyl chloride
**α-Halogenocarboxylic acids**
- special s.
  ethylene-α-halogenocarboxylic acids
- startg. m. f.
  2-piperazinone-5-acetic acid amides,
    polymer-based synthesis **55**, 158
**α-Halogeno-β,β'-dihydroxycarboxylic
  acids**
- special s.
  α-fluoro-β,β'-dihydroxycarboxylic
    acids
**Halogenoformamidinium salts**
- startg. m. f.
  guanidines, cyclic **55**, 156
**Halogenoformic acid esters**
- from
  oxalic acid ester halides
- startg. m. f.
  urethans **55**, 157
**α-Halogeno-β-ketocarboxylic acid
  esters**
- special s.
  α-fluoro-β-ketocarboxylic acid esters
- startg. m. f.
  α-halogenocarboxylic acid esters **55**,
    46
**Halogenoketones**
- special s.
  trihalogenoketones
- startg. m. f.
  lactols, bicyclic **55**, 395
**α-Halogenoketones**
- special s.
  aryl α-halogenoketones
  α,β-ethylene-α-halogenoketones
  α-fluoroketones
- startg. m. f.
  β,γ-epoxycarboxylic acids **55**, 376
  β,γ-ethyleneketones, with 3 extra C-
    atoms, 1,2-aryl migration **55**, 445
  furans **55**, 403
  2-ketothioethers **55**, 212
**β-Halogenoketones**
- special s.
  ethylene-β-halogenoketones
**α-Halogenolactones**

–, radical cross-coupling, asym., Lewis
    acid-catalyzed with allyltri-*n*-
    butylstannane **55**, 436
**δ-Halogeno-γ-lactones**
- special s.
  ethylene-δ-halogeno-γ-lactones
**ε-Halogenooxo compds.**
- special s.
  ethylene-ε-halogenooxo compds.
**α-Halogenophosphonic acid esters**
- special s.
  α,α-dihalogenophosphonic acid esters
- startg. m. f.
  β-hydroxyphosphonic acid esters **55**,
    249
**N-Halogenopyridinium salts**
- special s.
  N-fluoropyridinium salts
**Halogenosilanes**
- special s.
  bis(halogenosilanes)
  trihalogenosilanes
  trimethylsilyl bromide
  – chloride
**α-Halogenosilanes**
- special s.
  trifluoromethyltrimethylsilane
**N-Halogeno-N-sodiosulfonic acid amides**
- special s.
  Bromamine-T
  Chloramine-T
- startg. m. f.
  aziridines, 1-sulfonyl- **55**, 159
**Halogenostannanes** (s.a. Tin(IV) halides,
  organo-)
- special s.
  dihalogenostannanes
  tri-*n*-butyltin chloride
**N-Halogenosuccinimides**
- special s.
  N-bromosuccinimide
  N-chlorosuccinimide
  N-iodosuccinimide
**α-Halogenosulfones**
- special s.
  trihalogenomethyl sulfones
**N-Halogenosulfonic acid amides**
- special s.
  N-halogeno-N-sodiosulfonic acid
    amides
**Halogenothioethers, ar.**
-, radical ring closure **55**, 487
**Halogenothioformic acid esters**
- special s.
  phenyl chlorothionoformate
***o*-Halogenozinc halides**
- special s.
  *o*-bromophenylzinc iodide
**N-(2-Halogen)urethans**
- special s.
  2-carbalkoxyamino-3-siloxyhalides
**Heck arylation**
- using cyclopallad(II)ated phosphine
    complexes **55**, 412
- with
  arylcarboxylic acid anhydrides **55**, 476
  halides, ar., normally unreactive **55**,
    414
**Heck arylation, asym.**
- of furans, 2,3-dihydro-, 4-sulfinyl- **55**,
    410
- –, –, sequential **55**, 410

Heck arylation, copper(I)-catalyzed,
  stereospecific 55, 383
– –, double 55, 366
– –, intramolecular, reductive, asym.,
  regiospecific 55, 486
– –, intramolecular-Suzuki coupling 55,
  454
– –, polymer-based 55, 416
Heck-Diels-Alder reaction 55, 408
Heck reaction
–, implications, synthetic, review 27,
  871s55
– in carbon dioxide, supercritical 55, 417
– –, intramolecular
–, review 43, 962s55
Hemiacetals, cyclic
– special s.
  lactols
Heteroarenes, polymer-based
–, metalation 42, 597s55
Heterocyclics
– from
  (fluoroalkyl)carbonyl compds.,
  polyfunctionalized, review 35,
  152s55
Heterocyclics, 5-membered
– from
  acetylene derivs., terminal 55, 429
  tungsten alkoxycarbene complexes 55,
  429
N-Heterocyclics
– special s.
  amino-N-heterocyclics
  hydroxy-N-heterocyclics
  triflyloxy-N-heterocyclics
–, satd.
–, review (annual) 51, 376s55
O-Heterocyclics (s.a. Ethers, cyclic)
– special s.
  allyl-O-heterocyclics
  hydroxy-O-heterocyclics
  vinyl-O-heterocyclics
–, benzo-fused, medium-to-large ring
  49, 985s55
–, satd.
–, review (annual) 52, 407s55
–, seven-membered
–, synthesis, review 54, 160s55
Si-Heterocyclics
– special s.
  silacyclo...
(poly-Si)-Heterocyclics
– from
  bis(halogenosilanes) 55, 221
Hetero-Diels-Alder reaction, asym.
–, 4-pyrones, 2,3-dihydro- via – 55, 449
– with α,β-ethyleneacylphosphonic acid
  esters 55, 266
– –, asym., catalytic
–, 4(1H)-pyridones, 2,3-dihydro- via – 55,
  443
– –, regiostereospecific
–, 2H-pyrans, 3,4-dihydro-, 2-alkoxy-
  via – 55, 288
– with
  α-iminosulfines, in situ-generated 55,
  194
  2-siloxy-1,3-dienes 55, 274
– reaction-1,3-dipolar cycloaddition,
  asym.
–, 2,9-dioxa-1-azabicyclo[4.3.0]nonanes,
  3-alkoxy- via – 55, 258

Hexabutyldistannane
– as reagent 55, 400
Hexadecyltriethylammonium bromide
– as reagent 55, 52
Hexamethyldisilazane
– as reactant 55, 413
– as reagent 55, 279
Hexamethylenetetramine-bromine
  complex
– as reagent 55, 87
Hexamethylphosphoramide
– as reagent 55, 372, 441
Hexane
– as reagent 55, 33
Homoenolate equivalents
–, 1-aza-2-zircona-4-cyclopentenes as –
  55, 432
–, γ,γ-dialkoxyallylzirconium complexes
  as – 55, 348
Horner synthesis
– of pyrazoles 55, 425
Horner synthesis, asym.
– of enisocyclics 55, 464
– –, intramolecular
– via nucleophilic addition to α-allene-α-
  arylphosphonic acid esters 55, 426
– –, –, polymer-based 39, 964a55
Hydantoins
– from
  α-aminocarboxamides, polymer-based
  synthesis 21, 393s55
–, syntheses, polymer-based 31, 452s55
Hydrazine
– as reagent and medium 55, 207
Hydrazones
– special s.
  acylhydrazones
  aldose hydrazones
  ethylenehydrazones
  sulfonylhydrazones
Hydrazonolactones
– special s.
  aldonohydrazonolactones
α-(Hydridosilyl)carboxylic acid esters
– startg. m. f.
  β-hydroxycarboxylic acid esters 55,
  422
Hydroacylation in situ
–, aryl ketones via – 55, 323
Hydroacylation, chelation-assisted
–, review 52, 319s55
Hydroalumination, catalytic 36, 43s55
Hydroboration-cross-coupling 52,
  419s55
Hydrobromination, iron(III)-catalyzed
  22, 557s55
Hydrocarbon groups, quaternary
– by C-α-allylation 55, 357
– –, –, benzylic, chiral 55, 373
– –, –, chiral 55, 436
Hydrocarbons (s.a. Wurtz coupling)
–, C-alkylation, ar. with – 55, 322
–, functionalization, catalytic in protic
  media, review 41, 115s55
–, oxidation, homogeneous, late transition-
  metal catalyzed, review 50, 53s55
– special s.
  arenes
  methylene groups
Hydrocobaltation 41, 546s55
Hydroformylation, asym.

– in a highly cross-linked chiral polymer
  matrix 55, 295
Hydroformylation, double
–, ring closure via – 46, 669s55
Hydroformylation-reductive N-
  alkylation
–, amines, tert. by – 55, 356
Hydrogenation (s.a. HC⇅, Transfer-
  hydrogenation)
Hydrogenation, asym.
– special s.
  Noyori hydrogenation, asym.
  transfer-hydrogenation, asym.
–, –, sequential, one-pot
– with two different catalysts 55, 37
–, heterogeneous
– with (benzylamine-C,N)palladium(II)
  hydride complex, polymer-based 55,
  40
–, –, asym.
– of α-ketocarboxylic acid esters 55, 30
–, –, catalytic
–, review 32, 44s55
–, homogeneous, asym. 55, 36, 38
– of ketones 55, 28, 29
Hydrogen bromide
–, equivalent, neutral 13, 910s55
Hydrogen fluoride, polyacrylate-
  supported 12, 619s55
Hydrogen peroxide (s.a. Titanium
  silicate/hydrogen peroxide) 55, 68
– in fluorous media 55, 53
– –/triethylenediamine 37, 127s55
Hydrolysis
– of esters s. HO⇅C
Hydroperoxides
– special s.
  tert-butyl hydroperoxide
Hydroperoxides, chiral
– as reagent 39, 83s55
Hydrosilylation, homogeneous, asym.
– of azomethines 55, 31
–, intramolecular, thiyl-mediated,
  regiospecific 55, 218
–, polymer-based
– of oxo compds. 55, 24
–, regiospecific
– of enesilanes 55, 35
Hydrostannylation, Lewis acid-
  catalyzed
– with tri-n-butyltin hydride, in situ-
  generated 55, 216
Hydrotalcites (s.a. under Ruthenium) 55,
  22
–, basified 55, 335
Hydroxamic acid esters
– from
  N-alkoxycarbamyl halides, synthesis
  55, 462
  α-diazoketones, rearrangement 55, 150
– special s.
  acetylenehydroxamic acid esters
  aminohydroxamic – –
  ethylenehydroxamic – –
Hydroxamic acids
– special s.
  ethylenehydroxamic acids
– startg. m. f.
  ureas, via Lössen rearrangement 55,
  163
–, syntheses, polymer-based 47, 293s55
– –, O-acyl- s. Acyl hydroxamates

– –, heterocyclic
–, synthesis and reactivity, review **44**, 7s**55**
**Hydroximinohalides**
– startg. m. f.
  2-ethylenehydroxamic acids **55**, 128
  isothiocyanates **55**, 208
**α-Hydroxyacetals**
– from
  ketones, with 1 extra C-atom **55**, 419
–, chiral **9**, 741s**55**
**β-Hydroxyaldehydes**
– special s.
  α-amino-β-hydroxyaldehydes
**Hydroxyamines** s. Aminoalcohols
**N-Hydroxybenzotriazole, polymer-based**
– as reagent **55**, 139
*p*-**Hydroxybenzyl dithiocarbamates 55**, 359
**β-Hydroxycarbonyl compds.** (s.a. Aldol..., Reformatskii...)
**Hydroxycarboxylic acid amides**
– special s.
  (hydroxymethyl)carboxylic acid amides
**α-Hydroxycarboxylic acid esters**
–, dehydroxylation **13**, 733s**55**
– from
  α-ketocarboxylic acid esters, reduction, asym. **55**, 30
– special s.
  amino-α-hydroxycarboxylic acid esters
– startg. m. f.
  1,4-dioxane-2,5-diones, sym. **55**, 83
**β-Hydroxycarboxylic acid esters**
– from
  α-(hydridosilyl)carboxylic acid esters **55**, 422
  β-ketocarboxylic – – **33**, 46s**55**
– special s.
  amino-β-hydroxycarboxylic acid esters
  (arylselenomethyl)-β-hydroxy-carboxylic – –
  (arylthiomethyl)-β-hydroxycarboxylic – –
  cyano-β-hydroxycarboxylic – –
*o*-**Hydroxycarboxylic acid esters**
– startg. m. f.
  1,3-benzoxazine-2,4-diones **55**, 136
**α-Hydroxycarboxylic acids**
–, determination of abs. configuration **5**, 666s**55**
–, resolution, kinetic **49**, 995s**55**
– startg. m. f.
  ketones, decarboxylation, aerobic, catalytic **55**, 119
**β-Hydroxycarboxylic acids**
– from
  aldehydes, synthesis, asym. with 2 extra C-atoms **55**, 233
– special s.
  amino-β-hydroxycarboxylic acids
  β,β'-dihydroxycarboxylic –
**Hydroxy-N-heterocyclics**
– startg. m. f.
  amino-N-heterocyclics **55**, 135
**3-Hydroxy-O-heterocyclics**
– from
  ethylenealcohols **55**, 66
**α-Hydroxyketones 47**, 954s**55**
– from
  aldehydes, synthesis **55**, 244

– special s.
  ethylene-α-hydroxyketones
**α-Hydroxyketones, cyclic**
– from
  cyanoketones **55**, 482
**β-Hydroxyketones** (s.a. Aldol...)
– special s.
  α-arylseleno-β-hydroxyketones
  α,β-ethylene-β'-hydroxyketones
**β'-Hydroxy-β-lactones**
– as intermediates **55**, 374
**γ-Hydroxy-γ-lactones**
– startg. m. f.
  γ-allyl-γ-lactones, synthesis, stereospecific **55**, 393
**Hydroxylamines**
–, review (recent developments) **54**, 51s**55**
**Hydroxylamines, N,N-disubst.**
– from
  amines, sec. **55**, 49
**Hydroxymercaptans**
– special s.
  dihydroxymercaptans
*o*-**(Hydroxymethyl)arylacetylenes**
– startg. m. f.
  3-isochromanones, cyclocarbonylation **55**, 293
*o*-**(Hydroxymethyl)carboxylic acid amides**
– as intermediates **55**, 154
**β-Hydroxynitriles**
– special s.
  α-cyano-β-hydroxy...
**γ-Hydroxynitriles**
– startg. m. f.
  γ-lactols, (chiral compds.) **55**, 92
**2-Hydroxyphosphinic acid amides, chiral 43**, 45s**55**
**β-Hydroxyphosphonic acid esters**
– from
  α-halogenophosphonic acid esters **55**, 249
  oxo compds. **55**, 249
– – –, cyclic
– startg. m. f.
  enisocyclics, conversion, asym. **55**, 464
**2-Hydroxyselenides**
– from
  ethylene derivs. **29**, 180s**55**
**3-Hydroxyselenides**
– special s.
  α-(arylselenomethyl)-β-hydroxy...
**β-Hydroxy-α-siloxyketones 52**, 641s**55**
**1,1-Hydroxystannanes, O-protected**
– from
  1-stannylacetals, cyclic, synthesis, asym. **55**, 235
*o*-**Hydroxystyrenes, β-subst. 31**, 641s**55**
**γ-Hydroxysulfonic acid amides, chiral**
– as reagent **55**, 239
**Hydroxythioethers**
– special s.
  dihydroxythioethers
**2-Hydroxythioethers**
–, desulfurization **44**, 70s**55**
– from
  epoxides **50**, 335s**55**
**3-Hydroxythioethers**
– special s.
  α-(arylthiomethy)-β-hydroxy...
  ethylene-3-hydroxythioethers

**α-Hydroxythiolic acids, chiral 43**, 45s**55**
**Hyponitrous acid esters**
– special s.
  di-*tert*-butyl hyponitrite

**Imidazole**
– as reagent **55**, 70, 398
**Imidazole, 1,2-dimethyl-** s. under Zirconium aroxides, chiral
**Imidazoles**
– from
  N-sulfonylaldimines, polymer-based synthesis **47**, 927s**55**
–, 2-metalation **42**, 597s**55**
– special s.
  N-methylimidazole
**Imidazoles, 4-amino-**
– from
  N-imidoylisothioureas **55**, 420
–, **5-amino-, N-condensed**
– from
  aldehydes, *o*-amino-N-heterocyclics, and isonitriles, polymer-based synthesis **55**, 340
**Imidazolidines, 2-imino-, chiral 55**, 156
**2-Imidazolidone-4-acetic acid amides**
–, synthesis, polymer-based **55**, 152
**Δ²-Imidazolines, 2-benzyl-**
–, C-alkylation, asym., α-lateral **55**, 373
**Imidazo[1,2-*a*]pyr-azines and -idines, 3-amino-**
–, parallel synthesis, solution-phase **55**, 340
**Imides** s. Carbodiimides, Diacylamines, Dicarboxylic acid imides
**Imidoyl glycosides**
– special s.
  trichloroacetimidoyl glycosides
**N-Imidoylisothioureas**
– startg. m. f.
  imidazoles, 4-amino- **55**, 420
**Imines** (s.a. Azomethines)
– special s.
  silylimines
  sulfonylimines
– startg. m. f.
  β-aminoketones, synthesis, asym. **55**, 459
**Imines, N-protected**
– startg. m. f.
  aziridines, 2-acyl-, N-protected **55**, 367
**α-Iminocarboxylic acids**
– startg. m. f.
  aldimines **55**, 48
**Iminoiodinanes**
– special s.
  sulfonyliminoiodinanes
**α-Iminosulfines,** *in situ*-generated
–, hetero-Diels-Alder reaction, regiostereospecific with – **55**, 194
**Indane-1,3-diones, 2,2-diaryl- 2**, 680s**55**
**Indan ring,** *trans*-**hydr-**
–, synthesis, review **51**, 312s**55**
**Indans**
– from
  3-(*o*-fluoroaryl)halides, with 4-substitution **55**, 375

**Indans, arylseleno- 55,** 230
**2H-Indazoles**
– from
  o-nitrobenzylamines **55,** 121
**Indium 55,** 212, 392, 393
**Indium(III) chloride 55,** 345, 438
–**(III) fluoride 55,** 245
– hydride, dichloro-
–, reductions with – **55,** 23
**Indole-2-carboxamides 24,** 859s55
**Indoles**
–, N-arylation **8,** 563s55
– from
  acylsilanes **47,** 829s55
– special s.
  biindoles
  bis(indolyl)...
  tryptamines
–, syntheses, polymer-based **47,** 829s55
**Indoles, 3-(aminomethyl)- 55,** 344
–, **1,2-condensed 55,** 487
–, **2,3-α-disubst. 55,** 222
–, **4-hydroxy-**
– from
  benzofurans, 4-nitro- **28,** 297s55
–, **3-α-subst. 55,** 222
**Indolines, 2-alkylidene-3-arylimino- 55,** 404
–, **2-imino- 14,** 564s55
–, **2-(2-tosylvinyl)- 46,** 802s55
–, **2(E)-vinyl-, 1-tosyl- 55,** 405
**Iodides**
– special s.
  perfluoroalkyl iodides
**Iodides, ar.**
– from
  amines, ar., prim. **55,** 188
–, radical 1,4-addition, Cr(II)-mediated
  with – **55,** 287
**Iodides, functionalized**
– startg. m. f.
  zinc compds., organo-, functionalized
  **55,** 226
**Iodinanes**
– special s.
  iminoiodinanes
**Iodination, ar. 55,** 183
**Iodine**
– as reactant **55,** 175, 183
– as reagent **55,** 281, 429
**Iodine reagents, hypervalent**
– in carbohydrate chemistry, review **49,** 211s55
**Iodoaldehydes**
–, radical ring closure, deoxygenative **55,** 485
**4-Iodobutyl glycosides**
– from
  trichloroacetimidoyl glycosides **55,** 192
**p-Iodocarboxylic acid esters 55,** 324
**2-Iodo-2-deoxyglycosides**
– special s.
  acyl 2-iodo-2-deoxyglycosides
**Iododifluorides**
– special s.
  p-methyliodobenzene difluoride
**1-Iodoenetellurides 50,** 343s55
**Iodoetherification, intramolecular**
– of benzynes **55,** 187
**Iodonium salts**
– special s.
  acyleneiodonium salts

diaryliodonium –
  ethyleneiodonium –
**Iodonium salts, unsatd.**
–, Stille-type coupling, carbonylative
  with – **53,** 445s55
**Iodonium ylids**
– special s.
  ketoiodonium ylids
**Iodosocarboxylates, polymer-based**
– special s.
  poly[styrene(iodosoacetate)]
**Iodosobenzene**
– as reagent **55,** 52, 78, 500
**N-Iodosuccinimide**
– as reagent **55,** 187, 191
**Iridium hydride complexes 55,** 256
**Iron π-allyl complexes**
– special s.
  (π-allyl)tricarbonyliron-lactone
  complexes
**Iron carbonyl complexes, organo-**
–, stereocontrol, acyclic with –, review
  **47,** 549s55
**Iron(II) chloride 55,** 123
**Iron complexes** (s.a. Ferro...)
  1,1'-bis(di-*tert*-butylphosphino)
  ferrocene **55,** 160
  1,1'-bis(diphenylphosphino)ferrocene
  **55,** 73, 162, 211
**Iron(III) 2-ethylhexanoate**
– as reagent **55,** 288
**Isobutylamine**
– as reagent **55,** 31
**Isocarbostyrils 55,** 383
**3-Isochromanones**
– from
  o-(hydroxymethyl)arylacetylenes,
  cyclocarbonylation **55,** 293
–, **4-vinyl-**
– from
  3-oxatricyclo[4.4.0.0$^{1,5}$]deca-7,9-dien-
  4-ones, 5-vinyl- **55,** 304
**Isocyanates**
– startg. m. f.
  1,3-benzoxazine-2,4-diones **55,** 136
  carbodiimides **55,** 167
  β,γ-ethylenecarboxylic acid amides,
  with 3 extra C-atoms **55,** 254
  urethans **55,** 60
**Isocyanides** s. Isonitriles
**Isocyclics** (s.a. Benzene ring, Cyclo...)
– special s.
  enisocyclics
**1H-Isoindol-1-one..., 2,3-dihydro-** s.
  Phthalimidines
**Isoflavone epoxides, chiral 46,** 106s55
**Z→E-Isomerization**
– of ene-1,2-di-*tert*-amines **55,** 346
**Isonitriles**
– from
  formamides **55,** 174
– startg. m. f.
  α-(carbalkoxyamino)carboxylic acid
  amides **55,** 319
  imidazoles, 5-amino-, N-condensed,
  polymer-based synthesis **55,** 340
**Isonitriles, tert.**
– from
  alcohols, tert. **55,** 140
**Isopropanol**
– as H-donor **55,** 22
**Isothiochromans**

–, synthesis and reactions, review **34,** 238s55
**Isothiocyanates**
– from
  hydroximinohalides **55,** 208
– startg. m. f.
  β,γ-ethylenecarboxylic acid thioamides, with 3 extra C-atoms **55,** 254
**Isothioureas**
– special s.
  N-imidoylisothioureas
**Isoureas**
– special s.
  O-acylisoureas
**Isoxazoles, steroidal**
–, review **54,** 52s55
**Isoxazolidines, steroidal**
–, review **54,** 52s55
**Isoxazolidines, tricyclic**
– special s.
  2,8-dioxa-1-azabicyclo[3.3.0]octanes,
  peri-fused
**Isoxazolines, steroidal**
–, review **54,** 52s55


**Kaolinitic clay 55,** 202
**Ketals** (s.a. Acetals)
– from
  acetylene derivs., terminal **55,** 63
– special s.
  cyclopropanone ketals
– startg. m. f.
  ketimines **55,** 138
**Ketals, cyclic**
–, Baeyer-Villiger oxidation, asym. **55,** 65
**Ketene aminals, β,β-difunctionalized**
–, chemistry, review **43,** 587s55
**Ketene equivalents**
–, [4+2]-cycloaddition, review **37,** 669s55
**Ketenes**
– special s.
  bis(ketenes)
  silylketenes
**Ketene telluroacetals 50,** 343s55
**Ketenimines**
– special s.
  N-(alkynylaryl)ketenimines
– startg. m. f.
  pyrrolidines, 2-imino-, retention of
  configuration **55,** 255
**Ketimines** (s.a. Aldimines, Azomethines)
– from
  amines, prim. **55,** 138
  ketals **55,** 138
**2-Ketobismuthonium salts**
– startg. m. f.
  β-acoxy-α,β-ethyleneketones **55,** 427
**α-Ketocarboxylic acid esters**
–, decarbonylation **55,** 117
– startg. m. f.
  α-hydroxycarboxylic acid esters,
  reduction, asym. **55,** 30
**β-Ketocarboxylic acid esters**
– special s.
  acylamino-β-ketocarboxylic acid
  esters

aryl-β-ketocarboxylic – –
benzyl-β-ketocarboxylic – –
ethyl acetoacetate
ethylene-β-ketocarboxylic acid esters
halogeno-β-ketocarboxylic – –
– startg. m. f.
  β-ketothiolic acid esters **55**, 202
**γ-Ketocarboxylic acid esters**
– special s.
  amino-γ-ketocarboxylic acid esters
**β-Ketocarboxylic acids**
– from
  enol triflates, carboxylation, cathodic
  **55**, 418
**γ-Ketocarboxylic acids**
– special s.
  α-amino-γ-ketocarboxylic acids
**2-Ketoiodonium ylids**
– as intermediates **55**, 367
**Ketolactones, bicyclic, large-ring 49**,
  985s**55**
**β-Ketomalonic acid esters, cyclic**
– from
  halogenocarboxylic acid halides **55**,
  380
  malonic acid esters **55**, 380
**Ketones** (s.a. Carbonyl compds.,
  Hydroacylation, Oxo compds.)
–, aldol condensation, Lewis acid-
  catalyzed, regiostereospecific with –
  **55**, 248
–, aldol-type condensation with parallel
  differentiated recognition **55**, 446
–, α-arylation, asym. **55**, 411
– from
  alcohols, sec. s. under Oxo compds.
  and OC⇑H
  carboxylic acid selenoamides **55**, 428
  α-cyanoketones **54**, 473s**55**
  3-ethylene-*tert*-alcohols, C-cleavage
  **55**, 120
  α-hydroxycarboxylic acids,
  decarboxylation, aerobic, catalytic
  **55**, 119
  nitro compds., sec. **55**, 93
–, reduction s. under Oxo compds.
–, review (annual) **51**, 227s**55**
– special s.
  acoxyketones
  acylaminoketones
  aminoketones
  arylketones
  aryl ketones
  aryloxyketones
  (carbalkoxyamino)ketones
  cyanoketones
  cyclopropyl ketones
  diazoketones
  diketones
  epoxyketones
  ethyleneketones
  halogenoketones
  hydroxyketones
  methyl ketones
  nitroketones
  siloxyketones
  (sulfonyloxy)ketones
  vinyloxyketones
– startg. m. f.
  alcohols, sec. s. under Oxo compds.
  and OC⇓HC
  γ-aryl-β-diketones **55**, 390

benzylalcohols, tert., synthesis, asym.
  **55**, 239
epoxides, synthesis, asym. **55**, 421
α,β-ethylenehalides, with 1 extra C-
  atom **55**, 430
α,β-ethyleneketones, via aldol
  condensation **55**, 355
α-hydroxyacetals, with 1 extra C-atom
  **55**, 419
γ-lactols **55**, 432
γ-lactones, synthesis, asym. **55**, 343
pyridines, 2-amino- **55**, 326
4-pyrones, 2,3-dihydro- **55**, 399
–, –, 6-amino- **55**, 399
α,α',β-trihalogenoketones **55**, 185
**Ketones, cyclic**
– startg. m. f.
  enisocyclics, synthesis, asym. **55**, 464
**Ketones, sym.**
– from
  Grignard compds. **55**, 386
**α-Keto-β-nosyloxycarboxylic acid
  esters**
– startg. m. f.
  Δ⁴-2-oxazolones, 4-carbalkoxy- **55**,
  145
**β-Ketophosphonic acid esters**
– special s.
  ethylene-β-ketophosphonic acid esters
  α,β-ethylene-α-phosphonylketones
**Ketosteroids 49**, 971s**55**
**Δ⁴-3-Ketosteroids**
–, reduction, photochemical, regiostereospecific **55**, 33
**2-Ketothioethers**
– from
  α-halogenoketones **55**, 212
  thiosulfuric acid S-monoesters **55**, 212
**3-Ketothioethers**
– from
  1,1-acoxythioethers **37**, 891s**55**
  enamines **55**, 363
  sulfoxides **55**, 363
**β-Ketothiolactams**
– from
  α,β-ethylene-β-siloxy-α-(silyl)thio-
  lactams **55**, 252
  lactams, ring expansion **55**, 252
**β-Ketothiolic acid esters**
– from
  β-ketocarboxylic acid esters **55**, 202
**γ-Keto-α-(tosylamino)carboxylic acid
  esters**
– from
  enoxysilanes, asym. synthesis with 2
  extra C-atoms **55**, 450
**Ketoximes** (s.a. Oximes)
–, cleavage, selective **55**, 87
**Knoevenagel condensation,
  heterogeneous**
– with hydrotalcite as base **55**, 335
– –, polymer-based **3**, 632s**55**


**Lactams**
– special s.
  benzolactams
  dilactams

  ethylenelactams
– startg. m. f.
  α,β-ethylene-β-siloxy-α-(silyl)thio-
  lactams, ring expansion **55**, 252
  β-ketothiolactams **55**, 252
–, **macrocyclic 49**, 985s**55**
–, **peptidomimetic 49**, 985s**55**
**β-Lactams** s. 2-Azetidinones
**γ-Lactams** s. 2-Pyrrolidones
**δ-Lactams** (s.a. δ-Enaminolactams, 2-
  Piperidones)
– special s.
  alkylidene-δ-lactams
**Lactolides**
– special s.
  ethylenelactolides
**δ-Lactolides**
– special s.
  pyran-2-yl ethers, tetrahydro-
**Lactols, bicyclic**
– from
  α,β-ethylenecarboxylic acid esters **55**,
  395
  halogenoketones **55**, 395
**γ-Lactols**
– from
  1-aza-2-zircona-4-cyclopentenes **55**,
  432
  γ-hydroxynitriles (chiral compds.) **55**,
  92
  ketones **55**, 432
**Lactones**
–, review (annual) **53**, 322s**55**
– special s.
  allyllactones
  benzolactones
  dilactones
  ethylenelactones
  halogenolactones
**Lactones, macrocyclic 49**, 985s**55**
– special s.
  ansa macrolides
**β-Lactones**
– special s.
  hydroxy-β-lactones
**γ-Lactones**
– from
  cyclobutanone ketals, spirocyclic,
  asym., induction **55**, 65
  α,β-ethylenecarboxylic acid esters,
  synthesis, asym. **55**, 343
  ketones, –, – **55**, 343
– special s.
  acylamino-γ-lactones
  allyl-γ-lactones
  amino-γ-lactones
  aryl-γ-lactones
  arylseleno-γ-lactones
  carbalkoxy-γ-lactones
  ethylene-γ-lactones
  halogeno-γ-lactones
  hydroxy-γ-lactones
  methylene-γ-lactones
  spiro-γ-lactones
**γ-Lactones, cyclopropano-fused** s. 3-
  Oxabicyclo[3.1.0]hexan-2-ones
**δ-Lactones**
– special s.
  alkoxy-δ-lactones
  alkylidene-δ-lactones
**Lanthanide(III), cation exchanger-
  supported 47**, 893s**55**

**Lanthanum(III) 1,1′-bi-2-naphthoxides, chiral**
– as reagent **43**, 576s55
–(III) iodide **55**, 88
– tris[bis(trimethylsilyl)]amide
– as reagent **55**, 58
–(III) trisodium tris((R)-1,1′-bi-2-naphthoxide)
– as reagent **55**, 195, 196
**Lead(IV) tricarboxylates, organo-**
– special s.
aryllead triacetates
**Leaving group**
–, furan as – **55**, 111
**Lewis acids** (s.a. Radical reactions, Lewis acid-mediated)
– –, polymer-microencapsulated **55**, 440
**Libraries of compounds** s. Compound libraries
**Ligands**
–, design, optimum, review **42**, 616s55
**Lithiation** (s.a. Metalation)
–, reductive, heterogeneous **55**, 232
**Lithium** (s.a. under Titanium tetrachloride) **55**, 162
–/1,2-dibromoethane **55**, 360
–/naphthalene (s.a. Nickel(II) chloride dihydrate/lithium/naphthalene)
–/–, polymer-based
– as reagent **55**, 232
– acetate
– as reagent **55**, 186
– acetylides
– startg. m. f.
arylacetylenes **55**, 447
(E,E)-1-aryltelluro-1,3-dienes **55**, 272
(E)-1,3-enynes **55**, 447
– alkoxides
– ethoxide **55**, 367, 468
– **aluminum bis((R,R)-1,1′-bi-2-naphthoxide) 55**, 273
– amide
–, equivalent **6**, 367s55
– amides
– bis(trimethylsilyl)amide **55**, 430
– – (as reactant) **55**, 332
– diethylamide **55**, 376
– –, chiral
– as reagent **55**, 378
–, synthesis, asym. with –, review (annual) **4**, 3s55
– **bromide 55**, 183, 186, 190, 392
– **chloride 55**, 183, 378, 391
– compds., organo-
sec-butyllithium **55**, 373
tert-butyllithium **55**, 182, 221, 222, 303, 305, 374, 375
methyllithium **55**, 312
–, 1,4-addition with – **55**, 260
– special s.
silyllithium compds., organo-
vinyllithium compds.
– startg. m. f.
ketones, **55**, 428
selenolic acid esters, with 1 extra C-atom **55**, 382
– –, organo-, unsatd.
–, cross-coupling, oxidative with aluminum compds., organo- **55**, 447
– **cuprates, organo-**
– special s.
lithium organo(cyano)cuprates

– organo(α-sulfoximinyl)cuprates
– **dialkylcuprates**
– as reactant **55**, 235
– **dimethyl(silyl)zincates**
–, syntheses, cuprate-catalyzed with – **55**, 215
– **hydroxide 55**, 100, 327, 327
– **iodide** (s.a. bis(π-allylpalladium chloride)/lithium iodide under Palladium complexes) **55**, 287
– **organo(cyano)cuprates**
– as reactant **55**, 382
– **organo(α-sulfoximinyl)cuprates, chiral**
–, 1,4-addition, asym. with – **55**, 368
– **perchlorate 55**, 46, 147, 255, 332, 341, 494
– **tetrahydridoaluminate 55**, 32
– **trifluoromethanesulfonate 55**, 285
– **ynolates**
– as intermediates **55**, 374
**Lössen rearrangement**
–, ureas from hydroxamic acids via – **55**, 163


**Macrocyclics**
– by transacetalation, intramolecular, stereospecific **55**, 116
**Magnesium** (s.a. under Titanium complexes) **55**, 225
**Magnesium alkoxides, halogeno-**
bromomagnesium tert-butoxide **55**, 390
– amides, halogeno-
bromomagnesium diisopropylamide **55**, 363
– **bromide 55**, 129, 177
– **chloride 55**, 380
– halides, organo- (s.a. Grignard compds. and under Titanium(IV) alkoxides)
allylmagnesium bromide (as reactant) **55**, 384
ethynylmagnesium – **55**, 388
isopropylmagnesium – **55**, 391
– special s.
arylmagnesium halides
– **iodide 55**, 240
– triorganozincates, bromo-
– as reactant **55**, 270
**Maleic acid and derivs.**
–, addition of benzyl radicals to – **55**, 442
**Maleic anhydrides**
–, C-alkylation **42**, 531s55
**Maleimides**
– special s.
bis(indolyl)maleimides
N-carbamylmaleimides
**Malonamic acids**
– special s.
alkylidenemalonamic acids
**Malonic acid esters**
–, α-allylation with 2-ethylenecarbonic acid esters **55**, 357
– special s.
ketomalonic acid esters
– startg. m. f.
β-ketomalonic acid esters, cyclic **55**, 380

3-oxabicyclo[3.1.0]hexan-2-ones, 1-carbalkoxy-, asym. induction **55**, 333
– – –, functionalized **55**, 277
**Malononitriles**
– special s.
alkylidenemalononitriles
**Manganation** (s.a. Acylmanganation)
**Manganese 55**, 352, 402
Rieke manganese **52**, 413s55
**Manganese compds., organo-**
– special s.
allylmanganese compds.
methylmanganese pentacarbonyl
**Manganese dioxide 55**, 451
– –/silica **55**, 151
–(II) halides, organo-
– special s.
arylmanganese(II) bromides
**Manganese-mediated syntheses**
–, review **24**, 768s55
–(III) porphyrin complexes, Amberlite-supported **39**, 124s55
–(III) – –, water-soluble **55**, 70
–(III) salen – **55**, 78
–(III) – –, fluorous, chiral **48**, 134s55
–(III) Schiff base –, chiral **55**, 500
**Mannich reaction, polymer-based 55**, 344
**Meerwein-Ponndorf-Verley reduction, electrochemical 55**, 21
– –, heterogeneous **55**, 22
**Mercaptals**
– special s.
ethylenemercaptals
– startg. m. f.
(Z)-2-ethylenesilanes, with 2 extra C-atoms **55**, 473
silanes **55**, 228
**Mercaptals, cyclic**
– from
acetals **55**, 202, 204
dithiols **55**, 204
oxo compd. N-derivs. **55**, 202
oxo compds. **55**, 202, 204
**Mercaptals, unsym.**
– from
aldehydes **55**, 203
**Mercaptans**
–, Michael addition, asym. catalytic to enones **55**, 195
–, –, –, – to α,β-ethylenethiolic acid esters **55**, 196
–, reactions on kaolinitic clay **55**, 202
– review (annual) **53**, 16s55
– special s.
aminomercaptans
tert-dodecanethiol
hydroxymercaptans
siloxymercaptans
– startg. m. f.
2-aminothioethers, with retention of chirality **55**, 213
sulfenic acid esters **55**, 54
sulfenyl chlorides **55**, 54
thioethers **55**, 207
–, ar. polymer-based synthesis **55**, 211
**Mercaptans, ar.** s. Arylmercaptans
**α-Mercaptocarboxylic acid esters**
– special s.
ethyl thioglycolate
**o-Mercaptocarboxylic** – –
– startg. m. f.
thiochromans **55**, 362

**Mercury(II) chloride**
– as reactant **55**, 279
**Mercury compds., organo-** (s.a. Allylmercuration)
**Mesoporous materials, supramolecular-templated**
–, review **38**, 756s55
**Metalation**
– of heterocyclics **42**, 597s55
–, **asym.**
– of phospholane 1-oxides **55**, 378
–, **polymer-based 42**, 597s55
–, **α-lateral**
– of pyridines **28**, 732s55
*o*-**Metalation**
– of arylphosphine oxides **55**, 182
**Metal carbenes**
–, insertion, intramolecular, asym. in carbon-hydrogen bonds, review **47**, 955s55
**Metathesis** (s.a. Interchange in Vols. **1-50**)
– special s.
 ene-yne metathesis
 ring closing –
 ring opening –
**Metathesis, polymer-based**
– of ethylene derivs. **49**, 932s55
**O-*p*-Methoxybenzylation**
– with N-(*p*-methoxybenzyl)-*o*-benzenedisulfonimide **55**, 86
**N-(*p*-Methoxybenzyl)-*o*-benzene-disulfonimide**
–, O-*p*-methoxybenzylation with – **55**, 86
*p*-**Methoxybenzyl ethers**
–, cleavage **55**, 17
**1-Methoxy-3-trimethylsiloxy-1,3-butadiene**
– as reactant **55**, 449
**Methyl carbamate**
– as reactant **55**, 145
**Methyl(carboxysulfamyl)triethyl-ammonium hydroxide inner salt**
– as reagent **55**, 174
**3-Methylenealcohols, cyclic, medium-ring 38**, 952s55
**γ-Methylenealdehydes, cyclic 55**, 481
**Methylene compds.** (s.a. Ethylene derivs., terminal)
– from
 aldehydes, retention of keto groups **55**, 338
 oxo compds., with 1 extra C-atom **55**, 338
**5-Methylene-1,3-cyclohexadienes, 6-α-alkylthio-**
– from
 benzylsulfonium salts **55**, 314
**3-Methylene-1,5-diols 47**, 576s55
**Methylene groups, active**
–, C-acylation, polymer-based **55**, 349
–, α-alkylidenation with aldimines **55**, 364
–, C-monoalkylation **55**, 401
**α-Methyleneketones**
– special s.
 alkoxy-α-methyleneketones
**α-Methylene-γ-lactones**
–, 1,4-addition to – **47**, 450s55
**α-Methylene-γ-nitrocarboxylic acid esters 37**, 747s55
**α-Methylenephosphine oxides 55**, 217
**α-Methylene-β-(sulfonylamino)-**
 **carboxylic acids**
–, synthesis, polymer-based **55**, 334
**N-Methylimidazole** (s.a. under Zirconium aroxides, chiral)
*p*-**Methyliodobenzene difluoride**
– as reagent **55**, 181
**Methyl ketones**
– from
 acetylene derivs., terminal **55**, 63
**Methylmanganese pentacarbonyl**
– as reactant **55**, 301
**N-Methylmorpholine N-oxide**
– as reagent **55**, 74, 93, 128
**Methyl orthoformate**
– as reactant **55**, 107, 399
– as reagent **55**, 83
**Methyl α-siloxyketones, camphor-derived**
– as reactant **55**, 233
**Methyl trifluoromethanesulfonate**
– as reagent **55**, 75
**Micellar media**
– special s.
 reverse micelles
**Micellar media, aq.**
–, aldol-type condensation in – **52**, 447s55
–, epoxidation, catalytic in – **55**, 70
–, S-oxidation in – **55**, 52
–, tetrazoles from nitriles in – **13**, 371s55
**Michael addition** (s.a. 1,4-Addition)
– of azide ion **30**, 222s55
– to α,β-acetylenecarbonyl compds. **47**, 631s55
– with carbanions, benzotriazole-stabilized, review **53**, 386s55
**Michael addition, asym.**
–, review **50**, 498s55
– with phosphonic acid esters **55**, 273
– –, –, **catalytic**
– of
 mercaptans to α,β-ethyleneketones **55**, 195
– to α,β-ethylenethiolic acid esters **55**, 196
– –, –, **Lewis acid catalyzed**
– of O-benzylhydroxylamine **55**, 129
– –, **double, asym. 6**, 364s55
– –, **heterogeneous**
– with hydrotalcite as base **55**, 335
– –, **polymer-based**
–, β-aminoketones via – **55**, 349
– **addition-aldol condensation, stereospecific**
–, α-(arylthiomethyl)-β-hydroxy-carboxylic acid esters via – **55**, 261
**Michael-type addition**
– special s.
 radical Michael-type addition
– with
 heteroarenes **20**, 601s55
 homoenolate equivalents **55**, 348
– –, **indium(III)-catalyzed**
– without solvent **55**, 438
**Microwave irradiation**
–, N-acylation, selective **22**, 365s55
–, O-acylation, asym., enzymatic **44**, 214s55
–, 2-hydroxythioethers from epoxides **2**, 532s55
–, oxidation of alcohols with dichromate **42**, 235s55

–, pyridines, 2-amino- from α,β-ethyleneketones **55**, 326
–, trifluoromethyl thioethers, ar. **41**, 748s55
–, zeolite modification under –, review **44**, 651s55
– –, **solvent-less**
–, acetylation **55**, 79
–, benzimidazoles and benzoxazoles from carboxylic acids **12**, 432s55
–, cinnamic acids from aldehydes **1**, 569s55
–, cyclohexene-1,3-dicarboxylic acid esters, 2-amino-3-cyano-5-nitro- **55**, 263
–, Michael addition of amines **6**, 364s55
–, review (with focused microwaves) **55**, 79s55
–, retro-Diels-Alder reaction **55**, 493
– –, –, **solid-supported**
–, acylals from aldehydes **51**, 55s55
–, benzazoles from *o*-functionalized anilines **55**, 151
–, 4-chromones from *o*-hydroxy-β-diketones **8**, 342s55
–, coumarins, 3,4-dihydro- from α,β-acetylenecarboxylic acids **55**, 336
–, N-decarbo-*tert*-butoxylation **55**, 17
–, O-de(*p*-methoxybenzylation) **55**, 17
–, 1,2-disiloxy compds., sym. from oxo compds. **55**, 243
–, nitriles from aldehydes **55**, 146
–, sulfoxides from thioethers **54**, 54s55
–, transesterification of β-keto-esters **51**, 104s55
**Mitsunobu N-alkylation, polymer-based 28**, 753s55
**Molybdenum complexes**
 tricarbonyltris(propionitrile)-molybdenum(0) **55**, 353
**C-Monoalkylation**
– of methylene groups, active **55**, 401
**Mononitration, ar. 55**, 132
**Montmorillonite K 10 55**, 243, 336
**Morpholine, polymer-based**
– as base **55**, 340

**1-Naphthaldehyde**
– as reagent **55**, 321
**Naphthalene-1-carbonyl compds., 1,2,3,8a-tetrahydro-, η²-osmium-complexed 55**, 285
**Naphthalene-1-carboxylic acid derivs., 1,4-dihydro-, 4-amino-**
– from
 Δ²-oxazolines, 2-(1-naphthyl)-, synthesis, stereospecific **55**, 331
**Naphthalenes**
– special s.
 oxazolines, 2-(1-naphthyl)-
**1-Naphthol ring, 4-arylthio- 22**, 877s55
**Naphthols**
– special s.
 binaphthols
**2-Naphthols**
– from
 γ-aryl-β-diketones **41**, 927s55

**1,4-Naphthoquinone ring**
– via cyclobutane ring fragmentation, photochemical **55**, 492
**Negishi cross-coupling**
–, update **38**, 836s55
**Nickel**
Raney nickel **55**, 92
**Nickel, activated 55**, 210
–(0), active **55**, 25
–(II) acetoacetonate **55**, 270, 290
–(II) bromide **55**, 291
–(II) chloride (s.a. Electrolysis/nickel(II) chloride) **55**, 148
–(II) – dihydrate/lithium/naphthalene **55**, 25
–(II) –/potassium **55**, 209
**Nickel complexes**
dichloro[1,3-bis(diphenylphosphino)propane]nickel(II)/diisobutylaluminum hydride **55**, 10
dichlorobis(triphenylphosphine)nickel(II) **55**, 268
di(cyclooctadiene)nickel(0) **55**, 290
tetrakis(triethylphosphine)nickel(0) **55**, 491
**Nitration, ar.** (s.a. Mononitration, ar.)
**Nitrenes**
–, reactions, cryogenic in noble gas matrices, review **52**, 274s55
– special s.
carbo-*tert*-butoxynitrene
**Nitric acid esters**
–, review (recent developments) **54**, 51s55
**Nitrile oxides**
–, cycloaddition, 1,3-dipolar, polymer-based with –, **16**, 888s55
**Nitriles**
–, N-alkylation, reductive of 2-aminoalcohols with – **55**, 152
– from
aldehydes **55**, 146
carboxylic acid halides **55**, 144
– acids **55**, 144
halides, with 2 extra C-atoms **55**, 330
sulfonic acid esters, – – – – **55**, 330
– special s.
acetonitrile
acylaminonitriles
aminonitriles
ethylenenitriles
hydroxynitriles
siloxynitriles
– startg. m. f.
(Z)-β-amino-α,β-ethylenenitriles (from 2 different molecules) **55**, 256
carboxylic acid amides, without solvent **55**, 61
pyridine ring **55**, 431
*o*-**Nitrobenzylamines**
– startg. m. f.
2*H*-indazoles **55**, 121
**Nitrocarboxylic acids**
– special s.
bis(hydroxymethyl)-ω-nitrocarboxylic acids
**Nitro compds.**
–, review (recent developments) **54**, 51s55
– startg. m. f.
acyl hydroxamates **55**, 137
– startg. m. f.

amines, prim. **55**, 40
– –, aliphatic
– startg. m. f.
N,N-disiloxyenamines **55**, 56
– –, ar.
– startg. m. f.
amines, ar., prim. **55**, 13
– –, sec.
– startg. m. f.
ketones **55**, 93
**2-Nitro-1,3-diols**
– special s.
ω,ω-bis(hydroxymethyl)-ω-nitrocarboxylic acids
**1,1-Nitroethylene derivs.**
– from
2-nitrothioenolethers **29**, 854s55
– startg. m. f.
pyrrolidines, 3-nitro- **55**, 466
**1,2-Nitroethylene derivs.**
– special s.
α,β-ethylene-β-nitroiodides
**Nitrogen, atmospheric**
– startg. m. f.
δ-enaminolactams **55**, 141
pyrroles **55**, 141
–, molecular
– startg. m. f.
amines, ar., prim. **55**, 162
**Nitrogen dioxide, liq.**
–, diazotization with – **55**, 188
**1,2-Nitrohalides**
– special s.
α,β-ethylene-β-nitroiodides
**α-Nitroketones, cyclic**
– startg. m. f.
ω,ω-bis(hydroxymethyl)-ω-nitrocarboxylic acids **55**, 262
**Nitromethane**
– as reactant **55**, 263
**Nitrones**
–, review (recent developments) **54**, 51s55
**Nitronic acid silyl esters**
– as intermediates **55**, 56
*p*-**Nitrophenyl glycosides**
–, cleavage via *p*-acetamidophenyl glycosides **55**, 11
**Nitroso compds.**
– special s.
acylnitroso compds.
– startg. m. f.
Δ³-1,2,4-oxadiazolines, 5-carbalkoxy- **55**, 127
**1,1-Nitrosoethylene derivs.**
–, review **54**, 133s55
**1,1-Nitrosohalides**
– as intermediates **5**, 381s55
**Nitroxyls** s. N-Oxide radicals
**Noyori hydrogenation, asym., improved**
– of ketones **55**, 26
**Nucleopeptides 51**, 5s55
–, synthesis and properties, review **19**, 33s55
**Nucleoside-5′-carboxylic acids**
– from
nucleosides **55**, 77
**Nucleoside synthesis** (s.a. under Vorbrüggen)
**Nucleotides**
– special s.
dinucleoside...

**Nysted reagent**
–, methylenation with – **55**, 338

**Olefin aldol reaction, intramolecular, regiospecific**
– of ethylenehydrazones **55**, 303
**Oligonucleoside phosphorothioates 17**, 169s55
**Oligonucleotides, labelled 17**, 169s55
**Oligonucleotide synthesis**
–, update **17**, 169s55
**Oligosaccharides**
–, synthesis, solid-phase **17**, 169s55
(review); **20**, 12s55
**Oligosaccharides, cyclic**
–, synthesis, review **17**, 169s55
**Organometallics, main-group**
– in synthesis, review (annual) **53**, 407s55
**α-(Organoseleno)carbonyl compds.**
– from
α-halogenocarbonyl compds. **55**, 225
**2-Organoseleno-1,4-dienes 39**, 887s55
**(E)-1-(Organoseleno)enetellurides 50**, 343s55
**Orthocarboxylic acid esters**
– special s.
ethyleneorthocarboxylic acid esters
**Orthoformic acid esters**
– special s.
methyl orthoformate
**Osmium complexes, organo-**
– special s.
(η²-styrene)osmium complexes
**Osmium tetroxide 55**, 74, 169
**7-Oxabicyclo[2.2.1]hepta-2,5-dienes, 4-aryl-**
– startg. m. f.
fulvenes, 6-aryl-6-hydroxy- **55**, 306
**3-Oxabicyclo[3.1.0]hexan-2-ones, 1-carbalkoxy-**
– from
glycidyl sulfonates, asym. induction **55**, 333
malonic acid esters, – – **55**, 333
**8-Oxabicyclo[3.2.1]oct-2-ene ring, condensed**
– from
3,4-epoxyalcohols, unsatd. **55**, 479
**1,2,4-Oxadiazoles, 5-aryl-**
– from
amidoximes **55**, 415
halides, ar. **55**, 415
**1,3,4-Oxadiazoles, 2-mercapto-**
– as reagent **40**, 242s55
–, 2-organothio- **17**, 503s55
**Δ³-1,2,4-Oxadiazolines, 5-acyl- 55**, 127
–, 5-carbalkoxy-
– from
nitroso compds. **55**, 127
oxazoles, 5-alkoxy- **55**, 127
**Oxalic acid esters**
– startg. m. f.
carbonic acid esters **55**, 117
**Oxalimidoyl chlorides**
–, ring closures with – **55**, 404

Oxalyl chloride
- as reactant 55, 320
- as reagent 55, 144
Oxa-Pauson-Khand reaction 55, 292
1,2-Oxasilacycloalkanes 55, 218
1-Oxaspiro[5.4]decan-7-ol-2-ones 55, 275
1,2-Oxathianes, 4-hydroxy-
- from
  2,4-dihydroxymercaptans 55, 55
3-Oxatricyclo[4.4.0.0$^{1,5}$]deca-7,9-dien-4-ones, 5-vinyl-
- startg. m. f.
  3-isochromanones, 4-vinyl- 55, 304
1,3,2-Oxazaborolidines, chiral
- as catalysts for asym. reduction, review 43, 45s55
- as reducing agent 43, 45s55 (update)
1,3-Oxazin-2-ones, tetrahydro- 21, 393s55
4H-1,3-Oxazin-4-ones, tetrahydro-
- from
  aldehydes, parallel synthesis 55, 437
  3-siloxy-2-aza-1,3-dienes, – – 55, 437
Oxaziridines, 3-alkenyl-
- startg. m. f.
  epoxyaldehydes 55, 75
α-(Oxaziridin-2-yl)carboxylic acid esters
–, N-formylation of α-amino esters via – 55, 170
Oxazole-borane complexes
–, 2-metalation 42, 597s55
Oxazoles, 5-alkoxy-
- startg. m. f.
  Δ$^3$-1,2,4-oxadiazolines, 5-carbalkoxy- 55, 127
  Δ$^2$-oxazoline-4-carboxylic acid esters, asym. conversion 55, 241
Oxazoles, 2-aryl- 38, 836s55
Oxazolidines
–, N-alkylation, reductive of 2-aminoalcohols via – 55, 152
- from
  2-aminoalcohols, asym. induction 55, 152
  nitriles, – – 55, 152
- startg. m. f.
  pyrrolidines, 3-nitro- 55, 466
4-Oxazolidone ring, 2,5-bridged
- from
  oxazolium betaines, 4-hydroxy- 43, 740s55
2-Oxazolidones
- startg. m. f.
  2-aminothioethers, with retention of chirality 55, 213
  4H-1,4-thiazin-3(2H)-ones, 5,6-dihydro- 55, 213
2-Oxazolidones, 3-acyl-
–, dimerization, oxidative, asym. 4, 685s55
- startg. m. f.
  carboxylic acid esters 55, 88
–, –, 4-methylene-
–, hydrogenation, asym. 42, 45s55
–, 5-α-amino-
- from
  N-(2,3-epoxy)urethans, polymer-based 55, 147
  urethans, – 55, 147
–, 3-(β-hydroxyacyl)-, chiral 55, 247

–, 3-sulfonyl- 42, 108s55
Δ$^2$-Oxazoline-4-carboxylic acid esters
- from
  aldehydes, asym. conversion 55, 241
  oxazoles, 5-alkoxy-, – – 55, 241
Δ$^2$-Oxazolines
- special s.
  bis(Δ$^2$-oxazolines)
Δ$^2$-Oxazolines, chiral
- in asym. synthesis, review 51, 24s55
Δ$^2$-Oxazolines, 2-(1-naphthyl)-
- startg. m. f.
  naphthalene-1-carboxylic acid derivs., 1,4-dihydro-, 4-amino-, synthesis, stereospecific 55, 331
Δ$^4$-2-Oxazolones
- from
  α-hydroxycarboxamides 41, 624s55
Δ$^4$-2-Oxazolones, 4-carbalkoxy-
- from
  α-keto-β-nosyloxycarboxylic acid esters 55, 145
Δ$^2$-5-Oxazolones
- startg. m. f.
  α-acylaminocarboxylic acid esters, resolution, kinetic, dynamic 55, 57
Oxepane ring, condensed
- by radical ring closure 47, 983s55
2(3H)-Oxepinones, 6,7-dihydro- 29, 810s55
Oxepins s.a. O-Heterocyclics, seven-membered
2-Oxetanones s. β-Lactones
Oxidation, benzylic, manganese(III)-mediated 55, 78
–, catalytic, heterogeneous
- with dioxygen 55, 113
–, liquid-phase
- with catalysts, heterogeneous, review 47, 113s55
N-Oxide radicals
- special s.
  piperidine N-oxyl, tetramethyl-
N-Oxides
–, review (recent developments) 54, 51s55
Oxido compds. s. Epoxides
Oximes
–, cleavage 55, 87, 89
- special s.
  aldoximes
  ketoximes
- startg. m. f.
  mercaptals, cyclic 55, 202
(E)-Oximes
- startg. m. f.
  pyrroles, 1-vinyl- 55, 328
Oximes, O-alkyl- s. Alkoximes
–, O-silyl- s. Siloximes
Oxindoles, 3-vinyl-, chiral 43, 962s55
Oxo compds. (s.a. Aldehydes, Carbonyl compds., Ketones)
–, Friedel-Crafts alkylation, reductive with – 55, 345
- from
  alcohols, sec. (ketones) 55, 113
  1,3-dioxolanes, 4-sulfonylmethyl- 55, 4
  oximes 55, 89
- special s.
  aryloxo compds.
  ethyleneoxo –
  halogenooxo –

- startg. m. f.
  alcohols, reduction 55, 21, 23, 24, 25
  –, –, heterogeneous 55, 22
  –, (sec. alcohols), hydrogenation, homogeneous, asym. 55, 29
  – (– –), Noyori hydrogenation, asym. 55, 26
  – (– –), reduction, asym. 55, 26, 28, 29
  –, (– –), –, –, cathodic, enzyme-catalyzed 42, 22s55
  –, (– –) –, –, 1,3,2-oxazaborolidine-catalyzed, review 43, 45s55
  –, synthesis 55, 231, 238
  –, (sec. alcohols), synthesis 55, 242
  –, (– –), synthesis, asym. 55, 237
  –, (tert. alcohols), –, – 55, 239
  2-aryl-1,3-diols (from 2 molecules) 55, 360
  cyclopropanone ketals, 2-α-hydroxy- 55, 348
  1,2-disiloxy compds., sym. 55, 243
  (E)-α,β-ethylenecarboxylic acids 55, 374
  β-hydroxyphosphonic acid esters 55, 249
  mercaptals, cyclic 55, 204
  methylene compds., with 1 extra C-atom 55, 338
Oxyamination, asym.
–, effect of ligand on regioselectivity 55, 130
- of enoxysilanes 55, 169
Oxygen (s. Dioxygen)
Oxymethyl radicals
–, 1,4-addition with – 55, 442
Oxypalladation, intramolecular-cross-coupling 48, 831s55
Ozonolysis
–, 3-ethylenealcohols from ethylene derivs. via – 55, 472
Ozonolysis-aldol condensation, intramolecular, regiospecific 55, 496


Palladation (s.a. Carbopalladation, Oxypalladation, Silylpalladation, Vinylpalladation)
Palladium 55, 11
Palladium/carbon 55, 39, 152, 153
Palladium-on-polyolefin-fibre 55, 13
Palladium(II) acetate 55, 72, 186, 201, 324, 366, 405, 406, 407, 408, 409, 410, 453, 454, 480, 486
Palladium π-allyl complexes
- from
  allenes 55, 73, 297
–, ring closures of allenes via – 55, 410
– – –, chiral
- as reagent 55, 461
–(II) chloride 55, 413, 476
Palladium complexes
  bis(acetonitrile)dichloropalladium(II) 55, 414
  bis(η$^3$-allylpalladium chloride) 55, 460
  bis(π-allylpalladium –) 55, 300
  – –/lithium iodide 55, 358

**(Palladium complexes)**
bis(dibenzylideneacetone)palladium(0) **55**, 114, 160, 297, 455
[(1R,1'R)-2,6-bis[1-(diphenyl-phosphino)ethyl]phenyl]chloro-palladium(II) **42**, 612s**55**
cyclopallad(II)ated phosphine complexes **55**, 412
di(μ-acetato)bis(tri-*o*-tolylphosphine)-dipalladium **55**, 458
dichlorobis(benzonitrile)palladium(II) **55**, 255
dichloro[1,1'-bis(diphenylphosphino)-ferrocene]palladium(II) **55**, 463
dichlorobis(triphenylphosphine)-palladium(II) **55**, 415, 416, 462
dichloro[(S)-2-[2-(diphenylphosphino)-phenyl]-4-benzyl-Δ²-oxazoline]-palladium(II) **54**, 138s**55**
*cis*-dimethylbis[dimethyl(phenyl)-phosphine]palladium **55**, 217
methyl(phenanthroline)palladium(II) complexes, cationic **55**, 299
tetrakis(triphenylphosphine)-palladium(0) **55**, 280, 298, 388, 389, 457, 475, 478
tris(dibenzylideneacetone)dipalladium **55**, 73, 115, 161, 162, 211, 227, 411, 456, 481
– –, binuclear, chiral
[2,2'-bis(diarylphosphino)-1,1'-binaphthyl](μ-hydroxo)palladium(II) bis(fluoroborates], binuclear, chiral **55**, 459
– –, fluorous
dichlorobis[bis[2-(perfluorohexyl)-ethyl]phenylphosphino]palladium(II) **55**, 417
– –, polymer-based
(benzylamine-C,N)palladium(II) hydride complex, polymer-based **55**, 40
**Palladium-ene reaction, intramolecular**
– with α,β-ethyleneacylals **55**, 481
**Palladium(II) enolates**
– as intermediates **55**, 459
**Parallel differentiated recognition**
– of ketones and acetals (or aldehydes) **55**, 446
**Pauson-Khand reaction** (s.a. Oxa-Pauson-Khand reaction)
– –, asym.
–, review **54**, 316s**55**
– –, intramolecular, rhodium-catalyzed **55**, 296
– –, –, zirconium-catalyzed **55**, 282
– –, zirconocene-mediated **55**, 281
**Peptide alcohols 19**, 33s**55**
**Peptide amides**
–, synthesis, solid-phase **10**, 382s**55**
**Peptide esters**
– special s.
dipeptide esters
**Peptides** (s.a. Ureapeptoids)
–, Mitsunobu N-alkylation, polymer-based **28**, 753s**55**
– special s.
glycopeptides
nucleopeptides
–, **arginine-containing 19**, 33s**55**
–, **cyclic**
– special s.

tetrapeptides, cyclic
–, **cysteine-containing**
–, synthesis, review **19**, 33s**55**
–, **N-linked 19**, 33s**55**
**Peptide synthesis**
– using N-hydroxy couplers, side-reactions **22**, 394s**55**
– –, **asym. 41**, 344s**55**
– –, **solid-phase**
–, update **19**, 33s**55**
– using
7-azabenzotriazolyloxy-tris(pyrrolidino)phosphonium hexafluorophosphate **28**, 144s**55**
trimethylaluminum **26**, 358s**55**
– with real-time monitoring **10**, 382s**55**; **19**, 33s**55**; **22**, 394s**55**
– –, –, **inverse 19**, 33s**55**
**Per-O-acetylation 54**, 79s**55**
**Perbromides** s. Trimethylphenyl-ammonium tribromide
**Perchloric acid 55**, 340
**Perfluoroalkanes**
– as medium **55**, 189
**Perfluoroalkyl iodides**
–, addition to allyl ethers **55**, 5
**Peroxides**
– special s.
silyl peroxides
**Perrhenic acid 55**, 50
**2-Phase medium** s. Fluorous 2-phase medium
**Phenanthrenes, 9-amino- 10**, 562s**55**
**Phenolethers** (s.a. Aryloxy...)
– from
halides, ar., transition metal catalysis, review **51**, 171s**55**
–, monobromination, ar. **48**, 447s**55**; **54**, 192s**55**
– special s.
*tert*-butyl phenolethers
diaryl ethers
**Phenols**
–, O-alkylation with dialkyl sulfates **55**, 100
– special s.
allylphenols
aminophenols
– startg. m. f.
coumarins, 3,4-dihydro- **55**, 336
**Phenothiazines**
–, 4-metalation **42**, 597s**55**
**Phenyl chlorothionoformate**
– reactant **55**, 19, 400
**Phenyldimethylsilyllithium**
– as reagent **55**, 14
**P,P'-1,2-Phenylenebis(*endo*-2,5-dialkyl-7-phosphabicyclo[2.2.1]heptane), chiral**
– as reagent **55**, 29
*o*-**Phenylene dipole equivalent**
–, *o*-bromophenylzinc iodide as – **55**, 389
**Phenyl iodosoacetate** (s.a. Phosphonium iodides/phenyl iodosoacetate)
– –/**sodium iodide**
– as reagent **55**, 102
**Phenylsilane**
– as reagent **55**, 31
**Phenyl(tosylimino)iodinane**
– as reagent **55**, 124
**N-Phenyltriflimide**
– as reagent **55**, 135

**Phenyltrimethylammonium tribromide**
– as reagent **55**, 467
**7-Phosphabicyclo[2.2.1]heptanes**
– special s.
P,P'-1,2-phenylenebis(...
**Phosphazene base (EtP₂)**
– as reagent **55**, 421
**Phosphine-borane complexes**
–, review **55**, 220s**55**
– startg. m. f.
phosphines, synthesis, asym., review **55**, 220s**55**
– –, sec.
–, P-deprotonation, asym. with dynamic kinetic resolution **55**, 220
**Phosphine oxides**
– special s.
arylphosphine oxides
bis(phosphine oxides)
ethylenephosphine oxides
– –, sec. s. Phosphinous acids
– –, sym.
– from
halides **55**, 219
**Phosphines**
– from
phosphine-borane complexes, synthesis, asym., review **55**, 220s**55**
– special s.
di(phosphines)
tri(phosphines)
**Phosphines, sec.**
– startg. m. f.
phosphines, tert., kinetic resolution, dynamic **55**, 220
**Phosphines, tert.**
– from
phosphines, sec., kinetic resolution, dynamic **55**, 220
– special s.
bis(diphenylphosphino)...
tri-*n*-butylphosphine
triphenylphosphine
tris(diphenylphosphino...
–, –, **mixed**
– from
amino(halogeno)phosphines, synthesis **55**, 224
phosphinous acid amides, – **55**, 224
–, **water-soluble, functionalized**
–, review **46**, 736s**55**
**Phosphinic acid esters**
– special s.
enol phosphinates
**Phosphinic acid halides**
– special s.
diphenylphosphinyl chloride
**Phosphinic acids**
– special s.
diphenylphosphinic acid
**Phosphinoamidines, chiral**
– as reagent **55**, 460
**Phosphinic acid amides**
– from
amino(halogeno)phosphines, synthesis **55**, 224
– startg. m. f.
phosphines, tert., mixed, synthesis **55**, 224
**Phosphinous acids**
– special s.
diphenylphosphine oxide

**Phosphites** s. Phosphorous acid esters
**Phospholane 1-oxides**
–, 2-metalation, asym. **55,** 378
**Phospholanes, chiral 55,** 378
**Phosphonic acid amide esters**
– from
  phosphonic acid dihalides **55,** 126
**Phosphonic acid diamides, bicyclic, chiral**
– as reagent **42,** 616s55
**Phosphonic acid dihalides**
– startg. m. f.
  phosphonic acid amide esters **55,** 126
**Phosphonic acid esters**
–, Michael addition, asym. to α,β-ethyleneketones **55,** 273
– special s.
  acylphosphonic acid esters
  allenephosphonic – –
  epoxyphosphonic – –
  halogenophosphonic – –
  hydroxyphosphonic – –
  ketophosphonic – –
  (tosylhydrazono)phosphonic – –
– startg. m. f.
  enisocyclics, synthesis, asym. **55,** 464
  N′-phosphorylamidines, – **55,** 369
–, α-sulfonylation **34,** 547s55
**Phosphonium iodides/phenyl iodosoacetate**
– as reagent **55,** 180
**Phosphonium salts**
– special s.
  aminophosphonium salts
  tetraphenylphosphonium chloride
**Phosphonochloridates**
– as intermediates **55,** 126
**Phosphonous acid derivs.** (s.a. Amino(halogeno)phosphines)
**C→N-Phosphonyl group migration 55,** 369
**Phosphoranes**
– special s.
  alkylidenephosphoranes
**Phosphorazidates**
– special s.
  diphenyl phosphorazidate
**Phosphorodiamidates**
– special s.
  bis(phosphorodiamidates)
**Phosphorous acid esters**
– special s.
  triethyl phosphite
  trimethyl –
  triphenyl –
– – –, tripodal, chiral
– as ligand **49,** 42s55
**Phosphorous acid triamides**
– special s.
  tris(pyrrolidino)phosphine
**Phosphorus, white**
– as reactant **55,** 219
**Phosphorus compds.**
–, electrochemistry, review **46,** 572s55
**Phosphorylaldehydes**
–, review **42,** 557s55
**N′-Phosphorylamidines**
– from
  cyanamides, synthesis **55,** 369
  phosphonic acid esters, – **55,** 369
**Photosensitizers** s. Sensitizers
**Phthalamic acid esters**

– as intermediates **55,** 143
**Phthalazones**
– from
  N-aroylamidrazones **10,** 303s55
**Phthalic acid monoesters**
– startg. m. f.
  phthalimides **55,** 143
**Phthalides**
– from
  phthalic acid derivs. **11,** 123s55
**Phthalimide, polymer-based**
– as reagent **27,** 429s55
**Phthalimides**
– from
  amines, prim. **55,** 143
  phthalamic acid esters **55,** 143
  phthalic acid monoesters **55,** 143
– special s.
  N-alkoxyphthalimides
– startg. m. f.
  amines, sec. **55,** 154
  o-(hydroxymethyl)carboxylic acid amides **50,** 154
**Phthalimidines**
–, 3-metalation **10,** 617s55
–, **N-condensed 33,** 662s55
– by carbonylation **52,** 422s55
– via N-acyliminium ions, cyclic **55,** 138
**Pictet-Spengler ring closure**
– of tryptamines, N′-hydroxy-, review **33,** 730s55
– – –, **polymer-based 8,** 823s55
**Pictet-Spengler-type – –, oxidative 48,** 982s55
**Piperazic acids**
–, review **26,** 56s55
**Piperazine-2-carboxylic acid amides**
–, synthesis, polymer-based **12,** 453s55
**2,5-Piperazinediones**
–, 3-alkylation, asym. **37,** 657s55
– from
  dipeptide esters, polymer-based synthesis **19,** 559s55
**2,5-Piperazinediones, 3-alkylidene-**
– startg. m. f.
  α,β-dideuterio-α-*prim*-amino-carboxylic acids, asym. conversion **55,** 39
**Piperazines**
–, N-arylation **40,** 286s55; **52,** 171s55
**2-Piperazinone-5-acetic acid amides**
–, synthesis, polymer-based **55,** 158
**2-Piperazinones, 4-acyl-, condensed**
–, synthesis, polymer-based **38,** 982s55
**Piperidine**
– as reagent **55,** 31, 263
**Piperidine-2-carboxylic acid esters 52,** 321s55
**Piperidine N-oxyl, 2,2,6,6-tetramethyl-**
– as reagent **55,** 99
**Piperidines, alkylidene- 50,** 428s55
**2-Piperidones** (s.a. δ-Lactams)
–, α-alkylation, asym. **37,** 657s55
–, 1-β-hydroxy-, chiral **46,** 601s55
**Pivalaldehyde**
– as reagent **55,** 119
**Platinum cluster complex, polymer-stabilized 55,** 30
**Platinum complexes**
  ethylenebis(triphenylphosphine)-platinum **55,** 251

**Polarity reversal catalysis**
– of hydrogen atom abstraction, review **50,** 341s55
**Polyphosphoric acid ester 55,** 337
**Polymer-based reactions** (s.a. Combinatorial synthesis)
–, monitoring on-resin, review **50,** 555s55
– special s.
  C-acylation, polymer-based
  Baylis-Hillman-type reaction, –
  O-benzylation, –
  N-carbalkoxylation, –
  cycloaddition, 1,3-dipolar, –
  O-desilylation, –
  Diels-Alder reaction, –
  ene-yne metathesis, –
  glycosidation, –
  Grignard syntheses, –
  Heck arylation, –
  Horner synthesis, intramolecular, –
  hydrosilylation, –
  Knoevenagel condensation, –
  Mannich reaction, –
  metalation, –
  metatheses, –
  Michael addition, –
  Mitsunobu N-alkylation, –
  Pictet-Spengler ring closure, –
  radical ring closure, –
  Sonogashira coupling, –
  Stille coupling, –
**Polymer-based reagents**
–, purification with – in combinatorial synthesis, review **50,** 555s55
– special s.
  arylmagnesium halides, polymer-based
  N-hydroxybenzotriazole, –
  Lewis acids, polymer-microencapsulated
  lithium/naphthalene, polymer-based
  morpholine, –
  palladium complexes, –
  phthalimide, –
  platinum cluster complex, polymer-stabilized
  rhodium(I) phosphine-phosphite complexes, chiral, polymer-based
  silicon hydrides, organo-, –
  tartrate, –
  tetraamines, –
  tin hydrides, organo-, –
**Polymer-based synthesis**
– of
  acyl glycosides **55,** 104
  amidines **55,** 164
  arylacetylenes from halides, ar. **55,** 416
  2-azetidinones **55,** 379
  benzimidazoles from aldehydes **46,** 321s55
  benzofurans **44,** 781s55
  1,3-dienes, 2-α-functionalized **42,** 354s55
  α,β-ethyleneketones **55,** 327
  α,β-ethylenelactones, macrocyclic **39,** 964s55
  glycoconjugates (from glycals), review **17,** 169s55
  glycopeptides **17,** 169s55 (review); **19,** 33s55; **28,** 144s55
  guanidines from isothioureas **5,** 346s55
  N-heterocyclics from enones **55,** 327
  hydantoins **21,** 393s55; **31,** 452s55

(Polymer-based synthesis
- of)
  hydroxamic acids 47, 293s55
  imidazoles from N-sulfonylaldimines
    47, 927s55
  -, 5-amino-, N-condensed 55, 340
  imidazolidone-4-acetic acid amides 55,
    158
  indoles 47, 829s55
  α-methylene-β-sulfonylamino-
    carboxylic acids 55, 334
  oligonucleoside thionophosphates 45,
    303s55
  oligosaccharides (from glycals),
    review 17, 169s55; 20, 12s55
  2-oxazolidones, 5-α-amino- 55, 147
  peptides s. Peptide synthesis, solid-
    phase
  piperazine-2-carboxamides 12, 453s55
  2,5-piperazinediones 19, 559s55
  2-piperazinone-5-acetic acid amides
    55, 158
  2H-pyran-5-carboxylic acid esters,
    3,4-dihydro-, 2-alkoxy- 47, 698s55
  pyrazoles, 5-amino- 19, 461s55
  pyrimidine-4-carboxylic acids, 2-
    alkylthio- 27, 769s55
  Δ³-2-pyrrolones, 4-hydroxy- 54,
    481s55
  quinolines, 1,2,3,4-tetrahydro- 55, 342
  samarium(III) compds., organo- via
    radical ring closure 55, 396
  1,2-thiazetidine 1,1-dioxides 38, 266s55
  thioethers, ar. from halides, ar. 55, 211
  ureas via phenyl carbamates 51,
    141s55
-, review (annual) 50, 555s55
- via N-acylimmonium salts, cyclic 38,
    982s55
Polymers, chiral, synthetic
-, catalysis, asym. with -, review 53,
    266s55
Polymer supports
-, cleavage, decarboxylative 55, 349
Polymethylhydrosiloxane
- as reagent 55, 31
Poly[styrene(iodosoacetate)]
- as reagent 48, 439s55
Porphyrin derivs.
-, Wittig synthesis, review 10, 633s55
Porphyrins (s.a. Carbaporphyrins,
    Chlorins)
-, meso-alkylation 40, 273s55
(η⁶-Potassioarene)tricarbonyl-
    chromium complexes
- as intermediates 19, 104s55
Potassium (s.a. Germanium diiodide/
    potassium)
Potassium alkoxides
- tert-butoxide 55, 28, 154, 427, 499
- bromide 55, 29
- compds., organo-
- special s.
  benzylpotassium compds.
  (potassioarene)tricarbonylchromium
    complexes
- ene(trifluoro)borates
- startg. m. f.
  styrenes 55, 458
- enolates
- as intermediates 31, 890s55
- fluoride 55, 7, 189

- iodide 55, 179
- osmate 55, 130
- peroxymonosulfate/alumina 55, 146
o-(Prolylamino)ketones, chiral
- as reagent 55, 499
Propargyl cations
-, review 43, 715s55
Protection
- of amino groups as
  tert-butylsulfonamides 55, 15
  cyclohexanecarboxamides 2, 430s55
- of – –, prim. as
  phthalimides 55, 143
- of carbonyl groups as
  1,3-dioxolanes, 4-sulfonylmethyl- 55, 4
- of carboxyl groups with
  trichloroacetimidates 37, 152s55
- of hydroxyl groups as
  N-phenylcarbamates 55, 8
  1,1,3,3-tetraisopropyl-3-[2-(triphenyl-
    methoxy)ethoxy]disiloxan-1-yl
    ethers 55, 2
- of – – with
  trichloroacetimidates 37, 152s55
- of – – (alcohols) as
  tetrahydropyran-2-yl ethers 55, 69
- of – – (–, prim.) as
  9-phenyl-9-xanthyl ethers 55, 3
- of sulfate monoesters by
  2,2,2-trifluoroethylation 36, 493s55
Protective groups
-, review (annual) 46, 3s55
O-Protective groups, fluorous
-, cleavage of allyl ethers via – 55, 5
N-Protective groups, removal (s.a.
    HN↕S, HN↕C)
- of
  tert-butylsulfonyl 55, 15
  dimethylaminosulfonyl 51, 13s55
O-Protective groups, removal (s.a.
    HO↕S, HO↕Rem, HO↕C)
- of
  N-phenylcarbamyl 55, 8
  9-phenyl-9-xanthyl (photochemical
    removal) 55, 3
  tetrahydropyran-2-yl 55, 69
  1,1,3,3-tetraisopropyl-3-[2-(triphenyl-
    methoxy)ethoxy]disiloxan-1-yl 55, 2
S-Protective groups, removal
- of 9H-xanthen-9-yl 16, 172s55
Protonation, asym.
- of
  α-(alkylideneamino)carboxylic acid
    ester enolates 55, 499
  amide enolates 39, 993s55
Proton donors, polymeric 39, 993s55
Pyran-3-acetic acid esters, tetrahydro-,
    2-carbalkoxy- 49, 981s55
2H-Pyran-6-phosphonic acid esters, 3,4-
    dihydro-, 2-alkoxy-
- from
  enolethers, asym. cycloaddition 55, 266
2H-Pyrans, 3,4-dihydro-
- special s.
  2-spiro-2H-pyrans, 3,4-dihydro-
2H-Pyrans, 3,4-dihydro-, 2-alkoxy-
- from
  enolethers 55, 288
  α,β-ethylenealdehydes 55, 288
-, –, chiral 49, 985s55
-, 3,6-dihydro- 26, 827s55
-, –, 3-alkylidene- 55, 409

-, –, 4-siloxy-
- from
  aldehydes 55, 274
  2-siloxy-1,3-dienes 55, 274
Pyrans, tetrahydro-, 2-alkynyl- 45,
    449s55
-, –, trans-3-silyl-, 2-subst. 55, 76
2H-Pyran-2-ylcarboxylic acid esters,
    3,6-dihydro-
- by Claisen rearrangement-ring closing
    metathesis 55, 498
Pyran-2-yl ethers, tetrahydro- (s.a.
    under Protection)
- special s.
  allyl tetrahydropyran-2-yl ethers
    (tetrahydropyran-2-yloxy...
- startg. m. f.
  acoxy compds. 55, 110
Pyrazines
-, chemistry, review 37, 349s55
Pyrazines, 5,6-dihydro-
-, C-alkylation of α-diketones via – 55,
    377
Pyrazoles
- from
  aldehydes 55, 425
  β-(tosylhydrazono)phosphonic acid
    esters 55, 425
-, synthesis, review 41, 336s55
Pyrazoles, 5-amino-
-, synthesis, polymer-based 19, 461s55
Pyrazolidines
- from
  pyrazolium salts 55, 32
Pyrazolidinium ylids
-, review 43, 270s55
Δ²-Pyrazolines, 3,4-dimethylene-
- as intermediates 35, 393s55
Pyrazolium salts
- startg. m. f.
  pyrazolidines 55, 32
Pyrazolo[5,1-a]isoquinolines, 1,2,3,10b-
    tetrahydro- 22, 708s55
Pyridazine-3-carboxylic acids,
    hexahydro- s. Piperazic acids
Pyridazines
- from
  pyridazines, 1,4-dihydro- 55, 467
Pyridazines, 1,4-dihydro-
- from
  N-carbamylenazo compds. 55, 467
  β-diketones 55, 467
- startg. m. f.
  pyridazines 55, 467
-, 2,3,4,5-tetrahydro-
- from
  furans, tetrahydro-, 2,5-dialkoxy- 8,
    444s55
3(2H)-Pyridazones, 4,5-dihydro-
- from
  Meldrum's acid 40, 220s55
Pyrid[1,2-a]indoles, 1,2,3,4-tetrahydro-
    51, 422s55
Pyridine
- as reagent 55, 139
Pyridine-3,5-dicarboxylic acid esters 55,
    172
Pyridine N-oxide
- as reagent 55, 432
Pyridine N-oxide, 4-phenyl-
- as reagent 55, 500
Pyridine N-oxides

– from
  pyridines **55**, 50
**Pyridine ring**
– from
  η¹-(1,3-diene)tungsten complexes **55**, 431
  nitriles **55**, 431
  oxazolidines, 2-β-keto- **33**, 758s55
**Pyridines**
– from
  pyridines, 1,4-dihydro- **55**, 172
–, library **47**, 727s55
–, 2-α-metalation **28**, 732s55
– startg. m. f.
  pyridine N-oxides **55**, 50
**Pyridines, 2-amino-**
– from
  α,β-ethylenenitriles **55**, 326
  ketones **55**, 326
– special s.
  2-amino-4-picoline
–, 4-amino-
– special s.
  4-dimethylaminopyridine
–, 1,4-dihydro-
–, library **47**, 727s55
– startg. m. f.
  pyridines **55**, 172
–, synthesis, asym., enzymatic, review **28**, 13s55
–, 1,4-dihydro-, 4-silyl- **55**, 294
–, 4-stannyl- **26**, 833s55
–, 1,2,3,6-tetrahydro-, 3-alkylidene- **55**, 409
**2-Pyridinethiones, 6-amino-**
–, synthesis **27**, 680s55
**Pyridinium chlorochromate**
– as reagent **55**, 118
**Pyridinium salts**
– special s.
  N-halogenopyridinium salts
– startg. m. f.
  6-azabicyclo[3.1.0]hex-3-en-2-ols **55**, 62
– –, N-acyl-
–, O-acylation with – **38**, 158s55
**2-Pyridone ring**
– from
  1,3-oxazin-4(3H)-one ring **23**, 921s55
**3(2H)-Pyridone ring, 1,6-dihydro-, chiral 41**, 947s55
**2-Pyridones, 5,6-dihydro- 31**, 973s55
**2-Pyridones, hydro-** (s.a. δ-Enaminolactams)
**4(1H)-Pyridones, 2,3-dihydro-**
– from
  1-alkoxy-3-siloxy-1,3-dienes, asym. conversion **55**, 443
**Pyrimidine-4-carboxylic acids, 2-alkylthio-**
–, synthesis, polymer-based **27**, 769s55
**Pyrimidines**
–, synthesis, polymer-based **55**, 327
**4(3H)-Pyrimidinone ring, 2-carbalkoxyamino- 39**, 381s55
**2(1H)-Pyrimidinones, 3,4-dihydro-**
–, Biginelli synthesis, catalytic **55**, 337
–, –, 4-aryl-, 5-carbalkoxy- **55**, 337
**4(3H)-Pyrimidinones, N-condensed**
– by retrodiene scission **17**, 198s55
**2-Pyrones, 4-alkoxy-, 3(5)-aryl- 37**, 902s55

**2-Pyrones, tetrahydro-** s. δ-Lactones
**4-Pyrones, 2,3-dihydro-**
– from
  aldehydes, via asym. cycloaddition **55**, 449
  ketones **55**, 399
–, 2,3-dihydro-, 6-amino-
– from
  aldehydes **55**, 399
  ketones **55**, 399
–, 2-perfluoroalkyl- **36**, 819s55
**Pyrrole-3-carboxylic acid esters, 1-sulfonyl- 55**, 429
**2H-Pyrrolenines 45**, 43s55
**Pyrroles**
– from
  enephosphonium salts **19**, 911s55
  nitrogen, atmospheric **55**, 141
–, 2-metalation **42**, 597s55
–, 2-(pyridyl)-1-vinyl- **55**, 328
–, 3-sulfonyl- **32**, 845s55
–, 1-vinyl-
– from
  (E)-oximes **55**, 328
**Pyrrolidine-2-carboxylic acid esters, 4-nitro- 43**, 611s55
**Pyrrolidine-3-carboxylic – –, 1-alkoxy-**
– from
  alkoximes **55**, 257
  cyclopropanone ketals, 2-alkylidene- **55**, 257
**Pyrrolidine-2-carboxylic acids, 1-carbalkoxy-**
– startg. m. f.
  Δ²-pyrrolines, 1-carbalkoxy-, 3-trifluoroacetyl- **55**, 465
**Pyrrolidine ring**
– special s.
  fulleropyrrolidines
**Pyrrolidines, 3-α-arylseleno-4-α-tosyl-49**, 669s55
–, 2-imino-
– from
  aziridines, retention of configuration **55**, 255
  ketenimines, – – – **55**, 255
–, 3-nitro-
– from
  1,1-nitroethylene derivs. **55**, 466
  oxazolidines **55**, 466
–, 3-vinyl- **51**, 491s55
**2-Pyrrolidones, 3-(1-aminoene)-4,5-diimino- 55**, 404
–, 5-carbamyl- **52**, 351s55
–, 3-methylene-
– from
  N-silylimines, synthesis, asym. **55**, 423
–, tricyclic
–, α-alkylation, asym. **37**, 657s55
–, 4-vinyl- **44**, 938s55
**3-Pyrrolidones 51**, 491s55
**Δ²-Pyrrolines, 1-carbalkoxy-, 3-trifluoroacetyl-**
– from
  pyrrolidine-2-carboxylic acids, 1-carbalkoxy- **55**, 465
**Δ³-Pyrrolines, 3-α-,4-α-disubst. 55**, 222
**Pyrrolizidines, 1-nitro- 55**, 466
**Pyrrolizines, 3-alkylidene- 55**, 426
**1H-Pyrrolo[1,2-a]benzimidazoles, 1-(aminoalkylidene)-2,3-diimino- 55**, 404

**Δ³-2-Pyrrolones, 5-(1-carbalkoxyene)-, 3-amino- 55**, 404
–, 4-hydroxy-
–, synthesis, polymer-based **54**, 481s55
–, 5-subst.
– from
  Δ³-2-pyrrolones, 5-isopropoxy-, synthesis, asym., review **27**, 947s55
**Pyrrolo[3,2-b]pyrrole-2,5-diones 55**, 404
**Pyrrolo[1,2-a]quinoxalines, 4-α-hydroxy- 25**, 662s55

**Quadricyclanes**
–, review **22**, 761s55
**Quaternary C-atoms** s. Hydrocarbon groups, quaternary
**2(1H)-Quinazolones, 3,4-dihydro-, 4-carbalkoxymethyl- 44**, 362s55
**4(3H)-Quinazolones, 3-(acetoxyamino)-**
–, aziridination with –, review **23**, 381s55
**Quinidine p-chlorobenzoate, dihydro-**
– as reagent **55**, 169
**Quinoline N-oxides**
– special s.
  2,2′-biquinoline N,N′-dioxide...
**Quinolines**
– from
  quinolines, 3,4-dihydro- **10**, 639s55
–, 1,2-dihydro-, 1-tosyl- **55**, 405
–, 3-ferrocenyl- **39**, 887s55
–, hydro-
–, chemistry, review **54**, 349s55
–, 1,2,3,4-tetrahydro-
–, 3-component synthesis, polymer-based **55**, 342
–, –, 8-hydroxy- **50**, 254s55
**Quinolinium salts**
– from
  acetylene derivs. **53**, 386s55
**4(1H)-Quinolones, 2-aryl-**
– by dehydrogenation **29**, 52s55
**p-Quinone methids, 6-acyl-**
– from
  acetylene derivs. **55**, 259
  p-quinones **55**, 259
**p-Quinone monoketals**
–, 1,4-addition to – **39**, 578s55
–, [5+2]-cycloaddition, cationic, intramolecular, stereospecific with – **55**, 494
**p-Quinones**
– special s.
  2-(p-tolylsulfinyl)-5-tert-butyl-1,4-benzoquinone
– startg. m. f.
  p-quinone methids, 6-acyl- **55**, 259
–, benzo-fused, polycyclic, angular **55**, 492

Racemization, catalyzed
- of alcohols, sec. 53, 500s55
Radical addition, polarity reversed
- to ethylene derivs., electron-rich 55, 277
Radical 1,4-addition 55, 278
- -, asym. 55, 277
- -, Cr(II)-mediated
- to ethylene derivs., electron-deficient, terminal 55, 287
- with
  α-borylalkyl radicals 55, 287
  iodides, ar. 55, 287
- -, electron transfer-catalyzed, photo-induced 55, 442
- -, heterogeneous, nickel boride-mediated 48, 675s55
- o-alkylation
- of cyclimmonium salts 55, 278
- Claisen rearrangement 55, 309
- cross-coupling
- with β,γ-ethylenesulfones 41, 829s55
- -, asym., Lewis acid-catalyzed
- with α-halogenolactones 55, 436
- -, oxidative
- with enoxysilanes 55, 488
- Michael-type addition
- with 2-ethylenestannanes 32, 887s55
- reactions
- with
  1,1,2,2-tetraphenyldisilane 55, 278
  tin hydrides, organo-, polymer-based, in situ-generated 55, 45
- -, Lewis acid-catalyzed
- -, review 51, 435s55
- reagents, tin-free
- in synthesis, review 51, 38s55
Radical ring closure
- -, alkaloids via -, review 29, 970s55
- of ethyleneselenides 47, 983s55
- via vinyl radicals 50, 577s55
- with subsequent generation of samarium(III) compds., polymer-supported 55, 396
- - -, cobalt-mediated
- of halogenothioethers, ar. 55, 487
- - -, deoxygenative
- -, ethylene derivs., cyclic by - 55, 485
- - -, polymer-based
- via aryl radicals 55, 396
- - -, serial, regiostereospecific
- -, bicyclo[n.m.0]alkane-1,3-diols via - 55, 275
- - -, sulfur-mediated
- via fluoroalkyl radicals, review 41, 463s55
Radicals
- special s.
  alkoxyl radicals
  aryl -
  benzyl -
  α-borylalkyl -
  diradicals
  fluoroalkyl radicals
  oxymethyl -
- -, phosphorus-subst.
- -, reactions with alkenes, review 48, 356s55
Radical Wittig rearrangement
- via 1,5-hydrogen transfer 55, 484
Reduction, cathodic, enzyme-catalyzed 42, 22s55

-, photochemical, zeolite-supported
- of Δ⁴-3-ketosteroids 55, 33
Reformatskii reaction, stereospecific, germanium-mediated 55, 247
Replacement
- of chlorine by fluorine in a perfluorocarbon medium 55, 189
Resolution (s.a. Res section and under Stereoisomers in Vol. 1-50)
- of alcohols, tert. 44, 214s55
-, separation of enantiomers via selector/selectand hydrogen bonding, review 5, 666s55
- via host-guest complexation, update 5, 666s55
Resolution, kinetic
- of
  acylals 55, 6
  2-acylaminoalcohols 52, 497s55
  alcohols, sec. by asym. O-acetylation 55, 84
  allenes by asym. epoxidation 55, 500
  amines via asym. N-acetylation 55, 149
  α-hydroxycarboxylic acids 49, 995s55
- -, dynamic (s.a. Deracemization)
- -, α-acylaminocarboxylic acid esters from Δ²-5-oxazolones with - 55, 57
- -, Noyori reduction of ketones with - 55, 26
- of α-aminocarboxylic acid derivs., cyclic 45, 210s55
- -, phosphines, tert. from phosphines, sec. with - 55, 220
Retro-Dieckmann reaction 55, 381
Retro-Diels-Alder reaction
-, (Z)-4-amino-2-ethylenealcohols by - 55, 493
-, review of dienophiles with one or more heteroatoms 17, 198s55
Reverse micelles
-, S-oxidation in - 55, 52
Rhenates s. Bis(tetraethylammonium) tribromotricarbonylrhenate
Rhenic acids (s.a. Perrhenic acid)
Rhenium carbonyl complexes
- special s.
  tricarbonyl(acoxy-η⁵-cyclopenta-dienyl)rhenium complexes
- complexes
  chlorotetrakis(dimethylphenyl-phosphine)(dinitrogen)rhenium(I) 55, 403
- oxides, organo-
  methylrhenium oxide 55, 59
Rhodium/carbon 55, 152
Rhodium(II) acetate 55, 483
Rhodium bis(phospholane) complexes, chiral 55, 38
Rhodium complexes
  acetoacetonatobis(ethylene)rhodium(I) 55, 452
  acetoacetonato(dicarbonyl)rhodium(I) 55, 250
  1,2-bis[alkyl(methyl)phosphino]ethane-(norbornadiene)rhodium(I) fluoroborate, chiral 55, 36
  carbonylhydridotris(triphenyl-phosphine)rhodium(I) 55, 42
  chloro(1,5-cyclooctadiene)rhodium(I) dimer 55, 29
  chlorotris(triphenylphosphine)-rhodium(I) 55, 24, 318, 357

  cyclooctadiene[(S)-2,2'-bis(diphenyl-phosphino)-1,1'-binaphthyl]-rhodium(I) perchlorate 55, 37
  (1,5-cyclooctadiene)rhodium(I) tetraphenylborate 55, 294
  dicarbonyl(chloro)rhodium(I) dimer 55, 296
  hexadecacarbonyl hexarhodium 55, 293
  tris(triphenylphosphine)rhodium(I) fluoroborate 55, 317
- phosphine complexes, chiral 55, 29
- (I) phosphine-phosphite complexes, chiral, polymer-based
- as reagent 55, 295
Rhodium trichloride 55, 323
Ring closing metathesis (s.a. Interchange, intramolecular in Vol.1-50)
- of diynes 55, 497
-, update 49, 985s55
- - -, combinatorial 49, 985s55
- - metathesis-intramolecular arylation 49, 985s55
Ring closure
- special s.
  cyclo...
  radical ring closure
- - -, triple
-, 2,8-dioxa-1-azabicyclo[3.3.0]octanes, peri-fused by - 55, 398
Ring expansion
- of squaric acid derivs., review 49, 230s55
- -, double, regiospecific
- of (cyclopropylalkylidene)-cyclopropane ring 55, 316
Ring opening metathesis
-, review 53, 321s55
Ritter reaction, heterogeneous 3, 275s55
Ruthenate, per- s. Tetrapropylammonium perruthenate
Ruthenium/cerium dioxide 55, 113
Ruthenium(III) acetoacetonate 55, 43
- carbene complexes 55, 498
- complexes
  dichloro(p-cymene)(triphenyl-phosphine)ruthenium(II) 55, 71
  dichlorotris(triphenylphosphine)-ruthenium(II) 55, 27, 85, 120, 133
  dodecacarbonyltriruthenium 55, 71, 292
- -, chiral
  trans-(diamine)dichloro[di-(phosphine)]ruthenium(II) complexes, chiral 55, 28
  dibromo[(S)-2,2'-bis(diphenyl-phosphino)-1,1'-binaphthyl]-ruthenium(II) 55, 37
  dichloro(1,5-cyclooctadiene)-ruthenium(II)/2,2'-di(phosphino)-biphenyls, chiral 55, 26
- phosphine complex, water-soluble 23, 51s55
- trichloride 55, 172, 205, 355

**Sakurai-Hosomi reaction** (s.a. Diels-Alder-Sakurai-Hosomi reaction)
**Samarium 55,** 212, 254, 284, 339
**Samarium(III) compds., organo-**
– special s.
  alkylsamarium(III) compds.
–, synthesis, polymer-based via aryl radical ring closure **55,** 396
– **diiodide 55,** 192, 229, 339, 343, 395, 396, 397, 478
– –/hexamethylphosphoramide **55,** 60, 275, 308, 484
– **trichloride 55,** 246
**Scandium(III) triflate 55,** 138, 215, 340, 341, 439
– –, **polymer-microencapsulated 55,** 440
**Selenenic acid derivs.**
– special s.
  benzeneselenenyl compds.
**Selenides** (s.a. Organoseleno...)
– from
  halides **55,** 229
  selenoxides **43,** 995s55
  silyl selenides **55,** 229
–, review (annual) **53,** 16s55
– special s.
  aminoselen...
  eneselenides
  ethyleneselenides
  hydroxyselenides
  silyl selenides
**Selenides, ar.** (s.a. Arylseleno...)
– from
  halides **55,** 229
**Selenium compds., organo-, chiral**
–, review **49,** 515s55
– –, –, **chiral, 3-coordinate**
–, review **42,** 997s55
**Selenoamides** s. Carboxylic acid selenoamides
**Selenochromones 55,** 223
**Selenolates**
– special s.
  zinc selenolates, halogeno-
**Selenolic acid aryl esters**
– startg. m. f.
  (Z)-β-arylseleno-α,β-ethyleneketones **55,** 267
**Selenolic acid esters**
– from
  lithium compds., organo-, with 1 extra C-atom **55,** 382
– special s.
  ethyleneselenolic acid esters
**Selenols**
–, review (annual) **53,** 16s55
**Selenones [RSe(O₂)R′]**
–, review (annual) **53,** 16s55
**Selenophthalides, (Z)-3-(alkylidene)- 55,** 223
**Selenothiocarboxylic acid esters**
–, synthesis, review **47,** 552s55
**Selenoxides**
–, review (annual) **53,** 16s55
**Sensitizers**
– special s.
  benzophenone
**Separation techniques**
–, review **53,** 57s55
**Sharpless epoxidation**
– with a soluble poly(tartrate) **55,** 64
– –, **heterogeneous 55,** 64

**Silaboration, catalytic 55,** 251
**Silacycloalkanes, 5- and 6-membered**
– –, modification and applications, review (annual) **46,** 766s55
**Silacyclohexanes, 4-hydroxy-2-methylene- 36,** 682s55
**Silanes** (s.a. Hydrosilylation)
– from
  mercaptals **55,** 228
  silicon hydrides, organo- **55,** 228
– special s.
  alkoxysilanes
  aminosilanes
  arylsilanes
  (cyclopentylmethyl)silanes
  ethylenesilanes
  halogenosilanes
  sulfonylaminosilanes
**Silanethiols**
– special s.
  triisopropylsilanethiol
  triphenylsilanethiol
**Silica** (s.a. Tantalum pentachloride/silica) **55,** 98
**Silicates, organo-**
– special s.
  tetrabutylammonium triphenyldifluorosilicate
**Silicon hydrides, organo-**
– special s.
  chlorodimethylsilane
  diphenylsilane
  enoxy(hydrido)silanes (hydridosilyl)...
  phenylsilane
  polymethylhydrosiloxane
  1,1,2,2-tetraphenyldisilane
  triphenylsilane
– startg. m. f.
  arylsilanes **55,** 227
  silanes **55,** 228
– –, **organo-, polymer-based**
– as reagent **55,** 24
**Siloximes**
– startg. m. f.
  amines, prim. **55,** 12
**β-Siloxyaldehydes**
– from
  aldehydes, synthesis, asym. with 2 extra C-atoms **55,** 233
**3-Siloxy-2-aza-1,3-dienes**
– startg. m. f.
  4H-1,3-oxazin-4-ones, tetrahydro-, parallel synthesis **55,** 437
**α-Siloxycarboxylic acid esters**
– special s.
  amino-α-siloxycarboxylic acid esters
**2-Siloxy-1,3-dienes**
– special s.
  1-alkoxy-3-siloxy-1,3-dienes
– startg. m. f.
  2H-pyrans, 3,6-dihydro-, 4-siloxy- **55,** 274
**3-Siloxy-1,6-dienes**
– –, ene reaction, intramolecular, stereospecific **36,** 682s55
**5-Siloxyenesilanes 34,** 607s55
**1-Siloxy-1,ω-enynes**
– startg. m. f.
  α,β-ethyleneketones, cyclic **55,** 489
**5-Siloxy-2,3-epoxyalcohols 20,** 112s55
**γ′-Siloxy-γ,δ-ethyleneboronic acid**

esters
– from
  aldehydes, synthesis **55,** 251
  1,3-dienes, – **55,** 251
**Siloxy-3-ethylenes**
– from
  1,3-dienes, synthesis, regiostereospecific **55,** 290
**2-Siloxyhalides**
– from
  epoxides, desymmetrization **55,** 176
**3-Siloxyhalides**
– special s.
  carbalkoxyamino-3-siloxyhalides
**α-Siloxyketones, chiral**
– special s.
  methyl α-siloxyketones, camphorderived
**β-Siloxyketones**
– from
  aldehydes, synthesis, asym. **55,** 233
**Siloxylamines** (s.a. N,N-Disiloxyenamines)
**2-Siloxymercaptans**
– from
  epoxides **55,** 193
**α-Siloxynitriles**
– as intermediates **55,** 236
– from
  aldehydes, conversion, asym. **55,** 246
**β-Siloxy-α-(silyl)thiolactams**
– special s.
  ethylene-β-siloxy-α-(silyl)thiolactams
**5-Siloxy-1,3,6-trienes 17,** 968s55
**N-(2-Siloxy)urethans**
– special s.
  2-carbalkoxyamino-3-siloxyhalides
**Silver(I), supported** s. Zeolite, silver(I)-exchanged
**Silver acetate 55,** 93
– **benzoate 55,** 150
– **carbonate 55,** 408, 410
– **trifluoromethanesulfonate 55,** 91, 230, 318
**Silylacetylenes**
– from
  acylsilanes **29,** 920s55
**O-Silyl O-alkyl keteneacetals**
– startg. m. f.
  γ,δ-ethylenecarboxylic acid esters, synthesis, asym. **55,** 460
**Silylation** (s.a. 1,2-Allylsilylation)
**O-Silylation, preferential 55,** 81
**β-Silylazomethines**
– special s.
  ethylene-β-silylazomethines
**B-Silylboronic acid esters**
– as reactant **55,** 251
**N-Silylcarbodiimides 55,** 167
**N-Silylcarboxylic acid amides**
– startg. m. f.
  N-acylcarboxylic acid amides **55,** 165
**α-Silylcarboxylic acid esters**
– special s.
  α-(hydridosilyl)carboxylic acid esters
**1-Silyl-1,3-dienes, cyclic**
– special s.
  3-vinylcycloalkenes, 1-silyl-
**2-α-Silyl-1,3-dienes**
–, Diels-Alder reaction with – **22,** 721s55
**1-Silyl-1,4-dienes, cyclic**
– special s.
  3-vinylcycloalkenes, 1-silyl-

# Sil – Sul

**2-Silylenestannanes**
–, destannylation **47**, 77s55
**Silyl enol ethers** s. Enoxysilanes
**Silyl esters**
– special s.
  nitronic acid silyl esters
**Silyl ethers** (s.a. Alkoxysilanes, Aryloxysilanes, Siloxy..., O-Silylation)
– special s.
  *tert*-butyldimethylsilyl ethers
**Silylformylation, regiostereospecific**
–, (Z)-α,β-ethylene-β-silylaldimines by – **55**, 294
**1,2-Silyl group migration 55**, 76
**S→O-Silyl group migration 55**, 193
**N-Silylimines**
– startg. m. f.
  2-pyrrolidones, 3-methylene-, synthesis, asym. **55**, 423
**Silylketenes**
–, review (annual) **52**, 435s55
– special s.
  trimethylsilylketene
**Silyllithium compds., organo-**
– special s.
  dimethylphenylsilyllithium
**Silylpalladation**
–, ring closures of 1,6-dienes via – **55**, 299
**Silyl peroxides**
– special s.
  bis(trimethylsilyl)peroxide
**Silyl selenides**
– startg. m. f.
  selenides **55**, 229
**Silylthioketenes**
– special s.
  bis(trimethylsilyl)thioketene
**α-(Silyl)thiolactams**
– special s.
  siloxy-α-(silyl)thiolactams
**Silylzincates, organo-**
– special s.
  lithium dimethyl(silyl)zincates
**Smiles rearrangement**
– of N-acylsulfonic acid amides **55**, 144
**Sodium acetate 55**, 414
**Sodium alkoxides**
  – *tert*-butoxide **55**, 160, 161, 162, 411
**Sodium amides**
  – bis(trimethylsilyl)amide **55**, 165, 404
**Sodium bromide 55**, 476
– –/sodium perborate **55**, 178
– **compds. organo-**
– special s.
  benzylsodium compds.
– **formate 55**, 486
– **hydridotriacetoxoborate 55**, 35
– **hydrogen selenide 55**, 223
– – **telluride 55**, 223
– **hypochlorite 55**, 70, 78, 490
– **iodide** (s.a. Phenyl iodosoacetate/sodium iodide) **55**, 188, 352
– **mercaptides**
  – methylmercaptide **55**, 20
– **nitrate 55**, 179
– **perborate** s. Sodium bromide/sodium perborate
– **peroxide 55**, 94
– **tetrahydridoborate 55**, 41, 45, 154, 236
– –/carboxylic acids

– as reductant, review **46**, 317s55
– –/dialkyl sulfates **25**, 15s55
– –/lithium chloride **55**, 18
**Solid acids**
– special s.
  sulfonic acids, mesoporous silica-supported
**Solid bases** s. Bases, solid
**Solid-phase synthesis** s. Polymer-based...
**Solution-phase synthesis, parallel**
–, cycloaddition, 1,3-dipolar by – **16**, 888s55
– of
  amines, tert. from amines, sec. **21**, 499s55
  imidazo[1,2-*a*]pyr-azines and -idines, 3-amino- **55**, 340
  4*H*-1,3-oxazin-4-ones, tetrahydro- **55**, 437
– –, –, **automated**
– of 4*H*-3,1-benzoxazin-4-ones, 2-amino- **21**, 378s55
**Sommelet rearrangement** (s.a. Thia-Sommelet rearrangement)
**Sonogashira coupling**
–, update **27**, 851s55
– –, polymer-based **55**, 416
**(–)-Sparteine**
– as reagent **55**, 220
**Spirocyclopent-2-enones 1**, 554s55
**γ-Spiro-γ-lactones 31**, 105s55
– special s.
  1-oxaspiro[5.4]decan-7-ol-2-ones
**2-Spiro-2*H*-pyrans, 3,4-dihydro-, chiral 20**, 294s55
**Spiro[pyrrolidine-2,3′-oxindoles]**
–, library **44**, 897s55
**Squaric acid derivs.**
–, ring expansion to carbo- and heterocyclics, polyfunctionalized, review **49**, 230s55
**Stannanes** (s.a. Hydrostannylation and Stille...)
– special s.
  acetylenestannanes
  arylstannanes
  cyanostannanes
  enestannanes
  ethylenestannanes
  halogenostannanes
  hydroxystannanes
**Stannonic acids**
– special s.
  *n*-butylstannonic acid
**1-Stannylacetals, cyclic**
– startg. m. f.
  1,1-hydroxystannanes, O-protected, synthesis, asym. **55**, 235
**β-Stannylcarboxylic acids**
– special s.
  ethylene-β-stannylcarboxylic acids
**1-Stannyl-1,3-enynes**
– from
  acetylene derivs., synthesis **55**, 300
  acetylenestannanes, – **55**, 300
**Statine analogs 55**, 37
**Stille coupling**
– in carbon dioxide, supercritical **55**, 417
–, updates **34**, 862s55, **39**, 887s55
– –, polymer-based, copper(I)-catalyzed **52**, 439s55
**Stille-type coupling**

–, hydroxamic acid esters, unsatd. via – **55**, 462
– –, **carbonylative 53**, 445s55
**Steroids**
– special s.
  isoxazol..., steroidal
  ketosteroids
–, synthesis, partial and reactions, review **32**, 711s55
**Strecker synthesis, asym. 55**, 253
**(η²-Styrene)osmium complexes**
–, Diels-Alder reaction, regiostereo-specific with – **55**, 285
**Styrenes**
– from
  diazonium fluoroborates **55**, 458
  ethylene derivs. (s.a. Heck arylation)
  potassium ene(trifluoro)borates **55**, 458
– special s.
  *o*-aminostyrenes
**(E)-Styrenes**
– from
  acetylene derivs., terminal **55**, 280
  aryllead triacetates **55**, 456
  diaryliodonium salts **55**, 280
  α,β-ethyleneboronic acids **55**, 456
  –, oxyamination, asym. **55**, 130
  –, Wittig synthesis **26**, 686s55
**Substitution, ar.**
– with heteronucleophiles, review (annual) **51**, 171s55
**Succinic acid esters**
– special s.
  amino(arylseleno)succinic acid esters
**Succinic acid monoesters**
– special s.
  allylsuccinic acid monoesters
**Succinimides**
–, ring opening, review **7**, 541s55
– special s.
  N-acylsuccinimides
**Sugars** s. Carbohydrates
**Sulfenamides**
– special s.
  N-sulfonylsulfenamides
**Sulfenic acid esters**
– from
  alcohols **55**, 54
  mercaptans **55**, 54
**Sulfenylhalides**
– from
  mercaptans **55**, 54
**Sulfido compds.** s. Thiiranes from Vol.51
**Sulfilimines**
– special s.
  carbalkoxysulfilimines
  sulfonylsulfilimines
**Sulfines**
– special s.
  iminosulfines
**Sulfinic acid esters** (s.a. Sulfinyloxy...)
**2-Sulfinyl-1,3-dienes, chiral 39**, 887s55
**Sulfinyloxy-2-acetylenes, terminal**
– startg. m. f.
  α-allenesulfones, asym. induction **55**, 201
**Sulfones**
– from
  halides **55**, 210
  sulfonic acid halides **55**, 210
–, review (annual) **53**, 16s55
– special s.

allenesulfones
aryl benzyl sulfones
arylsulfones
ethylenesulfones
halogenosulfones
**Sulfonic acid amides**
 (s.a. N-Desulfonylation, N-Sulfonyl...,
 Sulfonylamin...)
–, α-alkylation, asym. **55**, 372
– from
 sulfonic acids (with amines) **55**, 122
– special s.
 N-acylsulfonic acid amides
 arenesulfonic – –
 2-(carbalkoxyoxy)sulfonic – –
 ethylenesulfonic – –
 halogenosulfonic – –
 hydroxysulfonic – –
**Sulfonic acid esters** (s.a.
 O-Desulfonylation, Sulfonyloxy...)
– special s.
 acoxysulfonates
 glycidyl sulfonates
– startg. m. f.
 nitriles, with 2 extra C-atoms **55**, 330
**Sulfonic acid halides**
– as intermediates **55**, 122
– special s.
 *p*-toluenesulfonyl chloride
 trifluoromethanesulfonyl –
– startg. m. f.
 sulfones **55**, 210
**Sulfonic acids**
– startg. m. f.
 sulfonic acid amides (with amines) **55**, 122
– –, silica-supported
– as reagent **55**, 351
**Sulfonium salts**
– special s.
 benzylsulfonium salts
 chloromethyl(dimethyl)sulfonium...
 di(sulfonium salts)
– startg. m. f.
 cyclopropanecarboxylic acid esters,
 synthesis, asym. **55**, 421
 epoxides, –, – **55**, 421
**Sulfonylamines** (s.a. Sulfonic acid
 amides)
– from
 N-sulfonylimines, synthesis **49**, 606s55
**α-(Sulfonylamino)alkylidenecarbenes**
–, cyclopropanation, intramolecular
 with – **55**, 370
**α-(Sulfonylamino)carboxylic acid esters**
– special s.
 keto-α-(tosylamino)carboxylic acid
 esters
**β-(Sulfonylamino)carboxylic acids**
– special s.
 ethylene-β′-(sulfonylamino)carboxylic
 acids
 α-methylene-β-(sulfonylamino)-
 carboxylic acids
**5-Sulfonylamino-1,3-dienes**
– startg. m. f.
 2-azabicyclo[3.3.0]octa-4,6-dienes, 2-
 sulfonyl- **55**, 370
**2-(Sulfonylamino)silanes**
– from
 aziridines, N-sulfonyl- **55**, 14
**Sulfonyl-1,3-dienes**

– in synthesis, review **41**, 622s55
**Sulfonylhydrazones**
– special s.
 tosylhydrazon...
**N-Sulfonylimines**
– special s.
 ethyl glyoxylate N-tosylimine
– startg. m. f.
 sulfonylamines, synthesis **49**, 606s55
**Sulfonyliminoiodinanes**
– special s.
 phenyl(tosylimino)iodinane
**β-Sulfonyloxycarboxylic acid esters**
– special s.
 keto-β-nosyloxycarboxylic acid esters
**1-Sulfonyloxy-2,3-epoxides**
– special s.
 glycidyl sulfonates
**α-Sulfonyloxyketones**
– from
 enoxysilanes, asym. conversion **55**, 169
– special s.
 α-keto-β-nosyloxy...
**N-Sulfonylsulfenamides**
– special s.
 N-allyl-N-tosylsulfenamides
**N-Sulfonylsulfilimines**
– from
 thioethers, asym. conversion **55**, 124
– special s.
 tosylsulfilimines
**N-Sulfonylurethans**
– special s.
 N-(carbo-*tert*-butoxy)methane-
 sulfonamides
**Sulfoxides**
– from
 thioethers, in fluorous media **55**, 53
–, in micellar media **55**, 52
–, review (annual) **53**, 16s55
– special s.
 ethylenesulfoxides
– startg. m. f.
 N-carbo-*tert*-butoxysulfoximines **55**, 123
 3-ketothioethers **55**, 363
**Sulfoximines**
– special s.
 carbalkoxysulfoximines
**Sulfoximines, cyclic**
–, syntheses, asym. with – **55**, 368
**Sulfur atom transfer**
– from sultenes **55**, 197
**Sulfur compds., organo-**
–, electrochemistry, review **46**, 572s55
–, synthesis, silicon-mediated, review **42**, 761s55
**Sulfuric acid esters**
– special s.
 dialkyl sulfates
**Sulfuric acid esters, cyclic** s. Diol
 sulfates, cyclic, Glycol –, –
**Sulfurous acid esters, cyclic** s. Diol
 sulfites, cyclic
**Sultams**
– special s.
 N-fluorosultams
**Sultenes**
– as reagent **55**, 197
**Sultones**
– in organic synthesis, review **25**, 594s55
**Superacids**

 carbon tetrabromide/aluminum bromide
 **55**, 322
**Superbases**
 2,5,8,9-tetraaza-1-phospha-
 bicyclo[3.3.3]undecane... **55**, 401
**Supercritical fluids**
–, alkylation, ar. in – **55**, 351
–, amines, ar. from nitro compds., ar. in –
 **55**, 13
–, reviews **53**, 31s55
**Supramolecular chemistry**
–, modular approach, review **51**, 30s55
**Surfactants**
– special s.
 Brij 25
**Suzuki coupling** (s.a. Carbopalladation,
 intramolecular, regiospecific-Suzuki
 coupling)
– with 9-borabicyclo[3.3.1]nonane, B-
 allyl- **55**, 463
– –, double **55**, 366
**Synthesis, asym.** (s.a. Catalysis, asym.,
 Deracemization, Desymmetrization,
 Resolution)
–, non-linear effects, review **47**, 646s55
– with
 Δ$^2$-oxazolines, chiral, review **51**, 24s55
 tartaric acid esters, review **36**, 117s55


**Takai-Utimoto reaction, catalytic**
–, *anti*-glycol monoethers via – **55**, 352
**Tantalum pentachloride/silica 55**, 84
**Tartaric acid esters**
–, synthesis, asym. with –, review **36**, 117s55
**Tartrate, polymer-based, chiral**
– as reagent **55**, 64
**Taxoid side chains**
–, synthesis, combinatorial **28**, 144s55
**Taxoids, 10-subst. 39**, 646s55
**Tellurides**
–, addition, regiostereospecific to
 acetylene derivs. **55**, 490
–, C-alkylation of acetylene derivs.,
 terminal with – **55**, 490
– special s.
 diaryl tellurides
 enetellurides
**Tellurium compds., organo-, 3-**
 **coordinate, chiral**
–, review **42**, 997s55
**Telluroacetals**
– special s.
 ketene telluroacetals
**Tellurochromones 55**, 223
**Tellurophthalides, (Z)-3-(alkylidene)- 55**, 223
**Tetraamines, polymer-based**
– as reagent **38**, 887s55
**2,5,8,9-Tetraaza-1-phospha-**
 **bicyclo[3.3.3]undecane, 2,8,9-**
 **trimethyl-**
– as reagent **55**, 401
**Tetra-*n*-butylammonium chloride**
– as reagent **55**, 185, 405, 409
– **fluoride**
– as reagent **55**, 2, 140, 354

Tetra-*n*-butylammonium hydrogen
   sulfate
– as reagent **55**, 223
– nitrite
– as reagent **55**, 8
– triphenyldifluorosilicate
– as reactant **55**, 455
Tetraethylammonium chloride
– as reagent **55**, 454
– hydrogen carbonate
– as reagent **55**, 155
Tetrahydridoborate, anion exchanger-
   supported **48**, 675s55
Tetrahydrofuran
– as reactant **55**, 192
*o*-(Tetrahydropyran-2-yloxymethyl)-
   carboxylic acid amides
– as intermediates **55**, 154
1,1,3,3-Tetraisopropyl-3-[2-(triphenylmethoxy)ethoxy]disiloxan-1-yl ethers
–, protection of alcohols as – **55**, 2
Tetralins, 2-arylseleno-, chiral **55**, 230
N,N,N′,N′-Tetramethylethylenediamine
– as reagent **55**, 222, 287, 312
Tetramethyl(fluoro)formamidinium
   hexafluorophosphate
– as reagent **31**, 336s55
Tetrapeptides, cyclic, sym.
– from
   dipeptide esters **55**, 148
1,1,2,2-Tetraphenyldisilane
–, radical reactions with – **55**, 278
Tetraphenylphosphonium chloride
– as reagent **55**, 117, 414
Tetra-*n*-propylammonium perruthenate
– as reagent **55**, 93
1*H*-Tetrazole
– as reagent **55**, 126
1*H*-Tetrazoles
–, metalation **42**, 597s95
–, 5-functionalized **21**, 256s55
2*H*-1,3,4-Thiadiazines, 3,6-dihydro-
– from
   α-diketone monohydrazones **37**,
   507s55
Thia-Sommelet rearrangement
–, 5-methylene-1,3-cyclohexadienes, 6-
   α-alkylthio- via – **55**, 314
1,2-Thiazetidine 1,1-dioxides
– startg. m. f.
   (E)-α,β-ethylenesulfonic acid amides
   **55**, 312
–, synthesis, polymer-based **38**, 266s55
1,2-Thiazetidin-3-one 1,1-dioxides
– startg. m. f.
   4-thiazolidone 1,1-dioxides **55**, 310
2*H*-1,4-Thiazine 1-oxides, 3,4-dihydro-,
   4-acoxy- **55**, 194
4*H*-1,4-Thiazin-3(2*H*)-ones, 5,6-dihydro-
– from
   2-oxazolidones **55**, 213
Thiazoles
– startg. m. f.
   aldehydes, review **43**, 877s55
–, 4-amino-, 5-carbalkoxy- **37**, 776s55
4-Thiazolidone 1,1-dioxides
– from
   1,2-thiazetidin-3-one 1,1-dioxides **55**,
   310
–, 3-α-acylamino- **55**, 310
Δ²-Thiazolines, 4,5-dimethylene-
– as intermediates **16**, 870s55

Δ⁴-Thiazoline-2-thiones, 3-acoxy-
– startg. m. f.
   alcohols, prim., oxidative
   decarboxylation **55**, 108
Thiiranes (s. under Sulfido compds. in
   Vol. 1-50)
– from
   enoxysilanes **47**, 981s55
   epoxides, inversion of configuration **55**,
   205
   ethylene derivs. **55**, 197
Thiiranes, 2-vinyl-
– startg. m. f.
   1,2-dithiins, 3,6-dihydro- **55**, 200
Thioacetals s. Mercaptals
Thioamides s. Carboxylic acid thioamides
Thiocarbamic acid esters s.
   Dithiocarbamic acid esters,
   Thionocarbamic – –
C-α-Thiocarbamyl glycosides **23**,
   879s55
Thiocarbonyl compds.
– startg. m. f.
   carbonyl compds., review **25**, 167s55
Thiochromans
– from
   acylhydrazones **55**, 362
   *o*-mercaptocarboxylic acid esters **55**,
   362
Thioenolethers
– from
   thiolic acid esters **51**, 423s55
– special s.
   ene-1,3-di(thioethers)
Thioethers (s.a. Alkylthio...,
   Organothio...)
– from
   disulfides **55**, 207
   halides **55**, 207
   mercaptans **55**, 207
–, review (annual) **53**, 16s55
– special s.
   aminothioethers
   di(thioethers)
   ethylenethioethers
   halogenothioethers
   hydroxythioethers
   ketothioethers
– startg. m. f.
   N-carbo-*tert*-butoxysulfilimines **55**, 123
   N-sulfonylsulfilimines, asym.
   conversion **55**, 124
   sulfoxides, in fluorous media **55**, 53
–, in micellar media **55**, 52
Thioethers, ar. (s.a. Arylthio...)
– from
   halides, ar., polymer-based synthesis
   **55**, 211
   mercaptans, – – **55**, 211
Thioketenes
– special s.
   silylthioketenes
Thiolactams
– special s.
   ketothiolactams
   (silyl)thiolactams
Thiolic acid esters (s.a. S-Deacylation)
– from
   halides, with 1 extra C-atom **55**, 400
– special s.
   ethylenethiolic acid esters
   ketothiolic – –

Thiolic acids
– startg. m. f.
   carboxylic acid amides, N-subst. **55**,
   163
Thionocarbamic acid esters, N,N-
   disubst.
– from
   amines, tert. **55**, 19
– startg. m. f.
   amines, sec. **55**, 19
Thiophene 1-oxides
–, Diels-Alder reaction with – **29**, 591s55
Thiophenes, alkynyl- **27**, 851s55
–, tetrahydro-, 3-hydroxy-
– from
   2,4-dihydroxythioethers **55**, 214
Thiophenol
– as reagent **55**, 7
Thiosulfuric acid S-monoesters
– startg. m. f.
   allyl thioethers **55**, 212
   2-ketothioethers **55**, 212
Thioureas
– as reagent **55**, 208
– startg. m. f.
   ureas **55**, 208
Thiourethans (s.a. Thiocarbamic acid
   esters)
1-Thiouronic acids **16**, 225s55
Tin(II) chloride **55**, 167, 445
–(IV) chloride **55**, 65, 479
–(IV) compds., organo-
– special s.
   distannanes
   stann...
–(IV) halides, organo- (s.a. Dihalogenostannanes, Halogenostannanes)
–(IV) –, –, polymer-based
– as reagent **55**, 45
– hydrides, organo-
–, alternatives, review **51**, 38s55
–, reductions, regio- and stereo-specific
   of halides with –, review **17**, 117s55
– special s.
   tributyltin hydride
– –, –, polymer-based, *in situ*-generated
–, radical reactions with – **55**, 45
– oxides, organo-
– special s.
   dibutyltin oxide
–(II) triflate **55**, 474
Tishchenko reaction **55**, 58
Titanium(IV) alkoxides
– tetraisopropoxide **55**, 64, 162, 239
– –/isopropylmagnesium chloride **55**,
   347
–(IV) –, halogeno-
   chlorotitanium triisopropoxide/
   ethylmagnesium bromide **55**, 269
– complexes
   bis(cyclopentadienyl)phenyl-
   titanium(III) **55**, 482
   (S,S)-ethylene-1,2-bis(η⁵-4,5,6,7-
   tetrahydro-1-indenyl)titanium
   difluoride **55**, 31
   titanocene dichloride/magnesium/
   triethyl phosphite **55**, 228, 473
–(IV) complexes, organo-
– special s.
   allenyltitanium(IV) complexes
–(IV) dialkoxides, bis(sulfonamido)-,
   chiral

– as reagent **44**, 565s55
– **dioxide 55**, 442
– **η²-olefin complexes** (s.a. under Titanium(IV) alkoxide/alkylmagnesium halides)
– as catalyst **55**, 269
– **silicate/hydrogen peroxide 55**, 49, 66
– **tetrachloride 55**, 76, 248, 283, 399
– –**/lithium/trimethylsilyl chloride 55**, 141
– –**/zinc 55**, 198, 284
**TMEDA** s. N,N,N′,N′-Tetramethylethylenediamine
**Tolans**
– from
diaryl ketones, synthesis with rearrangement **55**, 430
*p*-**Toluenesulfonic acid**
– as reactant **55**, 111
– as reagent **55**, 143, 496
*p*-**Toluenesulfonyl chloride**
– as reagent **55**, 55, 214
**2-(*p*-Tolylsulfinyl)-5-*tert*-butyl-1,4-benzoquinone**
– as reagent **55**, 72
**N-Tosylenamines, cyclic 43**, 271s55
**Tosylhydrazones**
–, cleavage, oxidative **55**, 87
– startg. m. f.
mercaptals, cyclic **55**, 202
**β-(Tosylhydrazono)phosphonic acid esters**
– startg. m. f.
pyrazoles **55**, 425
**Tosylsulfilimines**
– from
Grignard compds., synthesis, asym. **55**, 206
**Transacetalation, intramolecular, stereospecific**
–, macrocyclics by – **55**, 116
**Transesterification** (s.a. Epoxidation-transesterification)
–, O-acylation, preferential via – **55**, 110
– of
carbazic acid esters **55**, 103
carboxylic – – **55**, 109
**Transfer-hydrogenation, asym.**
– of
aryl ketones **55**, 27
ketones **51**, 26s55 (update)
–, **catalytic**
– of ethylene derivs., review **34**, 46s55
**Transition metal catalysis**
–, review (annual) **48**, 691s55
– – –, bimetallic
–, review **52**, 317s55
– **metals**
– in synthesis, review (annual) **48**, 691s55
**TRAP ligands**
– special s.
(R,R)-2,2″-bis[(S)-1-(diphenylphosphino)ethyl]-1,1″-biferrocene
**Trialkoxy(aryl)silanes 55**, 227
**Trialkylamines**
– as reagent **55**, 101
**Trialkylboranes** (s.a. Boranes, tert.)
– startg. m. f.
alcohols, synthesis **55**, 231
**Triaminophosphonium salts**
– special s.

(benzotriazol-1-yloxy)tris(dimethylamino)phosphonium...
(benzotriazol-1-yloxy)tris(pyrrolidino)phosphonium...
**1,2,4-Triazine N-oxide ring**
–, review **32**, 311s55
**1,2,3-Triazole-4-carbonyl compds.**
– from
enamines **25**, 250s55
**Triazolidinium ylids**
–, review **43**, 270s55
**Tribromides** s. Perbromides
**Tri-*n*-butyl(ethynyl)stannane**
– as reactant **55**, 388
**Tri-*n*-butylphosphine**
– as reagent **55**, 48, 480
**Tri-*n*-butyltin chloride/triethylsilane**
– as reactant **55**, 216
**Tri-*n*-butyltin cyanide**
– as reagent **55**, 341
**Tri-*n*-butyltin hydride**
–, alternative **45**, 35s55
– as reagent **55**, 1, 35, 309, 485
–, reductions with –, improved work-up **55**, 44
– –, *in situ*-generated
–, hydrostannylation, Lewis acid-catalyzed with – **55**, 216
**Tricarbonyl(acoxy-η⁵-cyclopentadienyl)rhenium complexes**
–, 3-component synthesis **55**, 91
**1,1,1-Tricarboxylic acid esters**
– special s.
ethylenetricarboxylic acid esters
**Trichloroacetimidates**
–, protection of hydroxyl groups with – **37**, 152s55
**Trichloroacetimidoyl glycosides**
– startg. m. f.
4-iodobutyl glycosides **55**, 192
**Trichloromethyl sulfones 55**, 209
**2,5(Z),8-Triene-1,10-diones**
– from
1,3-dienes **55**, 291
α,β-ethylene-β-halogenoketones (2 molecules) **55**, 291
**2,4,6-Trienones 55**, 435
**Triethylamine pentakis(hydrogen fluoride)**
– as reagent **55**, 181
**Triethylborane**
– as reagent **55**, 290, 436
**Triethylenediamine**
– as reagent **55**, 334
**Triethyl orthoacrylate**
– as reactant **55**, 348
**Triethyl phosphite** (s.a. under Titanium complexes)
**Triethylsilane** (s.a. Tri-*n*-butyltin chloride/triethylsilane) **55**, 290
**Trifluoroacetic acid**
– as reagent **55**, 197, 203
α-(**Trifluoroacetylamino)nitriles**
– from
aldimines, synthesis, asym. **55**, 253
**2,2,2-Trifluoroethyl dichlorovanadate**
– as reagent **55**, 488
**Trifluoromethanesulfonic acid**
– as reagent **55**, 15, 350
– – **esters** (s.a. Trifluoxy...)
– special s.
aryl triflates

enol –
methyl trifluoromethanesulfonate
– **anhydride**
– as reagent **55**, 90, 199
**Trifluoromethanesulfonyl chloride**
– as reactant **55**, 209
α-(**Trifluoromethyl)amines 46**, 601s55
**(Z)-1-(Trifluoromethyl)enolethers 37**, 902s55
**Trifluoromethyl ketones**
– from
carboxylic acid esters **55**, 354
**Trifluoromethyltrimethylsilane**
– as reactant **55**, 354
**Triflyloxy-N-heterocyclics**
– as intermediates **55**, 135
**1,1,1-Trihalides**
– special s.
trifluoromethyl...
α,α′,β-**Trihalogenoketones**
– from
ketones **55**, 185
**Trihalogenomethyl sulfones**
– from
alcohols **55**, 209
**Trihalogenosilanes**
– special s.
ethylene(trihalogeno)silanes
**Triisopropylsilanethiol**
– as reactant **55**, 193
**Trimethylamine N-oxide**
– as reagent **55**, 301, 431
**Trimethylenemethane 1,3-diradicals**
– special s.
cyclopropyltrimethylenemethane 1,3-diradicals
**Trimethylenemethane equivalents**
–, [3+2]-cycloaddition with alkoximes **55**, 257
**Trimethylphenylammonium tribromide**
– as reagent **55**, 159
**Trimethyl phosphite**
– as reagent **55**, 209, 357
**Trimethylsilyl azide**
– as reagent **55**, 176
**Trimethylsilyl bromide**
– as reactant **55**, 56
– **chloride** (s.a. under Titanium tetrachloride)
– as reagent **55**, 47, 61, 162, 284, 315, 352
– **cyanide**
– as reagent **55**, 140, 236, 245, 341
N-(**Trimethylsilyl)fluorosulfonimide**
– as reagent **55**, 9
**Trimethylsilyl halide/oxidant**
– in synthesis, review **44**, 410s55
**Trimethylsilylketene**
– as reactant **50**, 397s55
**Trimethylsilyl triflate**
– as reagent **55**, 348, 494
**N-Trimethylsilyltriflimide**
– as reagent **55**, 448
**1,3,5-Trioxanes**
– from
aldehydes, cyclotrimerization, catalytic **55**, 59
**Triphenylcarbonium tetrakis(pentafluorophenyl)borate**
– as reagent **55**, 97
**Triphenylphosphine**
– as reagent **55**, 108, 485

**Triphenylphosphine/bromine**
- as reagent **55**, 122

**–/carbon tetrabromide**
- as reagent **55**, 110

**–/diethyl azodicarboxylate**
- as reagent **55**, 142, 173

**Triphenyl phosphite**
- as reagent **55**, 357

**Triphenylsilane**
- as reagent **55**, 277

**Triphenylsilanethiol**
- as reagent **55**, 277

**Tri(phosphines)**
- special s.
  tris(diphenylphosphinomethyl)ethane

**Trisaccharides**
- special s.
  dideoxytrisaccharides

**1,1,1-Tris(diphenylphosphinomethyl)-ethane**
- as reagent **55**, 43

**Tris(pentafluorophenyl)borane**
- as reagent **55**, 216

**Tris(pyrrolidino)phosphine**
- as reagent **55**, 491

**Tris(trimethylsilyl)silane**
–, alternative **55**, 278

**Tri-o-tolylphosphine**
- as reagent **55**, 227, 481

**O-Tritylation**
- with benzyl trityl ether **55**, 106

**–, preferential 55**, 106

**Trityl salts** s. Triphenylcarbonium...

**Trofimov reaction 55**, 328

**Tryptamines, N′-hydroxy-**
–, Pictet-Spengler ring closure, review **33**, 730s55

**Tungsten alkoxycarbene complexes**
- startg. m. f.
  heterocyclics, 5-membered **55**, 429

**Tungsten carbyne complexes**
- as reagent **55**, 497

**Tungsten complexes**
acetonitrile(pentacarbonyl)tungsten **55**, 200

**– –, organo-**
- special s.
  (1,3-diene)tungsten complexes
- **hexachloride 55**, 204
- **pentacarbonyl 55**, 489

**Ugi 5-component synthesis 55**, 319
**Ureapeptides 9**, 536s55; **52, 141**
**Ureas** (s.a. N-Decarbamylation)
- from
  amines **55**, 133
  formamides **55**, 133
  hydroxamic acids, via Lössen
  rearrangement **55**, 163
  thioureas **55**, 208
- via carbamates, polymer-based **51**, 141s55

**Ureas, sym.**
- from
  amines, (N,N′-diaryl-derivs.) **55**, 131

**Urethans** (s.a. Carbalkoxyamino..., N-Carbalkoxylation, O-Carbamylation, N-Decarbalkoxylation)
- from
  alcohols **55**, 133
  –, tert. **55**, 60
  amines **55**, 155
  carbon dioxide, electro-activated **51**, 169s55
  formamides **55**, 133
  halides **55**, 155
  halogenoformic acid esters **55**, 157
  isocyanates **55**, 60
- special s.
  N-acylurethans
  eneurethans
  epoxyurethans
  halogenurethans
  methyl carbamate
  siloxyurethans
  sulfonylurethans

**Vanadates, dichloro-**
- special s.
  ethyl dichlorovanadate 2,2,2-trifluoroethyl –
**Vanadium tetrachloride 55**, 238
**Vanadyl trichloride 55**, 495
**– triisopropoxide 55**, 67
**– trinitrate 55**, 132
**Vilsmeier-type formylation**
- with bis(trichloromethyl) carbonate **55**, 365

**Vinyl...** s. En..., α,β-Ethylen...
**2-Vinyl-3-aminoalcohols, N-protected, chiral 51**, 281s55
**η³-Vinylcarbene complexes**
–, chemistry, review **23**, 819s55
**3-Vinylcycloalkenes, 1-silyl- 55**, 315
**Vinylcyclopentanes, polyoxy-, chiral 46**, 964s55
**2-Vinylcyclopentanols**
- from
  ε,ξ-ethylene-δ-lactolides **55**, 478
–, **polyoxy-, chiral 55**, 478
**Vinylcyclopropanes**
–, [5+2]-cycloaddition, intramolecular, stereospecific with – **55**, 318
- from
  acetylene derivs. **55**, 282
**Vinylcyclopropanes, fused**
- from
  enynes **55**, 269
**–, 2-homoallyl-**
- from
  α,β-ethyleneketones **55**, 392
**O-Vinyl derivs.**
- from
  O-allyl derivs., asym. induction **34**, 668s55
**C-β-Vinyl glycosides 26**, 827s55
**Vinyl halides** s. α,β-Ethylenehalides
**2-Vinyl-O-heterocyclics**
- from
  (Z)-2-ene-1,n-diol monocarbonates **55**, 115
**Vinyl ketones** s. α,β-Ethyleneketones

**Vinyllithium compds.**
–, carbolithiation, intramolecular **55**, 222
**O→C-Vinyl migration, stereospecific 55**, 308
**Vinyloxyketones**
- startg. m. f.
  1,2-ene-3,n-diols, O→C-vinyl migration, stereospecific **55**, 308
**Vinylpalladation-ring closure**
- of allenes **55**, 40
**Vinyl radicals**
- as intermediates **50**, 577s55
**Vinylsilanes** s. Enesilanes
**Vinylstannanes** s. Enestannanes
**Vorbrüggen nucleoside synthesis**
–, update **26**, 446s55
**– – –, bismuth(III)-catalyzed 55**, 168

**Water, supercritical**
–, reactions in –, review **53**, 31s55
**Wittig rearrangement**
- special s.
  radical Wittig rearrangement
**Wittig synthesis**
- of
  α,β-ethyleneketones, polymer-based **55**, 327
  porphyrin derivs., review **10**, 633s55
**– –, stereospecific**
- with in situ-generated aldehydes **55**, 451
**Wolff rearrangement**
–, hydroxamic acid esters by – **55**, 150
**Wurtz coupling**
- of alkyl halides in aq. medium **55**, 402

**Xenon fluorotriflate 49**, 399s55

**Yeast 55**, 34
**N-Ylids, cyclic**
- special s.
  azolium N-imides
**P-Ylids** s. Alkylidenephosphoranes
**Ynolates**
- special s.
  lithium ynolates
**Ytterbium 55**, 321
**Ytterbium(III) triflate 55**, 342

**Zeolite, copper(II)-exchanged** 55, 159
–, **silver(I)-exchanged** 55, 486
**Zeolites** 55, 131
–, reduction, photochemical in – 55, 33
–, **microwave-modified**
–, review 44, 651s55
**Zinc** (s.a. Titanium tetrachloride/zinc) 55, 96, 137, 157, 387, 389, 472
–/**ammonium chloride** 55, 5
–/**copper** 55, 420
**Zincates, organo-** s. Magnesium triorganozincates, bromo-, Silylzincates, organo-
**Zincation** s. Carbozincation
**Zinc azaenolates**
– as intermediates 55, 303
**Zinc bis(tetrahydridoborate)**
–, review 42, 54s55
– –/**triethylenediamine** 23, 27s55
– **bromide** 55, 140, 303, 371
– **chloride** 55, 225, 435
– **compds., dialkyl-**

diethylzinc 55, 269
– (as reactant) 55, 237
– as reactant 55, 226, 238
– –, **diaryl-**
– as reactant 55, 239
– –, **halogeno-** (s.a. Nysted reagent)
– –, **organo-, functionalized**
– from
iodides, functionalized 55, 226
– **halides, organo-**
– special s.
bis(iodozincio)methane
$o$-bromophenylzinc iodide
cyclopropylzinc chlorides
ethynylzinc bromide
– **iodide** 55, 236, 306
– **selenolates, halogeno-**
– as intermediates 55, 225
**Zirconacyclics**
– special s.
azazircona...
**Zirconia, sulfated** 37, 182s55

**Zirconium(IV) aminoalkoxides, chiral**
– as reagent 55, 176
**Zirconium(IV) aroxides, chiral**
– tetra-*tert*-butoxide/(R)-6,6'-dibromo-1,1'-bi-2-naphthol/1,2-dimethylimidazole 55, 444
–/N-methylimidazole 55, 443
**Zirconium complexes**
chlorobis(cyclopentadienyl)hydridozirconium 55, 280
zirconocene dichloride 55, 282
– –/*n*-butyllithium 55, 348
– –/ethylmagnesium bromide 55, 281
– –, **organo-**
– special s.
γ,γ-dialkoxyallylzirconium complexes
**Zirconocene chlorides, organo-**
– special s.
acylzirconocene chlorides
**Zirconocene η²-olefin and alkyne complexes**
–, chemistry, review 54, 365s55

## Supplementary References in Volume 55

| No. | Suppl. Ref. Vol. Page |
|---|---|
| **Volume 1** | |
| 397 | 55, 227 |
| 519 | 55, 163 |
| 554 | 55, 228 |
| 569 | 55, 225 |
| 570 | 55, 225 |
| 612 | 55, 175 |
| **Volume 2** | |
| 112 | 55, 26 |
| 113 | 55, 26 |
| 430 | 55, 80 |
| 532 | 55, 100 |
| 649 | 55, 889 |
| 657 | 55, 225 |
| 680 | 55, 170 |
| 703 | 55, 175 |
| 741 | 55, 234 |
| **Volume 3** | |
| 275 | 55, 65 |
| 440 | 55, 95 |
| 632 | 55, 162 |
| 635 | 55, 225 |
| 636 | 55, 225 |
| **Volume 4** | |
| 3 | 55, 245 |
| 117 | 55, 26 |
| 154 | 55, 33 |
| 274 | 55, 99 |
| 308 | 55, 64 |
| 435 | 55, 69 |
| 667 | 55, 147 |
| 685 | 55, 157 |
| 817 | 55, 228 |
| **Volume 5** | |
| 174 | 55, 45 |
| 346 | 55, 84 |
| 381 | 55, 92 |
| 452 | 55, 106 |
| 666 | 55, 242 (3), 243 (2), 245 |
| **Volume 6** | |
| 47 | 55, 12 |
| 54 | 55, 12 |
| 290 | 55, 48 |
| 357 | 55, 65 |
| 364 | 55, 65 |
| 367 | 55, 66 |
| 891 | 55, 48 |
| 902 | 55, 241 |
| 911 | 55, 242 |
| **Volume 7** | |
| 281 | 55, 245 |
| 365 | 55, 62 |
| 678 | 55, 117 |
| 746 | 55, 151 |
| 779 | 55, 225 |
| 836 | 55, 183 |
| 891 | 55, 230 |
| **Volume 8** | |
| 342 | 55, 59 |
| 444 | 55, 72 |
| 563 | 55, 80 |
| 593 | 55, 93 |
| 643 | 55, 108 |
| 656 | 55, 104 |
| 697 | 55, 117 |
| 823 | 55, 167 |
| 951 | 55, 240 |
| **Volume 9** | |
| 38 | 55, 7 |
| 287 | 55, 48 |
| 408 | 55, 106 |
| 536 | 55, 84 |
| 741 | 55, 120 |
| 831 | 55, 225 |
| 897 | 55, 175 |
| 917 | 55, 223 |
| **Volume 10** | |
| 177 | 55, 47 |
| 303 | 55, 232 |
| 367 | 55, 82 |
| 376 | 55, 85 |
| 382 | 55, 87 |
| 511 | 55, 117 |
| 562 | 55, 154 |
| 617 | 55, 182 |
| 633 | 55, 245 |
| 639 | 55, 227 |
| **Volume 11** | |
| 87 | 55, 38 |
| 123 | 55, 24 |
| 217 | 55, 41 |
| 283 | 55, 74 |

| No. | Suppl. Ref. Vol. Page |
|---|---|

**Volume 11** continued

| 618 | 55, 94 |
| 752 | 55, 127 |
| 799 | 55, 155 |

**Volume 12**

| 33 | 55, 58 |
| 110 | 55, 22 |
| 116 | 55, 24 |
| 206 | 55, 41 |
| 432 | 55, 71 |
| 453 | 55, 71 |
| 467 | 55, 79 |
| 619 | 55, 98 |

**Volume 13**

| 215 | 55, 96 |
| 371 | 55, 65 |
| 516 | 55, 65 |
| 573 | 55, 95 |
| 733 | 55, 27 |
| 838 | 55, 225 |
| 844 | 55, 228 |
| 879 | 55, 231 |
| 910 | 55, 241 |

**Volume 14**

| 400 | 55, 68 |
| 564 | 55, 89 |
| 597 | 55, 95 |
| 711 | 55, 205 |
| 876 | 55, 60 |

**Volume 15**

| 71 | 55, 22 |
| 261 | 55, 159 |
| 494 | 55, 111 |
| 609 | 55, 173 |

**Volume 16**

| 58 | 55, 62 |
| 72 | 55, 20 |
| 172 | 55, 12 |
| 201 | 55, 5 |
| 222 | 55, 43 |
| 225 | 55, 43 |
| 236 | 55, 45 |
| 257 | 55, 49 |
| 262 | 55, 71 |
| 644 | 55, 103 |
| 674 | 55, 7 |
| 828 | 55, 167 |
| 870 | 55, 183 |
| 888 | 55, 130 |

**Volume 17**

| 11 | 55, 2 |
| 117 | 55, 245 |
| 169 | 55, 31, 245 |
| 198 | 55, 237, 245 |
| 453 | 55, 74 |
| 503 | 55, 65, 79 |
| 735 | 55, 119 |
| 809 | 55, 159 |
| 821 | 55, 159 |
| 898 | 55, 224 |
| 968 | 55, 234 |

**Volume 18**

| 99 | 55, 23 |
| 193 | 55, 38 |
| 234 | 55, 46 |
| 647 | 55, 101 |
| 776 | 55, 144 |
| 954 | 55, 230 |

**Volume 19**

| 33 | 55, 77, 245 |
| 38 | 55, 12 |
| 104 | 55, 26 |
| 201 | 55, 35 |

| 226 | 55, 44 |
| 265 | 55, 245 |
| 382 | 55, 66 |
| 393 | 55, 66 |
| 461 | 55, 73 |
| 471 | 55, 72 |
| 559 | 55, 89 |
| 674 | 55, 80 |
| 854 | 55, 176 |
| 892 | 55, 185 |
| 896 | 55, 182 |
| 8897 | 55, 245 |
| 911 | 55, 223 |

**Volume 20**

| 12 | 55, 1 |
| 20 | 55, 3 |
| 71 | 55, 22 |
| 112 | 55, 36 |
| 116 | 55, 41 |
| 175 | 55, 91 |
| 239 | 55, 42 |
| 294 | 55, 138 |
| 334 | 55, 80 |
| 395 | 55, 69 |
| 447 | 55, 105 |
| 601 | 55, 176 |
| 680 | 55, 233 |
| 685 | 55, 234 |

**Volume 21**

| 9 | 55, 1 |
| 256 | 55, 52 |
| 378 | 55, 73 |
| 393 | 55, 69 |
| 499 | 55, 82 |
| 725 | 55, 136 |
| 858 | 55, 40 |
| 888 | 55, 205 |
| 927 | 55, 230 |
| 988 | 55, 241 |

## Supplementary References

| No. | Suppl. Ref. Vol. Page |
|---|---|

### Volume 22

| | |
|---|---|
| 24 | 55, 8 |
| 30 | 55, 10 |
| 106 | 55, 32 |
| 365 | 55, 71 |
| 394 | 55, 73 |
| 408 | 55, 90 |
| 420 | 55, 78 |
| 557 | 55, 94 |
| 580 | 55, 97 |
| 587 | 55, 100 |
| 655 | 55, 109 |
| 693 | 55, 125 |
| 708 | 55, 130 |
| 721 | 55, 137 |
| 761 | 55, 245 |
| 813 | 55, 48 |
| 836 | 55, 26 |
| 877 | 55, 223 |

### Volume 23

| | |
|---|---|
| 27 | 55, 8 |
| 51 | 55, 15 |
| 79 | 55, 22, 23 |
| 182 | 55, 42 |
| 261 | 55, 56 |
| 381 | 55, 245 |
| 577 | 55, 100 |
| 687 | 55, 144 |
| 703 | 55, 136 |
| 735 | 55, 152 |
| 776 | 55, 224 |
| 819 | 55, 174, 176, 245 |
| 871 | 55, 199 |
| 879 | 55, 203 |
| 921 | 55, 230 |

### Volume 24

| | |
|---|---|
| 5 | 55, 4 |
| 9 | 55, 2 |

| | |
|---|---|
| 61 | 55, 13 |
| 100 | 55, 29 |
| 261 | 55, 59 |
| 663 | 55, 118 |
| 694 | 55, 138 |
| 768 | 55, 158, 245 |
| 836 | 55, 173 |
| 859 | 55, 198 |
| 989 | 55, 240 |

### Volume 25

| | |
|---|---|
| 15 | 55, 7 (2) |
| 62 | 55, 24 |
| 167 | 55, 245 |
| 250 | 55, 70 |
| 330 | 55, 87 |
| 398 | 55, 97 |
| 484 | 55, 120 |
| 487 | 55, 119 |
| 533 | 55, 153 |
| 594 | 55, 245 |
| 628 | 55, 218 |
| 662 | 55, 128 |

### Volume 26

| | |
|---|---|
| 13 | 55, 6 |
| 56 | 55, 245 |
| 57 | 55, 22 |
| 203 | 55, 52 |
| 358 | 55, 72 |
| 446 | 55, 86 |
| 686 | 55, 205 |
| 808 | 55, 176 |
| 827 | 55, 172 (2) |
| 833 | 55, 173 |
| 875 | 55, 186 |

### Volume 27

| | |
|---|---|
| 15 | 55, 7 |
| 18 | 55, 8 |
| 57 | 55, 20 |
| 68 | 55, 23 |
| 110 | 55, 10 |

| | |
|---|---|
| 184 | 55, 28 |
| 402 | 55, 10 |
| 429 | 55, 74 |
| 527 | 55, 90 |
| 680 | 55, 200 |
| 738 | 55, 151 |
| 769 | 55, 71 |
| 822 | 55, 173 |
| 833 | 55, 177 |
| 838 | 55, 162 |
| 851 | 55, 196 |
| 871 | 55, 246 |
| 917 | 55, 230 |
| 947 | 55, 246 |
| 954 | 55, 230 |

### Volume 28

| | |
|---|---|
| 13 | 55, 4, 246 |
| 39 | 55, 20 |
| 141 | 55, 44 |
| 144 | 55, 73, 75 (2) |
| 148 | 55, 46 |
| 297 | 55, 68 |
| 524 | 55, 26 |
| 527 | 55, 107 |
| 652 | 55, 136 |
| 683 | 55, 151 |
| 730 | 55, 160 |
| 732 | 55, 119 |
| 753 | 55, 74 |
| 841 | 55, 200 |
| 851 | 55, 207 |
| 852 | 55, 203 |
| 854 | 55, 246 |
| 890 | 55, 227 |
| 909 | 55, 230 |
| 950 | 55, 233 |

### Volume 29

| | |
|---|---|
| 2 | 55, 3 |
| 36 | 55, 14 |
| 52 | 55, 227 |
| 84 | 55, 29 |
| 180 | 55, 111 |

| No. | Suppl. Ref. Vol. Page |
|---|---|
| **Volume 29** continued | |
| 201 | 55, 49 |
| 233 | 55, 58 |
| 325 | 55, 68 |
| 415 | 55, 2 |
| 547 | 55, 44 |
| 591 | 55, 137 |
| 617 | 55, 11 |
| 697 | 55, 246 |
| 786 | 55, 174 |
| 810 | 55, 150 |
| 824 | 55, 190 |
| 836 | 55, 193 |
| 845 | 55, 196 |
| 854 | 55, 200 |
| 910 | 55, 227 |
| 920 | 55, 228 |
| 959 | 55, 119, 232 |
| 970 | 55, 235, 246 |
| **Volume 30** | |
| 4 | 55, 1 |
| 222 | 55, 66 |
| 232 | 55, 69 |
| 239 | 55, 69 |
| 365 | 55, 96 |
| 514 | 55, 152 |
| 540 | 55, 157 |
| 561 | 55, 120 |
| 597 | 55, 190 |
| 621 | 55, 208 |
| 696 | 55, 240 |
| **Volume 31** | |
| 39 | 55, 18 |
| 65 | 55, 26 |
| 105 | 55, 36 |
| 163 | 55, 96, 246 |
| 336 | 55, 69 |
| 452 | 55, 89 |
| 501 | 55, 96 |
| 576 | 55, 109 |
| 641 | 55, 134 |
| 709 | 55, 176 (2) |
| 719 | 55, 157 |
| 753 | 55, 165 |
| 804 | 55, 182 |
| 847 | 55, 194 |
| 890 | 55, 211 |
| 973 | 55, 235 |
| 984 | 55, 238 |
| **Volume 32** | |
| 11 | 55, 246 |
| 26 | 55, 13 |
| 44 | 55, 246 |
| 85 | 55, 51 |
| 154 | 55, 4 |
| 161 | 55, 47 |
| 311 | 55, 246 |
| 593 | 55, 246 |
| 617 | 55, 128 |
| 668 | 55, 246 |
| 711 | 55, 246 |
| 845 | 55, 200 |
| 867 | 55, 185 |
| 885 | 55, 204 |
| 887 | 55, 210 |
| **Volume 33** | |
| 9 | 55, 3 |
| 46 | 55, 14 |
| 205 | 55, 51 |
| 252 | 55, 59 |
| 403 | 55, 246 |
| 662 | 55, 150 |
| 730 | 55, 246 |
| 758 | 55, 175 |
| 865 | 55, 206 |
| 930 | 55, 229 |
| 990 | 55, 240 |
| **Volume 34** | |
| 46 | 55, 22, 246 |
| 62 | 55, 184 |
| 112 | 55, 246 |
| 116 | 55, 36 |
| 238 | 55, 246 |
| 249 | 55, 61 |
| 358 | 55, 75 |
| 420 | 55, 85 |
| 547 | 55, 106 |
| 607 | 55, 118 |
| 627 | 55, 130 |
| 648 | 55, 140 |
| 649 | 55, 130 |
| 668 | 55, 151 |
| 693 | 55, 155 |
| 767 | 55, 178 |
| 825 | 55, 196 |
| 862 | 55, 219 |
| 897 | 55, 228 |
| 929 | 55, 231 |
| **Volume 35** | |
| 20 | 55, 12 |
| 34 | 55, 22 |
| 152 | 55, 246 |
| 157 | 55, 58 |
| 248 | 55, 71 |
| 311 | 55, 89 |
| 393 | 55, 199 |
| 430 | 55, 242 |
| 474 | 55, 139 |
| 506 | 55, 157 |
| 530 | 55, 163 |
| 549 | 55, 177 |
| 554 | 55, 180 |
| 642 | 55, 224 |
| 655 | 55, 227 |
| **Volume 36** | |
| 43 | 55, 19 |
| 117 | 55, 246 |
| 203 | 55, 50 |

| No. | Suppl. Ref. Vol. Page |
|---|---|

**Volume 36** continued

| | |
|---|---|
| 211 | 55, 95 |
| 285 | 55, 65 |
| 493 | 55, 2 |
| 667 | 55, 132, 138, 144 |
| 669 | 55, 139 |
| 670 | 55, 14 |
| 674 | 55, 137 |
| 682 | 55, 150, 152 |
| 766 | 55, 120 |
| 819 | 55, 161 |
| 884 | 55, 215 |

**Volume 37**

| | |
|---|---|
| 16 | 55, 8 |
| 49 | 55, 24 |
| 58 | 55, 24 |
| 76 | 55, 27 |
| 127 | 55, 38 |
| 128 | 55, 38 |
| 132 | 55, 16 |
| 182 | 55, 52 |
| 214 | 55, 56 |
| 226 | 55, 58 |
| 234 | 55, 57 |
| 330 | 55, 73 |
| 349 | 55, 246 |
| 441 | 55, 246 |
| 507 | 55, 105 |
| 657 | 55, 180 |
| 658 | 55, 134 |
| 669 | 55, 246 |
| 747 | 55, 177 |
| 776 | 55, 177 |
| 831 | 55, 213 |
| 841 | 55, 204 |
| 893 | 55, 213 |
| 902 | 55, 218, 219 (3) |
| 950 | 55, 234 |

**Volume 38**

| | |
|---|---|
| 32 | 55, 17 |
| 92 | 55, 33 |
| 100 | 55, 34 |
| 158 | 55, 47 |
| 232 | 55, 59 |
| 266 | 55, 184 |
| 584 | 55, 112, 115 |
| 632 | 55, 119, 123 |
| 756 | 55, 247 |
| 836 | 55, 186 (2) |
| 861 | 55, 200 |
| 887 | 55, 210 |
| 982 | 55, 89 |

**Volume 39**

| | |
|---|---|
| 83 | 55, 30 |
| 124 | 55, 38, 39 |
| 128 | 55, 3 |
| 189 | 55, 53 |
| 214 | 55, 54 |
| 228 | 55, 57 |
| 233 | 55, 58 |
| 381 | 55, 84 |
| 433 | 55, 90 |
| 469 | 55, 189 |
| 545 | 55, 109 |
| 578 | 55, 131 |
| 581 | 55, 48 |
| 612 | 55, 127 |
| 646 | 55, 142 |
| 673 | 55, 157 |
| 738 | 55, 200 |
| 740 | 55, 185 |
| 749 | 55, 182 |
| 882 | 55, 213 |
| 883 | 55, 214 |
| 887 | 55, 219 |
| 932 | 55, 230 |
| 952 | 55, 233 |
| 964 | 55, 235 |
| 993 | 55, 243 |

**Volume 40**

| | |
|---|---|
| 13 | 55, 11 |
| 122 | 55, 53 |
| 176 | 55, 64 |
| 220 | 55, 87 |
| 235 | 55, 73 |
| 242 | 55, 76 |
| 273 | 55, 204 |
| 286 | 55, 86 |
| 539 | 55, 182 |
| 567 | 55, 122 |
| 576 | 55, 188 |

**Volume 41**

| | |
|---|---|
| 38 | 55, 14 |
| 63 | 55, 23, 26 |
| 77 | 55, 25 |
| 115 | 55, 247 |
| 125 | 55, 35 |
| 132 | 55, 94 |
| 135 | 55, 37 |
| 139 | 55, 247 |
| 172 | 55, 46 |
| 175 | 55, 45, 244 |
| 199 | 55, 131 |
| 243 | 55, 59, 247 |
| 280 | 55, 247 |
| 336 | 55, 72, 247 |
| 344 | 55, 73 |
| 404 | 55, 85 |
| 463 | 55, 247 |
| 546 | 55, 103 |
| 622 | 55, 247 |
| 624 | 55, 202 |
| 671 | 55, 151 |
| 723 | 55, 166 |
| 731 | 55, 173 |
| 732 | 55, 176 |
| 748 | 55, 108 |
| 795 | 55, 186 |
| 829 | 55, 201 |

| No. | Suppl. Ref. Vol. Page |
|---|---|

**Volume 41** continued

| 832 | 55, 202 |
| 868 | 55, 204 |
| 913 | 55, 247 |
| 924 | 55, 227 |
| 927 | 55, 230 |
| 947 | 55, 232 |
| 995 | 55, 241 |

**Volume 42**

| 6 | 55, 4 |
| 22 | 55, 12 |
| 45 | 55, 20 |
| 54 | 55, 247 |
| 87 | 55, 107 |
| 108 | 55, 65 |
| 163 | 55, 46 |
| 173 | 55, 48 |
| 220 | 55, 55 |
| 233 | 55, 38 (2) |
| 234 | 55, 58 |
| 235 | 55, 58 (2) |
| 290 | 55, 66 |
| 308 | 55, 247 |
| 354 | 55, 78 |
| 462 | 5, 94 |
| 490 | 55, 81 |
| 531 | 55, 203 |
| 557 | 55, 247 |
| 597 | 55, 178 |
| 612 | 55, 126 |
| 616 | 55, 120, 121, 247 |
| 621 | 55, 127 |
| 679 | 55, 141 |
| 683 | 55, 151 |
| 761 | 55, 247 |
| 826 | 55, 188 |
| 970 | 55, 247 |
| 986 | 55, 156 |
| 997 | 55, 247 |

**Volume 43**

| 17 | 55, 6 |
| 45 | 55, 13, 247 |
| 51 | 55, 15, 16 |
| 89 | 55, 32 |
| 121 | 55, 41 |
| 270 | 55, 247 |
| 271 | 55, 68 |
| 299 | 55, 247 |
| 309 | 55, 77 |
| 498 | 55, 106 |
| 515 | 55, 110 |
| 556 | 55, 118 |
| 571 | 55, 124 |
| 576 | 55, 124 |
| 584 | 55, 129 |
| 587 | 55, 247 |
| 611 | 55, 144 |
| 699 | 55, 121 |
| 715 | 55, 247 |
| 721 | 55, 231 |
| 722 | 55, 247 |
| 740 | 55, 176 |
| 749 | 55, 80 |
| 756 | 55, 184 |
| 778 | 55, 207 |
| 825 | 55, 137 |
| 877 | 55, 247 |
| 912 | 55, 178 |
| 943 | 55, 176 (2) |
| 962 | 55, 234, 247 |
| 965 | 55, 151 |
| 981 | 55, 247 |
| 995 | 55, 241 |

**Volume 44**

| 7 | 55, 248 |
| 10 | 55, 44 |
| 42 | 55, 14 |
| 70 | 55, 25 |
| 82 | 55, 28 |
| 89 | 55, 32 |
| 104 | 55, 34 |
| 117 | 55, 36 |
| 131 | 55, 40, 145 |
| 211 | 55, 56 |
| 214 | 55, 55 |
| 229 | 55, 248 |
| 249 | 55, 61 |
| 362 | 55, 85 |
| 410 | 55, 248 |
| 431 | 55, 97 |
| 565 | 55, 121 (2) |
| 568 | 55, 125 |
| 577 | 55, 215 |
| 594 | 55, 142 |
| 611 | 55, 137 |
| 648 | 55, 151 |
| 651 | 55, 248 |
| 776 | 55, 182 |
| 781 | 55, 194 |
| 802 | 55, 163 |
| 805 | 55, 191 |
| 837 | 55, 205 |
| 884 | 55, 219 |
| 897 | 55, 222 |
| 907 | 55, 215 |
| 930 | 55, 229 |
| 938 | 55, 230 |

**Volume 45**

| 10 | 55, 3 |
| 35 | 55, 25 |
| 43 | 55, 27 |
| 70 | 55, 36 |
| 72 | 55, 39 |
| 96 | 55, 50 |
| 120 | 55, 57 |
| 210 | 55, 243 |
| 231 | 55, 82 |
| 285 | 55, 93 |
| 303 | 55, 100 |
| 319 | 55, 60 |
| 436 | 55, 152 |
| 439 | 55, 156 |
| 447 | 55, 172 |
| 449 | 55, 208 |
| 460 | 55, 175 |
| 473 | 55, 193 |

| No. | Suppl. Ref. Vol. Page |
|---|---|
| **Volume 45** continued | |
| 510 | 55, 24 |
| 533 | 55, 235 |
| 555 | 55, 220 |
| 557 | 55, 221 |
| **Volume 46** | |
| 3 | 55, 248 |
| 47 | 55, 248 |
| 106 | 55, 39 |
| 123 | 55, 37 |
| 214 | 55, 248 |
| 267 | 55, 65 |
| 317 | 55, 248 |
| 321 | 55, 73 |
| 437 | 55, 94 |
| 456 | 55, 99 |
| 533 | 55, 110 |
| 572 | 55, 248 |
| 601 | 55, 118, 120 |
| 661 | 55, 143 |
| 662 | 55, 133 (2), 135 |
| 669 | 55, 147 |
| 686 | 55, 153 |
| 713 | 55, 162 |
| 736 | 55, 248 |
| 766 | 55, 248 |
| 767 | 55, 248 |
| 798 | 55, 194 |
| 802 | 55, 194 |
| 811 | 55, 199 |
| 885 | 55, 207 |
| 906 | 55, 220 |
| 964 | 55, 233 |
| 989 | 55, 237 |
| **Volume 47** | |
| 35 | 55, 14 |
| 48 | 55, 21 |
| 54 | 55, 22 |
| 77 | 55, 26 |
| 113 | 55, 248 |
| 232 | 55, 92 |
| 287 | 55, 248 |
| 293 | 55, 71 |
| 303 | 55, 73 |
| 427 | 55, 248 |
| 435 | 55, 95 |
| 450 | 55, 131 |
| 462 | 55, 95, 99 |
| 468 | 55, 99 |
| 549 | 55, 248 |
| 552 | 55, 248 |
| 555 | 55, 110 |
| 568 | 55, 116 |
| 576 | 55, 117 |
| 614 | 55, 128 |
| 631 | 55, 132 |
| 640 | 55, 135 |
| 646 | 55, 248 |
| 656 | 55, 138 |
| 664 | 55, 142 |
| 687 | 55, 151 |
| 698 | 55, 225 |
| 727 | 55, 168 |
| 745 | 55, 169 |
| 806 | 55, 188 |
| 829 | 55, 194 |
| 893 | 55, 209 |
| 904 | 55, 214 |
| 927 | 55, 225 |
| 938 | 55, 208 |
| 940 | 55, 229 |
| 954 | 55, 178 |
| 955 | 55, 248 |
| 974 | 55, 234 |
| 981 | 55, 109 |
| 983 | 55, 236 |
| 984 | 55, 208 |
| **Volume 48** | |
| 38 | 55, 17 |
| 108 | 55, 244 |
| 120 | 55, 35 |
| 134 | 55, 39 |
| 269 | 55, 64 |
| 356 | 55, 248 |
| 381 | 55, 87 |
| 439 | 55, 94 |
| 447 | 55, 96 |
| 489 | 55, 104 |
| 547 | 55, 111 |
| 638 | 55, 130 |
| 640 | 55, 248 |
| 675 | 55, 136 |
| 691 | 55, 249 |
| 772 | 55, 173 |
| 812 | 55, 186 |
| 818 | 55, 190 |
| 831 | 55, 196 |
| 886 | 55, 209 |
| 982 | 55, 235 |
| 985 | 55, 240 |
| 988 | 55, 239, 240 |
| **Volume 49** | |
| 7 | 55, 6 |
| 8 | 55, 1 |
| 35 | 55, 12 |
| 42 | 55, 14 |
| 53 | 55, 18 |
| 211 | 55, 249 |
| 230 | 55, 249 |
| 256 | 55, 65 |
| 407 | 55, 93 |
| 510 | 55, 110 |
| 515 | 55, 110, 249 |
| 536 | 55, 113 |
| 557 | 55, 117 |
| 589 | 55, 118, 123 |
| 595 | 55, 125 |
| 606 | 55, 128 |
| 622 | 55, 130 |
| 638 | 55, 249 |
| 652 | 55, 137 |
| 661 | 55, 142 |
| 669 | 55, 139 |
| 674 | 55, 144 |
| 683 | 55, 147 |
| 703 | 55, 152, 249 |

| No. | Suppl. Ref. Vol. Page | | | | |
|---|---|---|---|---|---|
| **Volume 49** continued | | 555 | 55, 218, 249 | 422 | 55, 234 |
| | | 556 | 55, 218 | 423 | 55, 201 |
| | | 577 | 55, 232 | 435 | 55, 250 |
| | | 586 | 55, 234 | 443 | 55, 192, 216 |
| | | 591 | 55, 232 | 453 | 55, 216 |
| 713 | 55, 153 | | | 480 | 55, 233 |
| 763 | 55, 165 | | | 491 | 55, 235 |
| 797 | 55, 177 | **Volume 51** | | | |
| 898 | 55, 212 | | | **Volume 52** | |
| 909 | 55, 202 | 3 | 55, 1 | | |
| 932 | 55, 226 | 5 | 55, 4 | | |
| 938 | 55, 228 (2) | 13 | 55, 8 | 9 | 55, 250 |
| 946 | 55, 231 | 24 | 55, 249 | 24 | 55, 18 |
| 994 | 55, 30 | 26 | 55, 15, 16 | 40 | 55, 26 |
| 971 | 55, 236 | 30 | 55, 249 | 141 | 55, 70 |
| 981 | 55, 238 | 38 | 55, 249 | 145 | 55, 68 |
| 985 | 55, 239 (2), 240, 249 | 45 | 55, 28 | 147 | 55, 80 |
| 995 | 55, 244 | 55 | 55, 33 | 171 | 55, 83 |
| | | 65 | 55, 38 | 237 | 55, 116 |
| | | 72 | 55, 42 | 239 | 55, 116 |
| **Volume 50** | | 76 | 55, 42 | 249 | 55, 162 |
| | | 84 | 55, 46 | 267 | 55, 250 |
| 53 | 55, 249 | 91 | 55, 249 | 268 | 55, 126 |
| 70 | 55, 42 | 97 | 55, 53 | 273 | 55, 126 |
| 126 | 55, 58 | 104 | 55, 54 | 274 | 55, 250 |
| 195 | 55, 78 | 121 | 55, 65 | 278 | 55, 127 |
| 250 | 55, 17 | 132 | 55, 67 (2) | 284 | 55, 250 |
| 254 | 55, 89 | 135 | 55, 69 | 297 | 55, 135 |
| 272 | 55, 96 | 138 | 55, 249 | 303 | 55, 139 |
| 276 | 55, 41 | 162 | 55, 249 | 317 | 55, 250 |
| 292 | 55, 97 | 166 | 55, 10 | 319 | 55, 159, 250 |
| 302 | 55, 100 | 169 | 55, 81 | 321 | 55, 150 |
| 335 | 55, 108 | 171 | 55, 83 (2), 249 | 351 | 55, 159 |
| 341 | 55, 112, 249 | 227 | 55, 249 | 363 | 55, 167 |
| 343 | 55, 111 | 239 | 55, 112 | 387 | 55, 176 |
| 397 | 55, 212 | 258 | 55, 116 | 389 | 55, 177 |
| 402 | 55, 148 | 275 | 55, 123 | 400 | 55, 198 |
| 415 | 55, 144 | 281 | 55, 125 | 407 | 55, 232, 250 |
| 428 | 55, 141 | 312 | 55, 139, 249 | 413 | 55, 192 |
| 483 | 55, 177 | 317 | 55, 142 | 415 | 55, 194 |
| 498 | 55, 249 | 327 | 55, 146 | 419 | 55, 199 |
| 500 | 55, 182 | 337 | 55, 150 | 422 | 55, 198 |
| 531 | 55, 201 | 376 | 55, 250 | 425 | 55, 201 |
| 543 | 55, 212 | 399 | 55, 250 | 428 | 55, 202 |
| 551 | 55, 210 | 400 | 55, 178 | 435 | 55, 250 |
| 552 | 55, 216 | 416 | 55, 197 (2) | 439 | 55, 207 |

| No. | Suppl. Ref. Vol. Page |
|---|---|
| **Volume 52** continued | |
| 447 | *55*, 209 |
| 457 | *55*, 209 |
| 494 | *55*, 240 |
| 497 | *55*, 243, 250 |

| **Volume 53** | |
|---|---|
| 16 | *55*, 250 |
| 22 | *55*, 124 |
| 31 | *55*, 250 |
| 57 | *55*, 250 |
| 59 | *55*, 244 |
| 68 | *55*, 39 |
| 108 | *55*, 57 |
| 150 | *55*, 71 |
| 164 | *55*, 84 |
| 186 | *55*, 93 |
| 252 | *55*, 117 |
| 266 | *55*, 121 (2), 250 |
| 280 | *55*, 250 |
| 301 | *55*, 138 |
| 303 | *55*, 137 |
| 321 | *55*, 250 |

| 322 | *55*, 250 |
|---|---|
| 372 | *55*, 168 |
| 380 | *55*, 173 |
| 386 | *55*, 175, 250 |
| 395 | *55*, 250 |
| 407 | *55*, 250 |
| 437 | *55*, 201 |
| 445 | *55*, 216 |
| 494 | *55*, 191 |
| 500 | *55*, 41 |

| **Volume 54** | |
|---|---|
| 13 | *55*, 7 |
| 30 | *55*, 16 |
| 34 | *55*, 18 |
| 51 | *55*, 250 |
| 52 | *55*, 250 |
| 54 | *55*, 29 |
| 55 | *55*, 30 |
| 62 | *55*, 42 |
| 79 | *55*, 44 |
| 86 | *55*, 49 |
| 88 | *55*, 51 |
| 133 | *55*, 251 |
| 135 | *55*, 83 |
| 138 | *55*, 68 |
| 160 | *55*, 251 |

| 170 | *55*, 77 |
|---|---|
| 192 | *55*, 96 |
| 240 | *55*, 251 |
| 261 | *55*, 124 |
| 281 | *55*, 131 |
| 296 | *55*, 138 |
| 299 | *55*, 139 |
| 306 | *55*, 251 |
| 316 | *55*, 251 |
| 320 | *55*, 146 |
| 333 | *55*, 68 |
| 349 | *55*, 251 |
| 357 | *55*, 225 |
| 365 | *55*, 251 |
| 367 | *55*, 168 |
| 382 | *55*, 173 |
| 416 | *55*, 193 |
| 444 | *55*, 207 |
| 447 | *55*, 207 |
| 456 | *55*, 210 |
| 473 | *55*, 223 |
| 481 | *55*, 228 |

| **Volume 55** | |
|---|---|
| 79 | *55*, 251 |
| 220 | *55*, 220 |